Test Bank to Accompany

Elementary Linear Algebra
Eighth Edition

HOWARD ANTON
Drexel University

and

Elementary Linear Algebra
Applications Version
Eighth Edition

HOWARD ANTON
CHRIS RORRES
Drexel University

Prepared by
RANDY K. SCHWARTZ
Schoolcraft College

John Wiley & Sons, Inc.
New York   Chichester   Weinheim   Brisbane   Singapore   Toronto

To order books or for customer service call 1-800-CALL-WILEY (225-5945).

ISBN 0-471-38568-9

Printed in the United States of America

10 9 8 7 6 5 4 3 2 1

Printed and bound by Victor Graphics, Inc.

PREFACE

This test bank, to accompany *Elementary Linear Algebra, Eighth Edition* by Howard Anton and *Elementary Linear Algebra, Applications Version, Eighth Edition* by Howard Anton and Chris Rorres, was developed to assist instructors in formulating tests and quizzes as well as final exams.

The textbook is closely followed in the way that the topics are organized, the type of problems posed, and the methods and notation used in their solution. Problems are grouped by chapter, and their solutions are further grouped (and labeled) by the section of the chapter to which they pertain.

In addition, there are five or more "Writing Questions" posed for each chapter. They are intended to be answered by the student in a verbal, descriptive manner. Some of them can be addressed with short responses of one or two sentences, while others are more open-ended, even "philosophical" questions which a thoughtful student may address in several paragraphs.

At the end of the test bank, there are four versions of a Final Exam for the course.

The problems in this test bank vary greatly in their level of difficulty; instructors are urged to consult the solutions ahead of time. Great care has been taken to include complete solutions. No steps are omitted, and the problems are solved as they would be done "by hand" without the use of calculators or computers. Thus, the instructor is able to determine the content and difficulty level of each problem before selecting it.

For many topics, I have included a range of problems that differ only in their computational (not conceptual) difficulty. This is intended to meet the needs of different instructors, who vary as to the type of technology they allow their students to use during exams. Instructors who prohibit calculators and computers may wish to select problems whose solutions tend to involve small, whole numbers. Instructors who allow calculators or computers may wish to select some problems whose solutions involve larger numbers or fraction. In cases where advanced technology is allowed, instructors who want to avoid instant "push-button" answers can select problems which include unspecified parameters (a, b, c, k, etc.); or they can select problems whose solution involves fractional or irrational quantities and require that the student give the exact answer rather than a decimal approximation.

It is my hope that instructors who use this test bank will forward their comments and suggestions to the publisher. Your classroom experience will be invaluable to me in making improvements in the future.

Randy Schwartz

CONTENTS

CHAPTER 1: SYSTEMS OF LINEAR EQUATIONS AND MATRICES

1. Which of the following are linear equations in x_1, x_2, and x_3?

$$
\begin{array}{llll}
a) & 3x_1 & - & x_2 & + & 5x_3 & = & 4 \\
c) & x_1^2 & + & 2x_2 & - & 3x_3 & = & 0 \\
e) & & & \pi x_1 & + & \pi^2 x_2 & = & \pi^3 x_3
\end{array}
$$

$$
\begin{array}{llll}
b) & x_1 & - & 4x_2 x_3 & & & = & 3 \\
d) & \sqrt{3}x_1 & - & \sqrt{2}x_2 & + & x_3 & = & 5 \\
f) & \sqrt{5}x_1 & + & 5\sqrt{x_2} & - & x_3 & = & 1
\end{array}
$$

In questions 2–5, find the augmented matrix for the system of linear equations.

2.
$$
\begin{array}{rrrrr}
x_1 & + & 2x_2 & - & x_3 & = & 1 \\
x_1 & & & + & 3x_3 & = & 2 \\
2x_1 & + & x_2 & & & = & 5
\end{array}
$$

3.
$$
\begin{array}{rrrrr}
x_1 & + & x_2 & + & x_3 & + & x_4 & = & 7 \\
x_1 & - & x_2 & + & x_3 & - & x_4 & = & 12
\end{array}
$$

4.
$$
\begin{array}{rrrrr}
\sqrt{2}x_1 & + & \sqrt{6}x_2 & & & = & 2 \\
\sqrt{3}x_1 & + & \sqrt{2}x_2 & + & \sqrt{6}x_3 & = & 3 \\
& & \sqrt{3}x_2 & + & \sqrt{2}x_3 & = & 6
\end{array}
$$

5.
$$
\begin{array}{rrrr}
x_1 & - & x_2 & = & 5 \\
x_1 & + & x_2 & = & -1 \\
2x_1 & + & 3x_2 & = & 4
\end{array}
$$

In questions 6–9, find a system of linear equations corresponding to the augmented matrix.

6.
$$
\begin{bmatrix}
1 & 11 & 6 & 3 \\
9 & 4 & 0 & -2 \\
5 & 9 & -4 & 1
\end{bmatrix}
$$

7.
$$
\begin{bmatrix}
1 & 0 & 0 & 1 \\
0 & 1 & 0 & 5 \\
0 & 0 & 1 & 10
\end{bmatrix}
$$

8.
$$
\begin{bmatrix}
1/3 & 1/4 & 1/8 \\
1/6 & 1/2 & 1/8 \\
1/2 & 1/4 & 3/4
\end{bmatrix}
$$

9.
$$
\begin{bmatrix}
1 & -1 & 1 & -1 & 1 & 0 \\
1 & 0 & 1 & 0 & -1 & 4 \\
1 & 1 & 0 & 1 & 1 & 9
\end{bmatrix}
$$

10. In each part, determine whether the matrix is in row–echelon form, reduced row–echelon form, both, or neither.

a)
$$
\begin{bmatrix}
1 & 0 & -1 & 1 \\
0 & 1 & 2 & 0 \\
0 & 1 & 3 & 1
\end{bmatrix}
$$

b)
$$
\begin{bmatrix}
1 & 0 & 2 & 5 \\
0 & 1 & -7 & 5 \\
0 & 0 & 1 & 14
\end{bmatrix}
$$

c)
$$
\begin{bmatrix}
1 & -1 & 2 & 5 \\
0 & 1 & -1 & 0 \\
0 & 0 & -1 & 3
\end{bmatrix}
$$

d)
$$
\begin{bmatrix}
1 & 0 & 0 & 11 & -3 \\
0 & 0 & 0 & 1 & 4
\end{bmatrix}
$$

e)
$$
\begin{bmatrix}
1 & 2 & -1 & -4 \\
0 & 1 & 2 & 5 \\
0 & 0 & 0 & 0 \\
0 & 0 & 1 & 3 \\
0 & 0 & 0 & 0
\end{bmatrix}
$$

f)
$$
\begin{bmatrix}
1 & 0 & 0 & 0 & 6 \\
0 & 1 & 0 & 0 & 16 \\
0 & 0 & 0 & 1 & 20 \\
0 & 0 & 0 & 0 & 0 \\
0 & 0 & 0 & 0 & 0
\end{bmatrix}
$$

In questions 11–16, solve the system by Gaussian elimination or by Gauss–Jordan elimination.

11.
$$
\begin{array}{rrrr}
x & - & y & - & z & = & 0 \\
2x & + & y & + & z & = & 3 \\
3x & & & - & z & = & 0
\end{array}
$$

12.
$$
\begin{array}{rrrr}
x_1 & - & x_2 & - & 5x_3 & = & -1 \\
-2x_1 & + & 2x_2 & + & 11x_3 & = & 1 \\
3x_1 & - & x_2 & + & x_3 & = & 3
\end{array}
$$

13.
$$
\begin{array}{rrrr}
x_1 & + & x_2 & + & 3x_3 & = & a \\
x_1 & & & + & 2x_3 & = & b \\
2x_1 & - & x_2 & + & x_3 & = & c
\end{array}
$$

14.
$$
\begin{array}{rrrr}
2x_1 & + & 2x_2 & - & 2x_3 & = & 4 \\
3x_1 & + & 5x_2 & + & x_3 & = & -8 \\
-4x_1 & - & 7x_2 & - & 2x_3 & = & 13
\end{array}
$$

15.
$$\begin{aligned}
x_1 &+ 3x_2 && + 2x_4 &= 2 \\
2x_1 &+ x_2 &+ 5x_3 + 4x_4 &= -16 \\
2x_1 &+ 3x_2 &+ 3x_3 && = 4 \\
3x_1 &+ 11x_2 &- 2x_3 + 11x_4 &= -1
\end{aligned}$$

16.
$$\begin{aligned}
x &- y &= 2 \\
2x &+ y &= 1 \\
x &+ 3y &= -1
\end{aligned}$$

In questions 17–20, solve the system by Gaussian elimination or by Gauss–Jordan elimination

17.
$$\begin{aligned}
x &- 4y &+ z &= 0 \\
2x &- 3y &+ 7z &= 0 \\
x &- 2y && = 0
\end{aligned}$$

18.
$$\begin{aligned}
x_1 &+ 7x_2 &+ x_3 &= 0 \\
2x_1 &+ 14x_2 &+ 5x_3 &= 0 \\
3x_1 &+ 21x_2 &+ 5x_3 &= 0
\end{aligned}$$

19.
$$\begin{aligned}
2x_1 &+ 6x_2 &- 4x_3 &= 0 \\
3x_1 &+ 9x_2 &- 6x_3 &= 0 \\
-4x_1 &- 12x_2 &+ 8x_3 &= 0
\end{aligned}$$

20.
$$\begin{aligned}
w &+ 6x &- y &+ 2z &= 0 \\
-w &- 4x &+ 3y &+ 8z &= 0 \\
2w &+ 11x && + 5z &= 0 \\
2w &+ 14x &- 2y &+ 13z &= 0
\end{aligned}$$

21. Consider the matrices:

$$A = \begin{bmatrix} 3 & 1 \\ -1 & 1 \end{bmatrix} \quad, \quad B = \begin{bmatrix} 1 & 2 \\ 4 & 3 \end{bmatrix} \quad, \quad C = \begin{bmatrix} 1 & -1 \\ 2 & 0 \end{bmatrix} \quad, \quad I = \begin{bmatrix} 1 & 0 \\ 0 & 1 \end{bmatrix}$$

Compute the following.

a) $B - A$

b) $3B + 4C - 2A$

c) $AB - BA$

d) $BAI - IBC$

e) $(A - 2I)^2$

f) $(A^2 - B^2)C^2$

g) $A^{-1} + AA^{-1}$

h) $BC - (C^{-1}B^{-1})^{-1}$

i) CC^T

j) $(3AB)^T - B^T A^T$

k) $tr(A)$

l) $tr(3A^T - 4B^T C^T)$

22. Consider the matrices

$$A = \begin{bmatrix} 1 & 2 & 1 \\ 0 & -1 & 5 \\ 1 & 6 & 0 \end{bmatrix} \quad, \quad B = \begin{bmatrix} 1 & 3 & -2 \\ 4 & 0 & 1 \end{bmatrix} \quad, \quad C = \begin{bmatrix} 2 & 6 \\ 1 & -1 \\ 5 & 0 \end{bmatrix}$$

Compute the following.

a) BC

b) CB

c) $A^2 - 2CB$

d) $(AC + 3B^T)^T$

e) BCB

f) $tr(1/3BAC)$

23. Consider the matrices and scalars:

$$A = \begin{bmatrix} 1 & 1 & 5 \\ -1 & 1 & 0 \\ 1 & 0 & 1 \end{bmatrix} \quad, \quad B = \begin{bmatrix} 1 & 1 & 0 \\ 2 & 2 & -1 \\ 0 & 1 & -1 \end{bmatrix} \quad, \quad C = \begin{bmatrix} 0 & 1 & 3 \\ 2 & 0 & 0 \\ -2 & 4 & 1 \end{bmatrix} \quad, \quad a = 2 \quad, \quad b = 3$$

Use these to show the following:

a) $A + (B + C) = (A + B) + C$

b) $(AB)C = A(BC)$

c) $A(B + C) = AB + AC$

d) $a(bC) = (ab)C$

e) $(A + B)^T = A^T + B^T$

f) $(AB)^T = B^T A^T$

2

In questions 24–25, find matrices A, X, and B such that the given system of linear equations can be abbreviated $AX = B$.

24.
$$\begin{aligned} x + 2y - z &= 5 \\ 2x - y + 11z &= 19 \\ 3x + y + z &= 11 \end{aligned}$$

25.
$$\begin{aligned} - x_2 - x_3 - x_4 &= 1 \\ -x_1 - x_3 - x_4 &= 1 \\ -x_1 - x_2 - x_4 &= 1 \\ -x_1 - x_2 - x_3 &= 1 \end{aligned}$$

In questions 26–27, express the matrix equation as a system of linear equations.

26.
$$\begin{bmatrix} -1 & 7 & 0 \\ 0 & 4 & 3 \\ 6 & 0 & -2 \end{bmatrix} \begin{bmatrix} x \\ y \\ z \end{bmatrix} = \begin{bmatrix} 0 \\ 0 \\ 0 \end{bmatrix}$$

27.
$$\begin{bmatrix} 1/3 & 1/2 & 0 & -1/6 \\ 2/3 & 1/6 & -1/2 & 0 \end{bmatrix} \begin{bmatrix} x_1 \\ x_2 \\ x_3 \\ x_4 \end{bmatrix} = \begin{bmatrix} 1/2 \\ 1/4 \end{bmatrix}$$

28. For each matrix, indicate whether it is elementary and, if it is, indicate which row operation will restore the matrix to an identity matrix.

a) $\begin{bmatrix} 1 & 0 \\ 5 & 1 \end{bmatrix}$

b) $\begin{bmatrix} \sqrt{2} & 0 \\ 0 & \sqrt{2} \end{bmatrix}$

c) $\begin{bmatrix} 0 & 1 & 0 \\ 1 & 0 & 0 \\ 0 & 0 & 1 \end{bmatrix}$

b) $\begin{bmatrix} 1 & 0 & 0 \\ 0 & -2 & 0 \\ 0 & 0 & 1 \end{bmatrix}$

e) $\begin{bmatrix} 1 & 0 & 0 \\ 3 & 0 & 0 \\ 0 & 0 & 1 \end{bmatrix}$

f) $\begin{bmatrix} 1 & 0 & 0 & 0 \\ 0 & 1 & 0 & 0 \\ 0 & 0 & 1 & 0 \\ 0 & -9 & 0 & 1 \end{bmatrix}$

In questions 29–32, consider the matrices:

$$A = \begin{bmatrix} 1 & 4 & 6 \\ 0 & 0 & 1 \\ 2 & 10 & 9 \end{bmatrix} \quad, \quad B = \begin{bmatrix} 1 & 4 & 6 \\ 0 & 0 & 1 \\ 0 & 2 & -3 \end{bmatrix} \quad, \quad C = \begin{bmatrix} 1 & 4 & 6 \\ 0 & 2 & -3 \\ 0 & 0 & 1 \end{bmatrix}$$

Find elementary matrices E_1, E_2, E_3, and E_4 satisfying the given equation.

29. $E_1 A = B$ 30. $E_2 B = A$ 31. $E_3 B = C$ 32. $E_4 C = B$

In questions 33–40, use Gauss-Jordan elimination to find the inverse of the given matrix if the matrix is invertible.

33. $\begin{bmatrix} 2 & 3 \\ 5 & 6 \end{bmatrix}$

34. $\begin{bmatrix} 1 & 2 & 1 \\ 0 & 2 & 2 \\ 0 & 0 & 4 \end{bmatrix}$

35. $\begin{bmatrix} 1 & -5 & 3 \\ 2 & 0 & 1 \\ 1 & 1 & 1 \end{bmatrix}$

36. $\begin{bmatrix} 1 & -5 & 5 \\ 4 & 3 & 2 \\ 9 & 1 & 9 \end{bmatrix}$

37. $\begin{bmatrix} 1/2 & 0 & 0 \\ 1/4 & 1/2 & 0 \\ 1 & 1/4 & 1/2 \end{bmatrix}$

38. $\begin{bmatrix} 1 & -3 & 0 & 0 \\ -1 & 4 & 0 & 0 \\ 0 & 0 & 5 & 6 \\ 0 & 0 & 2 & 2 \end{bmatrix}$

3

39. $\begin{bmatrix} 0 & 0 & 1 \\ 0 & 1 & k_1 \\ 1 & k_2 & 0 \end{bmatrix}$

40. $\begin{bmatrix} 1 & 0 & 0 & 0 \\ k & 1 & 0 & 0 \\ 0 & k & 1 & 0 \\ 0 & 0 & k & 1 \end{bmatrix}$

In questions 41–48, use an inverse matrix to solve the system of equations.

41.
$$7x + 2y = 1$$
$$3x + y = 5$$

42.
$$x_1 + 4x_2 = 3$$
$$5x_1 + x_2 = -2$$

43.
$$x + 6y + 5z = 3$$
$$y + z = -1$$
$$2z = -4$$

44.
$$x_1 - x_2 + 2x_3 = 1$$
$$-2x_1 + x_2 + x_3 = -1$$
$$-3x_1 + x_2 + 5x_3 = -1$$

45.
$$2x_1 - 3x_2 + 10x_3 = 10$$
$$- x_2 + 2x_3 = 30$$
$$-4x_1 + 8x_2 - 19x_3 = -20$$

46.
$$x_1 - 2x_2 - 6x_3 - 2x_4 = 4$$
$$x_1 + x_2 + 2x_3 + x_4 = -2$$
$$x_1 - x_3 = 1$$
$$3x_1 + 3x_2 + 7x_3 + 4x_4 = 3$$

47.
$$.3x + .4y = b_1$$
$$.7x + .6y = b_2$$

48.
$$x_1 + x_2 + x_3 = b_1$$
$$3x_1 + 4x_2 + 5x_3 = b_2$$
$$-2x_1 + x_3 = b_3$$

In questions 49–52, find the conditions that the "b's" must satisfy for the system to be consistent.

49.
$$6x - 3y = b_1$$
$$-10x + 5y = b_2$$

50.
$$x_1 + 4x_2 - 3x_3 = b_1$$
$$2x_1 + 6x_2 + 5x_3 = b_2$$
$$x_1 = 6x_2 - 14x_3 = b_3$$

51.
$$x_1 + 3x_2 + x_3 = b_1$$
$$2x_1 + 7x_2 + 3x_3 = b_2$$
$$-x_1 - x_2 + 2x_3 = b_3$$

52.
$$x_1 + 4x_2 + 7x_3 = b_1$$
$$2x_1 + 5x_2 + x_3 = b_2$$
$$x_1 + 7x_2 + 20x_3 = b_3$$
$$-x_1 + 2x_2 + 19x_3 = b_4$$

WRITING QUESTIONS

53. Discuss the relative merits of these three methods of solving systems of linear equations:

   a) simple elimination
   b) Gaussian elimination
   c) Gauss–Jordan elimination

54. Why do we study row operations as opposed to column operations on a matrix?

55. In Gauss and Gauss–Jordan elimination, why is it that 0's and 1's established in one column are not disturbed by the pivoting done in columns further to the right?

56. Describe what you have observed as to the effect of the number of equations and the number of variables upon the size of the solution set of a linear system.

4

57. Describe some ways that multiplication of matrices has properties different from multiplication of real numbers.

58. What would be wrong with defining matrix multiplication for matrices of the same size by multiplying them entry–by–entry, as with addition and subtraction?

59. Why does a multiplicative identity matrix not consist entirely of 1's?

60. Why is it impossible for a linear system to have exactly two solutions? Explain it graphically so that a high school student could understand.

61. Why are multiplicative inverses of matrices so important in linear algebra?

62. Why is the method of solving a system of linear equations by using the inverse of the coefficient matrix not a general method for solving such systems?

SECTION 1.1 *INTRODUCTION TO SYSTEMS OF LINEAR EQUATIONS*

1. a) yes   b) no   c) no   d) yes   e) **yes**   f) **no**

2. $\begin{bmatrix} 1 & 2 & -1 & 1 \\ 1 & 0 & 3 & 2 \\ 2 & 1 & 0 & 5 \end{bmatrix}$

3. $\begin{bmatrix} 1 & 1 & 1 & 1 & 7 \\ 1 & -1 & 1 & -1 & 12 \end{bmatrix}$

4. $\begin{bmatrix} \sqrt{2} & \sqrt{6} & 0 & 2 \\ \sqrt{3} & \sqrt{2} & \sqrt{6} & 3 \\ 0 & \sqrt{3} & \sqrt{2} & 6 \end{bmatrix}$

5. $\begin{bmatrix} 1 & -1 & 5 \\ 1 & 1 & -1 \\ 2 & 3 & 4 \end{bmatrix}$

6. $\begin{aligned} x_1 + 11x_2 + 6x_3 &= 3 \\ 9x_1 + 4x_2 &= -2 \\ 5x_1 + 9x_2 - 4x_3 &= 1 \end{aligned}$

7. $\begin{aligned} x_1 &= 1 \\ x_2 &= 5 \\ x_3 &= 10 \end{aligned}$

8. $\begin{aligned} 1/3x_1 + 1/4x_2 &= 1/8 \\ 1/6x_1 + 1/2x_2 &= 1/8 \\ 1/2x_1 + 1/4x_2 &= 3/4 \end{aligned}$

9. $\begin{aligned} x_1 - x_2 + x_3 - x_4 + x_5 &= 0 \\ x_1 + x_3 - x_5 &= 4 \\ x_1 + x_2 + x_4 + x_5 &= 9 \end{aligned}$

SECTION 1.2 *GAUSSIAN ELIMINATION*

10. a) neither   b) row–echelon   c) neither

    d) row–echelon   e) neither   f) both

11. $\begin{bmatrix} 1 & -1 & -1 & 0 \\ 2 & 1 & 1 & 3 \\ 3 & 0 & -1 & 0 \end{bmatrix} \longrightarrow \begin{bmatrix} 1 & -1 & -1 & 0 \\ 0 & 3 & 3 & 3 \\ 3 & 0 & -1 & 0 \end{bmatrix} \longrightarrow \begin{bmatrix} 1 & -1 & -1 & 0 \\ 0 & 3 & 3 & 3 \\ 0 & 3 & 2 & 0 \end{bmatrix} \longrightarrow$

    $\begin{bmatrix} 1 & -1 & -1 & 0 \\ 0 & 1 & 1 & 1 \\ 0 & 3 & 2 & 0 \end{bmatrix} \longrightarrow \begin{bmatrix} 1 & -1 & -1 & 0 \\ 0 & 1 & 1 & 1 \\ 0 & 0 & -1 & -3 \end{bmatrix} \longrightarrow \begin{bmatrix} 1 & -1 & -1 & 0 \\ 0 & 1 & 1 & 1 \\ 0 & 0 & 1 & 3 \end{bmatrix}$

    To finish by Gaussian,
    $$z = 3$$
    $$y + z = 1 \quad \text{so} \quad y = 1 - z = 1 - 3 = -2$$
    $$x - y - z = 0 \quad \text{so} \quad x = y + z = -2 + 3 = 1$$

    To finish by Gauss–Jordan,

    $\begin{bmatrix} 1 & -1 & -1 & 0 \\ 0 & 1 & 1 & 1 \\ 0 & 0 & 1 & 3 \end{bmatrix} \longrightarrow \begin{bmatrix} 1 & 0 & 0 & 1 \\ 0 & 1 & 1 & 1 \\ 0 & 0 & 1 & 3 \end{bmatrix} \longrightarrow \begin{bmatrix} 1 & 0 & 0 & 1 \\ 0 & 1 & 0 & -2 \\ 0 & 0 & 1 & 3 \end{bmatrix}$

so $x = 1$, $y = -2$, $z = 3$.

12. $\begin{bmatrix} 1 & -1 & -5 & -1 \\ -2 & 2 & 11 & 1 \\ 3 & -1 & 1 & 3 \end{bmatrix} \longrightarrow \begin{bmatrix} 1 & -1 & -5 & -1 \\ 0 & 0 & 1 & -1 \\ 3 & -1 & 1 & 3 \end{bmatrix} \longrightarrow \begin{bmatrix} 1 & -1 & -5 & -1 \\ 0 & 0 & 1 & -1 \\ 0 & 2 & 16 & 6 \end{bmatrix} \longrightarrow$

$\begin{bmatrix} 1 & -1 & -5 & -1 \\ 0 & 2 & 16 & 6 \\ 0 & 0 & 1 & -1 \end{bmatrix} \longrightarrow \begin{bmatrix} 1 & -1 & -5 & -1 \\ 0 & 1 & 8 & 3 \\ 0 & 0 & 1 & -1 \end{bmatrix}$

To finish by Gaussian,

$x_3 = -1$

$x_2 + 8x_3 = 3$ so $x_2 = 3 - 8x_3 = 3 + 8 = 11$

$x_1 - x_2 - 5x_3 = -1$ so $x_1 = -1 + x_2 + 5x_3 = -1 + 11 - 5 = 5$

To finish by Gauss–Jordan,

$\begin{bmatrix} 1 & -1 & -5 & -1 \\ 0 & 1 & 8 & 3 \\ 0 & 0 & 1 & -1 \end{bmatrix} \longrightarrow \begin{bmatrix} 1 & 0 & 3 & 2 \\ 0 & 1 & 0 & 11 \\ 0 & 0 & 1 & -1 \end{bmatrix} \longrightarrow \begin{bmatrix} 1 & 0 & 0 & 5 \\ 0 & 1 & 0 & 11 \\ 0 & 0 & 1 & -1 \end{bmatrix}$

so $x_1 = 5$, $x_2 = 11$, $x_3 = -1$

13.

$\begin{bmatrix} 1 & 1 & 3 & a \\ 1 & 0 & 2 & b \\ 2 & -1 & 1 & c \end{bmatrix} \longrightarrow \begin{bmatrix} 1 & 1 & 3 & a \\ 0 & -1 & -1 & -a+b \\ 2 & -1 & 1 & c \end{bmatrix} \longrightarrow \begin{bmatrix} 1 & 1 & 3 & a \\ 0 & -1 & -1 & -a+b \\ 0 & -3 & -5 & -2a+c \end{bmatrix} \longrightarrow$

$\begin{bmatrix} 1 & 1 & 3 & a \\ 0 & 1 & 1 & a-b \\ 0 & -3 & -5 & -2a+c \end{bmatrix} \longrightarrow \begin{bmatrix} 1 & 1 & 3 & a \\ 0 & 1 & 1 & a-b \\ 0 & 0 & -2 & a-3b+c \end{bmatrix}$

$\longrightarrow \begin{bmatrix} 1 & 1 & 3 & a \\ 0 & 1 & 1 & a-b \\ 0 & 0 & 1 & (-1/2)a + (3/2)b - (1/2)c \end{bmatrix}$

To finish by Gaussian,

$x_3 = (-1/2)a + (3/2)b - (1/2)c$

$x_2 + x_3 = a - b$ so $x_2 = a - b - x_3 = a - b - \left((-1/2)a + (3/2)b - (1/2)c \right)$

$\qquad = (3/2)a - (5/2)b + (1/2)c$

$x_1 + x_2 + 3x_3 = a$ so $x_1 = a - x_2 - 3x_3$

$\qquad = a - \left((3/2)a - (5/2)b + (1/2)c \right) - 3\left((-1/2)a + (3/2)b - (1/2)c \right)$

$\qquad = a - 2b + c$

To finish by Gauss–Jordan,

$$\begin{bmatrix} 1 & 1 & 3 & a \\ 0 & 1 & 1 & a-b \\ 0 & 0 & 1 & (-1/2)a+(3/2)b-(1/2)c \end{bmatrix} \longrightarrow \begin{bmatrix} 1 & 0 & 2 & b \\ 0 & 1 & 1 & a-b \\ 0 & 0 & 1 & (-1/2)a+(3/2)b-(1/2)c \end{bmatrix} \longrightarrow$$

$$\begin{bmatrix} 1 & 0 & 0 & a-2b+c \\ 0 & 1 & 1 & a-b \\ 0 & 0 & 1 & (-1/2)a+(3/2)b-(1/2)c \end{bmatrix} \longrightarrow \begin{bmatrix} 1 & 0 & 0 & a-2b+c \\ 0 & 1 & 0 & (3/2)a-(5/2)b+(1/2)c \\ 0 & 0 & 1 & (-1/2)a+(3/2)b-(1/2)c \end{bmatrix}$$

so $x_1 = a-2b+c$, $x_2 = (3/2)a-(5/2)b+(1/2)c$, $x_3 = (-1/2)a+(3/2)b-(1/2)c$

14. $\begin{bmatrix} 2 & 2 & -2 & 4 \\ 3 & 5 & 1 & -8 \\ -4 & -7 & -2 & 13 \end{bmatrix} \longrightarrow \begin{bmatrix} 1 & 1 & -1 & 2 \\ 3 & 5 & 1 & -8 \\ -4 & -7 & -2 & 13 \end{bmatrix} \longrightarrow \begin{bmatrix} 1 & 1 & -1 & 2 \\ 0 & 2 & 4 & -14 \\ -4 & -7 & -2 & 13 \end{bmatrix} \longrightarrow$

$\begin{bmatrix} 1 & 1 & -1 & 2 \\ 0 & 2 & 4 & -14 \\ 0 & -3 & -6 & 21 \end{bmatrix} \longrightarrow \begin{bmatrix} 1 & 1 & -1 & 2 \\ 0 & 1 & 2 & -7 \\ 0 & -3 & -6 & 21 \end{bmatrix} \longrightarrow \begin{bmatrix} 1 & 1 & -1 & 2 \\ 0 & 1 & 2 & -7 \\ 0 & 0 & 0 & 0 \end{bmatrix}$

To finish by Gaussian,

Let $x_3 = t$;

then $x_2 + 2x_3 = -7$ so $x_2 = -7 - 2x_3 = -7 - 2t$

and $x_1 + x_2 - x_3 = 2$ so $x_1 = 2 - x_2 + x_3 = 2 - (-7 - 2t) + t = 9 + 3t$

To finish by Gauss–Jordan,

$\begin{bmatrix} 1 & 1 & -1 & 2 \\ 0 & 1 & 2 & -7 \\ 0 & 0 & 0 & 0 \end{bmatrix} \longrightarrow \begin{bmatrix} 1 & 0 & -3 & 9 \\ 0 & 1 & 2 & -7 \\ 0 & 0 & 0 & 0 \end{bmatrix}$

Let $x_3 = t$;

then $x_2 + 2x_3 = -7$ so $x_2 = -7 - 2x_3 = -7 - 2t$

and $x_1 - 3x_3 = 9$ so $x_1 = 9 + 3x_3 = 9 + 3t$

15. $\begin{bmatrix} 1 & 3 & 0 & 2 & 2 \\ 2 & 1 & 5 & 4 & -16 \\ 2 & 3 & 3 & 0 & 4 \\ 3 & 11 & -2 & 11 & -1 \end{bmatrix} \longrightarrow \begin{bmatrix} 1 & 3 & 0 & 2 & 2 \\ 0 & -5 & 5 & 0 & -20 \\ 2 & 3 & 3 & 0 & 4 \\ 3 & 11 & -2 & 11 & -1 \end{bmatrix} \longrightarrow \begin{bmatrix} 1 & 3 & 0 & 2 & 2 \\ 0 & -5 & 5 & 0 & -20 \\ 0 & -3 & 3 & -4 & 0 \\ 3 & 11 & -2 & 11 & -1 \end{bmatrix} \longrightarrow$

$\begin{bmatrix} 1 & 3 & 0 & 2 & 2 \\ 0 & -5 & 5 & 0 & -20 \\ 0 & -3 & 3 & -4 & 0 \\ 0 & 2 & -2 & 5 & -7 \end{bmatrix} \longrightarrow \begin{bmatrix} 1 & 3 & 0 & 2 & 2 \\ 0 & 1 & -1 & 0 & 4 \\ 0 & -3 & 3 & -4 & 0 \\ 0 & 2 & -2 & 5 & -7 \end{bmatrix} \longrightarrow \begin{bmatrix} 1 & 3 & 0 & 2 & 2 \\ 0 & 1 & -1 & 0 & 4 \\ 0 & 0 & 0 & -4 & 12 \\ 0 & 2 & -2 & 5 & -7 \end{bmatrix} \longrightarrow$

$\begin{bmatrix} 1 & 3 & 0 & 2 & 2 \\ 0 & 1 & -1 & 0 & 4 \\ 0 & 0 & 0 & -4 & 12 \\ 0 & 0 & 0 & 5 & -15 \end{bmatrix} \longrightarrow \begin{bmatrix} 1 & 3 & 0 & 2 & 2 \\ 0 & 1 & -1 & 0 & 4 \\ 0 & 0 & 0 & 1 & -3 \\ 0 & 0 & 0 & 5 & -15 \end{bmatrix} \longrightarrow \begin{bmatrix} 1 & 3 & 0 & 2 & 2 \\ 0 & 1 & -1 & 0 & 4 \\ 0 & 0 & 0 & 1 & -3 \\ 0 & 0 & 0 & 0 & 0 \end{bmatrix}$

To finish by Gaussian,

$x_4 = -3$

Let $\quad x_3 = t$

then $\quad x_2 - x_3 = 4 \quad$ so $\quad x_2 = 4 + x_3 = 4 + t$

and $\quad x_1 + 3x_2 + 2x_4 = 2 \quad$ so $\quad x_1 = 2 - 3x_2 - 2x_4 = 2 - 3(4 + t) - 2(-3) = -4 - 3t$

To finish by Gauss–Jordan,

$$
\begin{bmatrix} 1 & 3 & 0 & 2 & 2 \\ 0 & 1 & -1 & 0 & 4 \\ 0 & 0 & 0 & 1 & -3 \\ 0 & 0 & 0 & 0 & 0 \end{bmatrix}
\longrightarrow
\begin{bmatrix} 1 & 0 & 3 & 2 & -10 \\ 0 & 1 & -1 & 0 & 4 \\ 0 & 0 & 0 & 1 & -3 \\ 0 & 0 & 0 & 0 & 0 \end{bmatrix}
\longrightarrow
\begin{bmatrix} 1 & 0 & 3 & 0 & -4 \\ 0 & 1 & -1 & 0 & 4 \\ 0 & 0 & 0 & 1 & -3 \\ 0 & 0 & 0 & 0 & 0 \end{bmatrix}
$$

$x_4 = -3$

Let $\quad x_3 = t$;

then $\quad x_2 - x_3 = \quad 4 \quad$ so $\quad x_2 = 4 + x_3 = 4 + t$

and $\quad x_1 + 3x_3 = -4 \quad$ so $\quad x_1 = -4 - 3x_3 = -4 - 3t$

16.
$$
\begin{bmatrix} 1 & -1 & 2 \\ 2 & 1 & 1 \\ 1 & 3 & -1 \end{bmatrix}
\longrightarrow
\begin{bmatrix} 1 & -1 & 2 \\ 0 & 3 & -3 \\ 1 & 3 & -1 \end{bmatrix}
\longrightarrow
\begin{bmatrix} 1 & -1 & 2 \\ 0 & 3 & -3 \\ 0 & 4 & -3 \end{bmatrix}
\longrightarrow
\begin{bmatrix} 1 & -1 & 2 \\ 0 & 1 & -1 \\ 0 & 4 & -3 \end{bmatrix}
$$

$$
\longrightarrow
\begin{bmatrix} 1 & -1 & 2 \\ 0 & 1 & -1 \\ 0 & 0 & 1 \end{bmatrix}
$$

and since the last row is an inconsistency, there are no solutions.

17.
$$
\begin{bmatrix} 1 & -4 & 1 & 0 \\ 2 & -3 & 7 & 0 \\ 1 & -2 & 0 & 0 \end{bmatrix}
\longrightarrow
\begin{bmatrix} 1 & -4 & 1 & 0 \\ 0 & 5 & 5 & 0 \\ 1 & -2 & 0 & 0 \end{bmatrix}
\longrightarrow
\begin{bmatrix} 1 & -4 & 1 & 0 \\ 0 & 5 & 5 & 0 \\ 0 & 2 & -1 & 0 \end{bmatrix}
$$

$$
\longrightarrow
\begin{bmatrix} 1 & -4 & 1 & 0 \\ 0 & 1 & 1 & 0 \\ 0 & 2 & -1 & 0 \end{bmatrix}
\longrightarrow
\begin{bmatrix} 1 & -4 & 1 & 0 \\ 0 & 1 & 1 & 0 \\ 0 & 0 & -3 & 0 \end{bmatrix}
\longrightarrow
\begin{bmatrix} 1 & -4 & 1 & 0 \\ 0 & 1 & 1 & 0 \\ 0 & 0 & 1 & 0 \end{bmatrix}
$$

To finish by Gaussian,

$x_3 = 0$

$x_2 + x_3 = 0 \quad$ so $\quad x_2 = -x_3 = 0$

$x_1 - 4x_2 + x_3 = 0 \quad$ so $\quad x_1 = 4x_2 - x_3 = 0 - 0 = 0$

To finish by Gauss–Jordan,

$$
\begin{bmatrix} 1 & -4 & 1 & 0 \\ 0 & 1 & 1 & 0 \\ 0 & 0 & 1 & 0 \end{bmatrix}
\longrightarrow
\begin{bmatrix} 1 & 0 & 5 & 0 \\ 0 & 1 & 1 & 0 \\ 0 & 0 & 1 & 0 \end{bmatrix}
\longrightarrow
\begin{bmatrix} 1 & 0 & 0 & 0 \\ 0 & 1 & 1 & 0 \\ 0 & 0 & 1 & 0 \end{bmatrix}
$$

$$\longrightarrow \begin{bmatrix} 1 & 0 & 0 & 0 \\ 0 & 1 & 0 & 0 \\ 0 & 0 & 1 & 0 \end{bmatrix}$$

i.e., $x_1 = 0$, $x_2 = 0$, $x_3 = 0$

18. $\begin{bmatrix} 1 & 7 & 1 & 0 \\ 2 & 14 & 5 & 0 \\ 3 & 21 & 5 & 0 \end{bmatrix} \longrightarrow \begin{bmatrix} 1 & 7 & 1 & 0 \\ 0 & 0 & 3 & 0 \\ 3 & 21 & 5 & 0 \end{bmatrix} \longrightarrow \begin{bmatrix} 1 & 7 & 1 & 0 \\ 0 & 0 & 3 & 0 \\ 0 & 0 & 2 & 0 \end{bmatrix}$

$\longrightarrow \begin{bmatrix} 1 & 7 & 1 & 0 \\ 0 & 0 & 1 & 0 \\ 0 & 0 & 2 & 0 \end{bmatrix} \longrightarrow \begin{bmatrix} 1 & 7 & 1 & 0 \\ 0 & 0 & 1 & 0 \\ 0 & 0 & 0 & 0 \end{bmatrix}$

To finish by Gaussian,

$x_3 = 0$

Let $x_2 = t$;

then $x_1 + 7x_2 + x_3 = 0$ so $x_1 = -7x_2 - x_3 = -7t - 0 = -7t$

To finish by Gauss–Jordan,

$\begin{bmatrix} 1 & 7 & 1 & 0 \\ 0 & 0 & 1 & 0 \\ 0 & 0 & 0 & 0 \end{bmatrix} \longrightarrow \begin{bmatrix} 1 & 7 & 0 & 0 \\ 0 & 0 & 1 & 0 \\ 0 & 0 & 0 & 0 \end{bmatrix}$

$x_3 = 0$

Let $x_2 = t$;

then $x_1 + 7x_2 = 0$ so $x_1 = -7x_2 = -7t$

19.

$\begin{bmatrix} 2 & 6 & -4 & 0 \\ 3 & 9 & -6 & 0 \\ -4 & -12 & 8 & 0 \end{bmatrix} \longrightarrow \begin{bmatrix} 1 & 3 & -2 & 0 \\ 3 & 9 & -6 & 0 \\ -4 & -12 & 8 & 0 \end{bmatrix} \longrightarrow \begin{bmatrix} 1 & 3 & -2 & 0 \\ 0 & 0 & 0 & 0 \\ -4 & -12 & 8 & 0 \end{bmatrix}$

$\longrightarrow \begin{bmatrix} 1 & 3 & -2 & 0 \\ 0 & 0 & 0 & 0 \\ 0 & 0 & 0 & 0 \end{bmatrix}$

Let $x_3 = t$

and $x_2 = s$;

then $x_1 + 3x_2 - 2x_3 = 0$ so $x_1 = -3x_2 + 2x_3 = -3s + 2t$

20.

$\begin{bmatrix} 1 & 6 & -1 & 2 & 0 \\ -1 & -4 & 3 & 8 & 0 \\ 2 & 11 & 0 & 5 & 0 \\ 2 & 14 & -2 & 13 & 0 \end{bmatrix} \longrightarrow \begin{bmatrix} 1 & 6 & -1 & 2 & 0 \\ 0 & 2 & 2 & 10 & 0 \\ 2 & 11 & 0 & 5 & 0 \\ 2 & 14 & -2 & 13 & 0 \end{bmatrix} \longrightarrow \begin{bmatrix} 1 & 6 & -1 & 2 & 0 \\ 0 & 2 & 2 & 10 & 0 \\ 0 & -1 & 2 & 1 & 0 \\ 2 & 14 & -2 & 13 & 0 \end{bmatrix} \longrightarrow$

10

$$\begin{bmatrix} 1 & 6 & -1 & 2 & 0 \\ 0 & 2 & 2 & 10 & 0 \\ 0 & -1 & 2 & 1 & 0 \\ 0 & 2 & 0 & 9 & 0 \end{bmatrix} \rightarrow \begin{bmatrix} 1 & 6 & -1 & 2 & 0 \\ 0 & 1 & 1 & 5 & 0 \\ 0 & -1 & 2 & 1 & 0 \\ 0 & 2 & 0 & 9 & 0 \end{bmatrix} \rightarrow \begin{bmatrix} 1 & 6 & -1 & 2 & 0 \\ 0 & 1 & 1 & 5 & 0 \\ 0 & 0 & 3 & 6 & 0 \\ 0 & 2 & 0 & 9 & 0 \end{bmatrix} \rightarrow$$

$$\begin{bmatrix} 1 & 6 & -1 & 2 & 0 \\ 0 & 1 & 1 & 5 & 0 \\ 0 & 0 & 3 & 6 & 0 \\ 0 & 0 & -2 & -1 & 0 \end{bmatrix} \rightarrow \begin{bmatrix} 1 & 6 & -1 & 2 & 0 \\ 0 & 1 & 1 & 5 & 0 \\ 0 & 0 & 1 & 2 & 0 \\ 0 & 0 & -2 & -1 & 0 \end{bmatrix} \rightarrow \begin{bmatrix} 1 & 6 & -1 & 2 & 0 \\ 0 & 1 & 1 & 5 & 0 \\ 0 & 0 & 1 & 2 & 0 \\ 0 & 0 & 0 & 3 & 0 \end{bmatrix} \rightarrow$$

$$\begin{bmatrix} 1 & 6 & -1 & 2 & 0 \\ 0 & 1 & 1 & 5 & 0 \\ 0 & 0 & 1 & 2 & 0 \\ 0 & 0 & 0 & 1 & 0 \end{bmatrix}$$

To finish by Guassian,

$z = 0$

$y + 2z = 0$ so $y = -2z = 0$

$x + y + 5z = 0$ so $x = -y - 5z = 0 - 0 = 0$

$w + 6x - y + 2z = 0$ so $w = -6x + y - 2z = 0 + 0 - 0 = 0$

To finish by Gauss–Jordan

$$\begin{bmatrix} 1 & 6 & -1 & 2 & 0 \\ 0 & 1 & 1 & 5 & 0 \\ 0 & 0 & 1 & 2 & 0 \\ 0 & 0 & 0 & 1 & 0 \end{bmatrix} \rightarrow \begin{bmatrix} 1 & 0 & -7 & -28 & 0 \\ 0 & 1 & 1 & 5 & 0 \\ 0 & 0 & 1 & 2 & 0 \\ 0 & 0 & 0 & 1 & 0 \end{bmatrix} \rightarrow \begin{bmatrix} 1 & 0 & 0 & -14 & 0 \\ 0 & 1 & 1 & 5 & 0 \\ 0 & 0 & 1 & 2 & 0 \\ 0 & 0 & 0 & 1 & 0 \end{bmatrix} \rightarrow$$

$$\begin{bmatrix} 1 & 0 & 0 & -14 & 0 \\ 0 & 1 & 0 & 3 & 0 \\ 0 & 0 & 1 & 2 & 0 \\ 0 & 0 & 0 & 1 & 0 \end{bmatrix} \rightarrow \begin{bmatrix} 1 & 0 & 0 & 0 & 0 \\ 0 & 1 & 0 & 3 & 0 \\ 0 & 0 & 1 & 2 & 0 \\ 0 & 0 & 0 & 1 & 0 \end{bmatrix} \rightarrow \begin{bmatrix} 1 & 0 & 0 & 0 & 0 \\ 0 & 1 & 0 & 0 & 0 \\ 0 & 0 & 1 & 2 & 0 \\ 0 & 0 & 0 & 1 & 0 \end{bmatrix} \rightarrow$$

$$\begin{bmatrix} 1 & 0 & 0 & 0 & 0 \\ 0 & 1 & 0 & 0 & 0 \\ 0 & 0 & 1 & 0 & 0 \\ 0 & 0 & 0 & 1 & 0 \end{bmatrix}$$

i.e., $w = 0$, $x = 0$, $y = 0$, $z = 0$

21. (a) $B - A = \begin{bmatrix} 1 & 2 \\ 4 & 3 \end{bmatrix} - \begin{bmatrix} 3 & 1 \\ -1 & 1 \end{bmatrix} = \begin{bmatrix} -2 & 1 \\ 5 & 2 \end{bmatrix}$

(b) $3B + 4C - 2A = 3\begin{bmatrix} 1 & 2 \\ 4 & 3 \end{bmatrix} + 4\begin{bmatrix} 1 & -1 \\ 2 & 0 \end{bmatrix} - 2\begin{bmatrix} -3 & 1 \\ -1 & 1 \end{bmatrix}$

$= \begin{bmatrix} 3 & 6 \\ 12 & 9 \end{bmatrix} + \begin{bmatrix} 4 & -4 \\ 8 & 0 \end{bmatrix} - \begin{bmatrix} 6 & 2 \\ -2 & 2 \end{bmatrix} = \begin{bmatrix} 1 & 0 \\ 22 & 7 \end{bmatrix}$

(c) $AB - BA = \begin{bmatrix} 3 & 1 \\ -1 & 1 \end{bmatrix}\begin{bmatrix} 1 & 2 \\ 4 & 3 \end{bmatrix} - \begin{bmatrix} 1 & 2 \\ 4 & 3 \end{bmatrix}\begin{bmatrix} 3 & 1 \\ -1 & 1 \end{bmatrix}$

$= \begin{bmatrix} 7 & 9 \\ 3 & 1 \end{bmatrix} - \begin{bmatrix} 1 & 3 \\ 9 & 7 \end{bmatrix} = \begin{bmatrix} 6 & 6 \\ -6 & -6 \end{bmatrix}$

(d) $BAI - IBC = BA - BC = B(A - C) = \begin{bmatrix} 1 & 2 \\ 4 & 3 \end{bmatrix}\begin{bmatrix} 2 & 2 \\ -3 & 1 \end{bmatrix} = \begin{bmatrix} -4 & 4 \\ -1 & 11 \end{bmatrix}$

(e) $(A - 2I)^2 = \begin{bmatrix} 3-2 & 1-0 \\ -1-0 & 1-2 \end{bmatrix}^2 = \begin{bmatrix} 1 & 1 \\ -1 & -1 \end{bmatrix}^2 = \begin{bmatrix} 1 & 1 \\ -1 & -1 \end{bmatrix}\begin{bmatrix} 1 & 1 \\ -1 & -1 \end{bmatrix} = \begin{bmatrix} 0 & 0 \\ 0 & 0 \end{bmatrix}$

(f) $(A^2 - B^2)C^2 = \left(\begin{bmatrix} 3 & 1 \\ -1 & 1 \end{bmatrix}^2 - \begin{bmatrix} 1 & 2 \\ 4 & 3 \end{bmatrix}^2 \right) \begin{bmatrix} 1 & -1 \\ 2 & 0 \end{bmatrix}^2$

$= \left(\begin{bmatrix} 8 & 4 \\ -4 & 0 \end{bmatrix} - \begin{bmatrix} 9 & 8 \\ 16 & 17 \end{bmatrix} \right) \begin{bmatrix} -1 & -1 \\ 2 & -2 \end{bmatrix} = \begin{bmatrix} -1 & -4 \\ -20 & -17 \end{bmatrix} \begin{bmatrix} -1 & -1 \\ 2 & -2 \end{bmatrix}$

$= \begin{bmatrix} -7 & 9 \\ -14 & 54 \end{bmatrix}$

(g) $A^{-1} + AA^{-1} = A^{-1} + I = \frac{1}{4}\begin{bmatrix} 1 & -1 \\ 1 & 3 \end{bmatrix} + \begin{bmatrix} 1 & 0 \\ 0 & 1 \end{bmatrix} = \begin{bmatrix} \frac{5}{4} & -\frac{1}{4} \\ \frac{1}{4} & \frac{7}{4} \end{bmatrix}$

(h) $BC - (C^{-1}B^{-1})^{-1} = BC - (B^{-1})^{-1}(C^{-1})^{-1} = BC - BC = \begin{bmatrix} 0 & 0 \\ 0 & 0 \end{bmatrix}$

(i) $CC^T = \begin{bmatrix} 1 & -1 \\ 2 & 0 \end{bmatrix}\begin{bmatrix} 1 & -1 \\ 2 & 0 \end{bmatrix}^T = \begin{bmatrix} 1 & -1 \\ 2 & 0 \end{bmatrix}\begin{bmatrix} 1 & 2 \\ -1 & 0 \end{bmatrix} = \begin{bmatrix} 2 & 2 \\ 2 & 4 \end{bmatrix}$

(j) $(3AB)^T - B^T A^T = 3B^T A^T - B^T A^T = 2B^T A^T = 2\begin{bmatrix} 1 & 4 \\ 2 & 3 \end{bmatrix}\begin{bmatrix} 3 & -1 \\ 1 & 1 \end{bmatrix} = 2\begin{bmatrix} 7 & 3 \\ 9 & 1 \end{bmatrix}$

(k) $tr(A) = tr\begin{bmatrix} 3 & 1 \\ -1 & 1 \end{bmatrix} = 3 + 1 = 4$

(l) $tr(3A^T - 4B^T C^T) = 3tr(A^T) - 4tr(B^T C^T) = 3(4) - 4tr\left(\begin{bmatrix} 1 & 4 \\ 2 & 3 \end{bmatrix}\begin{bmatrix} 1 & 2 \\ -1 & 0 \end{bmatrix} \right)$

$= 12 - 4tr\begin{bmatrix} -3 & 2 \\ -1 & 4 \end{bmatrix} = 12 - 4(1) = 8$

22. (a) $BC = \begin{bmatrix} 1 & 3 & -2 \\ 4 & 0 & 1 \end{bmatrix}\begin{bmatrix} 2 & 6 \\ 1 & -1 \\ 5 & 0 \end{bmatrix} = \begin{bmatrix} -5 & 3 \\ 13 & 24 \end{bmatrix}$

(b) $CB = \begin{bmatrix} 2 & 6 \\ 1 & -1 \\ 5 & 0 \end{bmatrix} \begin{bmatrix} 1 & 3 & -2 \\ 4 & 0 & 1 \end{bmatrix} = \begin{bmatrix} 26 & 6 & 2 \\ -3 & 3 & -3 \\ 5 & 15 & -10 \end{bmatrix}$

(c) $A^2 - 2CB = \begin{bmatrix} 1 & 2 & 1 \\ 0 & -1 & 5 \\ 1 & 6 & 0 \end{bmatrix} \begin{bmatrix} 1 & 2 & 1 \\ 0 & -1 & 5 \\ 1 & 6 & 0 \end{bmatrix} - 2 \begin{bmatrix} 2 & 6 \\ 1 & -1 \\ 5 & 0 \end{bmatrix} \begin{bmatrix} 1 & 3 & -2 \\ 4 & 0 & 1 \end{bmatrix}$

$= \begin{bmatrix} 2 & 6 & 11 \\ 5 & 31 & -5 \\ 1 & -4 & 31 \end{bmatrix} - 2 \begin{bmatrix} 26 & 6 & 2 \\ -3 & 3 & -3 \\ 5 & 15 & -10 \end{bmatrix}$

$= \begin{bmatrix} -50 & -6 & 7 \\ 11 & 25 & 1 \\ -9 & -34 & 51 \end{bmatrix}$

(d) $\left(AC + 3B^T \right)^T = \left(\begin{bmatrix} 1 & 2 & 1 \\ 0 & -1 & 5 \\ 1 & 6 & 0 \end{bmatrix} \begin{bmatrix} 2 & 6 \\ 1 & -1 \\ 5 & 0 \end{bmatrix} + 3 \begin{bmatrix} 1 & 4 \\ 3 & 0 \\ -2 & 1 \end{bmatrix} \right)^T$

$= \left(\begin{bmatrix} 9 & 4 \\ 24 & 1 \\ 8 & 0 \end{bmatrix} + \begin{bmatrix} 3 & 12 \\ 9 & 0 \\ -6 & 3 \end{bmatrix} \right)^T$

$= \begin{bmatrix} 12 & 33 & 2 \\ 16 & 1 & 3 \end{bmatrix}$

(e) $BCB = \begin{bmatrix} 1 & 3 & -2 \\ 4 & 0 & 1 \end{bmatrix} \begin{bmatrix} 2 & 6 \\ 1 & -1 \\ 5 & 0 \end{bmatrix} = \begin{bmatrix} 1 & 3 & -2 \\ 4 & 0 & 1 \end{bmatrix}$

$= \begin{bmatrix} -5 & 3 \\ 13 & 24 \end{bmatrix} \begin{bmatrix} 1 & 3 & -2 \\ 4 & 0 & 1 \end{bmatrix}$

$= \begin{bmatrix} 7 & -15 & 13 \\ 109 & 39 & -2 \end{bmatrix}$

(f) $tr\left(\frac{1}{3}BAC\right) = \frac{1}{3}tr(BAC)$

$$= \frac{1}{3}tr\left(\begin{bmatrix} 1 & 3 & -2 \\ 4 & 0 & 1 \end{bmatrix} \begin{bmatrix} 1 & 2 & 1 \\ 0 & -1 & 5 \\ 1 & 6 & 0 \end{bmatrix} \begin{bmatrix} 2 & 6 \\ 1 & -1 \\ 5 & 0 \end{bmatrix} \right)$$

$$= \frac{1}{3}tr\left(\begin{bmatrix} -1 & -13 & 16 \\ 5 & 14 & 4 \end{bmatrix} \begin{bmatrix} 2 & 6 \\ 1 & -1 \\ 5 & 0 \end{bmatrix} \right)$$

$$= \frac{1}{3}tr\left(\begin{bmatrix} 65 & 7 \\ 44 & 16 \end{bmatrix} \right)$$

$$= \frac{1}{3}(81) = 27$$

23. (a) $A+(B+C)=\begin{bmatrix} 1 & 1 & 5 \\ -1 & 1 & 0 \\ 1 & 0 & 1 \end{bmatrix}+\left(\begin{bmatrix} 1 & 1 & 0 \\ 2 & 2 & -1 \\ 0 & 1 & -1 \end{bmatrix}+\begin{bmatrix} 0 & 1 & 3 \\ 2 & 0 & 0 \\ -2 & 4 & 1 \end{bmatrix}\right)$

$$=\begin{bmatrix} 1 & 1 & 5 \\ -1 & 1 & 0 \\ 1 & 0 & 1 \end{bmatrix}+\begin{bmatrix} 1 & 2 & 3 \\ 4 & 2 & -1 \\ -2 & 5 & 0 \end{bmatrix}$$

$$=\begin{bmatrix} 2 & 3 & 8 \\ 3 & 3 & -1 \\ -1 & 5 & 1 \end{bmatrix}$$

$(A+B)+C=\left(\begin{bmatrix} 1 & 1 & 5 \\ -1 & 1 & 0 \\ 1 & 0 & 1 \end{bmatrix}+\begin{bmatrix} 1 & 1 & 0 \\ 2 & 2 & -1 \\ 0 & 1 & -1 \end{bmatrix}\right)+\begin{bmatrix} 0 & 1 & 3 \\ 2 & 0 & 0 \\ -2 & 4 & 1 \end{bmatrix}$

$$=\begin{bmatrix} 2 & 2 & 5 \\ 1 & 3 & -1 \\ 1 & 1 & 0 \end{bmatrix}+\begin{bmatrix} 0 & 1 & 3 \\ 2 & 0 & 0 \\ -2 & 4 & 1 \end{bmatrix}$$

$$=\begin{bmatrix} 2 & 3 & 8 \\ 3 & 3 & -1 \\ -1 & 5 & 1 \end{bmatrix}$$

(b) $(AB)C=\left(\begin{bmatrix} 1 & 1 & 5 \\ -1 & 1 & 0 \\ 1 & 0 & 1 \end{bmatrix}\begin{bmatrix} 1 & 1 & 0 \\ 2 & 2 & -1 \\ 0 & 1 & -1 \end{bmatrix}\right)\begin{bmatrix} 0 & 1 & 3 \\ 2 & 0 & 0 \\ -2 & 4 & 1 \end{bmatrix}$

$$=\begin{bmatrix} 3 & 8 & -6 \\ 1 & 1 & -1 \\ 1 & 2 & -1 \end{bmatrix}\begin{bmatrix} 0 & 1 & 3 \\ 2 & 0 & 0 \\ -2 & 4 & 1 \end{bmatrix}=\begin{bmatrix} 28 & -21 & 3 \\ 4 & -3 & 2 \\ 6 & -3 & 2 \end{bmatrix}$$

$(AB)C=\begin{bmatrix} 1 & 1 & 5 \\ -1 & 1 & 0 \\ 1 & 0 & 1 \end{bmatrix}\left(\begin{bmatrix} 1 & 1 & 0 \\ 2 & 2 & -1 \\ 0 & 1 & -1 \end{bmatrix}\begin{bmatrix} 0 & 1 & 3 \\ 2 & 0 & 0 \\ -2 & 4 & 1 \end{bmatrix}\right)$

$$=\begin{bmatrix} 1 & 1 & 5 \\ -1 & 1 & 0 \\ 1 & 0 & 1 \end{bmatrix}\begin{bmatrix} 2 & 1 & 3 \\ 6 & -2 & 5 \\ 4 & -4 & -1 \end{bmatrix}=\begin{bmatrix} 28 & -21 & 3 \\ 4 & -3 & 2 \\ 6 & -3 & 2 \end{bmatrix}$$

(c) $A(B+C) = \begin{bmatrix} 1 & 1 & 5 \\ -1 & 1 & 0 \\ 1 & 0 & 1 \end{bmatrix} \left(\begin{bmatrix} 1 & 1 & 0 \\ 2 & 2 & -1 \\ 0 & 1 & -1 \end{bmatrix} + \begin{bmatrix} 0 & 1 & 3 \\ 2 & 0 & 0 \\ -2 & 4 & 1 \end{bmatrix} \right)$

$\quad = \begin{bmatrix} 1 & 1 & 5 \\ -1 & 1 & 0 \\ 1 & 0 & 1 \end{bmatrix} \begin{bmatrix} 1 & 2 & 3 \\ 4 & 2 & -1 \\ -2 & 5 & 0 \end{bmatrix} = \begin{bmatrix} -5 & 29 & 2 \\ 3 & 0 & -4 \\ -1 & 7 & 3 \end{bmatrix}$

$AB + AC = \begin{bmatrix} 1 & 1 & 5 \\ -1 & 1 & 0 \\ 1 & 0 & 1 \end{bmatrix} \begin{bmatrix} 1 & 1 & 0 \\ 2 & 2 & -1 \\ 0 & 1 & -1 \end{bmatrix} + \begin{bmatrix} 1 & 1 & 5 \\ -1 & 1 & 0 \\ 1 & 0 & 1 \end{bmatrix} \begin{bmatrix} 0 & 1 & 3 \\ 2 & 0 & 0 \\ -2 & 4 & 1 \end{bmatrix}$

$\quad = \begin{bmatrix} 3 & 8 & -6 \\ 1 & 1 & -1 \\ 1 & 2 & -1 \end{bmatrix} + \begin{bmatrix} -8 & 21 & 8 \\ 2 & -1 & -3 \\ -2 & 5 & 4 \end{bmatrix} = \begin{bmatrix} -5 & 29 & 2 \\ 3 & 0 & -4 \\ -1 & 7 & 3 \end{bmatrix}$

(d) $a(bC) = 2 \left(3 \begin{bmatrix} 0 & 1 & 3 \\ 2 & 0 & 0 \\ -2 & 4 & 1 \end{bmatrix} \right) = 2 \begin{bmatrix} 0 & 3 & 9 \\ 6 & 0 & 0 \\ -6 & 12 & 3 \end{bmatrix} = \begin{bmatrix} 0 & 6 & 18 \\ 12 & 0 & 0 \\ -12 & 24 & 6 \end{bmatrix}$

$(ab)C = (2 \cdot 3)C = 6C = 6 \begin{bmatrix} 0 & 1 & 3 \\ 2 & 0 & 0 \\ -2 & 4 & 1 \end{bmatrix} = \begin{bmatrix} 0 & 6 & 18 \\ 12 & 0 & 0 \\ -12 & 24 & 6 \end{bmatrix}$

(e) $(A+B)^T = \left(\begin{bmatrix} 1 & 1 & 5 \\ -1 & 1 & 0 \\ 1 & 0 & 1 \end{bmatrix} + \begin{bmatrix} 1 & 1 & 0 \\ 2 & 2 & -1 \\ 0 & 1 & -1 \end{bmatrix} \right)^T = \begin{bmatrix} 2 & 2 & 5 \\ 1 & 3 & -1 \\ 1 & 1 & 0 \end{bmatrix}^T = \begin{bmatrix} 2 & 1 & 1 \\ 2 & 3 & 1 \\ 5 & -1 & 0 \end{bmatrix}$

$A^T + B^T = \begin{bmatrix} 1 & 1 & 5 \\ -1 & 1 & 0 \\ 1 & 0 & 1 \end{bmatrix}^T + \begin{bmatrix} 1 & 1 & 0 \\ 2 & 2 & -1 \\ 0 & 1 & -1 \end{bmatrix}^T$

$\quad = \begin{bmatrix} 1 & -1 & 1 \\ 1 & 1 & 0 \\ 5 & 0 & 1 \end{bmatrix} + \begin{bmatrix} 1 & 2 & 0 \\ 1 & 2 & 1 \\ 0 & -1 & -1 \end{bmatrix} = \begin{bmatrix} 2 & 1 & 1 \\ 2 & 3 & 1 \\ 5 & -1 & 0 \end{bmatrix}$

(f) $(AB)^T = \left(\begin{bmatrix} 1 & 1 & 5 \\ -1 & 1 & 0 \\ 1 & 0 & 1 \end{bmatrix} \begin{bmatrix} 1 & 1 & 0 \\ 2 & 2 & -1 \\ 0 & 1 & -1 \end{bmatrix} \right)^T = \begin{bmatrix} 3 & 8 & -6 \\ 1 & 1 & -1 \\ 1 & 2 & -1 \end{bmatrix}^T = \begin{bmatrix} 3 & 1 & 1 \\ 8 & 1 & 2 \\ -6 & -1 & -1 \end{bmatrix}$

$B^T A^T = \begin{bmatrix} 1 & 1 & 0 \\ 2 & 2 & 1 \\ 0 & 1 & -1 \end{bmatrix}^T \begin{bmatrix} 1 & 1 & 5 \\ -1 & 1 & 0 \\ 1 & 0 & 1 \end{bmatrix}^T$

$\quad = \begin{bmatrix} 1 & 2 & 0 \\ 1 & 2 & 1 \\ 0 & -1 & -1 \end{bmatrix} \begin{bmatrix} 1 & -1 & 1 \\ 1 & 1 & 0 \\ 5 & 0 & 1 \end{bmatrix} = \begin{bmatrix} 3 & 1 & 1 \\ 8 & 1 & 2 \\ -6 & -1 & -1 \end{bmatrix}$

24. $A = \begin{bmatrix} 1 & 2 & -1 \\ 2 & -1 & 11 \\ 3 & 1 & 1 \end{bmatrix}$, $X = \begin{bmatrix} x \\ y \\ z \end{bmatrix}$, $B = \begin{bmatrix} 5 \\ 19 \\ 11 \end{bmatrix}$

25. $A = \begin{bmatrix} 0 & -1 & -1 & -1 \\ -1 & 0 & -1 & -1 \\ -1 & -1 & 0 & -1 \\ -1 & -1 & -1 & 0 \end{bmatrix}$, $X = \begin{bmatrix} x_1 \\ x_2 \\ x_3 \\ x_4 \end{bmatrix}$, $B = \begin{bmatrix} 1 \\ 1 \\ 1 \\ 1 \end{bmatrix}$

26.
$$\begin{aligned} -x + 7y &= 0 \\ + 4y + 3z &= 0 \\ 6x - 2z &= 0 \end{aligned}$$

27.
$$\begin{aligned} 1/3x_1 + 1/2x_2 - 1/6x_4 &= 1/2 \\ 2/3x_1 + 1/6x_2 - 1/2x_3 &= 1/4 \end{aligned}$$

28. (a) Add -5 times row 1 to row 2.
    (b) Not elementary.
    (c) Interchange rows 1 and 2.
    (d) Multiply row 2 by $-1/2$.
    (e) Not elementary.
    (f) Add 9 times row 2 to row 4.

29. The operation that transforms A into B is: add -2 times row 1 to row 3. Applying this same operation to I yields:

$$E_1 = \begin{bmatrix} 1 & 0 & 0 \\ 0 & 1 & 0 \\ -2 & 0 & 1 \end{bmatrix}$$

30. The operation that transforms B into A is: add 2 times row 1 to row 3. Applying this same operation to I yields:

$$E_2 = \begin{bmatrix} 1 & 0 & 0 \\ 0 & 1 & 0 \\ 2 & 0 & 1 \end{bmatrix}$$

31. The operation that transforms B into C is: interchange rows 2 and 3. Applying this same operation to I yields:

$$E_3 = \begin{bmatrix} 1 & 0 & 0 \\ 0 & 0 & 1 \\ 0 & 1 & 0 \end{bmatrix}$$

32. The operation that transforms C into B is: interchange rows 2 and 3. Applying this same operation to I yields:

$$E_4 = \begin{bmatrix} 1 & 0 & 0 \\ 0 & 0 & 1 \\ 0 & 1 & 0 \end{bmatrix}$$

33.
$$\left[\begin{array}{cc|cc} 2 & 3 & 1 & 0 \\ 5 & 6 & 0 & 1 \end{array}\right] \longrightarrow \left[\begin{array}{cc|cc} 1 & 3/2 & 1/2 & 0 \\ 5 & 6 & 0 & 1 \end{array}\right] \longrightarrow \left[\begin{array}{cc|cc} 1 & 3/2 & 1/2 & 0 \\ 0 & -3/2 & -3/2 & 1 \end{array}\right]$$

$$\left[\begin{array}{cc|cc} 1 & 3/2 & 1/2 & 0 \\ 0 & 1 & 5/3 & -2/3 \end{array}\right] \longrightarrow \left[\begin{array}{cc|cc} 1 & 0 & -2 & 1 \\ 0 & 1 & 5/3 & -2/3 \end{array}\right]$$

Thus, the inverse is: $\begin{bmatrix} -2 & 1 \\ 5/3 & -2/3 \end{bmatrix}$

18

34. $\begin{bmatrix} 1 & 2 & 1 & \cdot & 1 & 0 & 0 \\ 0 & 2 & 2 & \cdot & 0 & 1 & 0 \\ 0 & 0 & 4 & \cdot & 0 & 0 & 1 \end{bmatrix} \longrightarrow \begin{bmatrix} 1 & 2 & 1 & \cdot & 1 & 0 & 0 \\ 0 & 1 & 1 & \cdot & 0 & 1/2 & 0 \\ 0 & 0 & 1 & \cdot & 0 & 0 & 1/4 \end{bmatrix}$

$$\longrightarrow \begin{bmatrix} 1 & 0 & -1 & \cdot & 1 & -1 & 0 \\ 0 & 1 & 1 & \cdot & 0 & 1/2 & 0 \\ 0 & 0 & 1 & \cdot & 0 & 0 & 1/4 \end{bmatrix}$$

$$\longrightarrow \begin{bmatrix} 1 & 0 & 0 & \cdot & 1 & -1 & 1/4 \\ 0 & 1 & 0 & \cdot & 0 & 1/2 & -1/4 \\ 0 & 0 & 1 & \cdot & 0 & 0 & 1/4 \end{bmatrix}$$

Thus, the inverse is $\begin{bmatrix} 1 & -1 & 1/4 \\ 0 & 1/2 & -1/4 \\ 0 & 0 & 1/4 \end{bmatrix}$

35. $\begin{bmatrix} 1 & -5 & 3 & \cdot & 1 & 0 & 0 \\ 2 & 0 & 1 & \cdot & 0 & 1 & 0 \\ 1 & 1 & 1 & \cdot & 0 & 0 & 1 \end{bmatrix} \longrightarrow \begin{bmatrix} 1 & -5 & 3 & \cdot & 1 & 0 & 0 \\ 0 & 10 & -5 & \cdot & -2 & 1 & 0 \\ 0 & 6 & -2 & \cdot & -1 & 0 & 1 \end{bmatrix}$

$$\longrightarrow \begin{bmatrix} 1 & 0 & 1/2 & \cdot & 0 & 5/10 & 0 \\ 0 & 1 & -1/2 & \cdot & -2/10 & 1/10 & 0 \\ 0 & 0 & 1 & \cdot & 2/10 & -6/10 & 1 \end{bmatrix}$$

$$\longrightarrow \begin{bmatrix} 1 & 0 & 0 & \cdot & -1/10 & 8/10 & -5/10 \\ 0 & 1 & 0 & \cdot & -1/10 & -2/10 & 5/10 \\ 0 & 0 & 1 & \cdot & 2/10 & -6/10 & 10/10 \end{bmatrix}$$

Thus, the inverse is: $\begin{bmatrix} -1/10 & 8/10 & -5/10 \\ -1/10 & -2/10 & 5/10 \\ 2/10 & -6/10 & 10/10 \end{bmatrix}$

36. $\begin{bmatrix} 1 & -5 & 5 & \cdot & 1 & 0 & 0 \\ 4 & 3 & 2 & \cdot & 0 & 1 & 0 \\ 9 & 1 & 9 & \cdot & 0 & 0 & 1 \end{bmatrix} \longrightarrow \begin{bmatrix} 1 & -5 & 5 & \cdot & 1 & 0 & 0 \\ 0 & 23 & -18 & \cdot & -4 & 1 & 0 \\ 0 & 46 & -36 & \cdot & -9 & 0 & 1 \end{bmatrix}$

$$\longrightarrow \begin{bmatrix} 1 & -5 & 5 & \cdot & 1 & 0 & 0 \\ 0 & 1 & -18/23 & \cdot & -4/23 & 1/23 & 0 \\ 0 & 0 & 0 & \cdot & -1 & -2 & 1 \end{bmatrix}$$

Since we have obtained a row of zeros on the left side, the matrix is not invertible.

37. $\begin{bmatrix} 1/2 & 0 & 0 & \cdot & 1 & 0 & 0 \\ 1/4 & 1/2 & 0 & \cdot & 0 & 1 & 0 \\ 1 & 1/4 & 1/2 & \cdot & 0 & 0 & 1 \end{bmatrix} \longrightarrow \begin{bmatrix} 1 & 0 & 0 & \cdot & 2 & 0 & 0 \\ 0 & 1/2 & 0 & \cdot & -1/2 & 1 & 0 \\ 0 & 1/4 & 1/2 & \cdot & -2 & 0 & 1 \end{bmatrix}$

$$\longrightarrow \begin{bmatrix} 1 & 0 & 0 & \cdot & 2 & 0 & 0 \\ 0 & 1 & 0 & \cdot & -1 & 2 & 0 \\ 0 & 0 & 1/2 & \cdot & -7/4 & -1/2 & 1 \end{bmatrix}$$

$$\longrightarrow \begin{bmatrix} 1 & 0 & 0 & \cdot & 2 & 0 & 0 \\ 0 & 1 & 0 & \cdot & -1 & 2 & 0 \\ 0 & 0 & 1 & \cdot & -7/2 & -1 & 2 \end{bmatrix}$$

Thus, the inverse is: $\begin{bmatrix} 2 & 0 & 0 \\ -1 & 2 & 0 \\ -7/2 & -1 & 2 \end{bmatrix}$

38. $\left[\begin{array}{cccc|cccc} 1 & -3 & 0 & 0 & 1 & 0 & 0 & 0 \\ -1 & 4 & 0 & 0 & 0 & 1 & 0 & 0 \\ 0 & 0 & 5 & 6 & 0 & 0 & 1 & 0 \\ 0 & 0 & 2 & 2 & 0 & 0 & 0 & 1 \end{array}\right] \longrightarrow \left[\begin{array}{cccc|cccc} 1 & -3 & 0 & 0 & 1 & 0 & 0 & 0 \\ 0 & 1 & 0 & 0 & 1 & 1 & 0 & 0 \\ 0 & 0 & 5 & 6 & 0 & 0 & 1 & 0 \\ 0 & 0 & 2 & 2 & 0 & 0 & 0 & 1 \end{array}\right]$

$\longrightarrow \left[\begin{array}{cccc|cccc} 1 & 0 & 0 & 0 & 4 & 3 & 0 & 0 \\ 0 & 1 & 0 & 0 & 1 & 1 & 0 & 0 \\ 0 & 0 & 5 & 6 & 0 & 0 & 1 & 0 \\ 0 & 0 & 2 & 2 & 0 & 0 & 0 & 1 \end{array}\right] \longrightarrow \left[\begin{array}{cccc|cccc} 1 & 0 & 0 & 0 & 4 & 3 & 0 & 0 \\ 0 & 1 & 0 & 0 & 1 & 1 & 0 & 0 \\ 0 & 0 & 1 & 6/5 & 0 & 0 & 1/5 & 0 \\ 0 & 0 & 0 & -2/5 & 0 & 0 & -2/5 & 1 \end{array}\right]$

$\longrightarrow \left[\begin{array}{cccc|cccc} 1 & 0 & 0 & 0 & 4 & 3 & 0 & 0 \\ 0 & 1 & 0 & 0 & 1 & 1 & 0 & 0 \\ 0 & 0 & 1 & 0 & 0 & 0 & -1 & 3 \\ 0 & 0 & 0 & 1 & 0 & 0 & 1 & -5/2 \end{array}\right]$

Thus, the inverse is: $\begin{bmatrix} 4 & 3 & 0 & 0 \\ 1 & 1 & 0 & 0 \\ 0 & 0 & -1 & 3 \\ 0 & 0 & 1 & -5/2 \end{bmatrix}$

39. $\left[\begin{array}{ccc|ccc} 0 & 0 & 1 & 1 & 0 & 0 \\ 0 & 1 & k_1 & 0 & 1 & 0 \\ 1 & k_2 & 0 & 0 & 0 & 1 \end{array}\right] \longrightarrow \left[\begin{array}{ccc|ccc} 1 & k_2 & 0 & 0 & 0 & 1 \\ 0 & 1 & k_1 & 0 & 1 & 0 \\ 0 & 0 & 1 & 1 & 0 & 0 \end{array}\right]$

$\longrightarrow \left[\begin{array}{ccc|ccc} 1 & 0 & -k_1 k_2 & 0 & -k_2 & 1 \\ 0 & 1 & k_1 & 0 & 1 & 0 \\ 0 & 0 & 1 & 1 & 0 & 0 \end{array}\right]$

$\longrightarrow \left[\begin{array}{ccc|ccc} 1 & 0 & 0 & k_1 k_2 & -k_2 & 1 \\ 0 & 1 & 0 & -k_1 & 1 & 0 \\ 0 & 0 & 1 & 1 & 0 & 0 \end{array}\right]$

Thus the inverse is: $\begin{bmatrix} k_1 k_2 & -k_2 & 1 \\ -k_1 & 1 & 0 \\ 1 & 0 & 0 \end{bmatrix}$

40. $\left[\begin{array}{cccc|cccc} 1 & 0 & 0 & 0 & 1 & 0 & 0 & 0 \\ k & 1 & 0 & 0 & 0 & 1 & 0 & 0 \\ 0 & k & 1 & 0 & 0 & 0 & 1 & 0 \\ 0 & 0 & k & 1 & 0 & 0 & 0 & 1 \end{array}\right]$

$\longrightarrow \left[\begin{array}{cccc|cccc} 1 & 0 & 0 & 0 & 1 & 0 & 0 & 0 \\ 0 & 1 & 0 & 0 & -k & 1 & 0 & 0 \\ 0 & k & 1 & 0 & 0 & 0 & 1 & 0 \\ 0 & 0 & k & 1 & 0 & 0 & 0 & 1 \end{array}\right]$

$\longrightarrow \left[\begin{array}{cccc|cccc} 1 & 0 & 0 & 0 & 1 & 0 & 0 & 0 \\ 0 & 1 & 0 & 0 & -k & 1 & 0 & 0 \\ 0 & 0 & 1 & 0 & k^2 & -k & 1 & 0 \\ 0 & 0 & k & 1 & 0 & 0 & 0 & 1 \end{array}\right]$

$$\longrightarrow \begin{bmatrix} 1 & 0 & 0 & 0 & \cdot & 1 & 0 & 0 & 0 \\ 0 & 1 & 0 & 0 & \cdot & -k & 1 & 0 & 0 \\ 0 & 0 & 1 & 0 & \cdot & k^2 & -k & 1 & 0 \\ 0 & 0 & 0 & 1 & \cdot & -k^3 & k^2 & -k & 1 \end{bmatrix}$$

Thus, the inverse is: $\begin{bmatrix} 1 & 0 & 0 & 0 \\ -k & 1 & 0 & 0 \\ k^2 & -k & 1 & 0 \\ -k^3 & k^2 & -k & 1 \end{bmatrix}$

SECTION 1.6 *FURTHER RESULTS ON SYSTEMS OF EQUATIONS AND INVERTIBILITY*

41. $\begin{bmatrix} 7 & 2 \\ 3 & 1 \end{bmatrix}^{-1} \begin{bmatrix} 1 \\ 5 \end{bmatrix} = \frac{1}{1} \begin{bmatrix} 1 & -2 \\ -3 & 7 \end{bmatrix} \begin{bmatrix} 1 \\ 5 \end{bmatrix} = \begin{bmatrix} -9 \\ 32 \end{bmatrix}$ so $x = -9$, $y = 32$

42. $\begin{bmatrix} 1 & 4 \\ 5 & 1 \end{bmatrix}^{-1} \begin{bmatrix} 3 \\ -2 \end{bmatrix} = \frac{1}{-19} \begin{bmatrix} 1 & -4 \\ -5 & 1 \end{bmatrix} \begin{bmatrix} 3 \\ -2 \end{bmatrix} = \frac{-1}{19} \begin{bmatrix} 11 \\ -17 \end{bmatrix}$ so $x = -11/19$, $y = 17/19$

43. $\begin{bmatrix} 1 & 6 & 5 & \cdot & 1 & 0 & 0 \\ 0 & 1 & 1 & \cdot & 0 & 1 & 0 \\ 0 & 0 & 2 & \cdot & 0 & 0 & 1 \end{bmatrix} \longrightarrow \begin{bmatrix} 1 & 0 & -1 & \cdot & 1 & -6 & 0 \\ 0 & 1 & 1 & \cdot & 0 & 1 & 0 \\ 0 & 0 & 2 & \cdot & 0 & 0 & 1 \end{bmatrix}$

$$\longrightarrow \begin{bmatrix} 1 & 0 & 0 & \cdot & 1 & -6 & 1/2 \\ 0 & 1 & 0 & \cdot & 0 & 1 & -1/2 \\ 0 & 0 & 1 & \cdot & 0 & 0 & 1/2 \end{bmatrix}$$

$\begin{bmatrix} 1 & -6 & 1/2 \\ 0 & 1 & -1/2 \\ 0 & 0 & 1/2 \end{bmatrix} \begin{bmatrix} 3 \\ -1 \\ -4 \end{bmatrix} = \begin{bmatrix} 7 \\ 1 \\ -2 \end{bmatrix}$ so $x = 7$, $y = 1$, $z = -2$

44. $\begin{bmatrix} 1 & -1 & 2 & \cdot & 1 & 0 & 0 \\ -2 & 1 & 1 & \cdot & 0 & 1 & 0 \\ -3 & 1 & 5 & \cdot & 0 & 0 & 1 \end{bmatrix} \longrightarrow \begin{bmatrix} 1 & -1 & 2 & \cdot & 1 & 0 & 0 \\ 0 & -1 & 5 & \cdot & 2 & 1 & 0 \\ 0 & -2 & 11 & \cdot & 3 & 0 & 1 \end{bmatrix}$

$$\longrightarrow \begin{bmatrix} 1 & 0 & -3 & \cdot & -1 & -1 & 0 \\ 0 & 1 & -5 & \cdot & -2 & -1 & 0 \\ 0 & 0 & 1 & \cdot & -1 & -2 & 1 \end{bmatrix}$$

$$\longrightarrow \begin{bmatrix} 1 & 0 & 0 & \cdot & -4 & -7 & 3 \\ 0 & 1 & 0 & \cdot & -7 & -11 & 5 \\ 0 & 0 & 1 & \cdot & -1 & -2 & 1 \end{bmatrix}$$

$\begin{bmatrix} -4 & -7 & 3 \\ -7 & -11 & 5 \\ -1 & -2 & 1 \end{bmatrix} \begin{bmatrix} 1 \\ -1 \\ -1 \end{bmatrix} = \begin{bmatrix} 0 \\ -1 \\ 0 \end{bmatrix}$ so $x_1 = 0$, $x_2 = -1$, $x_3 = 0$

45. $\begin{bmatrix} 2 & -3 & 10 & \cdot & 1 & 0 & 0 \\ 0 & -1 & 2 & \cdot & 0 & 1 & 0 \\ -4 & 8 & -19 & \cdot & 0 & 0 & 1 \end{bmatrix}$

$$\longrightarrow \begin{bmatrix} 1 & -3/2 & 5 & \cdot & 1/2 & 0 & 0 \\ 0 & -1 & 2 & \cdot & 0 & 1 & 0 \\ 0 & 2 & 1 & \cdot & 2 & 0 & 1 \end{bmatrix}$$

$$\longrightarrow \begin{bmatrix} 1 & 0 & 2 & \cdot & 1/2 & -3/2 & 0 \\ 0 & 1 & -2 & \cdot & 0 & -1 & 0 \\ 0 & 0 & 5 & \cdot & 1 & 2 & 1 \end{bmatrix}$$

$$\longrightarrow \begin{bmatrix} 1 & 0 & 0 & \cdot & -3/10 & -23/10 & -2/5 \\ 0 & 1 & 0 & \cdot & 4/5 & -1/5 & 2/5 \\ 0 & 0 & 1 & \cdot & 2/5 & 2/5 & 1/5 \end{bmatrix}$$

$$\begin{bmatrix} -3/10 & -23/10 & -2/5 \\ 4/5 & -1/5 & 2/5 \\ 2/5 & 2/5 & 1/5 \end{bmatrix} \begin{bmatrix} 10 \\ 30 \\ -20 \end{bmatrix} = \begin{bmatrix} -64 \\ -6 \\ 12 \end{bmatrix} \quad \text{so} \quad x_1 = -64 \ , \quad x_2 = -6 \ , \quad x_3 = 12$$

46. $\begin{bmatrix} 1 & -2 & -6 & -2 & \cdot & 1 & 0 & 0 & 0 \\ 1 & 1 & 2 & 1 & \cdot & 0 & 1 & 0 & 0 \\ 1 & 0 & -1 & 0 & \cdot & 0 & 0 & 1 & 0 \\ 3 & 3 & 7 & 4 & \cdot & 0 & 0 & 0 & 1 \end{bmatrix} \longrightarrow \begin{bmatrix} 1 & -2 & -6 & -2 & \cdot & 1 & 0 & 0 & 0 \\ 0 & 3 & 8 & 3 & \cdot & -1 & 1 & 0 & 0 \\ 0 & 2 & 5 & 2 & \cdot & -1 & 0 & 1 & 0 \\ 0 & 9 & 25 & 10 & \cdot & -3 & 0 & 0 & 1 \end{bmatrix}$

$$\longrightarrow \begin{bmatrix} 1 & 0 & -2/3 & 0 & \cdot & 1/3 & 2/3 & 0 & 0 \\ 0 & 1 & 8/3 & 1 & \cdot & -1/3 & 1/3 & 0 & 0 \\ 0 & 0 & -1/3 & 0 & \cdot & -1/3 & -2/3 & 1 & 0 \\ 0 & 0 & 1 & 1 & \cdot & 0 & -3 & 0 & 1 \end{bmatrix}$$

$$\longrightarrow \begin{bmatrix} 1 & 0 & 0 & 0 & \cdot & 1 & 2 & -2 & 0 \\ 0 & 1 & 0 & 1 & \cdot & -3 & -5 & 8 & 0 \\ 0 & 0 & 1 & 0 & \cdot & 1 & 2 & -3 & 0 \\ 0 & 0 & 0 & 1 & \cdot & -1 & -5 & 3 & 1 \end{bmatrix}$$

$$\longrightarrow \begin{bmatrix} 1 & 0 & 0 & 0 & \cdot & 1 & 2 & -2 & 0 \\ 0 & 1 & 0 & 0 & \cdot & -2 & 0 & 5 & -1 \\ 0 & 0 & 1 & 0 & \cdot & 1 & 2 & -3 & 0 \\ 0 & 0 & 0 & 1 & \cdot & -1 & -5 & 3 & 1 \end{bmatrix}$$

$$\begin{bmatrix} 1 & 2 & -2 & 0 \\ -2 & 0 & 5 & -1 \\ 1 & 2 & -3 & 0 \\ -1 & -5 & 3 & 1 \end{bmatrix} \begin{bmatrix} 4 \\ -2 \\ 1 \\ 3 \end{bmatrix} = \begin{bmatrix} -2 \\ -6 \\ -3 \\ 12 \end{bmatrix} \quad \text{so} \quad x_1 = -2 \ , \quad x_2 = -6 \ , \quad x_3 = -3 \ , \quad x_4 = 12$$

47. $\begin{bmatrix} .3 & .4 \\ .7 & .6 \end{bmatrix}^{-1} \begin{bmatrix} b_1 \\ b_2 \end{bmatrix} = \frac{1}{-.1} \begin{bmatrix} .6 & -.4 \\ -.7 & .3 \end{bmatrix} \begin{bmatrix} b_1 \\ b_2 \end{bmatrix} = \begin{bmatrix} -6 & 4 \\ 7 & -3 \end{bmatrix} \begin{bmatrix} b_1 \\ b_2 \end{bmatrix} = \begin{bmatrix} -6b_1 + 4b_2 \\ 7b_1 - 3b_2 \end{bmatrix}$

so $\quad x = -6b_1 + 4b_2 \quad$ and $\quad y = 7b_1 - 3b_2$.

48. $\begin{bmatrix} 1 & 1 & 1 & \cdot & 1 & 0 & 0 \\ 3 & 4 & 5 & \cdot & 0 & 1 & 0 \\ -2 & 0 & 1 & \cdot & 0 & 0 & 1 \end{bmatrix} \longrightarrow \begin{bmatrix} 1 & 1 & 1 & \cdot & 1 & 0 & 0 \\ 0 & 1 & 2 & \cdot & -3 & 1 & 0 \\ 0 & 2 & 3 & \cdot & 2 & 0 & 1 \end{bmatrix}$

$$\longrightarrow \begin{bmatrix} 1 & 0 & -1 & \cdot & 4 & -1 & 0 \\ 0 & 1 & 2 & \cdot & -3 & 1 & 0 \\ 0 & 0 & -1 & \cdot & 8 & -2 & 1 \end{bmatrix}$$

22

$$\longrightarrow \begin{bmatrix} 1 & 0 & 0 & \cdot & -4 & 1 & -1 \\ 0 & 1 & 0 & \cdot & 13 & -3 & 2 \\ 0 & 0 & 1 & \cdot & -8 & 2 & -1 \end{bmatrix}$$

$$\begin{bmatrix} -4 & 1 & -1 \\ 13 & -3 & 2 \\ -8 & 2 & -1 \end{bmatrix} \begin{bmatrix} b_1 \\ b_2 \\ b_3 \end{bmatrix} = \begin{bmatrix} -4b_1 + b_2 - b_3 \\ 13b_1 - 3b_2 + 2b_3 \\ -8b_1 + 2b_2 - b_3 \end{bmatrix}$$

so $x_1 = -4b_1 + b_2 - b_3$, $x_2 = 13b_1 - 3b_2 + 2b_3$, $x_3 = -8b_1 + 2b_2 - b_3$.

49. $\begin{bmatrix} 6 & -3 & b_1 \\ -10 & 5 & b_2 \end{bmatrix} \longrightarrow \begin{bmatrix} 1 & -1/2 & b_1/6 \\ 0 & 0 & b_2 + 10b_1/6 \end{bmatrix}$

Thus, the only condition required for consistency is:

$$b_2 + \tfrac{10}{6}b_1 = 0$$

i.e., $b_2 + \tfrac{5}{3}b_1 = 0$

$$b_2 = -\tfrac{5}{3}b_1$$

50. $\begin{bmatrix} 1 & 4 & -3 & b_1 \\ 2 & 6 & 5 & b_2 \\ 1 & 6 & -14 & b_3 \end{bmatrix} \longrightarrow \begin{bmatrix} 1 & 4 & -3 & b_1 \\ 0 & -2 & 11 & b_2 - 2b_1 \\ 0 & 2 & -11 & b_3 - b_1 \end{bmatrix}$

$\longrightarrow \begin{bmatrix} 1 & 4 & -3 & b_1 \\ 0 & 1 & -11/2 & -1/2(b_2 - 2b_1) \\ 0 & 0 & 0 & (b_3 - b_1) + (b_2 - 2b_1) \end{bmatrix}$

Thus, the only condition required for consistency is:

$$(b_3 - b_1) + (b_2 - 2b_1) = 0$$

i.e., $b_3 + b_2 - b_1 = 0$

$$b_3 = b_1 - b_2$$

51. $\begin{bmatrix} 1 & 3 & 1 & b_1 \\ 2 & 7 & 3 & b_2 \\ -1 & -1 & 2 & b_3 \end{bmatrix} \longrightarrow \begin{bmatrix} 1 & 3 & 1 & b_1 \\ 0 & 1 & 1 & b_2 - 2b_1 \\ 0 & 2 & 3 & b_3 + b_1 \end{bmatrix} \longrightarrow \begin{bmatrix} 1 & 3 & 1 & b_1 \\ 0 & 1 & 1 & b_2 - 2b_1 \\ 0 & 0 & 1 & (b_3 + b_1) - 2(b_2 - 2b_1) \end{bmatrix}$

Thus, there are no conditions required for consistency.

52. $\begin{bmatrix} 1 & 4 & 7 & b_1 \\ 2 & 5 & 1 & b_2 \\ 1 & 7 & 20 & b_3 \\ -1 & 2 & 19 & b_4 \end{bmatrix} \longrightarrow \begin{bmatrix} 1 & 4 & 7 & b_1 \\ 0 & -3 & -13 & b_2 - 2b_1 \\ 0 & 3 & 13 & b_3 - b_1 \\ 0 & 6 & 26 & b_4 + b_1 \end{bmatrix} \longrightarrow \begin{bmatrix} 1 & 4 & 7 & b_1 \\ 0 & 1 & 13/3 & -1/3(b_2 - 2b_1) \\ 0 & 0 & 0 & (b_3 - b_1) + (b_2 - 2b_1) \\ 0 & 0 & 0 & (b_4 + b_1) + 2(b_2 - 2b_1) \end{bmatrix}$

23

Thus, the only conditions required for consistency are:

$$(b_3 - b_1) + (b_2 - 2b_1) = 0 \quad \text{and} \quad (b_4 + b_1) + 2(b_2 - 2b_1) = 0$$

i.e., $\quad b_3 + b_2 - 3b_1 = 0 \quad \text{and} \quad b_4 + 2b_2 - 3b_1 = 0$

$$b_3 = 3b_1 - b_2 \quad \text{and} \quad b_4 = 3b_1 - 2b_2$$

CHAPTER 2: DETERMINANTS

In questions 1–6, find the number of inversions in the permuation of $(1,2,3,4,5)$.

1. $(3,4,1,2,5)$ 2. $(4,5,1,3,2)$ 3. $(2,5,1,3,4)$

4. $(1,3,5,4,2)$ 5. $(5,4,2,1,3)$ 6. $(1,2,3,5,4)$

In questions 7–12, evaluate the determinant by using signed elementary products.

7. $\begin{vmatrix} 0 & -1 & 0 \\ 2 & 0 & 0 \\ 0 & 0 & 8 \end{vmatrix}$

8. $\begin{vmatrix} 0 & 0 & 3 & 0 \\ 1 & 0 & 0 & 0 \\ 0 & -2 & 0 & 0 \\ 0 & 0 & 0 & 4 \end{vmatrix}$

9. $\begin{vmatrix} 0 & 0 & 0 & 2 \\ 0 & 0 & 1 & 0 \\ 0 & 4 & 0 & 0 \\ 3 & 0 & 0 & 0 \end{vmatrix}$

10. $\begin{vmatrix} 0 & 0 & 0 & -3 & 0 \\ 0 & 0 & 0 & 0 & 2 \\ 0 & 0 & 1 & 0 & 0 \\ 5 & 0 & 0 & 0 & 0 \\ 0 & 4 & 0 & 0 & 0 \end{vmatrix}$

11. $\begin{vmatrix} 3 & 0 & 0 & 0 & 0 \\ 0 & 0 & 0 & 0 & -5 \\ 0 & 0 & 0 & 0 & 0 \\ 0 & 0 & -4 & 1 & 0 \\ 0 & 2 & 0 & 0 & 0 \end{vmatrix}$

12. $\begin{vmatrix} 1 & 0 & 0 & 0 & 0 & 0 \\ 0 & -3 & 0 & 0 & 0 & 0 \\ 0 & 0 & 2 & 0 & 0 & 0 \\ 0 & 0 & 0 & 4 & 0 & 0 \\ 0 & 0 & 0 & 0 & 2 & 1 \\ 0 & 0 & 0 & 0 & 3 & 1 \end{vmatrix}$

In questions 13–18, evaluate the determinant by inspection.

13. $\begin{vmatrix} 2 & 0 & 0 \\ 43 & 14 & 0 \\ \sqrt{43} & 43 & -1 \end{vmatrix}$

14. $\begin{vmatrix} 1 & -2 & 3 & -4 \\ 0 & 5 & -6 & 7 \\ 0 & 0 & -8 & 9 \\ 0 & 0 & 0 & 1 \end{vmatrix}$

15. $\begin{vmatrix} 3 & 2 & 5 \\ 1 & 0 & -7 \\ 1 & 0 & -7 \end{vmatrix}$

16. $\begin{vmatrix} 12 & 1 & 9 \\ 7 & 7 & 6 \\ 12 & 1 & 9 \end{vmatrix}$

17. $\begin{vmatrix} 1 & 8 & 6 \\ -3 & -24 & -18 \\ 5 & 5 & 4 \end{vmatrix}$

18. $\begin{vmatrix} 6 & 3 & 9 & -12 \\ 5 & 0 & 1 & 2 \\ \frac{4}{5} & \frac{2}{5} & \frac{6}{5} & \frac{-8}{5} \\ \frac{2}{3} & \frac{-1}{3} & \frac{5}{3} & \frac{8}{3} \end{vmatrix}$

In questions 19–22, evaluate the determinant by reducing the matrix to row–echelon form.

19. $\begin{vmatrix} 1 & 3 & 5 \\ 4 & 14 & 12 \\ -2 & -3 & -20 \end{vmatrix}$

20. $\begin{vmatrix} 1 & 3 & -2 \\ 4 & 2 & 5 \\ 0 & 1 & 1 \end{vmatrix}$

21. $\begin{vmatrix} 1 & 2 & 7 \\ 2 & 5 & -3 \\ 8 & 19 & 5 \end{vmatrix}$

22. $\begin{vmatrix} 0 & 1 & 3 & 4 \\ 2 & -7 & 2 & 4 \\ -3 & 11 & 4 & 0 \\ 1 & -3 & 2 & 2 \end{vmatrix}$

In questions 23–26,

given that $\begin{vmatrix} r & s & t \\ u & v & w \\ x & y & z \end{vmatrix} = 4$, evaluate the determinant.

23. $\begin{vmatrix} -r & -s & -t \\ 3u & 3v & 3w \\ 2x & 2y & 2z \end{vmatrix}$ 24. $\begin{vmatrix} x & y & z \\ u & v & w \\ r & s & t \end{vmatrix}$ 25. $\begin{vmatrix} -x & -y & -z \\ r & s & t \\ u & v & w \end{vmatrix}$ 26. $\begin{vmatrix} r & s & t \\ 8u & 8v & 8w \\ x-8r & y-8s & z-8t \end{vmatrix}$

In questions 27–32, given that $A = \begin{bmatrix} r & s & t \\ u & v & w \\ x & y & z \end{bmatrix}$ and $\det(A) = 5$, evaluate the determinant.

27. $\det(-4A)$ 28. $\det(A^{-1})$ 29. $\det(A^2)$

30. $\det(A^T)$ 31. $\det([3A^{-1}]^T)$ 32. $\det \begin{bmatrix} t & r & s \\ w & u & v \\ z & x & y \end{bmatrix}$

In questions 33–36, determine whether the given matrix is invertible.

33. $\begin{bmatrix} 3 & 0 & 0 \\ \frac{1}{3} & 5 & 0 \\ \frac{2}{3} & \frac{2}{3} & -2 \end{bmatrix}$ 34. $\begin{bmatrix} 7 & 1 & -1 \\ 2 & 4 & 3 \\ -14 & -2 & 2 \end{bmatrix}$ 35. $\begin{bmatrix} 5 & 0 & 3 \\ 5 & 0 & -3 \\ 4 & 0 & 2 \end{bmatrix}$ 36. $\begin{bmatrix} 0 & -2 & 0 \\ 0 & 0 & 1 \\ 4 & 0 & 0 \end{bmatrix}$

In questions 37–42, evaluate the determinant by using cofactor expansion.

37. $\begin{vmatrix} 4 & 1 & 3 \\ 0 & 1 & -2 \\ 1 & 2 & 5 \end{vmatrix}$ 38. $\begin{vmatrix} -1 & 1 & 2 \\ 0 & 12 & 0 \\ 3 & 0 & 2 \end{vmatrix}$ 39. $\begin{vmatrix} 2 & 4 & 3 \\ 2 & 6 & 5 \\ 1 & 0 & 1 \end{vmatrix}$

40. $\begin{vmatrix} 4 & 3 & 1 \\ 2 & 1 & 2 \\ 1 & 3 & 4 \end{vmatrix}$ 41. $\begin{vmatrix} 2 & k & 3 & 0 \\ k & 4 & 1 & 1 \\ 0 & -1 & 5 & 1 \\ 0 & 1 & 4 & 2 \end{vmatrix}$ 42. $\begin{vmatrix} 1 & 7 & 2 & 0 \\ 2 & 5 & 5 & 0 \\ 1 & 1 & -1 & 0 \\ 0 & 0 & 0 & 2 \end{vmatrix}$

In questions 43–48, compute A^{-1} by using the adjoint matrix.

43. $A = \begin{bmatrix} 2 & 4 & 1 \\ 0 & 1 & 4 \\ 0 & 0 & 3 \end{bmatrix}$ 44. $A = \begin{bmatrix} 1 & 2 & 3 \\ 2 & -1 & 0 \\ 3 & 0 & 3 \end{bmatrix}$ 45. $A = \begin{bmatrix} 1 & -2 & 0 \\ 2 & 3 & 0 \\ 0 & 0 & 5 \end{bmatrix}$

46. $A = \begin{bmatrix} 3 & 0 & 0 \\ 0 & 0 & -2 \\ 0 & 8 & 0 \end{bmatrix}$ 47. $A = \begin{bmatrix} 5 & 0 & 2 \\ 0 & 1 & 1 \\ 3 & 4 & 7 \end{bmatrix}$ 48. $A = \begin{bmatrix} 1 & 3 & 5 \\ 2 & 1 & 4 \\ -1 & 6 & 2 \end{bmatrix}$

In questions 49–54, solve the system of equations by using Cramer's Rule.

49. $\begin{aligned} 2x - 3y &= 7 \\ x + 5y &= 1 \end{aligned}$ 50. $\begin{aligned} x + y - z &= 2 \\ 3x - y + z &= 5 \\ 3x + 2y + 4z &= 0 \end{aligned}$ 51. $\begin{aligned} 4x - z &= 5 \\ 3y + z &= 1 \\ x - y &= 2 \end{aligned}$

52.
$$\begin{aligned} x_1 + x_2 + x_3 &= 0 \\ 2x_1 - x_2 - x_3 &= 1 \\ x_2 + 2x_3 &= 2 \end{aligned}$$

53.
$$\begin{aligned} -p + q - 2r &= 1 \\ p - q + 9r &= -2 \\ 5q + r &= 4 \end{aligned}$$

54.
$$\begin{aligned} x_1 - x_2 + x_3 + x_4 &= 4 \\ x_1 + x_2 - x_3 - x_4 &= 0 \\ -x_1 + x_2 + x_3 - x_4 &= -2 \\ -x_1 + x_2 - x_3 + x_4 &= 4 \end{aligned}$$

WRITING QUESTIONS

55. Discuss the relative merits of these three methods of computing determinants:

a) signed elementary products
b) row reduction
c) cofactor expansion

56. Suppose that you needed to compute by hand a 10×10 determinant as quickly as possible, and you had 10 friends to help you. How would you divide up the work, and what would you tell your friends to do?

57. What does a determinant allow you to "determine"?

58. Discuss the relative merits of athese three methods of solving systems of linear equations:

a) Gauss or Gauss–Jordan elimination
b) multiplying by the inverse of the coefficient matrix
c) Cramer's rule of determinants

59. Use your study of determinants to refute the following: "Mathematical theorems aren't important if all we're doing is trying to solve a problem."

CHAPTER 2: SOLUTIONS

SECTION 2.1. THE DETERMINANT FUNCTION

1. The number of inversions in $(3,4,1,2,5)$ is $2+2+0+0=4$

2. The number of inversions in $(4,5,1,3,2)$ is $3+3+0+1=7$

3. The number of inversions in $(2,5,1,3,4)$ is $1+3+0+0=4$

4. The number of inversions in $(1,3,5,4,2)$ is $0+1+2+1=4$

5. The number of inversions in $(5,4,2,1,3)$ is $4+3+1+0=8$

6. The number of inversions in $(1,2,3,5,4)$ is $0+0+0+1=1$

7. The only nonzero elementary product is $(-1)(2)(8) = -16$.
   The associated permutation of the columns is $(2,1,3)$ which is odd.
   Thus, $\det = 16$.

8. The only nonzero elementary product is $(3)(1)(-2)(4) = -24$.
   The associated permutation of the columns is $(3,1,2,4)$ which is even.
   Thus, $\det = -24$.

9. The only nonzero elementary product is $(2)(1)(4)(3) = 24$.
   The associated permutation of the columns is $(4,3,2,1)$ which is even.
   Thus, $\det = 24$.

10. The only nonzero elementary product is $(-3)(2)(1)(5)(4) = -120$.
    The associated permutation of the columns is $(4,5,3,1,2)$ which is even.
    Thus, $\det = -120$.

11. All of the elementary products equal zero, since row 3 has only zero entries.
    Thus, $\det = 0$.

12. The only nonzero elementary products are $(1)(-3)(2)(4)(2)(1) = -48$
    and $(1)(-3)(2)(4)(1)(3) = -72$.
    The associated permutations of the columns are $(1,2,3,4,5,6)$ and $(1,2,3,4,6,5)$
    which are even and odd, respectively.
    Thus, $\det = -48 + 72 = 24$.

13. Since the matrix is lower triangular, its determinant equals the product of the diagonal entries, or -28.

14. Since the matrix is upper triangular, its determinant equals the product of the diagonal entries, or -40.

15. Since rows 2 and 3 are proportional, the determinant equals 0.

16. Since rows 1 and 3 are proportional, the determinant equals 0.

17. Since rows 1 and 2 are proportional, the determinant equals 0.

18. Since rows 1 and 3 are proportional, the determinant equals 0.

19.
$$
\begin{vmatrix} 1 & 3 & 5 \\ 4 & 14 & 12 \\ -2 & -3 & -20 \end{vmatrix} = \begin{vmatrix} 1 & 3 & 5 \\ 0 & 2 & -8 \\ -2 & -3 & -20 \end{vmatrix}
$$

$$
= \begin{vmatrix} 1 & 3 & 5 \\ 0 & 2 & -8 \\ 0 & 3 & -10 \end{vmatrix}
$$

$$
= 2\begin{vmatrix} 1 & 3 & 5 \\ 0 & 1 & -4 \\ 0 & 3 & -10 \end{vmatrix}
$$

$$
= 2\begin{vmatrix} 1 & 3 & 5 \\ 0 & 1 & -4 \\ 0 & 0 & 2 \end{vmatrix}
$$

$$
= (2)(2)\begin{vmatrix} 1 & 3 & 5 \\ 0 & 1 & -4 \\ 0 & 0 & 1 \end{vmatrix}
$$

$$
= (2)(2)(1) = 4
$$

20.
$$
\begin{vmatrix} 1 & 3 & -2 \\ 4 & 2 & 5 \\ 0 & 1 & 1 \end{vmatrix} = \begin{vmatrix} 1 & 3 & -2 \\ 0 & -10 & 13 \\ 0 & 1 & 1 \end{vmatrix}
$$

$$
= -10\begin{vmatrix} 1 & 3 & -2 \\ 0 & 1 & -13/10 \\ 0 & 1 & 1 \end{vmatrix}
$$

$$
= -10\begin{vmatrix} 1 & 3 & -2 \\ 0 & 1 & -13/10 \\ 0 & 0 & 23/10 \end{vmatrix}
$$

$$
= (-10)\left(\frac{23}{10}\right)\begin{vmatrix} 1 & 3 & -2 \\ 0 & 1 & -13/10 \\ 0 & 0 & 1 \end{vmatrix}
$$

$$
= (-10)\left(\frac{23}{10}\right)(1) = -23
$$

21. $\begin{vmatrix} 1 & 2 & 7 \\ 2 & 5 & -3 \\ 8 & 19 & 5 \end{vmatrix} = \begin{vmatrix} 1 & 2 & 7 \\ 0 & 1 & -17 \\ 8 & 19 & 5 \end{vmatrix}$

$$= \begin{vmatrix} 1 & 2 & 7 \\ 0 & 1 & -17 \\ 0 & 3 & -51 \end{vmatrix}$$

$$= \begin{vmatrix} 1 & 2 & 7 \\ 0 & 1 & -17 \\ 0 & 0 & 0 \end{vmatrix}$$

$$= 0$$

22. $\begin{vmatrix} 0 & 1 & 3 & 4 \\ 2 & -7 & 2 & 4 \\ -3 & 11 & 4 & 0 \\ 1 & -3 & 2 & 2 \end{vmatrix} = -\begin{vmatrix} 1 & -3 & 2 & 2 \\ 2 & -7 & 2 & 4 \\ -3 & 11 & 4 & 0 \\ 0 & 1 & 3 & 4 \end{vmatrix}$

$$= -\begin{vmatrix} 1 & -3 & 2 & 2 \\ 0 & -1 & -2 & 0 \\ -3 & 11 & 4 & 0 \\ 0 & 1 & 3 & 4 \end{vmatrix}$$

$$= -\begin{vmatrix} 1 & -3 & 2 & 2 \\ 0 & -1 & -2 & 0 \\ 0 & 2 & 10 & 6 \\ 0 & 1 & 3 & 4 \end{vmatrix}$$

$$= \begin{vmatrix} 1 & -3 & 2 & 2 \\ 0 & 1 & 2 & 0 \\ 0 & 2 & 10 & 6 \\ 0 & 1 & 3 & 4 \end{vmatrix}$$

$$= \begin{vmatrix} 1 & -3 & 2 & 2 \\ 0 & 1 & 2 & 0 \\ 0 & 0 & 6 & 6 \\ 0 & 1 & 3 & 4 \end{vmatrix}$$

$$= \begin{vmatrix} 1 & -3 & 2 & 2 \\ 0 & 1 & 2 & 0 \\ 0 & 0 & 6 & 6 \\ 0 & 0 & 1 & 4 \end{vmatrix}$$

$$= 6\begin{vmatrix} 1 & -3 & 2 & 2 \\ 0 & 1 & 2 & 0 \\ 0 & 0 & 1 & 1 \\ 0 & 0 & 1 & 4 \end{vmatrix}$$

$$= 6\begin{vmatrix} 1 & -3 & 2 & 2 \\ 0 & 1 & 2 & 0 \\ 0 & 0 & 1 & 1 \\ 0 & 0 & 0 & 3 \end{vmatrix}$$

$$= (6)(3)\begin{vmatrix} 1 & -3 & 2 & 2 \\ 0 & 1 & 2 & 0 \\ 0 & 0 & 1 & 1 \\ 0 & 0 & 0 & 1 \end{vmatrix}$$

$$= (6)(3)(1) = 18$$

23.
$$\begin{vmatrix} -r & -s & -t \\ 3u & 3v & 3w \\ 2x & 2y & 2z \end{vmatrix} = -\begin{vmatrix} r & s & t \\ 3u & 3v & 3w \\ 2x & 2y & 2z \end{vmatrix}$$

$$= (-3)\begin{vmatrix} r & s & t \\ u & v & w \\ 2x & 2y & 2z \end{vmatrix}$$

$$= (-6)\begin{vmatrix} r & s & t \\ u & v & w \\ x & y & z \end{vmatrix}$$

$$= -6(4) = -24$$

24.
$$\begin{vmatrix} x & y & z \\ u & v & w \\ r & s & t \end{vmatrix} = -\begin{vmatrix} r & s & t \\ u & v & w \\ x & y & z \end{vmatrix} \qquad \text{(interchange rows 1 and 3)}$$

$$= -4$$

25.
$$\begin{vmatrix} -x & -y & -z \\ r & s & t \\ u & v & w \end{vmatrix} = -\begin{vmatrix} x & y & z \\ r & s & t \\ u & v & w \end{vmatrix}$$

$$= \begin{vmatrix} r & s & t \\ x & y & z \\ u & v & w \end{vmatrix} \qquad \text{(interchange rows 1 and 2)}$$

$$= -\begin{vmatrix} r & s & t \\ u & v & w \\ x & y & z \end{vmatrix} \qquad \text{(interchange rows 2 and 3)}$$

$$= -4$$

26.
$$\begin{vmatrix} r & s & t \\ 8u & 8v & 8w \\ x-8r & y-8s & z-8t \end{vmatrix} = 8\begin{vmatrix} r & s & t \\ u & v & w \\ x-8r & y-8s & z-8t \end{vmatrix}$$

$$= 8\begin{vmatrix} r & s & t \\ u & v & w \\ x & y & z \end{vmatrix}$$

$$= 8(4) = 32$$

SECTION 2.3. PROPERTIES OF THE DETERMINANT FUNCTION

27. $\det(-4A) = (-4)^3 \det(A) = (-64)(5) = -320$

28. $\det(A^{-1}) = [\det(A)]^{-1} = (5)^{-1} = \frac{1}{5}$

29. $\det(A^2) = \det(AA) = \det(A)\det(A) = (5)(5) = 25$

30. $\det(A^T) = \det(A) = 5$

31. $\det\left(\left[3A^{-1}\right]^T\right) = \det(3A^{-1}) = (3^3)\det(A^{-1}) = 27[\det A]^{-1} = 27(5)^{-1} = \frac{27}{5}$

32. $\begin{vmatrix} t & r & s \\ w & u & v \\ z & x & y \end{vmatrix} = - \begin{vmatrix} r & t & s \\ u & w & v \\ x & z & y \end{vmatrix}$ (interchange columns 1 and 2)

$\qquad\qquad = \begin{vmatrix} r & s & t \\ u & v & w \\ x & y & z \end{vmatrix}$ (interchange columns 2 and 3)

$\qquad\qquad = 5$

33. Since the matrix is triangular, its determinant equals the product of the diagonal entries, or -30. Since the determinant is not zero, the matrix is invertible.

34. Since rows 1 and 3 of the matrix are proportional, its determinant equals 0. Hence, it is not invertible.

35. Since column 2 of the matrix has only zero entries, its determinant equals 0. Hence, it is not invertible.

36. Since the only nonzero elementary product of the matrix is (-2)(1)(4) = -8, and the associated permutation of the columns is (2,3,1) which is even, the determinant is $-8 \neq 0$. Hence, it is invertible.

SECTION 2.4. COFACTOR EXPANSION; CRAMER'S RULE

37. Expanding along column 1,

$$\det(A) = 4 \begin{vmatrix} 1 & -2 \\ 2 & 5 \end{vmatrix} - 0 + 1 \begin{vmatrix} 1 & 3 \\ 1 & -2 \end{vmatrix}$$
$$= (4)(9) + (1)(-5) = 31$$

38. Expanding along row 2,

$$\det(A) = 0 + 12 \begin{vmatrix} -1 & 2 \\ 3 & 2 \end{vmatrix} + 0$$
$$= (12)(-8) = -96$$

39. Exapnding along row 3,

$$\det(A) = 1 \begin{vmatrix} 4 & 3 \\ 6 & 5 \end{vmatrix} + 0 + 1 \begin{vmatrix} 2 & 4 \\ 2 & 6 \end{vmatrix}$$
$$= (1)(2) + (1)(4) = 6$$

40. Expanding along row 1,

$$\det(A) = 4 \begin{vmatrix} 1 & 2 \\ 3 & 4 \end{vmatrix} - 3 \begin{vmatrix} 2 & 2 \\ 1 & 4 \end{vmatrix} + 1 \begin{vmatrix} 2 & 1 \\ 1 & 3 \end{vmatrix}$$
$$= (4)(-2) - (3)(6) + (1)(5) = -21$$

41. Expanding along column 1,

$$\det(A) = 2 \begin{vmatrix} 4 & 1 & 1 \\ -1 & 5 & 1 \\ 1 & 4 & 2 \end{vmatrix} - k \begin{vmatrix} k & 3 & 0 \\ -1 & 5 & 1 \\ 1 & 4 & 2 \end{vmatrix}$$

Now expanding along row 1,

$$\det(A) = 2\left[4\begin{vmatrix} 5 & 1 \\ 4 & 2 \end{vmatrix} - 1\begin{vmatrix} -1 & 1 \\ 1 & 2 \end{vmatrix} + 1\begin{vmatrix} -1 & 5 \\ 1 & 4 \end{vmatrix}\right] - k\left[k\begin{vmatrix} 5 & 1 \\ 4 & 2 \end{vmatrix} - 3\begin{vmatrix} -1 & 1 \\ 1 & 2 \end{vmatrix} + 0\right]$$

$$= 2[(4)(6) - (1)(-3) + (1)(-9)] - k[(k)(6) - (3)(-3)]$$

$$= 2[18] - k[6k + 9] = -6k^2 - 9k + 36$$

42. Expanding along row 4,

$$\det(A) = 0 + 0 + 0 + 2\begin{vmatrix} 1 & 7 & 2 \\ 2 & 5 & 5 \\ 1 & 1 & -1 \end{vmatrix}$$

Now expanding along row 1,

$$\det(A) = 2\left[1\begin{vmatrix} 5 & 5 \\ 1 & -1 \end{vmatrix} - 7\begin{vmatrix} 2 & 5 \\ 1 & -1 \end{vmatrix} + 2\begin{vmatrix} 2 & 5 \\ 1 & 1 \end{vmatrix}\right]$$

$$= 2[(1)(-10) - (7)(-7) + (2)(-3)] = 2[33] = 66$$

43. $A = \begin{bmatrix} 2 & 4 & 1 \\ 0 & 1 & 4 \\ 0 & 0 & 3 \end{bmatrix}$

The matrix of cofactors is $\begin{bmatrix} 3 & 0 & 0 \\ -12 & 6 & 0 \\ 15 & -8 & 2 \end{bmatrix}$

$\det(A) = (0)(15) + (0)(-8) + (3)(2) = 6$

$\mathrm{adj}(A) = \begin{bmatrix} 3 & -12 & 15 \\ 0 & 6 & -8 \\ 0 & 0 & 2 \end{bmatrix}$

$A^{-1} = \dfrac{1}{6}\begin{bmatrix} 3 & -12 & 15 \\ 0 & 6 & -8 \\ 0 & 0 & 2 \end{bmatrix}$

44. $A = \begin{bmatrix} 1 & 2 & 3 \\ 2 & -1 & 0 \\ 3 & 0 & 3 \end{bmatrix}$

The matrix of cofactors is $\begin{bmatrix} -3 & -6 & 3 \\ -6 & -6 & 6 \\ 3 & 6 & -5 \end{bmatrix}$

$\det(A) = (3)(3) + (0)(6) + (3)(-5) = -6$

$\mathrm{adj}(A) = \begin{bmatrix} -3 & -6 & 3 \\ -6 & -6 & 6 \\ 3 & 6 & -5 \end{bmatrix}$

$A^{-1} = \dfrac{1}{6}\begin{bmatrix} 3 & 6 & -3 \\ 6 & 6 & -6 \\ -3 & -6 & 5 \end{bmatrix}$

45. $A = \begin{bmatrix} 1 & -2 & 0 \\ 2 & 3 & 0 \\ 0 & 0 & 5 \end{bmatrix}$

The matrix of cofactors is $\begin{bmatrix} 15 & -10 & 0 \\ 10 & 5 & 0 \\ 0 & 0 & 7 \end{bmatrix}$

$\det(A) = (0)(0) + (0)(0) + (5)(7) = 35$

$\text{adj}(A) = \begin{bmatrix} 15 & 10 & 0 \\ -10 & 5 & 0 \\ 0 & 0 & 7 \end{bmatrix}$

$A^{-1} = \dfrac{1}{35} \begin{bmatrix} 15 & 10 & 0 \\ -10 & 5 & 0 \\ 0 & 0 & 7 \end{bmatrix}$

46. $A = \begin{bmatrix} 3 & 0 & 0 \\ 0 & 0 & -2 \\ 0 & 8 & 0 \end{bmatrix}$

The matrix of cofactors is $\begin{bmatrix} 16 & 0 & 0 \\ 0 & 0 & -24 \\ 0 & 6 & 0 \end{bmatrix}$

$\det(A) = (0)(0) + (8)(6) + (0)(0) = 48$

$\text{adj}(A) = \begin{bmatrix} 16 & 0 & 0 \\ 0 & 0 & 6 \\ 0 & -24 & 0 \end{bmatrix}$

$A^{-1} = \dfrac{1}{48} \begin{bmatrix} 16 & 0 & 0 \\ 0 & 0 & 6 \\ 0 & -24 & 0 \end{bmatrix} = \dfrac{1}{24} \begin{bmatrix} 8 & 0 & 0 \\ 0 & 0 & 3 \\ 0 & -12 & 0 \end{bmatrix}$

47. $A = \begin{bmatrix} 5 & 0 & 2 \\ 0 & 1 & 1 \\ 3 & 4 & 7 \end{bmatrix}$

The matrix of cofactors is $\begin{bmatrix} 3 & 3 & -3 \\ 8 & 29 & -20 \\ -2 & -5 & 5 \end{bmatrix}$

$\det(A) = (5)(3) + (0)(3) + (2)(-3) = 9$

$\text{adj}(A) = \begin{bmatrix} 3 & 8 & -2 \\ 3 & 29 & -5 \\ -3 & -20 & 5 \end{bmatrix}$

$A^{-1} = \dfrac{1}{9} \begin{bmatrix} 3 & 8 & -2 \\ 3 & 29 & -5 \\ -3 & -20 & 5 \end{bmatrix}$

34

48. $A = \begin{bmatrix} 1 & 3 & 5 \\ 2 & 1 & 4 \\ -1 & 6 & 2 \end{bmatrix}$

The matrix of cofactors is $\begin{bmatrix} -22 & -8 & 13 \\ 24 & 7 & -9 \\ 7 & 6 & -5 \end{bmatrix}$

$\det(A) = (1)(-22) + (3)(-8) + (5)(13) = 19$

$\text{adj}(A) = \begin{bmatrix} -22 & 24 & 7 \\ -8 & 7 & 6 \\ 13 & -9 & -5 \end{bmatrix}$

$A^{-1} = \dfrac{1}{19} \begin{bmatrix} -22 & 24 & 7 \\ -8 & 7 & 6 \\ 13 & -9 & -5 \end{bmatrix}$

49. By direct computation, we obtain

$$\det(A) = \begin{vmatrix} 2 & -3 \\ 1 & 5 \end{vmatrix} = 13$$

$$\det(A_1) = \begin{vmatrix} 7 & -3 \\ 1 & 5 \end{vmatrix} = 38$$

$$\det(A_2) = \begin{vmatrix} 2 & 7 \\ 1 & 1 \end{vmatrix} = -5$$

Thus, $x = 38/13$ and $y = -5/13$.

50. By direct computation, we obtain

$$\det(A) = \begin{vmatrix} 1 & 1 & -1 \\ 3 & -1 & 1 \\ 3 & 2 & 4 \end{vmatrix} = -24$$

$$\det(A_1) = \begin{vmatrix} 2 & 1 & -1 \\ 5 & -1 & 1 \\ 0 & 2 & 4 \end{vmatrix} = -42$$

$$\det(A_2) = \begin{vmatrix} 1 & 2 & -1 \\ 3 & 5 & 1 \\ 3 & 0 & 4 \end{vmatrix} = 17$$

$$\det(A_3) = \begin{vmatrix} 1 & 1 & 2 \\ 3 & -1 & 5 \\ 3 & 2 & 0 \end{vmatrix} = 23$$

Thus, $x = -42/(-24) = 7/4$, $y = 17/(-24) = -17/24$, and $z = 23/-24 = -23/24$.

51. By direct computation, we obtain

$$\det(A) = \begin{vmatrix} 4 & 0 & -1 \\ 0 & 3 & 1 \\ 1 & -1 & 0 \end{vmatrix} = 7$$

$$\det(A_1) = \begin{vmatrix} 5 & 0 & -1 \\ 1 & 3 & 1 \\ 2 & -1 & 0 \end{vmatrix} = 12$$

$$\det(A_2) = \begin{vmatrix} 4 & 5 & -1 \\ 0 & 1 & 1 \\ 1 & 2 & 0 \end{vmatrix} = -2$$

$$\det(A_3) = \begin{vmatrix} 4 & 0 & 5 \\ 0 & 3 & 1 \\ 1 & -1 & 2 \end{vmatrix} = 13$$

Thus, $x = 12/7$, $y = -2/7$, and $z = 13/7$.

52. By direct computation, we obtain

$$\det(A) = \begin{vmatrix} 1 & 1 & 1 \\ 2 & -1 & -1 \\ 0 & 1 & 2 \end{vmatrix} = -3$$

$$\det(A_1) = \begin{vmatrix} 0 & 1 & 1 \\ 1 & -1 & -1 \\ 2 & 1 & 2 \end{vmatrix} = -1$$

$$\det(A_2) = \begin{vmatrix} 1 & 0 & 1 \\ 2 & 1 & -1 \\ 0 & 2 & 2 \end{vmatrix} = 8$$

$$\det(A_3) = \begin{vmatrix} 1 & 1 & 0 \\ 2 & -1 & 1 \\ 0 & 1 & 2 \end{vmatrix} = -7$$

Thus, $x_1 = -1/(-3) = 1/3$, $y_2 = 8/(-3) = -8/3$, and $x_3 = -7/(-3) = 7/3$.

53. By direct computation, we obtain

$$\det(A) = \begin{vmatrix} -1 & 1 & -2 \\ 1 & -1 & 9 \\ 0 & 5 & 1 \end{vmatrix} = 35$$

$$\det(A_1) = \begin{vmatrix} 1 & 1 & -2 \\ -2 & -1 & 9 \\ 4 & 5 & 1 \end{vmatrix} = 4$$

$$\det(A_2) = \begin{vmatrix} -1 & 1 & -2 \\ 1 & -2 & 9 \\ 0 & 4 & 1 \end{vmatrix} = 29$$

$$\det(A_3) = \begin{vmatrix} -1 & 1 & 1 \\ 1 & -1 & -2 \\ 0 & 5 & 4 \end{vmatrix} = -5$$

Thus, $p = 4/35$, $\quad q = 29/35$, $\quad$ and $\quad r = -5/35 = -1/7$.

54. By direct computation, we obtain

$$
\det(A) = \begin{vmatrix} 1 & -1 & 1 & 1 \\ 1 & 1 & -1 & -1 \\ -1 & 1 & 1 & -1 \\ -1 & 1 & -1 & 1 \end{vmatrix} = 8
$$

$$
\det(A_1) = \begin{vmatrix} 4 & -1 & 1 & 1 \\ 0 & 1 & -1 & -1 \\ -2 & 1 & 1 & -1 \\ 4 & 1 & -1 & 1 \end{vmatrix} = 16
$$

$$
\det(A_2) = \begin{vmatrix} 1 & 4 & 1 & 1 \\ 1 & 0 & -1 & -1 \\ -1 & -2 & 1 & -1 \\ -1 & 4 & -1 & 1 \end{vmatrix} = 24
$$

$$
\det(A_3) = \begin{vmatrix} 1 & -1 & 4 & 1 \\ 1 & 1 & 0 & -1 \\ -1 & 1 & -2 & -1 \\ -1 & 1 & 4 & 1 \end{vmatrix} = 8
$$

$$
\det(A_4) = \begin{vmatrix} 1 & -1 & 1 & 4 \\ 1 & 1 & -1 & 0 \\ -1 & 1 & 1 & -2 \\ -1 & 1 & -1 & 4 \end{vmatrix} = 32
$$

Thus, $x_1 = 16/8 = 2$, $\quad x_2 = 24/8 = 3$, $\quad x_3 = 8/8 = 1$, $\quad$ and $\quad x_4 = 32/8 = 4$.

CHAPTER 3: VECTORS IN 2–SPACE AND 3–SPACE

1. Let $\mathbf{u} = (1,7)$, $\mathbf{v} = (3,-2)$. Compute the following.

   (a) $\mathbf{u} + \mathbf{v}$ (b) $2\mathbf{u} - 3\mathbf{v}$ (c) $\|\mathbf{u} - \mathbf{v}\|$

   (d) $\|\mathbf{u}\| - \|\mathbf{v}\|$ (e) $2\mathbf{u}\cdot\mathbf{v}$ (f) $\mathbf{u}\cdot\mathbf{v} - \mathbf{v}\cdot\mathbf{u}$

2. Let $\mathbf{u} = (1,0,-2)$, $\mathbf{v} = (3,2,4)$, $\mathbf{w} = (2,2,-1)$. Compute the following.

   (a) $\mathbf{u} - \mathbf{v}$ (b) $2\mathbf{u} + \mathbf{v}$ (c) $3\mathbf{u} + \mathbf{v} - \mathbf{w}$

   (d) $\mathbf{u}\cdot\mathbf{v}$ (e) $\|\mathbf{u} + \mathbf{v} - 2\mathbf{w}\|$ (f) $\|\mathbf{u} + \mathbf{v}\| - \|2\mathbf{w}\|$

3. Let $\mathbf{u} = (1,1,3)$, $\mathbf{v} = (2,0,1)$, $\mathbf{w} = (0,-1,5)$. Compute the following.

   (a) $2\mathbf{u} + \mathbf{w}$ (b) $2(\mathbf{u} + \mathbf{v}) - 3\,(\mathbf{v} - 2\,\mathbf{w})$ (c) $(\mathbf{u}\cdot\mathbf{v})\mathbf{w}$

   (d) $\mathbf{u}\cdot(\mathbf{v} \times \mathbf{w})$ (e) $\|\mathbf{v}\|(\mathbf{u}\cdot\mathbf{w})$ (f) $\|\mathbf{u} \times (\mathbf{v} + \mathbf{w})\|$

4. Let $\mathbf{u} = (1,-1,1)$, $\mathbf{v} = (2,1,2)$, $\mathbf{w} = (1,0,-3)$. Compute the following.

   (a) $\mathbf{u} - 2\mathbf{v} + \mathbf{w}$ (b) $\mathbf{w}\cdot\mathbf{u} - \|5\mathbf{v}\|$ (c) $(2\mathbf{u} - \mathbf{v}) \times \mathbf{w}$

   (d) $(\mathbf{u} \times \mathbf{v}) \times \mathbf{w}$ (e) $(\mathbf{u} \times \mathbf{w}) \times (\mathbf{u} \times \mathbf{v})$ (f) $(\mathbf{v} \times \mathbf{w})\cdot\mathbf{u}$

5. Let $\mathbf{u} = (4,2,-1)$, $\mathbf{v} = (3,1,1)$, $\mathbf{w} = (0,2,1)$. Compute the following.

   (a) $2\mathbf{v} - 3\mathbf{w} - \mathbf{u}$ (b) $(\mathbf{u}\cdot\mathbf{w})\|\mathbf{u} \times \mathbf{w}\|$ (c) $\mathbf{w}\cdot(5\mathbf{v} - \mathbf{u})$

   (d) $\mathbf{v}\cdot(\mathbf{w} \times \mathbf{u})$ (e) $\mathbf{v} \times (\mathbf{u} \times \mathbf{w})$ (f) $\mathbf{v} \times (\mathbf{u} \times 2\mathbf{u})$

6. Find the terminal point Q of a vetor $\mathbf{u}$ with initial point $P(4,-3,6)$ such that

   (a) $\mathbf{u}$ has the same direction as $\mathbf{v} = (1,1,7)$

   (b) $\mathbf{u}$ is oppositely directed to $\mathbf{v} = (1,1,7)$.

7. Find the terminal point Q of a vector $\mathbf{u}$ with initial point $P(-2,6,5)$ such that

   (a) $\mathbf{u}$ has the same direction as $\mathbf{v} = (4,0,3)$

   (b) $\mathbf{u}$ is oppositely directed to $\mathbf{v} = (4,0,3)$.

8. Find the initial point P of a vector $\mathbf{u}$ with terminal point $Q(3,5,5)$ such that

   (a) $\mathbf{u}$ has the same direction as $\mathbf{v} = (6,-2,1)$

   (b) $\mathbf{u}$ is oppositely directed to $\mathbf{v} = (6,-2,1)$.

9. Find the initial point P of a vector $\mathbf{u}$ with terminal point $Q(2,0,2)$ such that

   (a) $\mathbf{u}$ has the same direction as $\mathbf{v} = (5,4,-1)$

   (b) $\mathbf{u}$ is oppositely directed to $\mathbf{v} = (5,4,-1)$.

10. Find the distance between P and Q

(a) $P(1,7)$, $Q(2,3)$

(c) $P(1,0,6)$, $Q(4,3,-2)$

(b) $P(-1,4)$, $Q(3,-5)$

(d) $P(7,-4,5)$, $Q(8,-2,-3)$

11. Find the distance between R and S.

(a) $R(6,1)$, $S(1,-11)$

(c) $R(4,3,-8)$, $S(7,7,4)$

(b) $R(4,0)$, $S(0,-8)$

(d) $R(3,4,1)$, $S(4,3,4)$

12. Find the vector component of $\mathbf{u}$ parallel to $\mathbf{a}$.

(a) $\mathbf{u} = (6,5)$, $\mathbf{a} = (-3,4)$

(c) $\mathbf{u} = (3,0,2)$, $\mathbf{a} = (1,1,3)$

(b) $\mathbf{u} = (1,2)$, $\mathbf{a} = (7,-3)$

(d) $\mathbf{u} = (1,0,7)$, $\mathbf{a} = (0,5,0)$

13. Find the vector component of $\mathbf{u}$ orthogonal to $\mathbf{a}$.

(a) $\mathbf{u} = (4,1)$, $\mathbf{a} = (2,-3)$

(c) $\mathbf{u} = (1,5,-5)$, $\mathbf{a} = (1,2,3)$

(b) $\mathbf{u} = (5,-2)$, $\mathbf{a} = (1,1)$

(d) $\mathbf{u} = (4,-1-1)$, $\mathbf{a} = (1,-2,4)$

14. Consider the points $A(2,6)$, $B(3,7)$, $C(3,8)$. Compute the following.

(a) $\cos \angle ABC$

(b) $\cos \angle BAC$

(c) $\cos \angle ACB$

15. Consider the points $L(-1,3,5)$, $M(1,4,3)$, $N(7,2,6)$.

(a) $\cos \angle MLN$

(b) $\cos \angle MNL$

(c) $\cos \angle LMN$

16. Calculate the distance between the given point and line using the formula

$$D = \frac{|ax_0 + by_0 + c|}{\sqrt{a^2 + b^2}}.$$

(a) $x - 2y + 3 = 0$; $(2,1)$

(b) $5x + 12y - 2 = 0$; $(2,-1)$

(c) $15x = 8y + 4$; $(1,1)$

(d) $y = \frac{3}{4}x + 3$; $(0,2)$

17. Consider the points $P(1,1,1)$, $Q(2,-1,3)$, $R(3,-1,4)$. Compute the following.

(a) $\sin \angle QPR$

(b) $\sin \angle PQR$

(c) $\sin \angle PRQ$

18. Find the area of the triangle PQR.

(a) $P(1,3,2), Q(2,3,1), R(2,2,3)$

(c) $P(3,0,-1), Q(2,2,2), R(4,2,3)$

(b) $P(3,-3,1), Q(1,-3,2), R(5,-2,-1)$

(d) $P(1,1,-1), Q(1,2,0), R(2,0,1)$

19. Find the area of the triangle determined by $\mathbf{u}$ and $\mathbf{v}$.

(a) $\mathbf{u} = (1,2,4), \mathbf{v} = (3,1,2)$

(c) $\mathbf{u} = (6,1,0), \mathbf{v} = (2,1,-2)$

(b) $\mathbf{u} = (1,-1,2), \mathbf{v} = (2,0,3)$

(d) $\mathbf{u} = (-3,0,1), \mathbf{v} = (0,1,2)$

20. Find the area of the parallelogram determined by **u** and **v**.

(a) $\mathbf{u} = (1,0,-2), \mathbf{v} = (0,3,2)$
(c) $\mathbf{u} = (1,4,1)$, $\mathbf{v} = (3,2,2)$

(b) $\mathbf{u} = (2,0,2), \mathbf{v} = (0,2,1)$
(d) $\mathbf{u} = (0,1,1), \mathbf{v} = (1,0,2)$

21. Consider the parallelopiped determined by $\mathbf{u} = (1,-1,0)$, $\mathbf{v} = (1,0,-1)$, $\mathbf{w} = (3,-1,2)$. Compute the following.

(a) the volume of the parallelopiped
(b) the area of the face determined by **u** and **v**
(c) the cosine of the angle between **v** and the plane containing the face determined by **u** and **w**.

22. Consider the parallelopiped determined by $\mathbf{u} = (2,0,5)$, $\mathbf{v} = (1,-1,0)$, $\mathbf{w} = (1,3,8)$. Compute the following.

(a) the volume of the parallelopiped
(b) the area of the face determined by **v** and **w**
(c) the sine of the angle between **w** and the plane containing the face determined by **u** and **v**.

23. Find a parametric equation for the line passing through P and parallel to **n**.

(a) $P(5,1,2)$; $\mathbf{n} = (1,2,6)$
(c) $P(0,0,0)$; $\mathbf{n} = (2,2,5)$

(b) $P(-1,2,3)$; $\mathbf{n} = (1,1,1)$
(d) $P(6,2,6)$; $\mathbf{n} = (1,0,0)$

24. Find a symmetric equation for the line passing through P and parallel to **n**.

(a) $P(1,3,5)$; $\mathbf{n} = (2,2,7)$
(c) $P(4,5,0)$; $\mathbf{n} = (\frac{1}{2},\frac{1}{4},-1)$

(b) $P(2,-6,3)$; $\mathbf{n} = (1,-1,3)$
(d) $P(0,0,8)$; $\mathbf{n} = (1,2,\sqrt{2})$

25. Determine whether the lines are parallel.

(a) $\begin{array}{ccc} x &=& 2 + t \\ y &=& 1 + 2t \\ z &=& 1 + t \end{array}$ and $\begin{array}{ccc} x &=& 4 + t \\ y &=& 2 + 2t \\ z &=& 4 + t \end{array}$

(b) $\begin{array}{ccc} x &=& 5 - t \\ y &=& 6 + t \\ z &=& -1 - 2t \end{array}$ and $\begin{array}{ccc} x &=& 3 + t \\ y &=& -t \\ z &=& 5 + 2t \end{array}$

(c) $\begin{array}{ccc} x &=& 4t \\ y &=& 7 \\ z &=& 1 - t \end{array}$ and $\begin{array}{ccc} x &=& 6 + 4t \\ y &=& 6 + 7t \\ z &=& -t \end{array}$

(d) $\begin{array}{ccc} x &=& -8 + 1/2t \\ y &=& 5 + 1/3t \\ z &=& 3 - t \end{array}$ and $\begin{array}{ccc} x &=& -3t \\ y &=& 11 - 2t \\ z &=& -6t \end{array}$

26. Determine whether the planes are parallel.

(a) $4x+y-7z=1$ and $4x+y-7z=0$
(b) $-x+2y-z=1$ and $3x+6y+3z=5$

(c) $6x = 21y - 3z$ and $2x - 7y + z = 11$
(d) $2z = 3 - x$ and $2z - x = 4$

27. Determine whether the planes are perpendicular.

    (a) $2x - 3y + z = 0$ and $4x - 6y + 2z = 3$ (b) $x - 3y + 5z = 2$ and $4x + 3y + z = 0$

    (c) $2x = 3z$ and $y = 7$ (d) $2y = 5x + z - 9$ and $x = -4y - 2z$

28. Determine whether the line and plane are parallel.

    (a) $x = 2 + 4t, y = 1 - 3t, z = t; x + y - z = 5$ (b) $x = 3, y = -4t, z = 1 + 5t; x + y + z = 9$

    (c) $x = 1 + \frac{1}{2}t, y = 1 - \frac{1}{3}t, z = 2 + \frac{1}{6}t; 6x + 6y = 6z + 1$ (d) $x = t, y = 2, z = 3 + 9t; 11y = 15$

29. Determine whether the line and plane are perpendicular.

    (a) $x = 3 + 2t, y = 14t, z = 1 + 12t; x + 7y = 2 + 6z$

    (b) $x = 2t, y = 1 + \sqrt{10}t, z = 3 - \sqrt{6}t; 3z = \sqrt{6}x + \sqrt{15}y + 9$

    (c) $x = 5 - 2t, y = 0, z = 3t; \frac{1}{2}x + \frac{1}{3}z = 19$

    (d) $x = 4t + 5, y = 2t + 1, z = 2; 4x + 2y + 2z = 7$

30. Give the point of intersection, if any, of the two lines.

    (a)
$$\begin{aligned} x &= -9 + 5t \\ y &= 1 + t \\ z &= 10 - 4t \end{aligned}$$
  and
$$\begin{aligned} x &= -2 - 3t \\ y &= 5 + 2t \\ z &= 5 + 3t \end{aligned}$$

    (b)
$$\begin{aligned} x &= \tfrac{13}{2} + t \\ y &= \tfrac{3}{2} + 3t \\ z &= -1 \end{aligned}$$
  and
$$\begin{aligned} x &= 6 \\ y &= 4 - 2t \\ z &= -11 + 5t \end{aligned}$$

    (c)
$$\begin{aligned} x &= 10 + t \\ y &= 2 + 3t \\ z &= 6 + t \end{aligned}$$
  and
$$\begin{aligned} x &= 7 + t \\ y &= 7 - 4t \\ z &= -3 + 4t \end{aligned}$$

    (d)
$$\begin{aligned} x &= 3 - t \\ y &= 2t \\ z &= 1 + t \end{aligned}$$
  and
$$\begin{aligned} x &= 4 + 3t \\ y &= 1 - 2t \\ z &= 5 - 5t \end{aligned}$$

31. Give the point of intersection, if any, of the line and plane.

    (a) $x = 4 + 2t, y = 7 - t, z = 3t; 2x - y - z = 7$

    (b) $x = 2 + 2t, y = 5, z = \frac{1}{2} - t; 3x + 5z = 10$

    (c) $x = t - 3, y = 2t, z = t + 5; x - 4y - z = 0$

    (d) $x = 1 - t, y = 3 + 2t, z = -2 + 3t; x + z = y + 4$

32. Find a parametric equation for the line of intersection of the planes.

    (a) $x + 2y - z = 1$, $2x - y + 3z = 7$ (b) $3x + y + z = 5$, $y - 7z = 1$

(c) $5x + y - 7z = 2$, $4x + 2y + z = 4$ (d) $2x + 3y + z = 11$, $4x + 9y - z = 31$

33. Find a parametric equation for the line passing through the given points.

  (a) $P(1, 6, 3)$, $Q(2, 7, 1)$ (b) $P(4, 1, \frac{2}{3})$, $Q(8, 0, \frac{5}{3})$

  (c) $P(0, -1, 1)$, $Q(2, -1, 2)$ (d) $P(2, 2, 3)$, $Q(-1, -1, 0)$

34. Find a symmetric equation for the line passing through the given points.

  (a) $P(3, -5, 1)$, $Q(2, 2, 2)$ (b) $P(4, 1, 6)$, $Q(3, 2, 3)$

  (c) $P(4, 3, \frac{-5}{2})$, $Q(\frac{9}{2}, 0, \frac{-3}{2})$ (d) $P(0, 0, 0)$, $Q(1, 7, 7)$

35. Find a point–normal form of the equation for the plane passing through P and having **n** as normal.

  (a) $P(1, -1, 5)$, $\mathbf{n} = (1, 2, 3)$ (b) $P(0, 2, 0)$, $\mathbf{n} = (\frac{4}{13}, \frac{-3}{13}, \frac{12}{13})$

  (c) $P(2, 6, -3)$, $\mathbf{n} = (1, 1, 1)$ (d) $P(4, 1, -7)$, $\mathbf{n} = (\frac{1}{4}, \frac{-1}{2}, \frac{5}{4})$

36. Find a general form of the equation for the plane passing through P and having **n** as normal.

  (a) $P(2, 3, 4)$, $\mathbf{n} = (6, 1, 6)$ (b) $P(-7, 2, 3)$, $\mathbf{n} = (0, 0, 1)$

  (c) $P(8, -8, 2)$, $\mathbf{n} = (\frac{-2}{3}, \frac{1}{3}, \frac{2}{3})$ (d) $P(0, 0, 0)$, $\mathbf{n} = (2, 5, 5)$

37. Find a point–normal form of the equation for the plane passing through the given points.

  (a) $P(3, 1, 1), Q(1, 6, 7), R(4, 2, 2)$ (b) $P(3, 4, 4), Q(0, 1, -11), R(1, 3, -17)$

  (c) $P(0, 2, -1), Q(\frac{3}{2}, \frac{5}{2}, 0), R(\frac{-1}{2}, 1, \frac{3}{2})$ (d) $P(7, 2, 7), Q(9, 1, 9), R(8, -1, 6)$

38. Find a general foarm of the equation for the plane passing through the given points.

  (a) $P(8, -5, 2), Q(6, -6, 1), R(10, 0, 0)$ (b) $P(1, 5, 4), Q(2, 6, 7), R(-1, 5, 0)$

  (c) $P(4, 4, 3), Q(10, 4, -1), R(-1, 8, 12)$ (d) $P(\frac{1}{3}, 0, \frac{-2}{3}), Q(\frac{5}{3}, 1, \frac{5}{3}), R(\frac{4}{3}, \frac{2}{3}, 1)$

39. Find an equation for the plane through $P(1, 1, 3)$ that is perpendicular to the line $x = 2 - 3t$, $y = 1 + t$, $z = 2t$.

40. Find an equation for the plane through $P(2, 7, -1)$ that is parallel to the plane $4x - y + 3z = 3$.

41. Find an equation for the plane that contains the line $x = 3 + t$, $y = 5$, $z = 5 + 2t$, and is perpendicular to the plane $x + y + z = 4$.

42. Find an equation for the plane through $P(1, 4, 4)$ that contains the line of intersection of the planes $x - y + 3z = 5$ and $2x + 2y + 7z = 0$.

43. Find an equation for the line through $P(2, -3, 0)$ that is parallel to the planes $2x + 2y + z = 2$ and $x - 3y = 5$.

44. Find an equation for the plane through $P(-1, 7, 4)$ that is perpendicular to the planes $3x + y - z = 5$ and $11x + 2y + 3z = 0$.

45. Find an equation for the plane through $P(4,5,3)$ and $Q(6,3,-2)$ that is perpendicular to the plane $2x - y - z = 8$.

46. Find an equation for the plane through $P(1,1,7)$ that contains the line $x = 2t+4$, $y = 4t-1$, $z = t+1$.

47. Find an equation for the plane containing the line $x = 3+6t$, $y = 4$, $z = t$ and that is parallel to the line of intersection of the planes $2x + y + z = 1$ and $x - 2y + 3z = 2$.

48. Find an equation for the plane parallel to the line $x = 1 - 2t$, $y = 2+3t$, $z = 1+2t$ and that contains the line of intersection of the planes $x + 3y - 7z = 2$ and $3x + 11y - 17z = 2$.

49. Find an equation for the plane each of whose points is equidistant from P and Q.

   (a) $P(1,4,\ 3)$, $Q(-1,6,5)$.

   (b) $P(5,0,-2)$, $Q(-5,1,1)$.

50. Calculate the distance between the given point and plane using the formula

$$D = \frac{|ax_0 + by_0 + cz_0 + d|}{\sqrt{a^2 + b^2 + c^2}}$$

   (a) $2x - 3y + 6z + 4 = 0$; $(1,1,-1)$

   (b) $z = 2x + 2y + 8$; $(11,-2,3)$

   (c) $4x - z = 5$; $(10,7,6)$

   (d) $3x - 12y + 4z + 1 = 0$; $(4,1,1)$

WRITING QUESTIONS

51. How do vectors differ from simple numerical quantities such as length and mass?

52. With the help of a labeled diagram, translate the Pythagorean Theorem into a statement about vectors.

53. If $\mathbf{u}$ and $\mathbf{v}$ are vectors in 3–space, describe the geometric meaning of the following:

$$\text{if} \quad \mathbf{x} \cdot \mathbf{u} = 0 \quad \text{and} \quad \mathbf{x} \cdot \mathbf{v} = 0$$

$$\text{then} \quad \mathbf{x} \cdot (c_1 \mathbf{u} + c_2 \mathbf{v}) = 0 \quad \text{for all real numbers} \quad c_1 \quad \text{and} \quad c_2.$$

54. Describe the geometric significance of the cross–product.

55. Discuss the relative merits of the parametric and symmetric forms of the line equation.

56. Describe in words the procedure you would use to determine whether two lines (given in parametric form) are parallel, intersecting or skew.

57. Suppose you were carried by time machine to Alexandria, Egypt in 300 B.C. and had the opportunity to meet Euclid, the geometer. Assuming he could speak English, what sorts of things would you say or do to try to convince him that vectors are a good tool for studying geometry?

SECTIONS 3.1–3.4. VECTOR OPERATIONS

1. (a) $\mathbf{u} + \mathbf{v} = (1,7) + (3,-2) = (4,5)$

    (b) $2\mathbf{u} - 3\mathbf{v} = (2,14) - (9,-6) = (-7,20)$

    (c) $\|\mathbf{u} - \mathbf{v}\| = \|(1,7) - (3,-2)\| = \|(-2,9)\| = \sqrt{85}$

    (d) $\|\mathbf{u}\| - \|\mathbf{v}\| = \|(1,7)\| - \|(3,-2)\| = \sqrt{50} - \sqrt{13} = 5\sqrt{2} - \sqrt{13}$

    (e) $2\mathbf{u}\cdot\mathbf{v} = 2(1,7)\cdot(3,-2) = 2(3 - 14) = 2(-11) = -22$

    (f) $\mathbf{u}\cdot\mathbf{v} - \mathbf{v}\cdot\mathbf{u} = \mathbf{u}\cdot\mathbf{v} - \mathbf{u}\cdot\mathbf{v} = 0$

2. (a) $\mathbf{u} - \mathbf{v} = (1,0,-2) - (3,2,4) = (-2,-2,-6)$

    (b) $2\mathbf{u} + \mathbf{v} = (2,0,-4) + (3,2,4) = (5,2,0)$

    (c) $3\mathbf{u} + \mathbf{v} - \mathbf{w} = (3,0,-6) + (3,2,4) - (2,2,-1) = (4,0,-1)$

    (d) $\mathbf{u}\cdot\mathbf{v} = (1,0,-2)\cdot(3,2,4) = 3 + 0 - 8 = -5$

    (e) $\|\mathbf{u} + \mathbf{v} - 2\mathbf{w}\| = \|(1,0,-2) + (3,2,4) - (4,4,-2)\| = \|(0,-2,4)\| = \sqrt{0 + 4 + 16} = \sqrt{20} = 2\sqrt{5}$

    (f) $\|\mathbf{u} + \mathbf{v}\| - \|2\mathbf{w}\| = \|(1,0,-2) + (3,2,4)\| - \|(4,4,-2)\| = \|(4,2,2)\| - \|(4,4,-2)\| = \sqrt{24} - \sqrt{36} = 2\sqrt{6} - 6$

3. (a) $2\mathbf{u} + \mathbf{w} = (2,2,6) + (0,-1,5) = (2,1,11)$

    (b) $2(\mathbf{u} + \mathbf{v}) - 3(\mathbf{v} - 2\mathbf{w}) = 2\mathbf{u} - \mathbf{v} + 6\mathbf{w} = (2,2,6) - (2,0,1) + (0,-6,30) = (0,-4,35)$

    (c) $(\mathbf{u}\cdot\mathbf{v})\mathbf{w} = (2 + 0 + 3)(0,-1,5) = 5(0,-1,5) = (0,-5,25)$

    (d) $\mathbf{u}\cdot(\mathbf{v} \times \mathbf{w}) = (1,1,3)\cdot(1,-10,-2) = 1 - 10 - 6 = -15$

    (e) $\|\mathbf{v}\|(\mathbf{u}\cdot\mathbf{w}) = \|(2,0,1)\|(0 - 1 + 15) = \sqrt{5}(14) = 14\sqrt{5}$

    (f) $\|\mathbf{u} \times (\mathbf{v} + \mathbf{w})\| = \|(1,1,3) \times (2,-1,6)\| = \|(9,0,-3)\| = \sqrt{90} = 3\sqrt{10}$

4. (a) $\mathbf{u} - 2\mathbf{v} + \mathbf{w} = (1,-1,1) - (4,2,4) + (1,0,-3) = (-2,-3,-6)$

    (b) $\mathbf{w}\cdot\mathbf{u} - \|5\mathbf{v}\| = (1,0,-3)\cdot(1,-1,1) - 5\|(2,1,2)\| = -2 - 5\sqrt{9} = -2 - 15 = -17$

    (c) $(2\mathbf{u} - \mathbf{v}) \times \mathbf{w} = ((2,-2,2) - (2,1,2)) \times (1,0,-3) = (0,-3,0) \times (1,0,-3) = (9,0,3)$

    (d) $(\mathbf{u} \times \mathbf{v}) \times \mathbf{w} = ((1,-1,1) \times (2,1,2)) \times (1,0,-3) = (-3,0,3) \times (1,0,-3) = (0,-6,0)$

    (e) $(\mathbf{u} \times \mathbf{w}) \times (\mathbf{u} \times \mathbf{v}) = ((1,-1,1) \times (1,0,-3)) \times ((1,-1,1) \times (2,1,2)) = (3,4,1) \times (-3,0,3) = (12,-12,12)$

    (f) $(\mathbf{v} \times \mathbf{w})\cdot\mathbf{u} = ((2,1,2) \times (1,0,-3))\cdot(1,-1,1) = (-3,8,-1)\cdot(1,-1,1) = -12$

5. (a) $2\mathbf{v} - 3\mathbf{w} - \mathbf{u} = (6,2,2) - (0,6,3) - (4,2,-1) = (2,-6,0)$

    (b) $(\mathbf{u}\cdot\mathbf{w})\|\mathbf{u} \times \mathbf{w}\| = 3\|(4,2,-1) \times (0,2,1)\| = 3\|(4,-4,8)\| = 12\|(1,-1,2)\| = 12\sqrt{6}$

    (c) $\mathbf{w}\cdot(5\mathbf{v} - \mathbf{u}) = (0,2,1) \cdot ((15,5,5) - (4,2,-1)) = (0,2,1) \cdot (11,3,6) = 12$

(d) $\mathbf{v}\cdot(\mathbf{w}\times\mathbf{u}) = (3,1,1)\cdot((0,2,1)\times(4,2,-1)) = (3,1,1)\cdot(-4,4,-8) = -16$

(e) $\mathbf{v}\times(\mathbf{u}\times\mathbf{w}) = (3,1,1)\times((4,2,-1)\times(0,2,1)) = (3,1,1)\times(4,-4,8) =$
$\quad 4(3,1,1)\times(1,-1,2) = 4(3,-5,-4)$

(f) $\mathbf{v}\times(\mathbf{u}\times 2\mathbf{u}) = 2\mathbf{v}\times(\mathbf{u}\times\mathbf{u}) = 2\mathbf{v}\times\mathbf{0} = \mathbf{0} = (0,0,0)$

SECTION 3.1. INTRODUCTION TO VECTORS (GEOMETRIC)

6. (a) $Q = P+\mathbf{v} = (4,-3,6)+(1,1,7) = (5,-2,13),$ or any other point $P+k\mathbf{v}$ with $k>0$

   (b) $Q = P+-\mathbf{v} = (4,-3,6)+(-1,-1,-7) = (3,-4,-1),$ or any other point $P+k\mathbf{v}$ with $k<0$

7. (a) $Q = P+\mathbf{v} = (-2,6,5)+(4,0,3) = (2,6,8),$ or any other point $P+k\mathbf{v}$ with $k>0$

   (b) $Q = P+-\mathbf{v} = (-2,6,5)+(-4,0,-3) = (-6,6,2),$ or any other point $P+k\mathbf{v}$ with $k<0$

8. (a) $P = Q+-\mathbf{v} = (3,5,5)+(-6,2,-1) = (-3,7,4),$ or any other point $Q+k\mathbf{v}$ with $k<0$

   (b) $P = Q+\mathbf{v} = (3,5,5)+(6,-2,1) = (9,3,6),$ or any other point $Q+k\mathbf{v}$ with $k>0$

9. (a) $P = Q+-\mathbf{v} = (2,0,2)+(-5,-4,1) = (-3,-4,3),$ or any other point $Q+k\mathbf{v}$ with $k<0$

   (b) $P = Q+\mathbf{v} = (2,0,2)+(5,4,-1) = (7,4,1),$ or any other point $Q+k\mathbf{v}$ with $k>0$

SECTION 3.2. NORM OF A VECTOR; VECTOR ARITHMETIC

10. (a) $d = \|(2,3)-(1,7)\| = \|(1,-4)\| = \sqrt{1+16} = \sqrt{17}$

    (b) $d = \|(3,-5)-(-1,4)\| = \|(4,-9)\| = \sqrt{16+81} = \sqrt{97}$

    (c) $d = \|(4,3,-2)-(1,0,6)\| = \|(3,3,-8)\| = \sqrt{9+9+64} = \sqrt{82}$

    (d) $d = \|(8,-2,-3)-(7,-4,5)\| = \|(1,2,-8)\| = \sqrt{1+4+64} = \sqrt{69}$

11. (a) $d = \|(1,-11)-(6,1)\| = \|(-5,-12)\| = \sqrt{25+144} = \sqrt{169} = 13$

    (b) $d = \|(0,-8)-(4,0)\| = \|(-4,-8)\| = \sqrt{16+64} \doteq \sqrt{80} = 4\sqrt{5}$

    (c) $d = \|(7,7,4)-(4,3,-8)\| = \|(3,4,12)\| = \sqrt{9+16+144} = \sqrt{169} = 13$

    (d) $d = \|(4,3,4)-(3,4,1)\| = \|(1,-1,3)\| = \sqrt{1+1+9} = \sqrt{11}$

SECTION 3.3. DOT PRODUCT; PROJECTIONS

12. (a) $\frac{\mathbf{u}\cdot\mathbf{a}}{\mathbf{a}\cdot\mathbf{a}}\mathbf{a} = \frac{(6,5)\cdot(-3,4)}{(-3,4)\cdot(-3,4)}(-3,4) = \frac{2}{25}(-3,4)$

    (b) $\frac{\mathbf{u}\cdot\mathbf{a}}{\mathbf{a}\cdot\mathbf{a}}\mathbf{a} = \frac{(1,2)\cdot(7,-3)}{(7,-3)\cdot(7,-3)}(7,-3) = \frac{1}{58}(7,-3)$

    (c) $\frac{\mathbf{u}\cdot\mathbf{a}}{\mathbf{a}\cdot\mathbf{a}}\mathbf{a} = \frac{(3,0,2)\cdot(1,1,3)}{(1,1,3)\cdot(1,1,3)}(1,1,3) = \frac{9}{11}(1,1,3)$

    (d) $\frac{\mathbf{u}\cdot\mathbf{a}}{\mathbf{a}\cdot\mathbf{a}}\mathbf{a} = \frac{(1,0,7)\cdot(0,5,0)}{(0,5,0)\cdot(0,5,0)}(0,5,0) = \frac{0}{25}(0,5,0) = (0,0,0)$

13. (a) $\mathbf{u} - \frac{\mathbf{u} \cdot \mathbf{a}}{\mathbf{a} \cdot \mathbf{a}} \mathbf{a} = (4, 1) - \frac{(4,1) \cdot (2,-3)}{(2,-3) \cdot (2,-3)} (2, -3)$
$$= (4, 1) - \frac{5}{13}(2, -3)$$
$$= \left(\frac{42}{13}, \frac{28}{13}\right) = \frac{14}{13}(3, 2)$$

(b) $\mathbf{u} - \frac{\mathbf{u} \cdot \mathbf{a}}{\mathbf{a} \cdot \mathbf{a}} \mathbf{a} = (5, -2) - \frac{(5,-2) \cdot (1,1)}{(1,1) \cdot (1,1)} (1, 1)$
$$= (5, -2) - \frac{3}{2}(1, 1)$$
$$= \left(\frac{7}{2}, \frac{-7}{2}\right) = \frac{7}{2}(1, -1)$$

(c) $\mathbf{u} - \frac{\mathbf{u} \cdot \mathbf{a}}{\mathbf{a} \cdot \mathbf{a}} \mathbf{a} = (1, 5, -5) - \frac{(1,5,-5) \cdot (1,2,3)}{(1,2,3) \cdot (1,2,3)} (1, 2, 3)$
$$= (1, 5, -5) - \frac{-4}{14}(1, 2, 3)$$
$$= \left(\frac{18}{14}, \frac{78}{14}, \frac{-58}{14}\right) = \frac{1}{7}(9, 39, -29)$$

(d) $\mathbf{u} - \frac{\mathbf{u} \cdot \mathbf{a}}{\mathbf{a} \cdot \mathbf{a}} \mathbf{a} = (4, -1, -1) - \frac{(4,-1,-1) \cdot (1,-2,4)}{(1,-2,4) \cdot (1,-2,4)} (1, -2, 4)$
$$= (4, -1, -1) - \frac{2}{21}(1, -2, 4)$$
$$= \left(\frac{82}{21}, \frac{-17}{21}, \frac{-29}{21}\right) = \frac{-1}{21}(-82, 17, 29)$$

14. (a) $\mathbf{u} = \overrightarrow{BA} = (-1, -1), \mathbf{v} = \overrightarrow{BC} = (0, 1),$ $\qquad \cos\theta = \frac{\mathbf{u} \cdot \mathbf{v}}{\|\mathbf{u}\|\|\mathbf{v}\|} = \frac{-1}{\sqrt{2}\sqrt{1}} = \frac{-1}{2}\sqrt{2}$

(b) $\mathbf{u} = \overrightarrow{AB} = (1, 1), \mathbf{v} = \overrightarrow{AC} = (1, 2),$ $\qquad \cos\theta = \frac{\mathbf{u} \cdot \mathbf{v}}{\|\mathbf{u}\|\|\mathbf{v}\|} = \frac{3}{\sqrt{2}\sqrt{5}} = \frac{3}{10}\sqrt{10}$

(c) $\mathbf{u} = \overrightarrow{CA} = (-1, -2), \mathbf{v} = \overrightarrow{CB} = (0, -1),$ $\qquad \cos\theta = \frac{\mathbf{u} \cdot \mathbf{v}}{\|\mathbf{u}\|\|\mathbf{v}\|} = \frac{2}{\sqrt{5}\sqrt{1}} = \frac{2}{5}\sqrt{5}$

15. (a) $\mathbf{u} = \overrightarrow{LM} = (2, 1, -2), \mathbf{v} = \overrightarrow{LN} = (-8, -1, 1),$ $\qquad \cos\theta = \frac{\mathbf{u} \cdot \mathbf{v}}{\|\mathbf{u}\|\|\mathbf{v}\|} = \frac{13}{\sqrt{9}\sqrt{66}} = \frac{13}{198}\sqrt{66}$

(b) $\mathbf{u} = \overrightarrow{NM} = (-6, 2, -3), \mathbf{v} = \overrightarrow{LN} = (-8, 1, -1),$ $\qquad \cos\theta = \frac{\mathbf{u} \cdot \mathbf{v}}{\|\mathbf{u}\|\|\mathbf{v}\|} = \frac{53}{\sqrt{49}\sqrt{66}} = \frac{53}{462}\sqrt{66}$

(c) $\mathbf{u} = \overrightarrow{ML} = (-2, -1, 2), \mathbf{v} = \overrightarrow{MN} = (6, -2, 3),$ $\qquad \cos\theta = \frac{\mathbf{u} \cdot \mathbf{v}}{\|\mathbf{u}\|\|\mathbf{v}\|} = \frac{-4}{\sqrt{9}\sqrt{49}} = \frac{-4}{21}$

16. (a) $D = \frac{|(1)(2)+(-2)(1)+3|}{\sqrt{1+4}} = \frac{3}{\sqrt{5}} = \frac{3}{5}\sqrt{5}$

(b) $D = \frac{|(5)(2)+(12)(-1)+-2|}{\sqrt{25+144}} = \frac{4}{\sqrt{169}} = \frac{4}{13}$

(c) $15x - 8y - 4 = 0,$ so $D = \frac{|(15)(1)+(-8)(1)+-4|}{\sqrt{225+64}} = \frac{3}{\sqrt{289}} = \frac{3}{17}$

(d) $3x - 4y + 12 = 0,$ so $D = \frac{|(3)(0)+(-4)(2)+12|}{\sqrt{9+16}} = \frac{4}{\sqrt{25}} = \frac{4}{5}$

SECTION 3.4. CROSS PRODUCT

17. (a) $\mathbf{u} = \overrightarrow{PQ} = (1, -2, 2), \mathbf{v} = \overrightarrow{PR} = (2, -2, 3),$ $\qquad \sin\theta = \frac{\|\mathbf{u} \times \mathbf{v}\|}{\|\mathbf{u}\|\|\mathbf{v}\|} = \frac{\|(-2,1,2)\|}{\|\mathbf{u}\|\|\mathbf{v}\|} = \frac{\sqrt{9}}{\sqrt{9}\sqrt{17}} = \frac{1}{17}\sqrt{17}$

(b) $\mathbf{u} = \overrightarrow{QP} = (-1, 2, -2), \mathbf{v} = \overrightarrow{QR} = (1, 0, 1),$ $\qquad \sin\theta = \frac{\|\mathbf{u} \times \mathbf{v}\|}{\|\mathbf{u}\|\|\mathbf{v}\|} = \frac{\|(2,-1,-2)\|}{\|\mathbf{u}\|\|\mathbf{v}\|} = \frac{\sqrt{9}}{\sqrt{9}\sqrt{2}} = \frac{1}{2}\sqrt{2}$

(c) $\mathbf{u} = \overrightarrow{RP} = (-2, 2, -3), \mathbf{v} = \overrightarrow{RP} = (-1, 0, -1),$ $\qquad \sin\theta = \frac{\|\mathbf{u} \times \mathbf{v}\|}{\|\mathbf{u}\|\|\mathbf{v}\|} = \frac{\|(-2,1,2)\|}{\|\mathbf{u}\|\|\mathbf{v}\|} = \frac{\sqrt{9}}{\sqrt{17}\sqrt{2}} = \frac{3}{34}\sqrt{34}$

18. (a) $A = \frac{1}{2}\|\overrightarrow{PQ} \times \overrightarrow{PR}\| = \frac{1}{2}\|(1, 0, -1) \times (1, -1, 1)\| = \frac{1}{2}\|(-1, -2, -1)\| = \frac{1}{2}\sqrt{6}$

(b) $A = \frac{1}{2}\|\overrightarrow{PQ} \times \overrightarrow{PR}\| = \frac{1}{2}\|(-2, 0, 1) \times (2, 1, -2)\| = \frac{1}{2}\|(-1, -2, -2)\| = \frac{1}{2}\sqrt{9} = \frac{3}{2}$

(c) $A = \frac{1}{2}\|\overrightarrow{PQ} \times \overrightarrow{PR}\| = \frac{1}{2}\|(-1,2,3) \times (1,2,4)\| = \frac{1}{2}\|(2,7,-4)\| = \frac{1}{2}\sqrt{69}$

(d) $A = \frac{1}{2}\|\overrightarrow{PQ} \times \overrightarrow{PR}\| = \frac{1}{2}\|(0,1,1) \times (1,-1,2)\| = \frac{1}{2}\|(3,1,-1)\| = \frac{1}{2}\sqrt{11}$

19. (a) $A = \frac{1}{2}\|\mathbf{u} \times \mathbf{v}\| = \frac{1}{2}\|(1,2,4) \times (3,1,2)\| = \frac{1}{2}\|(0,10,-5)\| = \frac{5}{2}\sqrt{5}$

(b) $A = \frac{1}{2}\|\mathbf{u} \times \mathbf{v}\| = \frac{1}{2}\|(1,-1,2) \times (2,0,3)\| = \frac{1}{2}\|(-3,1,2)\| = \frac{1}{2}\sqrt{14}$

(c) $A = \frac{1}{2}\|\mathbf{u} \times \mathbf{v}\| = \frac{1}{2}\|(6,1,0) \times (2,1,-2)\| = \frac{1}{2}\|(-2,12,4)\| = \sqrt{41}$

(d) $A = \frac{1}{2}\|\mathbf{u} \times \mathbf{v}\| = \frac{1}{2}\|(-3,0,1) \times (0,1,2)\| = \frac{1}{2}\|(-1,6,-3)\| = \frac{1}{2}\sqrt{46}$

20. (a) $A = \|\mathbf{u} \times \mathbf{v}\| = \|(1,0,-2) \times (0,3,2)\| = \|(6,-2,3)\| = \sqrt{49} = 7$

(b) $A = \|\mathbf{u} \times \mathbf{v}\| = \|(2,0,2) \times (0,2,1)\| = \|(-4,-2,4)\| = \sqrt{36} = 6$

(c) $A = \|\mathbf{u} \times \mathbf{v}\| = \|(1,4,1) \times (3,2,2)\| = \|(6,1,-10)\| = \sqrt{137}$

(d) $A = \|\mathbf{u} \times \mathbf{v}\| = \|(0,1,1) \times (1,0,2)\| = \|(2,1,-1)\| = \sqrt{6}$

21. (a) $V = |\mathbf{u}\cdot(\mathbf{v} \times \mathbf{w})| = |(1,-1,0)\cdot(-1,-5,-1)| = 4$

(b) $A = \|\mathbf{u} \times \mathbf{v}\| = \|(1,1,1)\| = \sqrt{3}$

(c) $\mathbf{n} = \mathbf{u} \times \mathbf{w} = (-2,-2,2), \quad \cos\theta = \frac{\|\mathbf{v} \times \mathbf{n}\|}{\|\mathbf{v}\|\|\mathbf{n}\|} = \frac{\|(-2,0,-2)\|}{\|\mathbf{v}\|\|\mathbf{n}\|} = \frac{\sqrt{8}}{\sqrt{2}\sqrt{12}} = \frac{1}{3}\sqrt{3}$

22. (a) $V = |\mathbf{u}\cdot(\mathbf{v} \times \mathbf{w})| = |(2,0,5)\cdot(-8,-8,4)| = 4$

(b) $A = \|\mathbf{v} \times \mathbf{w}\| = \|(-8,-8,4)\| = 12$

(c) $\mathbf{n} = \mathbf{u} \times \mathbf{v} = (5,5,-2), \quad \sin\theta = \frac{\|\mathbf{w}\cdot\mathbf{n}\|}{\|\mathbf{w}\|\|\mathbf{n}\|} = \frac{4}{\sqrt{74}\sqrt{54}} = \frac{2}{333}\sqrt{111}$

SECTION 3.5. LINES AND PLANES IN 3–SPACE

23. (a) $x = 5 + t,$ $\qquad y = 1 + 2t$ $\qquad z = 2 + 6t$

(b) $x = -1 + t,$ $\qquad y = 2 + t,$ $\qquad z = 3 + t$

(c) $x = 2t,$ $\qquad y = 2t,$ $\qquad z = 5t$

(d) $x = 6 + t,$ $\qquad y = 2,$ $\qquad z = 6$

24. (a) $\frac{x-1}{2} = \frac{y-3}{2} = \frac{z-5}{7}$

(b) $\frac{x-2}{1} = \frac{y+6}{-1} = \frac{z-3}{3}$

(c) $2(x - 4) = 4(y - 5) = -z$

(d) $\frac{x}{1} = \frac{y}{2} = \frac{z-8}{\sqrt{2}}$

25. (a) $\mathbf{n_1} = (1,2,1),$ $\qquad \mathbf{n_2} = (1,2,1)$ $\qquad;\qquad$ yes: $\mathbf{n_1} = \mathbf{n_2}$

(b) $\mathbf{n_1} = (-1,1,-2),$ $\qquad \mathbf{n_2} = (1,-1,2)$ $\qquad;\qquad$ yes: $\mathbf{n_1} = -\mathbf{n_2}$

(c) $\mathbf{n_1} = (4,0,-1),$ $\qquad \mathbf{n_2} = (4,7,-1)$ $\qquad;\qquad$ no: $\mathbf{n_1} \neq k\mathbf{n_2}$

(d) $\mathbf{n_1} = (\frac{1}{2},\frac{1}{3},-1),$ $\qquad \mathbf{n_2} = (-3,-2,-6)$ $\;;\qquad$ no: $\mathbf{n_1} \neq k\mathbf{n_2}$

26. (a) $\mathbf{n_1} = (4, 1, -7)$, $\qquad$ $\mathbf{n_2} = (4, 1, -7)$ $\qquad$; $\qquad$ yes: $\mathbf{n_1} = \mathbf{n_2}$

$\quad$ (b) $\mathbf{n_1} = (-1, 2, -1)$, $\qquad$ $\mathbf{n_2} = (3, 6, 3)$ $\qquad$; $\qquad$ no: $\mathbf{n_1} \neq k\mathbf{n_2}$

$\quad$ (c) $\mathbf{n_1} = (6, -21, 3)$, $\qquad$ $\mathbf{n_2} = (2, -7, 1)$ $\qquad$; $\qquad$ yes: $\mathbf{n_1} = 3\mathbf{n_2}$

$\quad$ (d) $\mathbf{n_1} = (1, 0, 2)$, $\qquad$ $\mathbf{n_2} = (-1, 0, 2)$ $\qquad$; $\qquad$ no: $\mathbf{n_1} \neq k\mathbf{n_2}$

27. (a) $\mathbf{n_1} = (2, -3, 1)$, $\qquad$ $\mathbf{n_2} = (4, -6, 2)$ $\qquad$; $\qquad$ no: $\mathbf{n_1} \cdot \mathbf{n_2} = 28 \neq 0$

$\quad$ (b) $\mathbf{n_1} = (1, -3, 5)$, $\qquad$ $\mathbf{n_2} = (4, 3, 1)$ $\qquad$; $\qquad$ yes: $\mathbf{n_1} \cdot \mathbf{n_2} = 0$

$\quad$ (c) $\mathbf{n_1} = (2, 0, -3)$, $\qquad$ $\mathbf{n_2} = (0, 1, 0)$ $\qquad$; $\qquad$ yes: $\mathbf{n_1} \cdot \mathbf{n_2} = 0$

$\quad$ (d) $\mathbf{n_1} = (5, -2, 1)$, $\qquad$ $\mathbf{n_2} = (1, 4, 2)$ $\qquad$; $\qquad$ no: $\mathbf{n_1} \cdot \mathbf{n_2} = -1 \neq 0$

28. (a) $\mathbf{n_1} = (4, -3, 1)$, $\qquad$ $\mathbf{n_2} = (1, 1, -1)$ $\qquad$; $\qquad$ yes: $\mathbf{n_1} \cdot \mathbf{n_2} = 0$

$\quad$ (b) $\mathbf{n_1} = (0, -4, 5)$, $\qquad$ $\mathbf{n_2} = (1, 1, 1)$ $\qquad$; $\qquad$ no: $\mathbf{n_1} \cdot \mathbf{n_2} = 1 \neq 0$

$\quad$ (c) $\mathbf{n_1} = (\frac{1}{2}, \frac{-1}{3}, \frac{1}{6})$, $\qquad$ $\mathbf{n_2} = (6, 6, -6)$ $\qquad$; $\qquad$ yes: $\mathbf{n_1} \cdot \mathbf{n_2} = 0$

$\quad$ (d) $\mathbf{n_1} = (1, 0, 9)$, $\qquad$ $\mathbf{n_2} = (0, 11, 0)$ $\qquad$; $\qquad$ yes: $\mathbf{n_1} \cdot \mathbf{n_2} = 0$

29. (a) $\mathbf{n_1} = (2, 14, 12)$, $\qquad$ $\mathbf{n_2} = (1, 7, -6)$ $\qquad$; $\qquad$ no: $\mathbf{n_1} = k\mathbf{n_2}$

$\quad$ (b) $\mathbf{n_1} = (2, \sqrt{10}, -\sqrt{6})$, $\quad$ $\mathbf{n_2} = (\sqrt{6}, \sqrt{15}, -3)$; $\qquad$ yes: $\mathbf{n_1} = \frac{1}{3}\sqrt{6}\mathbf{n_2}$

$\quad$ (c) $\mathbf{n_1} = (-2, 0, 3)$, $\qquad$ $\mathbf{n_2} = (\frac{1}{2}, 0, \frac{1}{3})$ $\qquad$; $\qquad$ no: $\mathbf{n_1} \neq k\mathbf{n_2}$

$\quad$ (d) $\mathbf{n_1} = (4, 2, 0)$, $\qquad$ $\mathbf{n_2} = (4, 2, 2)$ $\qquad$; $\qquad$ no: $\mathbf{n_1} \neq k\mathbf{n_2}$

30. (a) $-9 + 5t_1 = -2 - 3t_2$ $\qquad$ so $\qquad$ $5t_1 + 3t_2 = 7$

$\qquad \quad$ $1 + t_1 = 5 + 2t_2$ $\qquad$ so $\qquad$ $t_1 - 2t_2 = 4$

$\qquad \quad$ $10 - 4t_1 = 5 + 3t_2$ $\qquad$ so $\qquad$ $4t_1 + 3t_2 = 5$

$$
\begin{bmatrix} 5 & 3 & 7 \\ 1 & -2 & 4 \\ 4 & 3 & 5 \end{bmatrix} \longrightarrow \begin{bmatrix} 1 & -2 & 4 \\ 5 & 3 & 7 \\ 4 & 3 & 5 \end{bmatrix} \longrightarrow \begin{bmatrix} 1 & -2 & 4 \\ 0 & 13 & -13 \\ 0 & 11 & -11 \end{bmatrix} \longrightarrow \begin{bmatrix} 1 & 0 & 2 \\ 0 & 1 & -1 \\ 0 & 0 & 0 \end{bmatrix}
$$

Thus, $\quad t_1 = 2, \quad t_2 = -1 \quad$ so $\qquad x = -9 + 5t_1 = 1$

$\qquad\qquad\qquad\qquad\qquad\qquad\qquad\qquad y = 1 + t_1 = 3$

$\qquad\qquad\qquad\qquad\qquad\qquad\qquad\qquad z = 10 - 4t_1 = 2$

$\quad$ (b) $\frac{13}{2} + t_1 = 6$ $\qquad\qquad$ so $\qquad$ $t_1 = \frac{-1}{2}$

$\qquad \quad$ $\frac{3}{2} + 3t_1 = 4 - 2t_2$ $\qquad$ so $\qquad$ $2t_2 = \frac{5}{2} - 3t_1 = \frac{5}{2} + \frac{3}{2} = 4$ $\qquad$ so $\qquad$ $t_2 = 2$

$\qquad \quad$ $-1 = -11 + 5t_2$ $\qquad$ so $\qquad$ $5t_2 = 10$ $\qquad$ so $\qquad$ $t_2 = 2$

Thus, $\quad t_1 = \frac{-1}{2}, \quad t_2 = 2 \quad$ so $\qquad x = \frac{13}{2} + t_1 = 6$

$\qquad\qquad\qquad\qquad\qquad\qquad\qquad\qquad y = \frac{3}{2} + 3t_1 = 0$

$\qquad\qquad\qquad\qquad\qquad\qquad\qquad\qquad z = -1$

$\quad$ (c) $10 + t_1 = 7 + t_2$ $\qquad$ so $\qquad$ $t_1 - t_2 = -3$

$\qquad \quad$ $2 + 3t_1 = 7 - 4t_2$ $\qquad$ so $\qquad$ $3t_1 + 4t_2 = 5$

$\qquad \quad$ $6 + t_1 = -3 + 4t_2$ $\qquad$ so $\qquad$ $t_1 - 4t_2 = -9$

$$\begin{bmatrix} 1 & -1 & -3 \\ 3 & 4 & 5 \\ 1 & -4 & -9 \end{bmatrix} \longrightarrow \begin{bmatrix} 1 & -1 & -3 \\ 0 & 7 & 14 \\ 0 & -3 & -6 \end{bmatrix} \longrightarrow \begin{bmatrix} 1 & 0 & -1 \\ 0 & 1 & 2 \\ 0 & 0 & 0 \end{bmatrix}$$

Thus, $t_1 = -1$, $t_2 = 2$ so

$$\begin{aligned} x &= 10 + t_1 = 9 \\ y &= 2 + 3t_1 = -1 \\ z &= 6 + t_1 = 5 \end{aligned}$$

(d) $3 - t_1 = 4 + 3t_2$ so $t_1 + 3t_2 = -1$

$2t_1 = 1 - 2t_2$ so $2t_1 + 2t_2 = 1$

$1 + t_1 = 5 - 5t_2$ so $t_1 + 5t_2 = 4$

$$\begin{bmatrix} 1 & 3 & -1 \\ 2 & 2 & 1 \\ 1 & 5 & 4 \end{bmatrix} \longrightarrow \begin{bmatrix} 1 & 3 & -1 \\ 0 & -4 & 3 \\ 0 & 2 & 5 \end{bmatrix} \longrightarrow \begin{bmatrix} 1 & 0 & 5/4 \\ 0 & 1 & -3/4 \\ 0 & 0 & 13/2 \end{bmatrix} \quad , \quad \text{inconsistent}$$

Thus, the lines do not intersect.

31. (a) $2(4 + 2t) - (7 - t) - (3t) = 7$

$8 + 4t - 7 + t - 3t = 7$

$2t + 1 = 7$

$2t = 6$

$t = 3$

so $x = 4 + 2t = 4 + 6 = 10$

$y = 7 - t = 7 - 3 = 4$

$z = 3t = 9$

(b) $3(2 + 2t) + 5(\frac{1}{2} - t) = 10$

$6 + 6t + \frac{5}{2} - 5t = 10$

$t + \frac{17}{2} = 10$

$t = \frac{3}{2}$

so $x = 2 + 2t = 2 + 3 = 5$

$y = 5$

$z = \frac{1}{2} - t = \frac{1}{2} - \frac{3}{2} = -1$

(c) $(t - 3) - 4(2t) - (t + 5) = 0$

$t - 3 - 8t - t - 5 = 0$

$-8t - 8 = 0$

$8t = -8$

$t = -1$

so $x = t - 3 = -1 - 3 = -4$

$y = 2t = -2$

$z = t + 5 = -1 + 5 = -4$

(d) $(1 - t) + (-2 + 3t) = (3 + 2t) + 4$

$2t - 1 = 2t + 7$ has no solution,

so there is no point of intersection

32. (a) $\begin{bmatrix} 1 & 2 & -1 & 1 \\ 2 & -1 & 3 & 7 \end{bmatrix} \longrightarrow \begin{bmatrix} 1 & 2 & -1 & 1 \\ 0 & -5 & 5 & 5 \end{bmatrix} \longrightarrow \begin{bmatrix} 1 & 2 & -1 & 1 \\ 0 & 1 & -1 & -1 \end{bmatrix} \longrightarrow$

$\begin{bmatrix} 1 & 0 & 1 & 3 \\ 0 & 1 & -1 & -1 \end{bmatrix}$

Let $z = t$;

then $y - t = -1$ so $y = -1 + t$

and $x + t = 3$ so $x = 3 + -t$

50

(b) $\begin{bmatrix} 3 & 1 & 1 & 5 \\ 0 & 1 & -7 & 1 \end{bmatrix} \longrightarrow \begin{bmatrix} 1 & 1/3 & 1/3 & 5/3 \\ 0 & 1 & -7 & 1 \end{bmatrix} \longrightarrow \begin{bmatrix} 1 & 0 & 8/3 & 4/3 \\ 0 & 1 & -7 & 1 \end{bmatrix}$

Let $z = t$;

then $y - 7t = 1$ so $y = 1 + 7t$

and $x + \dfrac{8}{3}t = \dfrac{4}{3}$ so $x = \dfrac{4}{3} - \dfrac{8}{3}t$

(c) $\begin{bmatrix} 5 & 1 & -7 & 2 \\ 4 & 2 & 1 & 4 \end{bmatrix} \longrightarrow \begin{bmatrix} 1 & 1/5 & -7/5 & 2/5 \\ 0 & 6/5 & 33/5 & 12/5 \end{bmatrix} \longrightarrow \begin{bmatrix} 1 & 1/5 & -7/5 & 2/5 \\ 0 & 1 & 11/2 & 2 \end{bmatrix} \longrightarrow$
$\begin{bmatrix} 1 & 0 & -5/2 & 0 \\ 0 & 1 & 11/2 & 2 \end{bmatrix}$

Let $z = t$;

then $y + \dfrac{11}{2}t = 2$ so $y = 2 - \dfrac{11}{2}t$

and $x - \dfrac{5}{2}t = 0$ so $x = \dfrac{5}{2}t$

(d) $\begin{bmatrix} 2 & 3 & 1 & 11 \\ 4 & 9 & -1 & 31 \end{bmatrix} \longrightarrow \begin{bmatrix} 1 & 3/2 & 1/2 & 11/2 \\ 4 & 9 & -1 & 31 \end{bmatrix} \longrightarrow \begin{bmatrix} 1 & 3/2 & 1/2 & 11/2 \\ 0 & 3 & -3 & 9 \end{bmatrix} \longrightarrow$
$\begin{bmatrix} 1 & 3/2 & 1/2 & 11/2 \\ 0 & 1 & -1 & 3 \end{bmatrix} \longrightarrow \begin{bmatrix} 1 & 0 & 2 & 1 \\ 0 & 1 & -1 & 3 \end{bmatrix}$

Let $z = t$;

then $y - t = 3$ so $y = 3 + t$

and $x + 2t = 1$ so $x = 1 - 2t$

33.   (a) Let $\mathbf{u} = \overrightarrow{PQ} = (1, 1, -2)$,   so $x = 1 + t$, $y = 6 + t$, $z = 3 - 2t$

     (b) Let $\mathbf{u} = \overrightarrow{PQ} = (4, -1, 1)$,   so $x = 4 + 4t$, $y = 1 - t$, $z = 2/3 + t$

     (c) Let $\mathbf{u} = \overrightarrow{PQ} = (2, 0, 1)$,   so $x = 2t$, $y = -1$, $z = 1 + t$

     (d) Let $\mathbf{u} = \overrightarrow{PQ} = (-3, -3, -3) = -3(1, 1, 1)$,   so $x = 2 + t$, $y = 2 + t$, $z = 3 + t$

34.   (a) Let $\mathbf{u} = \overrightarrow{PQ} = (-1, 7, 1)$,   so $\frac{x-3}{-1} = \frac{y-{}^-5}{7} = \frac{z-1}{1}$ or $3 - x = \frac{1}{7}(y + 5) = z - 1$

     (b) Let $\mathbf{u} = \overrightarrow{PQ} = (-1, 1, -3)$,   so $\frac{x-4}{-1} = \frac{y-1}{1} = \frac{z-6}{-3}$ or $4 - x = y - 1 = 3(6 - z)$

     (c) Let $\mathbf{u} = \overrightarrow{PQ} = (\frac{1}{2}, -3, 1)$,   so $\frac{x-4}{\frac{1}{2}} = \frac{y-3}{-3} = \frac{z-\frac{-5}{2}}{1}$ or $2(x - 4) = 3(3 - y) = z + \frac{5}{2}$

     (d) Let $\mathbf{u} = \overrightarrow{PQ} = (1, 7, 7)$,   so $\frac{x-0}{1} = \frac{y-0}{7} = \frac{z-0}{7}$ or $x = \frac{1}{7}y = \frac{1}{7}z$

35.   (a) $1(x - 1) + 2(y - {}^- 1) + 3(z - 5) = 0$ or $(x - 1) + 2(y + 1) + 3(z - 5) = 0$

     (b) $\frac{4}{13}(x - 0) + \frac{-3}{13}(y - 2) + \frac{12}{13}(z - 0) = 0$ or $4x - 3(y - 2) + 12z = 0$

     (c) $1(x - 2) + 1(y - 6) + 1(z - {}^- 3) = 0$ or $(x - 2) + (y - 6) + (z + 3) = 0$

     (d) $\frac{1}{4}(x - 4) + \frac{-1}{2}(y - 1) + \frac{5}{4}(z - {}^- 7) = 0$ or $(x - 4) - 2(y - 1) + 5(z + 7) = 0$

36. (a) $6(x-2)+1(y-3)+6(z-4)=0$

$\quad\quad 6x-12+y-3+6z-24=0$

$\quad\quad\quad 6x+y+6z-39=0$, $\quad\quad\quad$ or $\quad\quad$ $6x+y+6z=39$

(b) $0(x-^-7)+0(y-2)+1(z-3)=0$

$\quad\quad\quad\quad z-3=0$ $\quad\quad$ or $\quad\quad$ $z=3$

(c) $\frac{-2}{3}(x-8)+\frac{1}{3}(y-^-8)+\frac{2}{3}(z-2)=0$

$\quad\quad -2(x-8)+1(y+8)+2(z-2)=0$

$\quad\quad -2x+16+y+8+2z-4=0$

$\quad\quad\quad -2x+y+2z+20=0$ $\quad\quad$ or $\quad\quad$ $-2x+y+2z=-20$

(d) $2(x-0)+5(y-0)+5(z-0)=0$

$\quad\quad 2x+5y+5z=0$

37. (a) Let $\mathbf{n}=\overrightarrow{PQ}\times\overrightarrow{PR}=(-2,5,6)\times(1,1,1)=(-1,8,-7)$

$\quad$ so $\quad -1(x-3)+8(y-1)+^-7(z-1)-0$ $\quad\quad$ or $\quad\quad$ $-(x-3)+8(y-1)-7(z-1)=0$

(b) Let $\mathbf{n}=\overrightarrow{PQ}\times\overrightarrow{PR}=(-3,-3,-15)\times(-2,-1,-21)=(48,-33,-3)=3(16,-11,-1)$

$\quad$ so $\quad 16(x-3)+-11(y-4)+-1(z-4)=0$ $\quad\quad$ or $\quad\quad$ $16(x-3)-11(y-4)-(z-4)=0$

(c) Let $\mathbf{n}=\overrightarrow{PQ}\times\overrightarrow{PR}=(\frac{3}{2},\frac{1}{2},1)\times(\frac{-1}{2},-1,\frac{5}{2})=(\frac{9}{4},\frac{-17}{4},\frac{-5}{4}=\frac{1}{4}(9,-17,-5)$

$\quad$ so $\quad 9(x-0)+-17(y-2))+-5(z--1)=0$ $\quad$ or $\quad$ $9x-17(y-2)-5(z+1)=0$

(d) Let $\mathbf{n}=\overrightarrow{PQ}\times\overrightarrow{PR}=(2,-1,2)\times(1,-3,-1)=(7,4,-5)$

$\quad$ so $\quad 7(x-7)+4(y-2)+-5(z-7)=0$ $\quad\quad$ or $\quad\quad$ $7(x-7)+4(y-2)-5(z-7)=0$

38. (a) Let $\mathbf{n}=\overrightarrow{PQ}\times\overrightarrow{PR}=(-2,-1,-1)\times(2,5,-2)=(7,-6,-8)$

$\quad$ so $\quad 7(x-8)+-6(y--5)+-8(z-2)=0$

$\quad\quad\quad 7x-56-6y-30-8z+16=0$

$\quad\quad\quad\quad 7x-6y-8z-70=0$ $\quad$ or $\quad$ $7x-6y-8z=70$

(b) Let $\mathbf{n}=\overrightarrow{PQ}\times\overrightarrow{PR}=(1,1,3)\times(-2,0,-4)=(-4,-2,2)=-2(2,1,-1)$

$\quad$ so $\quad 2(x-1)+1(y-5)+-1(z-4)=0$

$\quad\quad\quad 2x-2+y-5-z+4=0$

$\quad\quad\quad\quad 2x+y-z-3=0$ $\quad\quad$ or $\quad\quad$ $2x+y-z=3$

(c) Let $\mathbf{n}=\overrightarrow{PQ}\times\overrightarrow{PR}=(6,0,-4)\times(-5,4,9)=(16,-34,24)=2(8,-17,12)$

$\quad$ so $\quad 8(x-4)+-17(y-4)+12(z-3)=0$

$\quad\quad\quad 8x-32-17y+68+12z-36=0$

$\quad\quad\quad\quad 8x-17y+12z=0$

(d) Let $\mathbf{n}=\overrightarrow{PQ}\times\overrightarrow{PR}=(\frac{4}{3},1,\frac{7}{3})\times(1,\frac{2}{3},\frac{5}{3})=(\frac{1}{9},\frac{1}{9},\frac{-1}{9})=\frac{1}{9}(1,1,-1)$

$\quad$ so $\quad 1(x-\frac{1}{3})+1(y-0)+-1(z-\frac{-2}{3})=0$

$\quad\quad\quad x-\frac{1}{3}+y-z-\frac{2}{3}=0$

$\quad\quad\quad\quad x+y-z-1=0$ $\quad\quad$ or $\quad\quad$ $x+y-z=1$

39. Let $\mathbf{n} = (-3, 1, 2)$ so $-3(x-1) + 1(y-1) + 2(z-3) = 0$ or $-3x + y + 2z = 4$

40. Let $\mathbf{n} = (4, -1, 3)$ so $4(x-2) + -1(y-7) + 3(z--1) = 0$ or $4x - y + 3z = -2$

41. Let $\mathbf{n} = (1, 0, 2) \times (1, 1, 1) = (-2, 1, 1)$, and note $t = 0$ implies $x = 3$, $y = 5$, $z = 5$

   so $-2(x-3) + 1(y-5) + 1(z-5) = 0$ or $-2x + y + z = 4$

42. $\begin{bmatrix} 1 & -1 & 3 & 5 \\ 2 & 2 & 7 & 0 \end{bmatrix} \longrightarrow \begin{bmatrix} 1 & -1 & 3 & 5 \\ 0 & 4 & 1 & -10 \end{bmatrix} \longrightarrow \begin{bmatrix} 1 & 0 & 13/4 & 5/2 \\ 0 & 1 & 1/4 & -5/2 \end{bmatrix}$

   so $z = t$, $y = \frac{-5}{2} - \frac{1}{4}t$ and $x = \frac{5}{2} - \frac{13}{4}t$ is the line of intersection,

   with direction $\mathbf{u} = \left(\frac{-13}{4}, \frac{-1}{4}, 1\right)$ and point $Q(\frac{5}{2}, \frac{-5}{2}, 0)$.

   Let $\mathbf{n} = \mathbf{u} \times \overrightarrow{PQ} = \left(\frac{-13}{4}, \frac{-1}{4}, 1\right) \times \left(\frac{3}{2}, \frac{-13}{2}, -4\right) = \left(\frac{15}{2}, \frac{-23}{2}, \frac{43}{2}\right) = \frac{1}{2}(15, -23, 43)$

   so $15(x-1) + -23(y-4) + 43(z-4) = 0$ or $15x - 23y + 43z = 95$.

43. Let $\mathbf{n} = (2, 2, 1) \times (1, -3, 0) = (3, 1, -8)$
   so $x = 2 + 3t$, $y = -3 + t$ and $z = -8t$.

44. Let $\mathbf{n} = (3, 1, -1) \times (11, 2, 3) = (5, -20, -5) = 5(1, -4, -1)$
   so $1(x--1) + -4(y-7) + -1(z-4) = 0$ or $x - 4y - z = -33$.

45. Let $\mathbf{n} = \overrightarrow{PQ} \times \mathbf{n_1} = (2, -2, -5) \times (2, -1, -1) = (-3, -8, 2)$
   so $-3(x-4) + -8(y-5) + 2(z-3) = 0$ or $3x + 8y - 2z = 46$.

46. Note $t = 0$ implies $x = 4$, $y = -1$, $z = 1$ or $Q(4, -1, 1)$
   Let $\mathbf{n} = \overrightarrow{PQ} \times \mathbf{u} = (3, -2, -6) \times (2, 4, 1) = (22, -15, 16)$
   so $22(x-1) + -15(y-1) + 16(z-7) = 0$ or $22x - 15y + 16z = 119$

47. Note the line of intersection has direction $\mathbf{u_1} = \mathbf{n_1} \times \mathbf{n_2} = (2, 1, 1) \times (1, -2, 3)$
$$= (5, -5, -5) = 5(1, -1, -1)$$

   and the given line has direction $\mathbf{u_2} = (6, 0, 1)$
   Let $\mathbf{n} = (1, -1, -1) \times (6, 0, 1) = (-1, -7, 6)$
   and note $t = 0$ implies $x = 3$, $y = 4$ and $z = 0$
   so $-1(x-3) + -7(y-4) + 6(z-0) = 0$ or $x + 7y - 6z = 31$.

48.
$$\begin{bmatrix} 1 & 3 & -7 & 2 \\ 3 & 11 & -17 & 2 \end{bmatrix} \rightarrow \begin{bmatrix} 1 & 3 & -7 & 2 \\ 0 & 2 & 4 & -4 \end{bmatrix} \rightarrow \begin{bmatrix} 1 & 3 & -7 & 2 \\ 0 & 1 & 2 & -2 \end{bmatrix} \rightarrow$$
$$\begin{bmatrix} 1 & 0 & -13 & 8 \\ 0 & 1 & 2 & -2 \end{bmatrix}$$

so $z = t$, $y = -2 - 2t$, $x = 8 + 13t$ is the line of intersection,

with direction $\mathbf{u}_1 = (13, -2, 1)$ and point $Q(8, -2, 0)$.

Let $\mathbf{n} = \mathbf{u}_1 \times \mathbf{u}_2 = (13, -2, 1) \times (-2, 3, 2) = (-7, -28, 35) = -7(1, 4, -5)$

so $1(x - 8) + 4(y - -2) + -5(z - 0) = 0$ or $x + 4y - 5z = 0$.

49. (a) Let $M = P + \frac{1}{2}\overrightarrow{PQ} = (1, 4, 3) + \frac{1}{2}(-2, 2, 2) = (1, 4, 3) + (-1, 1, 1) = (0, 5, 4)$

and $\mathbf{n} = \overrightarrow{PQ} = (-2, 2, 2) = -2(1, -1, -1)$

so $1(x - 0) + -1(y - 5) + -1(z - 4) = 0$ or $x - y - z = -9$.

50. (a) $D = \dfrac{|(2)(1)+(-3)(1)+(6)(-1)+4|}{\sqrt{4+9+36}} = \dfrac{3}{\sqrt{49}} = \dfrac{3}{7}$

(b) $2x + 2y - z + 8 = 0$, so $D = \dfrac{|(2)(11)+(2)(-2)+(-1)(3)+8|}{\sqrt{4+4+1}} = \dfrac{23}{\sqrt{9}} = \dfrac{23}{3}$

(c) $4x - z - 5 = 0$, so $D = \dfrac{|(4)(10)+(0)(7)+(-1)(6)+-5|}{\sqrt{16+0+1}} = \dfrac{29}{\sqrt{17}} = \dfrac{29}{17}\sqrt{17}$

(d) $D = \dfrac{|(3)(4)+(-12)(1)+(4)(1)+1|}{\sqrt{9+144+16}} = \dfrac{4}{\sqrt{169}} = \dfrac{4}{13}$

CHAPTER 4: EUCLIDEAN VECTOR SPACES

1. Let $\mathbf{u} = (2, 1, 0, -4)$, $\mathbf{v} = (4, -1, 4, 4)$, $\mathbf{w} = (2, 5, -1, 5)$. Compute following.
   - (a) $2\mathbf{u} - \mathbf{v} + 3\mathbf{w}$
   - (b) $3(\mathbf{u} - \mathbf{v}) - 2(3\mathbf{w} - \mathbf{v})$
   - (c) $(\mathbf{v} - 3\mathbf{u}) \cdot \mathbf{w}$
   - (d) $(\mathbf{u} \cdot \mathbf{w})\|\mathbf{v}\|$

2. Let $\mathbf{u} = (1, 7, 0, 7)$, $\mathbf{v} = (2, 1, 3, -1)$, $\mathbf{w} = (3, 0, 1, 3)$. Compute following.
   - (a) $(\mathbf{w} - \mathbf{v}) - 2(\mathbf{u} + 4\mathbf{w})$
   - (b) $\|\mathbf{u} + \mathbf{v} - \mathbf{w}\|$
   - (c) $(3\mathbf{v} + \mathbf{w}) \cdot (3\mathbf{v} - \mathbf{w})$
   - (d) $\frac{1}{\|\mathbf{w}\|}\mathbf{w}$

3. Find the Euclidean distance between $\mathbf{u}$ and $\mathbf{v}$.
   - (a) $\mathbf{u} = (1, 1, 6)$, $\mathbf{v} = (1, 5, 4)$
   - (b) $\mathbf{u} = (1, 0, 6, -5)$, $\mathbf{v} = (3, 1, 3, -3)$
   - (c) $\mathbf{u} = (1, 2, -1, 0)$, $\mathbf{v} = (2, 1, \frac{-3}{4}, 1)$
   - (d) $\mathbf{u} = (4, 1, 3, 2, 10)$, $\mathbf{v} = (-4, 5, 0, 6, 2)$

In questions 4–9, find the standard matrix for the linear transformation defined by the equations.

4. $\begin{aligned} w_1 &= x_1 - x_2 \\ w_2 &= 2x_1 + x_2 \\ w_3 &= 5x_1 - 3x_2 \end{aligned}$

5. $\begin{aligned} w_1 &= x_1 + 4x_2 - 6x_3 \\ w_2 &= 4x_1 \qquad - 5x_3 \end{aligned}$

6. $\begin{aligned} w_1 &= 6x_1 - x_2 - x_3 + x_4 \\ w_2 &= \quad x_2 + x_3 - 2x_4 \\ w_3 &= \qquad\quad 3x_3 + x_4 \\ w_2 &= \qquad\qquad\quad 5x_4 \end{aligned}$

7. $T(x_1, x_2) = (x_1 - 7x_2, \ 6x_1 + x_2)$

8. $T(x_1, x_2, x_3) = (4x_1 - x_2 + 2x_3, 3x_1 - x_3, 2x_1 + x_2 + 5x_3)$

9. $T(x_1, x_2, x_3) = (8x_1, -x_1 + x_3, x_2 - x_3, 2x_1 + x_2, x_2 + 3x_3)$

In questions 10–13, the standard matrix $[T]$ of a linear transformation T is given. Use it to find $T(\mathbf{x})$.

10. $[T] = \begin{bmatrix} 1 & 6 \\ 1 & 7 \end{bmatrix}$; $\mathbf{x} = \begin{bmatrix} 1 \\ 2 \end{bmatrix}$

11. $[T] = \begin{bmatrix} 1 & 1 \\ 2 & 3 \\ 6 & 8 \end{bmatrix}$; $\mathbf{x} = \begin{bmatrix} 3 \\ -2 \end{bmatrix}$

12. $[T] = \begin{bmatrix} 2 & -1 \\ -1 & 1 \\ 3 & -2 \end{bmatrix}$; $\mathbf{x} = \begin{bmatrix} x_1 \\ x_2 \end{bmatrix}$

13. $[T] = \begin{bmatrix} 1 & 5 & 9 \\ 6 & 1 & -1 \\ 0 & 2 & 5 \end{bmatrix}$; $\mathbf{x} = \begin{bmatrix} x_1 \\ x_2 \\ x_3 \end{bmatrix}$

In questions 14–17, determine whether the linear operator $T : R^2 \to R^2$ defined by the equations is one-to-one; if so, find the standard matrix for the inverse operator, and find $T^{-1}(w_1, w_2)$.

14. $\begin{aligned} w_1 &= x_1 + x_2 \\ w_2 &= 6x_1 + 7x_2 \end{aligned}$

15. $\begin{aligned} w_1 &= 3x_1 - 9x_2 \\ w_2 &= 4x_1 - 12x_2 \end{aligned}$

16. $\begin{aligned} w_1 &= 2x_1 - x_2 \\ w_2 &= 8x_1 - 5x_2 \end{aligned}$

17. $\begin{aligned} w_1 &= 2x_2 \\ w_2 &= 3x_1 \end{aligned}$

In questions 18–21, determine whether the linear operator $T : R^3 \to R^3$ defined by the equations is one-to-one; if so, find the standard matrix for the inverse operator, and find $T^{-1}(w_1, w_2, w_3)$.

18. $\begin{aligned} w_1 &= x_1 + 3x_2 + 2x_3 \\ w_2 &= \quad x_2 - x_3 \\ w_3 &= \qquad\quad x_3 \end{aligned}$

19. $\begin{aligned} w_1 &= x_1 + 3x_2 \\ w_2 &= 3x_1 + 7x_2 - 4x_3 \\ w_3 &= x_1 + 5x_2 + 5x_3 \end{aligned}$

20. $\begin{aligned} w_1 &= x_1 - 7x_2 + 7x_3 \\ w_2 &= -2x_1 + 2x_2 + x_3 \\ w_3 &= 3x_1 - 5x_2 + x_3 \end{aligned}$

21. $\begin{aligned} w_1 &= 2x_1 + 4x_2 + x_3 \\ w_2 &= \qquad 9x_2 + 2x_3 \\ w_3 &= 2x_1 - 8x_2 - 2x_3 \end{aligned}$

In questions 22–25, show how whether the function is a linear transformation from R^n to R^m.

55

22. $T(x, y) = (x - 2y, 3x + y)$

23. $T(x, y) = (x + y, 2xy)$

24. $T(x, y) = (.3y, .4x)$

25. $T(x, y, z) = (x - y, y - z, z - x)$

In questions 26–29, determine the standard matrix for the linear operator.

26. The operator on R^2 which rotates by $\pi/3$ radian about the origin.

27. The operator on R^2 which contracts with factor $1/2$, then reflects about the line $y = x$.

28. The operator on R^3 which projects orthogonally onto the yz–plane.

29. The operator on R^3 which rotates by $\pi/4$ radian about the z–axis, then reflects about the yz–plane.

In questions 30–33, determine the eigenvalues and corresponding eigenvectors of the linear operator T.

30. $T : R^2 \to R^2$ is the dilation with factor 3.

31. $T : R^2 \to R^2$ is the rotation by $\pi/6$ radian about the origin.

32. $T : R^3 \to R^3$ is the orthogonal projection on the xy–plane.

33. $T : R^3 \to R^3$ is the reflection about the yz–plane.

WRITING QUESTIONS

34. Explain in words the difference between a function from R^n to R^m and a linear transformation from R^n to R^m.

35. Explain in words what is meant by a **one–to–one** function or transformation.

36. Explain in words the meaning of equation $[T^{-1}] = [T]^{-1}$.

37. Use both geometric arguments and properties of matrices to refute the following: "When two or more linear operators follow one another, the order in which they are carried out is irrelevant."

38. Suppose you were carried by time machine to Alexandria, Egypt in 300 B.C. and had the opportunity to meet Euclid, the geometer. Assuming he could speak English, what sorts of things would you say or do to try to convince him that matrices are a good tool for studying geometry?

CHAPTER 4: SOLUTIONS

SECTION 4.1 *EUCLIDEAN n–SPACE*

1. (a) $2\mathbf{u} - \mathbf{v} + 3\mathbf{w} = (4,2,0,-8) - (4,-1,4,4) + (6,15,-3,15) = (6,18,-7,3)$

   (b) $3(\mathbf{u} - \mathbf{v}) - 2(3\mathbf{w} - \mathbf{v}) \;=\; 3\mathbf{u} - 3\mathbf{v} - 6\mathbf{w} + 2\mathbf{v} = 3\mathbf{u} - \mathbf{v} - 6\mathbf{w}$
$$= (6,3,0,-12) - (4,-1,4,4) - (12,30,-6,30) = (-10,-26,2,-46)$$

   (c) $(\mathbf{v} - 3\mathbf{u}) \cdot \mathbf{w} \;=\; ((4,-1,4,4) - (6,3,0,-12)) \cdot (2,5,-1,5)$
$$= (-2,-4,4,16) \cdot (2,5,-1,5) = -4 + -20 + -4 + 80 = 52$$

   (d) $(\mathbf{u} \cdot \mathbf{w})\|\mathbf{v}\| = (4 + 5 + 0 + -20)\sqrt{16 + 1 + 16 + 16} = -11\sqrt{49} = -77$

2. (a) $(\mathbf{w} - \mathbf{v}) - 2(\mathbf{u} + 4\mathbf{w}) \;=\; \mathbf{w} - \mathbf{v} - 2\mathbf{u} - 8\mathbf{w} = -7\mathbf{w} - \mathbf{v} - 2\mathbf{u}$
$$= (-21,0,-7,-21) - (2,1,3,-1) - (2,14,0,14) = (-25,-15,-10,-34)$$

   (b) $\|\mathbf{u} + \mathbf{v} - \mathbf{w}\| \;=\; \|(1,7,0,7) + (2,1,3,-1) - (3,0,1,3)\|$
$$\|(0,8,2,3)| = \sqrt{0 + 64 + 4 + 9} = \sqrt{77}$$

   (c) $(3\mathbf{v} + \mathbf{w}) \cdot (3\mathbf{v} - \mathbf{w}) = 9\mathbf{v} \cdot \mathbf{v} - 3\mathbf{v} \cdot \mathbf{w} + \mathbf{w} \cdot 3\mathbf{v} - \mathbf{w} \cdot \mathbf{w}$
$$= 9\mathbf{v} \cdot \mathbf{v} - \mathbf{w} \cdot \mathbf{w} = 9(4 + 1 + 9 + 1) - (9 + 0 + 1 + 9) = 135 - 19 = 116$$

   (d) $\frac{1}{\|\mathbf{w}\|}\mathbf{w} = \frac{1}{\sqrt{9+0+1+9}}(3,0,1,3) = \frac{\sqrt{19}}{19}(3,0,1,3)$

3. (a) $d(\mathbf{u},\mathbf{v}) = \|\mathbf{u} - \mathbf{v}\| = \|(0,-4,2)\| = \sqrt{0 + 16 + 4} = \sqrt{20} = 2\sqrt{5}$

   (b) $d(\mathbf{u},\mathbf{v}) = \|\mathbf{u} - \mathbf{v}\| = \|(-2,-1,3,-2)\| = \sqrt{4 + 1 + 9 + 4} = \sqrt{18} = 3\sqrt{2}$

   (c) $d(\mathbf{u},\mathbf{v}) = \|\mathbf{u} - \mathbf{v}\| = \|(-1,1,\frac{-1}{4},-1)\| = \sqrt{1 + 1 + \frac{1}{16} + 1} = \sqrt{\frac{49}{16}} = \frac{7}{4}$

   (d) $d(\mathbf{u},\mathbf{v}) = \|\mathbf{u} - \mathbf{v}\| = \|(8,-4,3,-4,8)\| = \sqrt{64 + 16 = 9 + 16 + 64} = \sqrt{169} = 13$

SECTION 4.2 *LINEAR TRANSFORMATIONS FROM R^n to R^m*

4. $A = \begin{bmatrix} 1 & -1 \\ 2 & 1 \\ 5 & -3 \end{bmatrix}$

5. $A = \begin{bmatrix} 1 & 4 & -6 \\ 4 & 0 & -5 \end{bmatrix}$

6. $A = \begin{bmatrix} 6 & -1 & -1 & 1 \\ 0 & 1 & 1 & -2 \\ 0 & 0 & 3 & 1 \\ 0 & 0 & 0 & 5 \end{bmatrix}$

7. $A = \begin{bmatrix} 1 & -7 \\ 6 & 1 \end{bmatrix}$

8. $A = \begin{bmatrix} 4 & -1 & 2 \\ 3 & 0 & -1 \\ 2 & 1 & 5 \end{bmatrix}$

9. $A = \begin{bmatrix} 8 & 0 & 0 \\ -1 & 0 & 1 \\ 0 & 1 & -1 \\ 1 & 1 & 0 \\ 0 & 1 & 3 \end{bmatrix}$

10. $T(\mathbf{x}) = \begin{bmatrix} 1 & 6 \\ 1 & 7 \end{bmatrix}\begin{bmatrix} 1 \\ 2 \end{bmatrix} = \begin{bmatrix} 13 \\ 15 \end{bmatrix}$

11. $T(\mathbf{x}) = \begin{bmatrix} 1 & 1 \\ 2 & 3 \\ 6 & 8 \end{bmatrix}\begin{bmatrix} 3 \\ -2 \end{bmatrix} = \begin{bmatrix} 1 \\ 0 \\ 2 \end{bmatrix}$

57

12. $T(\mathbf{x}) = \begin{bmatrix} 2 & -1 \\ -1 & 1 \\ 3 & -2 \end{bmatrix} \begin{bmatrix} x_1 \\ x_2 \end{bmatrix} = \begin{bmatrix} 2x_1 - x_2 \\ -x_1 + x_2 \\ 3x_1 - 2x_2 \end{bmatrix}$ 13. $T(\mathbf{x}) = \begin{bmatrix} 1 & 5 & 9 \\ 6 & 1 & -1 \\ 0 & 2 & 5 \end{bmatrix} \begin{bmatrix} x_1 \\ x_2 \\ x_3 \end{bmatrix} = \begin{bmatrix} x_1 + 5x_2 + 9x_3 \\ 6x_1 + x_2 - x_3 \\ 2x_2 + 5x_3 \end{bmatrix}$

SECTION 4.3 *PROPERTIES OF LINEAR TRANSFORMATIONS FROM R^n to R^m*

14. $[T] = \begin{bmatrix} 1 & 1 \\ 6 & 7 \end{bmatrix}$, $\det[T] = 7 - 6 = 1 \neq 0$ so T is one-to-one.

$[T^{-1}] = [T]^{-1} = \begin{bmatrix} 1 & 1 \\ 6 & 7 \end{bmatrix}^{-1} = \frac{1}{1}\begin{bmatrix} 7 & -1 \\ -6 & 1 \end{bmatrix} = \begin{bmatrix} 7 & -1 \\ -6 & 1 \end{bmatrix}.$

$T^{-1}(w_1, w_2) = [T^{-1}]\begin{bmatrix} w_1 \\ w_2 \end{bmatrix}\begin{bmatrix} 7 & -1 \\ -6 & 1 \end{bmatrix}\begin{bmatrix} w_1 \\ w_2 \end{bmatrix} = \begin{bmatrix} 7w_1 - w_2 \\ -6w_1 + w_2 \end{bmatrix}.$

15. $[T] = \begin{bmatrix} 3 & -9 \\ 4 & -12 \end{bmatrix}$, $\det[T] = -36 - (-36) = 0$ so T is not one-to-one.

16. $[T] = \begin{bmatrix} 2 & -1 \\ 8 & -5 \end{bmatrix}$, $\det[T] = -10 - (-8) = -2 \neq 0$ so T is one-to-one.

$[T^{-1}] = [T]^{-1} = \begin{bmatrix} 2 & -1 \\ 8 & -5 \end{bmatrix}^{-1} = \frac{1}{-2}\begin{bmatrix} -5 & 1 \\ -8 & 2 \end{bmatrix} = \begin{bmatrix} 5/2 & -1/2 \\ 4 & -1 \end{bmatrix}.$

$T^{-1}(w_1, w_2) = [T^{-1}]\begin{bmatrix} w_1 \\ w_2 \end{bmatrix}\begin{bmatrix} 5/2 & -1/2 \\ 4 & -1 \end{bmatrix}\begin{bmatrix} w_1 \\ w_2 \end{bmatrix} = \begin{bmatrix} (5/2)w_1 - (1/2)w_2 \\ 4w_1 - w_2 \end{bmatrix}.$

17. $[T] = \begin{bmatrix} 0 & 2 \\ 3 & 0 \end{bmatrix}$, $\det[T] = 0 - 6 = -6 \neq 0$ so T is one-to-one.

$[T^{-1}] = [T]^{-1} = \begin{bmatrix} 0 & 2 \\ 3 & 0 \end{bmatrix}^{-1} = \frac{1}{-6}\begin{bmatrix} 0 & -2 \\ -3 & 0 \end{bmatrix} = \begin{bmatrix} 0 & 1/3 \\ 1/2 & 0 \end{bmatrix}.$

$T^{-1}(w_1, w_2) = [T^{-1}]\begin{bmatrix} w_1 \\ w_2 \end{bmatrix}\begin{bmatrix} 0 & 1/3 \\ 1/2 & 0 \end{bmatrix}\begin{bmatrix} w_1 \\ w_2 \end{bmatrix} = \begin{bmatrix} (1/3)w_2 \\ (1/2)w_1 \end{bmatrix}.$

18. $[T] = \begin{bmatrix} 1 & 3 & 2 \\ 0 & 1 & -1 \\ 0 & 0 & 1 \end{bmatrix}$, $\det[T] = 1 \neq 0$ so T is one-to-one.

$[T^{-1}] = [T]^{-1} = \frac{1}{1}\begin{bmatrix} 1 & 0 & 0 \\ -3 & 1 & 0 \\ -5 & 1 & 1 \end{bmatrix}^T = \begin{bmatrix} 1 & -3 & -5 \\ 0 & 1 & 1 \\ 0 & 0 & 1 \end{bmatrix}.$

$T^{-1}(w_1, w_2, w_3) = [T^{-1}]\begin{bmatrix} w_1 \\ w_2 \\ w_3 \end{bmatrix} = \begin{bmatrix} 1 & -3 & -5 \\ 0 & 1 & 1 \\ 0 & 0 & 1 \end{bmatrix}\begin{bmatrix} w_1 \\ w_2 \\ w_3 \end{bmatrix} = \begin{bmatrix} w_1 - 3w_2 - 5w_3 \\ w_2 + w_3 \\ w_3 \end{bmatrix}.$

19. $[T] = \begin{bmatrix} 1 & 3 & 0 \\ 3 & 7 & -4 \\ 1 & 5 & 5 \end{bmatrix}$, $\det[T] = 1(5) - 3(19) = -2 \neq 0$ so T is one-to-one.

$[T^{-1}] = [T]^{-1} = \frac{1}{-2}\begin{bmatrix} 55 & -19 & 8 \\ -15 & 5 & -2 \\ -12 & 4 & -2 \end{bmatrix}^T = \begin{bmatrix} -55/2 & 15/2 & 6 \\ 19/2 & -5/2 & -2 \\ -4 & 1 & 1 \end{bmatrix}.$

$T^{-1}(w_1, w_2, w_3) = [T^{-1}]\begin{bmatrix} w_1 \\ w_2 \\ w_3 \end{bmatrix} = \begin{bmatrix} -55/2 & 15/2 & 6 \\ 19/2 & -5/2 & -2 \\ -4 & 1 & 1 \end{bmatrix}\begin{bmatrix} w_1 \\ w_2 \\ w_3 \end{bmatrix} = \begin{bmatrix} (-55/2)w_1 + (15/2)w_2 + 6w_3 \\ (19/2)w_1 - (5/2)w_2 - 2w_3 \\ -4w_1 + w_2 + w_3 \end{bmatrix}.$

20. $[T] = \begin{bmatrix} 1 & -7 & 7 \\ -2 & 2 & 1 \\ 3 & -5 & 1 \end{bmatrix}$, $\det[T] = 1(7) - 7(5) + 7(4) = 0$ so T is not one-to-one.

21. $[T] = \begin{bmatrix} 2 & 4 & 1 \\ 0 & 9 & 2 \\ 2 & -8 & -2 \end{bmatrix}$, $\det[T] = 2(-2) + 2(-1) = -6 \neq 0$ so T is one-to-one.

$$[T^{-1}] = [T]^{-1} = \frac{1}{-6}\begin{bmatrix} -2 & 4 & -18 \\ 0 & -6 & 24 \\ -1 & -4 & 18 \end{bmatrix}^T = \begin{bmatrix} 1/3 & 0 & 1/6 \\ -2/3 & 1 & 2/3 \\ 3 & -4 & -3 \end{bmatrix}.$$

$$T^{-1}(w_1, w_2, w_3) = [T^{-1}]\begin{bmatrix} w_1 \\ w_2 \\ w_3 \end{bmatrix} = \begin{bmatrix} 1/3 & 0 & 1/6 \\ -2/3 & 1 & 2/3 \\ 3 & -4 & -3 \end{bmatrix}\begin{bmatrix} w_1 \\ w_2 \\ w_3 \end{bmatrix} = \begin{bmatrix} (1/3)w_1 + (1/6)w_3 \\ (-2/3)w_1 + w_2 + (2/3)w_3 \\ 3w_1 - 4w_2 - 3w_3 \end{bmatrix}.$$

22.
$$\begin{aligned}
T(\mathbf{u} + \mathbf{v}) &= T((x_1, y_1) + (x_2, y_2)) \\
&= T(x_1 + x_2, y_1 + y_2) \\
&= ((x_1 + x_2) - 2(y_1 + y_2), 3(x_1 + x_2) + (y_1 + y_2)) \\
&= (x_1 + x_2 - 2y_1 - 2y_2, 3x_1 + 3x_2 + y_1 + y_2)
\end{aligned}$$

$$\begin{aligned}
T(\mathbf{u}) + T(\mathbf{v}) &= T(x_1, y_1) + T(x_2, y_2) \\
&= (x_1 - 2y_1, 3x_1 + y_1) + (x_2 - 2y_2, 3x_2 + y_2) \\
&= (x_1 - 2y_1 + x_2 - 2y_2, 3x_1 + y_1 + 3x_2 + y_2) \\
&= T(\mathbf{u} + \mathbf{v})
\end{aligned}$$

$$\begin{aligned}
T(c\mathbf{u}) &= T(c(x, y)) \\
&= T(cx, cy) \\
&= (cx - 2cy, 3cx + cy)
\end{aligned}$$

$$\begin{aligned}
cT(\mathbf{u}) &= cT((x, y)) \\
&= c(x - 2y, 3x + y) \\
&= (cx - 2cy, 3cx + cy) \\
&= T(c\mathbf{u})
\end{aligned}$$

Thus, T is a linear transformation.

23.
$$\begin{aligned}
T(\mathbf{u} + \mathbf{v}) &= T((x_1, y_1) + (x_2, y_2)) \\
&= T(x_1 + x_2, y_1 + y_2) \\
&= ((x_1 + x_2) + (y_1 + y_2), 2(x_1 + x_2)(y_1 + y_2)) \\
&= (x_1 + x_2 + y_1 + y_2, 2x_1y_1 + 2x_1y_2 + 2x_2y_1 + 2x_2y_2)
\end{aligned}$$

$$\begin{aligned}
T(\mathbf{u}) + T(\mathbf{v}) &= T(x_1, y_1) + T(x_2, y_2) \\
&= (x_1 + y_1, 2x_1y_1) + (x_2 + y_2, 2x_2y_2) \\
&= (x_1 + y_1 + x_2 + y_2, 2x_1y_1 + 2x_2y_2) \\
&\neq T(\mathbf{u} + \mathbf{v})
\end{aligned}$$

Thus, T is not a linear transformation.

24.
$$\begin{aligned}
T(\mathbf{u} + \mathbf{v}) &= T((x_1, y_1) + (x_2, y_2)) \\
&= T(x_1 + x_2, y_1 + y_2) \\
&= (.3(y_1 + y_2), .4(x_1 + x_2)) \\
&= (.3y_1 + .3y_2, .4x_1 + .4x_2)
\end{aligned}$$

$$\begin{aligned}
T(\mathbf{u}) + T(\mathbf{v}) &= T(x_1, y_1) + T(x_2, y_2) \\
&= (.3y_1, .4x_1) + (.3y_2, .4x_2) \\
&= (.3y_1 + .3y_2, .4x_1 + .4x_2) \\
&= T(\mathbf{u} + \mathbf{v})
\end{aligned}$$

$$\begin{aligned}
T(c\mathbf{u}) &= T(c(x, y)) \\
&= T(cx, cy) \\
&= (.3cy, .4cx)
\end{aligned}$$

$$
\begin{aligned}
cT(\mathbf{u}) &= cT((x, y)) \\
&= c(.3y, .4x) \\
&= (.3cy, .4cx) \\
&= T(c\mathbf{u})
\end{aligned}
$$

Thus, T is a linear transformation.

25.
$$
\begin{aligned}
T(\mathbf{u} + \mathbf{v}) &= T((x_1, y_1, z_1) + (x_2, y_2, z_2)) \\
&= T(x_1 + x_2, y_1 + y_2, z_1 + z_2) \\
&= ((x_1 + x_2) - (y_1 + y_2), (y_1 + y_2) - (z_1 + z_2), (z_1 + z_2) - (x_1 + x_2)) \\
&= (x_1 + x_2 - y_1 - y_2, y_1 + y_2 - z_1 - z_2, z_1 + z_2 - x_1 - x_2)
\end{aligned}
$$

$$
\begin{aligned}
T(\mathbf{u}) + T(\mathbf{v}) &= T(x_1, y_1, z_1) + T(x_2, y_2, z_2) \\
&= (x_1 - y_1, y_1 - z_1, z_1 - x_1) + (x_2 - y_2, y_2 - z_2, z_2 - x_2) \\
&= (x_1 - y_1 + x_2 - y_2, y_1 - z_1 + y_2 - z_2, z_1 - x_1 + z_2 - x_2) \\
&= T(\mathbf{u} + \mathbf{v})
\end{aligned}
$$

$$
\begin{aligned}
T(c\mathbf{u}) &= T(c(x, y, z)) \\
&= T(cx, cy, cz) \\
&= (cx - cy, cy - cz, cz - cx)
\end{aligned}
$$

$$
\begin{aligned}
cT(\mathbf{u}) &= cT(x, y, z) \\
&= c(x - y, y - z, z - x) \\
&= (cx - cy, cy - cz, cz - cx) \\
&= T(c\mathbf{u})
\end{aligned}
$$

Thus, T is a linear transformation.

26.
$$
\begin{aligned}
T\left(\begin{bmatrix} 1 \\ 0 \end{bmatrix}\right) &= \begin{bmatrix} \cos \pi/3 \\ \sin \pi/3 \end{bmatrix} = \begin{bmatrix} 1/2 \\ \sqrt{3}/2 \end{bmatrix} \\
T\left(\begin{bmatrix} 0 \\ 1 \end{bmatrix}\right) &= \begin{bmatrix} -\sin \pi/3 \\ \cos \pi/3 \end{bmatrix} = \begin{bmatrix} -\sqrt{3}/2 \\ 1/2 \end{bmatrix} \\
[T] &= \begin{bmatrix} 1/2 & -\sqrt{3}/2 \\ \sqrt{3}/2 & 1/2 \end{bmatrix}
\end{aligned}
$$

27.
$$
\begin{aligned}
T_1\left(\begin{bmatrix} 1 \\ 0 \end{bmatrix}\right) &= \begin{bmatrix} 1/2 \\ 0 \end{bmatrix} \\
T_1\left(\begin{bmatrix} 0 \\ 1 \end{bmatrix}\right) &= \begin{bmatrix} 0 \\ 1/2 \end{bmatrix} \\
[T_1] &= \begin{bmatrix} 1/2 & 0 \\ 0 & 1/2 \end{bmatrix}
\end{aligned}
$$

$$
\begin{aligned}
T_2\left(\begin{bmatrix} 1 \\ 0 \end{bmatrix}\right) &= \begin{bmatrix} 0 \\ 1 \end{bmatrix} \\
T_2\left(\begin{bmatrix} 0 \\ 1 \end{bmatrix}\right) &= \begin{bmatrix} 1 \\ 0 \end{bmatrix} \\
[T_2] &= \begin{bmatrix} 0 & 1 \\ 1 & 0 \end{bmatrix}
\end{aligned}
$$

$$
[T] = [T_2 \circ T_1] = [T_2][T_1] = \begin{bmatrix} 0 & 1 \\ 1 & 0 \end{bmatrix} \begin{bmatrix} 1/2 & 0 \\ 0 & 1/2 \end{bmatrix} = \begin{bmatrix} 0 & 1/2 \\ 1/2 & 0 \end{bmatrix}
$$

28. $T\left(\begin{bmatrix} 1 \\ 0 \\ 0 \end{bmatrix}\right) = \begin{bmatrix} 0 \\ 0 \\ 0 \end{bmatrix}$

$T\left(\begin{bmatrix} 0 \\ 1 \\ 0 \end{bmatrix}\right) = \begin{bmatrix} 0 \\ 1 \\ 0 \end{bmatrix}$

$T\left(\begin{bmatrix} 0 \\ 0 \\ 1 \end{bmatrix}\right) = \begin{bmatrix} 0 \\ 0 \\ 1 \end{bmatrix}$

$[T] = \begin{bmatrix} 0 & 0 & 0 \\ 0 & 1 & 0 \\ 0 & 0 & 1 \end{bmatrix}$

29. $T_1\left(\begin{bmatrix} 1 \\ 0 \\ 0 \end{bmatrix}\right) = \begin{bmatrix} \cos \pi/4 \\ \sin \pi/4 \\ 0 \end{bmatrix} = \begin{bmatrix} \sqrt{2}/2 \\ \sqrt{2}/2 \\ 0 \end{bmatrix}$

$T_1\left(\begin{bmatrix} 0 \\ 1 \\ 0 \end{bmatrix}\right) = \begin{bmatrix} -\sin \pi/4 \\ \cos \pi/4 \\ 0 \end{bmatrix} = \begin{bmatrix} -\sqrt{2}/2 \\ \sqrt{2}/2 \\ 0 \end{bmatrix}$

$T_1\left(\begin{bmatrix} 0 \\ 0 \\ 1 \end{bmatrix}\right) = \begin{bmatrix} 0 \\ 0 \\ 1 \end{bmatrix}$

$[T_1] = \begin{bmatrix} \sqrt{2}/2 & -\sqrt{2}/2 & 0 \\ \sqrt{2}/2 & \sqrt{2}/2 & 0 \\ 0 & 0 & 1 \end{bmatrix}$

$T_2\left(\begin{bmatrix} 1 \\ 0 \\ 0 \end{bmatrix}\right) = \begin{bmatrix} -1 \\ 0 \\ 0 \end{bmatrix}$

$T_2\left(\begin{bmatrix} 0 \\ 1 \\ 0 \end{bmatrix}\right) = \begin{bmatrix} 0 \\ 1 \\ 0 \end{bmatrix}$

$T_2\left(\begin{bmatrix} 0 \\ 0 \\ 1 \end{bmatrix}\right) = \begin{bmatrix} 0 \\ 0 \\ 1 \end{bmatrix}$

$[T_2] = \begin{bmatrix} -1 & 0 & 0 \\ 0 & 1 & 0 \\ 0 & 0 & 1 \end{bmatrix}$

$[T] = [T_2 \circ T_1] = [T_2][T_1] = \begin{bmatrix} \sqrt{2}/2 & -\sqrt{2}/2 & 0 \\ \sqrt{2}/2 & \sqrt{2}/2 & 0 \\ 0 & 0 & 1 \end{bmatrix} \begin{bmatrix} -1 & 0 & 0 \\ 0 & 1 & 0 \\ 0 & 0 & 1 \end{bmatrix}$

$= \begin{bmatrix} -\sqrt{2}/2 & -\sqrt{2}/2 & 0 \\ -\sqrt{2}/2 & \sqrt{2}/2 & 0 \\ 0 & 0 & 1 \end{bmatrix}$

30. $T\left(\begin{bmatrix} 1 \\ 0 \end{bmatrix}\right) = \begin{bmatrix} 3 \\ 0 \end{bmatrix}, T\left(\begin{bmatrix} 0 \\ 1 \end{bmatrix}\right) = \begin{bmatrix} 0 \\ 3 \end{bmatrix}, A = [T] = \begin{bmatrix} 3 & 0 \\ 0 & 3 \end{bmatrix}$

$\det(\lambda I - A) = \begin{vmatrix} \lambda - 3 & 0 \\ 0 & \lambda - 3 \end{vmatrix} = (\lambda - 3)^2 = 0$, so $\lambda = 3$

Substituting $\lambda = 3$ gives the system $\begin{bmatrix} 0 & 0 & 0 \\ 0 & 0 & 0 \end{bmatrix}$ so $x = s, y = t$.

Thus $\begin{bmatrix} x \\ y \end{bmatrix} = \begin{bmatrix} s \\ t \end{bmatrix}$.

31. $T\left(\begin{bmatrix} 1 \\ 0 \end{bmatrix}\right) = \begin{bmatrix} \cos \pi/6 \\ \sin \pi/6 \end{bmatrix} = \begin{bmatrix} \sqrt{3}/2 \\ 1/2 \end{bmatrix}, T\left(\begin{bmatrix} 0 \\ 1 \end{bmatrix}\right) = \begin{bmatrix} -\sin \pi/6 \\ \cos \pi/6 \end{bmatrix} = \begin{bmatrix} -1/2 \\ \sqrt{3}/2 \end{bmatrix},$

$$A = [T] = \begin{bmatrix} \sqrt{3}/2 & -1/2 \\ 1/2 & \sqrt{3}/2 \end{bmatrix}.$$

$$\det(\lambda I - A) = \begin{vmatrix} \lambda - \sqrt{3}/2 & 1/2 \\ -1/2 & \lambda - \sqrt{3}/2 \end{vmatrix} = \lambda^2 - \sqrt{3}\lambda + 1 = 0$$

There are no real roots λ, so T has no real eigenvalues or eigenvectors.

32. $T\left(\begin{bmatrix} 1 \\ 0 \\ 0 \end{bmatrix}\right) = \begin{bmatrix} 0 \\ 0 \\ 0 \end{bmatrix}, T\left(\begin{bmatrix} 0 \\ 1 \\ 0 \end{bmatrix}\right) = \begin{bmatrix} 0 \\ 1 \\ 0 \end{bmatrix}, T\left(\begin{bmatrix} 0 \\ 0 \\ 1 \end{bmatrix}\right) = \begin{bmatrix} 0 \\ 0 \\ 1 \end{bmatrix},$

$$A = [T] = \begin{bmatrix} 0 & 0 & 0 \\ 0 & 1 & 0 \\ 0 & 0 & 1 \end{bmatrix}.$$

$$\det(\lambda I - A) = \begin{vmatrix} \lambda & 0 & 0 \\ 0 & \lambda - 1 & 0 \\ 0 & 0 & \lambda - 1 \end{vmatrix} = \lambda(\lambda - 1)^2 = 0 \text{ so } \lambda = 0, 1.$$

Substituting $\lambda = 0$ gives the system

$$\begin{bmatrix} 0 & 0 & 0 & 0 \\ 0 & -1 & 0 & 0 \\ 0 & 0 & -1 & 0 \end{bmatrix} \rightarrow \begin{bmatrix} 0 & 1 & 0 & 0 \\ 0 & 0 & 1 & 0 \\ 0 & 0 & 0 & 0 \end{bmatrix} \text{ so } x = t, y = 0, z = 0.$$

Thus, $\begin{bmatrix} x \\ y \\ z \end{bmatrix} = \begin{bmatrix} t \\ 0 \\ 0 \end{bmatrix}.$

Substituting $\lambda = 1$ gives the system

$$\begin{bmatrix} 1 & 0 & 0 \\ 0 & 0 & 0 \\ 0 & 0 & 0 \end{bmatrix} \text{ so } x = 0, y = r, z = s.$$

Thus, $\begin{bmatrix} x \\ y \\ z \end{bmatrix} = \begin{bmatrix} 0 \\ r \\ s \end{bmatrix}.$

33. $T\left(\begin{bmatrix} 1 \\ 0 \\ 0 \end{bmatrix}\right) = \begin{bmatrix} 1 \\ 0 \\ 0 \end{bmatrix}, T\left(\begin{bmatrix} 0 \\ 1 \\ 0 \end{bmatrix}\right) = \begin{bmatrix} 0 \\ 1 \\ 0 \end{bmatrix}, T\left(\begin{bmatrix} 0 \\ 0 \\ 1 \end{bmatrix}\right) = \begin{bmatrix} 0 \\ 0 \\ -1 \end{bmatrix},$

$$A = [T] = \begin{bmatrix} 1 & 0 & 0 \\ 0 & 1 & 0 \\ 0 & 0 & -1 \end{bmatrix}.$$

$$\det(\lambda I - A) = \begin{vmatrix} \lambda - 1 & 0 & 0 \\ 0 & \lambda - 1 & 0 \\ 0 & 0 & \lambda + 1 \end{vmatrix} = (\lambda - 1)^2(\lambda + 1) = 0 \text{ so } \lambda = 1, -1$$

Substituting $\lambda = 1$ gives the system

$$\begin{bmatrix} 0 & 0 & 0 & 0 \\ 0 & 0 & 0 & 0 \\ 0 & 0 & 2 & 0 \end{bmatrix} \rightarrow \begin{bmatrix} 0 & 0 & 1 & 0 \\ 0 & 0 & 0 & 0 \\ 0 & 0 & 0 & 0 \end{bmatrix} \text{ so } x = s, y = t, z = 0.$$

Thus, $\begin{bmatrix} x \\ y \\ z \end{bmatrix} = \begin{bmatrix} s \\ t \\ 0 \end{bmatrix}$.

Substituting $\lambda = -1$ gives the system

$$\begin{bmatrix} -2 & 0 & 0 & 0 \\ 0 & -2 & 0 & 0 \\ 0 & 0 & 2 & 0 \end{bmatrix} \rightarrow \begin{bmatrix} 1 & 0 & 0 & 0 \\ 0 & 1 & 0 & 0 \\ 0 & 0 & 0 & 0 \end{bmatrix} \text{ so } x = 0, y = 0, z = r.$$

Thus, $\begin{bmatrix} x \\ y \\ z \end{bmatrix} = \begin{bmatrix} 0 \\ 0 \\ r \end{bmatrix}$.

CHAPTER 5: GENERAL VECTOR SPACES

In questions 1–4, a set of objects is given together with operations of addition and scalar multiplication. Determine whether the set is a vector space under the given operations.

1. The set of all pairs of real numbers of the form (x, y), where $x \geq 0$ and $y \geq 0$, with the standard operations on R^2.

2. The set of all triples of real numbers of the form (x, y, z) with the operations

$$(x, y, z) + (x', y', z') = (x + x', y + y', z + z') \text{ and}$$
$$k(x, y, z) = (kx, ky, 2kz)$$

3. The set of all positive real numbers with operations $x + x' = xx'$ and $kx = x^k$.

4. The set of all functions of the form $\sin(cx)$ where c is real, with the operations $\sin(c_1 x) + \sin(c_2 x) = \sin[(c_1 + c_2)x]$ and $k\sin(cx) = \sin(kcx)$.

5. Consider the set of all real triples of the form (a, b, c), where $c = a - 2b$. Prove whether the set is a subspace of R^3.

6. Consider the set of all 3×3 magic squares. (A magic square is a real square matrix in which the total along each row, each column and each diagonal is the same.) Prove whether the set is a subspace of M_{33}.

7. Consider the set of all real triples of the form (a, b, c), where $a^2 + b^2 = c^2$. Prove whether the set is a subspace of R^3.

8. Consider the set of all polynomials of the form $a_0 + a_1 x + a_2 x^2$, where a_0, a_1 and a_2 are integers. Prove whether the set is subspace of P_3.

9. Determine whether the solution space of the system $A\mathbf{x} = \mathbf{0}$ is a line through the origin, a plane through the origin, or the origin only. If it is a plane, find an equation for it, and if it is a line find parametric equations for it.

(a) $A = \begin{bmatrix} 2 & -8 & 6 \\ -3 & 12 & -9 \\ 7 & -28 & 21 \end{bmatrix}$
(b) $A = \begin{bmatrix} 2 & 6 & 8 \\ 3 & 3 & 15 \\ 2 & 4 & 12 \end{bmatrix}$
(c) $A = \begin{bmatrix} 1 & 6 & 2 \\ 3 & 3 & -1 \\ -1 & 9 & 5 \end{bmatrix}$

10. In each part determine whether $\mathbf{w}$ is in span$\{\mathbf{v}_1, \mathbf{v}_2, \ldots\}$ and if it is, express $\mathbf{w}$ as a linear combination of $\mathbf{v}_1, \mathbf{v}_2, \ldots$

(a) $\mathbf{w} = (-1, 4, 15)$, $\mathbf{v}_1 = (1, 2, 8)$, $\mathbf{v}_2 = (3, 0, 1)$.

(b) $\mathbf{w} = (4, 5, 10)$, $\mathbf{v}_1 = (1, 2, 3)$, $\mathbf{v}_2 = (3, 1, 2)$, $\mathbf{v}_3 = (4, 1, 0)$.

(c) $\mathbf{w} = 1 + x^2$, $\mathbf{v}_1 = 1 - x$, $\mathbf{v}_2 = 2 + x + 3x^2$.

(d) $\mathbf{w} = 4x + 6x^2$, $\mathbf{v}_1 = 1 + x + x^2$, $\mathbf{v}_2 = -2 + 2x + 3x^2$, $\mathbf{v}_3 = 1 + 5x + 6x^2$.

(e) $\mathbf{w} = \begin{bmatrix} 0 & 5 \\ -4 & -1 \end{bmatrix}$, $\mathbf{v}_1 = \begin{bmatrix} 1 & 2 \\ -1 & 0 \end{bmatrix}$, $\mathbf{v}_2 = \begin{bmatrix} 3 & 1 \\ 1 & 1 \end{bmatrix}$.

(f) $\mathbf{w} = \begin{bmatrix} 7 & 19 \\ -3 & 8 \end{bmatrix}$, $\mathbf{v}_1 = \begin{bmatrix} 2 & 4 \\ 0 & 2 \end{bmatrix}$, $\mathbf{v}_2 = \begin{bmatrix} 3 & 1 \\ 3 & 2 \end{bmatrix}$, $\mathbf{v}_3 = \begin{bmatrix} 0 & 10 \\ -6 & 2 \end{bmatrix}$.

11. In each part determine whether the given vectors span R^3.

(a) $(1, 3, 4)$, $(2, 0, 1)$, $2, 1, 0$.

(b) $(2, 0, 2)$, $(3, 1, 1)$, $(-3, 5, 5)$.

(c) $(1, 5, 1)$, $(2, 6, 1)$, $(3, 3, 0)$, $(4, 6, 2)$.

12. In each part determine whether the given polynomials span P_2.

(a) $2 + 5x + 6x^2$, $1 + x^2$, $1 - x^2$.
(b) $7 - x + x^2$, $1 + x + x^2$, $2 + 3x + 5x^2$.
(c) $1 + 4x - x^2$, $2 + 5x + 3x^2$, $3x - 5x^2$, $3 + 15x - 8x^2$.

13. In each part determine whether the set of vectors in R^3 is linearly independent.

(a) $(3, 6, -12)$, $(-2/5, -4/5, 8/5)$
(b) $(1, -4, 2)$, $(2, 0, 1)$, $(3, 2, 2)$
(c) $(1, 1, 1)$, $(1, 1, 0)$, $(1, 0, 0)$, $(1, 0, 1)$.

14. In each part determine whether the set of vectors in R^4 is linearly independent.

(a) $(1, 2, 4, -3)$, $(1, 1, 0, 1)$, $(2, 1, 1, 3)$
(b) $(3, 2, 2, 2)$, $(12, 5, 2, 2)$, $(6, 2, 5, 2)$, $(3, 2, 2, 5)$
(c) $(1, a, 0, 0)$, $(0, 1, a, 0)$, $(0, 0, 1, a)$, $(0, 0, 0, 1)$

15. In each part determine whether the set of vectors in P_2 is linearly independent.

(a) $1 - x$, $1 - x^2$.
(b) $1 + 5x + 6x^2$, $3 + x + x^2$, $5x - 7x^2$.
(c) $\pi + x + 2x^2$, $\pi + 3x$, π.

16. Assume that v_1, v_2 and v_3 are vectors in R^3 that have their initial points at the origin. In each part determine whether the three vectors lie in a plane.

(a) $v_1 = (5, -1, 6)$, $v_2 = (2, 4, 1)$, $v_3 = (0, 1, 1)$.
(b) $v_1 = (1, 1, 3)$, $v_2 = (2, 0, 5)$, $v_3 = (1, -3, 1)$.
(c) $v_1 = (2, 5, 7)$, $v_2 = (0, 2, 0)$, $v_3 = (6, 6, 1)$.

17. Assume that v_1, v_2, v_3 are vectors in R^3 that have their initial points at the origin. In each part determine whether the three vectors lie on the same line.

(a) $v_1 = (1, -7, 4)$, $v_2 = (2, -14, 8)$, $v_3 = (-3, 21, -12)$.
(b) $v_1 = (1, 6, 5)$, $v_2 = (2, 12, 11)$, $v_3 = (3, 18, 15)$.
(c) $v_1 = (2/3, 1/3, -5/3)$, $v_2 = (-2/5, -1/5, 1)$, $v_3 = (1/2, 1/4, -5/4)$.

18. In each part, use the Wronskian to determine whether the set of vectors is linearly independent.

(a) x, x^2, x^3
(b) x, e^x, xe^x
(c) $\sin x, \cos x, \sin 2x$

19. In each part, determine whether the set of vectors is a basis for R^2.

(a) $(1, 3)$, $(0, -2)$
(b) $(7, 1)$, $(6, 1)$
(c) $(10, -15)$, $(-8, 12)$
(d) $(3/5, 4/5)$, $(-4/5, 3/5)$

20. In each part, determine whether the set of vectors is a basis for R^3.

(a) $(1, 1, 1)$, $(2, 2, 0)$, $(3, 0, 0)$

(b) $(0, 17, 8)$, $(1, 7, 5)$, $(2, -3, 2)$

(c) $(2, 5, 2)$, $(1, -1, 3)$, $(0, 1, 1)$

(d) $(\sqrt{2}, 0, \sqrt{2})$, $(\sqrt{3}, 0, \sqrt{6})$, $(0, -\sqrt{6}, \sqrt{3})$

21. In each part, determine whether the set of vectors is a basis for P_2.

(a) 1, $1 + x$, $1 + x + x^2$

(b) $1 - x$, $1 + x$, $1 - x^2$

(c) $3 + x - 2x^2$, $1 - x - x^2$, $5 + x$

(d) $1 + x + x^2$, $1 + 3x + 5x^2$, $5 + 3x + x^2$

22. In each part, determine whether the set of vectors is a basis for M_{22}.

(a) $\begin{bmatrix} 1 & 0 \\ 0 & 1 \end{bmatrix}$, $\begin{bmatrix} 0 & -1 \\ -1 & 0 \end{bmatrix}$, $\begin{bmatrix} 2 & 2 \\ 2 & 0 \end{bmatrix}$, $\begin{bmatrix} 0 & 3 \\ 3 & 3 \end{bmatrix}$

(b) $\begin{bmatrix} 1 & 1 \\ 1 & 0 \end{bmatrix}$, $\begin{bmatrix} 1 & 1 \\ 0 & 1 \end{bmatrix}$, $\begin{bmatrix} 1 & 0 \\ 1 & 1 \end{bmatrix}$, $\begin{bmatrix} 0 & 1 \\ 1 & 1 \end{bmatrix}$

(c) $\begin{bmatrix} 1 & 7 \\ 0 & 0 \end{bmatrix}$, $\begin{bmatrix} 0 & 0 \\ 2 & -3 \end{bmatrix}$, $\begin{bmatrix} 0 & 5 \\ 5 & 0 \end{bmatrix}$, $\begin{bmatrix} 0 & 1 \\ 4 & 4 \end{bmatrix}$

(d) $\begin{bmatrix} \frac{1}{2} & \frac{1}{2} \\ \frac{1}{2} & \frac{1}{2} \end{bmatrix}$, $\begin{bmatrix} \frac{1}{2} & \frac{-5}{6} \\ \frac{1}{6} & \frac{1}{6} \end{bmatrix}$, $\begin{bmatrix} \frac{1}{2} & \frac{1}{6} \\ \frac{1}{6} & \frac{-5}{6} \end{bmatrix}$, $\begin{bmatrix} \frac{1}{2} & \frac{1}{6} \\ \frac{-5}{6} & \frac{1}{6} \end{bmatrix}$

23. In each part, determine the coördinate vector of $\mathbf{w}$ relative to the basis $S = \{\mathbf{v}_1, \mathbf{v}_2\}$.

(a) $\mathbf{v}_1 = (0, 1)$, $\mathbf{v}_2 = (1, 0)$; $\mathbf{w} = (5, 4)$

(b) $\mathbf{v}_1 = (1, 4)$, $\mathbf{v}_2 = (1, 5)$; $\mathbf{w} = (7, -3)$

(c) $\mathbf{v}_1 = (2, 0)$, $\mathbf{v}_2 = (3, -1)$; $\mathbf{w} = (6, 5)$

24. In each part, determine the coördinate vector of $\mathbf{w}$ relative to the basis $S = \{\mathbf{v}_1, \mathbf{v}_2, \mathbf{v}_3\}$.

(a) $\mathbf{v}_1 = (1, 1, 1)$, $\mathbf{v}_2 = (1, 5, -3)$, $\mathbf{v}_3 = (2, 2, 1)$; $\mathbf{w} = (8, -4, -12)$

(b) $\mathbf{v}_1 = (2, 0, -1)$, $\mathbf{v}_2 = (1, 1, 0)$, $\mathbf{v}_3 = (0, 1, 0)$; $\mathbf{w} = (7, 1, -3)$

(c) $\mathbf{v}_1 = (3, 4, 5)$, $\mathbf{v}_2 = (-1, 1, 8)$, $\mathbf{v}_3 = (1, 1, 0)$; $\mathbf{w} = (1, 1, 1)$

25. In each part, determine the coördinate vector of $\mathbf{p}$ relative to the basis $S = \{\mathbf{p}_1, \mathbf{p}_2, \mathbf{p}_3\}$.

(a) $\mathbf{p}_1 = 1 - x$, $\mathbf{p}_2 = x - x^2$, $\mathbf{p}_3 = x^2$; $\mathbf{p} = 6 + 2x + 3x^2$

(b) $\mathbf{p}_1 = 1 + x^2$, $\mathbf{p}_2 = 3x + x^2$, $\mathbf{p}_3 = -3 + x$; $\mathbf{p} = x$

(c) $\mathbf{p}_1 = 1 - x^2$, $\mathbf{p}_2 = 1 + x^2$, $\mathbf{p}_3 = 1 + x + x^2$; $\mathbf{p} = -2 + 4x^2$

26. In each part, determine the coördinate vector of $\mathbf{A}$ relative to the basis $S = \{\mathbf{A}_1, \mathbf{A}_2, \mathbf{A}_3, \mathbf{A}_4\}$.

(a) $\mathbf{A}_1 = \begin{bmatrix} 1 & 0 \\ 0 & 0 \end{bmatrix}$, $\mathbf{A}_2 = \begin{bmatrix} 0 & 0 \\ 3 & 0 \end{bmatrix}$, $\mathbf{A}_3 = \begin{bmatrix} 0 & 2 \\ 0 & 2 \end{bmatrix}$ $\mathbf{A}_4 = \begin{bmatrix} 1 & 1 \\ 1 & 0 \end{bmatrix}$; $\mathbf{A} = \begin{bmatrix} 1 & 2 \\ 0 & -1 \end{bmatrix}$

(b) $\mathbf{A}_1 = \begin{bmatrix} 1 & -2 \\ 1 & 0 \end{bmatrix}$, $\mathbf{A}_2 = \begin{bmatrix} 0 & 0 \\ 1 & 1 \end{bmatrix}$, $\mathbf{A}_3 = \begin{bmatrix} 1 & 0 \\ 0 & 0 \end{bmatrix}$, $\mathbf{A}_4 = \begin{bmatrix} 0 & 0 \\ 0 & 1 \end{bmatrix}$; $\mathbf{A} = \begin{bmatrix} 1 & 2 \\ -1 & 3 \end{bmatrix}$

(c) $\mathbf{A}_1 = \begin{bmatrix} 0 & 3 \\ 2 & 5 \end{bmatrix}$, $\mathbf{A}_2 = \begin{bmatrix} 2 & 6 \\ -2 & 0 \end{bmatrix}$, $\mathbf{A}_3 = \begin{bmatrix} -1 & 1 \\ 1 & 3 \end{bmatrix}$, $\mathbf{A}_4 = \begin{bmatrix} 3 & 0 \\ 4 & 3 \end{bmatrix}$; $\mathbf{A} = \begin{bmatrix} 1 & 0 \\ 0 & 0 \end{bmatrix}$

In questions 27–30, determine the dimension of and a basis for the solution space of the system.

27.
$$\begin{aligned} x_1 + 3x_2 - x_3 &= 0 \\ 2x_1 - x_2 + x_3 &= 0 \end{aligned}$$

28.
$$\begin{aligned} x_1 + x_2 + 3x_3 &= 0 \\ 2x_1 + x_2 + 5x_3 - 3x_4 &= 0 \end{aligned}$$

29.
$$\begin{aligned} 2x_1 + 5x_2 + x_3 &= 0 \\ x_1 + 3x_2 + 2x_3 &= 0 \\ 3x_1 + 4x_2 - 9x_3 &= 0 \end{aligned}$$

30.
$$\begin{aligned} x_1 + x_2 - x_3 &= 0 \\ 2x_1 + x_2 &= 0 \\ 2x_1 + x_3 &= 0 \\ -x_1 + 3x_2 &= 0 \end{aligned}$$

31. In each part, determine the dimension of and a basis for the vector space.

(a) the set of all vectors of the form (x, y, z).

(b) the set of all polynomials of the form $a_0 + a_1 x + a_2 x^2 + a_3 x^3$.

(c) the set of all matrices of the form $\begin{bmatrix} a & b & c \\ d & e & f \end{bmatrix}$.

(d) the line $x = t$, $y = 7t$, $z = -3t$.

(e) the plane $5x + 3y - 2z = 0$.

(f) the set of all vectors of the form (a, b, c, d) where $a + b + c = d$.

(g) the set of all polynomials $a_0 + a_1 x + a_2 x^2 + a_3 x^3$ for which $a_3 = -a_0$.

32. In each part, express the product $A\mathbf{x}$ as a linear combination of the column vectors of A.

(a) $\begin{bmatrix} 1 & 7 \\ 2 & -3 \end{bmatrix} \begin{bmatrix} 3 \\ 4 \end{bmatrix}$

(b) $\begin{bmatrix} 2 & -2 & 1 \\ 1 & 0 & 3 \\ 3 & 5 & -1 \end{bmatrix} \begin{bmatrix} 4 \\ 4 \\ 1 \end{bmatrix}$

(c) $\begin{bmatrix} 2 & 3 & 0 & 1 \\ 6 & 1 & -6 & 6 \\ 5 & 5 & 0 & -1 \end{bmatrix} \begin{bmatrix} 1 \\ 1 \\ 1 \\ 1 \end{bmatrix}$

33. Determine whether $\mathbf{b}$ is in the column space of A, and if so, express $\mathbf{b}$ as a linear combination of the column vectors of A.

(a) $A = \begin{bmatrix} -1 & 6 \\ 2 & 5 \end{bmatrix}$, $\mathbf{b} = \begin{bmatrix} 19 \\ 13 \end{bmatrix}$

(b) $A = \begin{bmatrix} 1 & 7 & 2 \\ 2 & 4 & -6 \\ 3 & 19 & 4 \end{bmatrix}$, $\mathbf{b} = \begin{bmatrix} -1 \\ 3 \\ -4 \end{bmatrix}$

(c) $A = \begin{bmatrix} 3 & -9 & -6 \\ 3 & -10 & -6 \\ 0 & 1 & 0 \\ -3 & 11 & 8 \end{bmatrix}$, $\mathbf{b} = \begin{bmatrix} -20 \\ -19 \\ -1 \\ 28 \end{bmatrix}$

34. Find the vector form of the general solution of the given linear system $A\mathbf{x} = \mathbf{b}$; then use that result to find the vector form of the general solution of $A\mathbf{x} = \mathbf{0}$.

(a)
$$\begin{aligned} 3x_1 + 9x_2 &= -6 \\ -2x_1 - 6x_2 &= 4 \end{aligned}$$

(b)
$$\begin{aligned} 2x_1 + 2x_2 + 2x_3 &= 2 \\ 3x_1 + 5x_2 + 5x_3 &= 11 \\ 4x_1 + 3x_2 + 3x_3 &= 0 \end{aligned}$$

(c)
$$\begin{aligned} x_1 + 2x_2 - 2x_3 + 8x_4 &= 0 \\ x_1 + 2x_2 + 2x_4 &= 4 \\ x_1 + 2x_2 - 3x_3 + 5x_4 &= 2 \\ 2x_1 + 4x_2 - 2x_3 + 10x_4 &= 4 \end{aligned}$$

35. For each matrix below, find a basis for the nullspace, row space, and column space.

(a) $\begin{bmatrix} 1 & -3 & 3 \\ 2 & -6 & 8 \\ 3 & -9 & 11 \end{bmatrix}$

(b) $\begin{bmatrix} 5 & -5 & -1 & 0 \\ 5 & 0 & 3 & 10 \\ 10 & -5 & 2 & 10 \end{bmatrix}$

(c) $\begin{bmatrix} 1 & 0 & 0 & 3 \\ 1 & 0 & 1 & 4 \\ 1 & 0 & -1 & 2 \\ 1 & 1 & 2 & 7 \end{bmatrix}$

36. Find a basis for the span of the given vectors.

(a) $(1, 3, 2)$, $(1, -5, 5)$, $(3, 1, 9)$

(b) $(-1, 2, 2, 3)$, $(2, 1, 1, 5)$, $(7, -4, -4, 1)$

(c) $(1, 0, 2, -1)$, $(3, 3, 0, 1)$, $(0, -3, 6, -4)$, $(1, 3, -4, 3)$

37. In each part, find a subset of the vectors that forms a basis for the span of the vectors; then express each vector not in the basis as a linear combination of the basis vectors.

(a) $\mathbf{v}_1 = (1, 1, -1)$, $\mathbf{v}_2 = (1, 0, 1)$, $\mathbf{v}_3 = (1, -2, 5)$, $\mathbf{v}_4 = (5, 3, 2)$

(b) $\mathbf{v}_1 = (1, 2, 1, 2)$, $\mathbf{v}_2 = (3, 6, 3, 6)$, $\mathbf{v}_3 = (2, 1, 3, 3)$, $\mathbf{v}_4 = (3, 0, 5, 4)$

(c) $\mathbf{v}_1 = (1, 1, -1, 2)$, $\mathbf{v}_2 = (1, -1, 1, 1)$, $\mathbf{v}_3 = (3, -5, 5, 2)$, $\mathbf{v}_4 = (6, 2, -3, 8)$ $\mathbf{v}_5 = (8, 2, -4, 9)$.

38. Find the rank and nullity of the matrix.

(a) $\begin{bmatrix} 1 & 1 & 7 \\ 1 & 2 & 0 \\ 2 & 3 & 10 \end{bmatrix}$

(b) $\begin{bmatrix} 1 & -4 & 5 & 1 \\ 2 & -8 & 9 & 0 \\ 1 & -4 & 3 & -3 \\ -1 & 4 & -2 & 5 \end{bmatrix}$

(c) $\begin{bmatrix} 1 & -2 & 0 & 1 & 0 \\ 2 & -4 & 2 & 4 & 6 \\ 3 & -6 & 1 & 4 & 1 \\ 1 & -2 & -2 & -1 & -3 \end{bmatrix}$

39. In each part use the information in the table to find the dimension of the row space of A, of the column space of A, of the nullspace of A, and of the nullspace of A^T.

	size of A	rank(A)
(a)	3×3	2
(b)	4×4	1
(c)	3×5	3
(d)	5×3	3
(e)	4×6	3
(f)	7×5	0

40. In each part use the information in the table to determine whether the linear system $A\mathbf{x} = \mathbf{b}$ is consistent and, if so, determine the number of parameters in its general solution.

	size of A	rank(A)	rank $[A|b]$
(a)	3×3	1	3
(b)	3×4	3	3
(c)	3×5	3	5
(d)	5×3	3	3
(e)	6×9	5	5
(f)	2×7	2	3

WRITING QUESTIONS

41. We have defined general vector spaces with the help of a list of ten axioms. Expalin what an "axiom" is. How is this axiomatic approach to mathematics similar to or different from other mathematical work that you have done in the past?

42. Suppose you were attempting to define a cross product for vector spaces other than R^3. What properties of the cross product would you take as axiomatic?

43. Explain why the following statement is wrong: "A subspace is any subset of a vector space."

44. Describe geometrically why a plane in R^3 is a subspace if and only if it passes through the origin.

45. Explain why the word "span" is a good term for the set of linear combinations of a set of vectors.

46. Explain in your own words why every basis for R^3 must consist of three vectors.

47. Summarize what was needed in order for us to define "dimension" for general vector spaces.

48. Suppose you landed on an alien planet where matrix multiplication is defined as we define it, but where linear systems are written $XA = B$ instead of $AX = B$. Try to predict how linear algebra would "look" on this planet, including such questions as: echelon form of a matrix; notation for linear operators and their compositions; significance of row space and column space of a matrix.

SECTION 5.1 *GENERAL VECTOR SPACES*

1. Axiom (1): If (x_1, y_1), (x_2, y_2) are such that $x_1 \geq 0$, $y_1 \geq 0$, $x_2 \geq 0$, $y_2 \geq 0$
then $(x_1, y_1) + (x_2, y_2) = (x_1 + x_2, y_1 + y_2)$ satisfies $x_1 + x_2 \geq 0$, $y_1 + y_2 \geq 0$.

(2): $(x_1, y_1) + (x_2, y_2) = (x_1 + x_2, y_1 + y_2)$
$(x_2, y_2) + (x_1, y_1) = (x_2 + x_1, y_2 + y_1) = (x_1 + x_2, y_1 + y_2)$

$$(3): \quad (x_1, y_1) + ((x_2, y_2) + (x_3, y_3)) = (x_1, y_1) + (x_2 + x_3, y_2 + y_3)$$
$$= (x_1 + x_2 + x_3, y_1 + y_2 + y_3)$$
$$((x_1, y_1) + (x_2, y_2)) + (x_3, y_3) = (x_1 + x_2, y_1 + y_2) + (x_3, y_3)$$
$$= (x_1 + x_2 + x_3, y_1 + y_2 + y_3)$$

(4): There is an object $\mathbf{0} = (0, 0)$ such that $0 \geq 0$, $0 \geq 0$ and
$(x, y) + \mathbf{0} = (x, y) + (0, 0) = (x + 0, y + 0) = (x, y)$
$\mathbf{0} + (x, y) = (0, 0) + (x, y) = (0 + x, 0 + y) = (x, y)$.

(5) fails: The only possible zero vector is $-(x, y) = (-x, -y)$,
but if $x \geq 0$, $y \geq 0$ then $-x \geq 0$, $-y \geq 0$ only if $x = 0, y = 0$.

(6) fails: If (x, y) is such that $x \geq 0$, $y \geq 0$
then $k(x, y) = (kx, ky)$ satisfies $kx \geq 0$, $ky \geq 0$ only if $k \geq 0$.

$$(7): \quad k((x_1, y_1) + (x_2, y_2)) = k(x_1 + x_2, y_1 + y_2))$$
$$= (kx_1 + kx_2, ky_1 + ky_2)$$
$$k(x_1, y_1) + k(x_2, y_2) = (kx_1, ky_1) + (kx_2, ky_2)$$
$$= (kx_1 + kx_2, ky_1 + ky_2)$$

$$(8): \quad (k + l)(x, y) = ((k + l)x, (k + l)y)$$
$$= (kx + lx, ky + ly)$$
$$k(x, y) + l(x, y) = (kx, ky) + (lx, ly)$$
$$= (kx + lx, ky + ly)$$

$$(9): \quad k(l(x, y)) = k(lx, ly)$$
$$= (klx, kly)$$
$$(kl)(x, y) = (klx, kly)$$

(10): $1(x, y) = (1x, 1y) = (x, y)$

Since Axioms (5) and (6) fail, this is not a vector space.

2. Axioms (1) through (5) follow since the objects and the addition operation
are identical with those of R^3.

Axiom (6): If (x, y, z) is such that x, y, and z are real
then $k(x, y, z) = (kx, ky, 2kz)$ satisfies kx, ky and $2kz$ are real for any real k.

$$(7): \quad k((x_1, y_1, z_1) + (x_2, y_2, z_2)) = k(x_1 + y_1, x_2 + y_2, z_1 + z_2))$$
$$= (k(x_1 + y_1), k(x_2 + y_2), 2k(z_1 + z_2))$$
$$= (kx_1 + ky_1, kx_2 + ky_2, 2kz_1 + 2kz_2)$$
$$k(x_1, y_1, z_1) + k(x_2, y_2, z_2) = (kx_1, ky_1, 2kz_1) + (kx_2, ky_2, 2kz_2)$$
$$= (kx_1 + kx_2, ky_1 + ky_2, 2kz_1 + 2kz_2)$$

(8):
$$(k+l)(x,y,z) = ((k+l)x, (k+l)y, 2(k+l)z)$$
$$= (kx + lx, ky + ly, 2kz + 2lz)$$
$$k(x,y,z) + l(x,y,z) = (kx, ky, 2kz) + (lx, ly, 2lz)$$
$$= (kx + lx, ky + ly, 2kz + 2lz)$$

(9) fails:
$$k(l(x,y,z)) = k(lx, ly, 2lz)$$
$$= (klx, kly, 4klz)$$
$$(kl)(x,y,z) = (klx, kly, 2klz)$$
$$\neq (klx, kly, 4klz) \text{ unless } k = 0 \text{ or } l = 0 \text{ or } z = 0.$$

(10) fails:
$$1(x,y,z) = (1x, 1y, 1z)$$
$$= (x, y, 2z)$$
$$\neq (x, y, z) \text{ unless } z = 0.$$

Since Axioms (9) and (10) fail, this is not a vector space.

3. Axiom (1): If x, y are positive reals,
then $x + y = xy$ is positive real.

(2):
$$x + y = xy$$
$$y + x = yx = xy$$

(3):
$$x + (y + z) = x + (yz)$$
$$= x(yz)$$
$$(x + y) + z = (xy) + z$$
$$= (xy)z = x(yz)$$

(4): There is an object $0 = 1$ such that 1 is positive real and
$$x + 0 = x + 1 = x1 = x$$
$$0 + x = 1 + x = 1x = x$$

(5): For each positive real x, there is an object $\frac{1}{x}$ which is positive real and
$$x + \frac{1}{x} = x \cdot \frac{1}{x} = 1 = 0$$
$$\frac{1}{x} + x = \frac{1}{x} \cdot x = 1 = 0$$

(6): If x is positive real and k is real
then $kx = x^k$ is positive real.

(7):
$$k(x + y) = k(xy) = (xy)^k$$
$$kx + ky = x^k + y^k = x^k y^k = (xy)^k$$

(8):
$$(k + l)x = x^{k+l}$$
$$kx + lx = x^k x^l = x^{k+l}$$

(9):
$$k(lx) = k(x^l) = \left(x^l\right)^k$$
$$(kl)(x) = x^{kl} = \left(x^l\right)^k$$

(10): $1x = x^1 = x$

Since Axioms (1)–(10) hold, this is a vector space.

4. Axiom (1): If $\sin c_1 x$, $\sin c_2 x$ are such that c_1, c_2 are real
then $\sin c_1 x + \sin c_2 x = \sin[(c_1 + c_2)x]$ satisfies $c_1 + c_2$ is real.

(2):
$$\sin c_1 x + \sin c_2 x = \sin[(c_1 + c_2)x]$$
$$\sin c_2 x + \sin c_1 x = \sin[(c_2 + c_1)x] = \sin[(c_1 + c_2)x]$$

(3): $\sin c_1 x + (\sin c_2 x + \sin c_3 x)$ $=$ $\sin c_1 x + \sin[(c_2 + c_3)x]$
$=$ $\sin[(c_1 + c_2 + c_3)x]$
$(\sin c_1 x + \sin c_2 x) + \sin c_3 x$ $=$ $\sin[(c_1 + c_2)x] + \sin c_3 x$
$=$ $\sin[(c_1 + c_2 + c_3)x]$

(4): There is an object $\mathbf{0} = 0 = \sin 0x$ such that
$\sin cx + \mathbf{0} = \sin cx + \sin 0x = \sin[(c + 0)x] = \sin cx$
$\mathbf{0} + x = \sin 0x + \sin cx = \sin[(0 + c)x] = \sin cx$

(5): For each $\sin cx$, there is an object $-\sin cx = \sin(-cx)$ such that
$\sin cx + \sin(-cx) = \sin[(c + -c)x] = \sin 0x = \mathbf{0}$
$\sin(-cx) + \sin cx = \sin[(-c + c)x] = \sin 0x = \mathbf{0}$

(6): If $\sin cx$ is such that c is real and if k is real
then $k \sin cx = \sin(kcx)$ satisfies that kc is real.

(7): $k(\sin c_1 x + \sin c_2 x)$ $=$ $k(\sin[(c_1 + c_2)x])$
$=$ $\sin[k(c_1 + c_2)x]$
$k \sin c_1 x + k \sin c_2 x$ $=$ $\sin(kc_1 x) + \sin(kc_2 x)$
$=$ $\sin[(kc_1 + kc_2)x]$
$=$ $\sin[k(c_1 + c_2)x]$

(8): $(k + l) \sin cx$ $=$ $\sin[(k + l)cx]$
$k \sin cx + l \sin cx$ $=$ $\sin(kcx) + \sin(lcx)$
$=$ $\sin[(kc + lc)x]$
$=$ $\sin[(k + l)cx]$

(9): $k(l \sin cx)$ $=$ $k(\sin(lcx))$
$=$ $\sin(klcx)$
$(kl) \sin cx$ $=$ $\sin(klcx)$

(10): $1 \sin cx$ $=$ $sin(1cx)$
$=$ $\sin cx$

Since Axioms (1)–(10) hold, this is a vector space.

SECTION 5.2 *SUBSPACES*

5. closure under addition: (a, b, c) such that $c = a - 2b$
$+ (d, e, f)$ such that $f = d - 2e$
$= (a + d, b + e, c + f)$ such that $c + f$ $=$ $(a - 2b) + (d - 2e)$
$=$ $(a + d) + (-2b - 2e)$
$=$ $(a + d) - 2(b + e)$

closure under multiplication: k such that k is real
$\cdot (a, b, c)$ such that $c = a - 2b$
$= (ka, kb, kc)$ such that kc $=$ $k(a - 2b)$
$=$ $(a + d) + (-2b - 2e)$
$=$ $ka - k(2b)$
$=$ $ka - 2(kb)$

Since both closures hold, the set is a subspace.

6. closure under addition: M_1 such that each row, column and diagonal totals c_1
$+ M_2$ such that each row, column and diagonal totals c_2
$= M_1 + M_2$ such that each row, column and diagonal totals $c_1 + c_2$

73

closure under multiplication: k such that k is real

· M such that each row, column and diagonal totals c

= kM such that each row, column and diagonal totals kc

Since both closures hold, the set is a subspace.

7. closure under addition: (a, b, c) such that $a^2 + b^2 = c^2$

$+ (d, e, f)$ such that $d^2 + e^2 = f^2$

$= (a + d, b + e, c + f)$ such that

$$
\begin{aligned}
(a+d)^2 + (b+e)^2 &= (a^2 + 2ad + d^2) + (b^2 + 2be + e) \\
&= (a^2 + d^2 + b^2 + e^2) + (2ad + 2b \\
&= (c^2 + f^2) + (2ad + 2be) \\
&\neq (c + f)^2 \text{ in general}
\end{aligned}
$$

For example, $(3, 4, 5) + (5, 12, 13) = (8, 16, 18)$
but $8^2 + 16^2 = 320 \neq 18^2$

Since closure under addition fails, the set is not a subspace.

closure under multiplication: k such that k is real

· (a, b, c) such that $a^2 + b^2 = c^2$

$= (ka, kb, kc)$ such that

$$
\begin{aligned}
(ka)^2 + (kb)^2 &= k^2 a^2 + k^2 b^2 \\
&= k^2 (a^2 + b^2) \\
&= k^2 c^2 \\
&= (kc)^2
\end{aligned}
$$

8. closure under addition: $(a_0 + a_1 x + a_2 x^2)$ such that a_0, a_1, a_2 are integers

$+ (b_0 + b_1 x + b_2 x^2)$ such that b_0, b_1, b_2 are integers

$= (a_0 + a_1 x + a_2 x^2) + (b_0 + b_1 x + b_2 x^2)$

$= (a_0 + b_0) + (a_1 x + b_1 x) + (a_2 x^2 + b_2 x^2)$

$= (a_0 + b_0) + (a_1 + b_1)x + (a_2 + b_2)x^2$ such that
$(a_0 + b_0), (a_1 + b_1), (a_2 + b_2)$ are integers

closure under multiplication: k such that k is real

· $(a_0 + a_1 x + a_2 x^2)$ such that a_0, a_1, a_2 are integers

$= k(a_0 + a_1 x + a_2 x^2)$

$= ka_0 + ka_1 x + ka_2 x^2$ such that ka_0, ka_1, ka_2 are not integers in general
For example, $\frac{1}{2}(1 + x + x^2) = \frac{1}{2} + \frac{1}{2}x + \frac{1}{2}x^2$.

Since closure under multiplication fails, the set is not a subspace.

9. (a) $\begin{bmatrix} 2 & -8 & 6 & 0 \\ -3 & 12 & -9 & 0 \\ 7 & -28 & 21 & 0 \end{bmatrix} \rightarrow \begin{bmatrix} 1 & -4 & 3 & 0 \\ 0 & 0 & 0 & 0 \\ 0 & 0 & 0 & 0 \end{bmatrix}$ so $x - 4y + 3z = 0$ (plane).

(b) $\begin{bmatrix} 2 & 6 & 8 & 0 \\ 3 & 3 & 15 & 0 \\ 2 & 4 & 12 & 0 \end{bmatrix} \rightarrow \begin{bmatrix} 1 & 3 & 4 & 0 \\ 0 & -6 & 3 & 0 \\ 0 & -2 & 4 & 0 \end{bmatrix} \rightarrow \begin{bmatrix} 1 & 3 & 4 & 0 \\ 0 & 1 & -\frac{1}{2} & 0 \\ 0 & 0 & 3 & 0 \end{bmatrix} \rightarrow \begin{bmatrix} 1 & 3 & 4 & 0 \\ 0 & 1 & -\frac{1}{2} & 0 \\ 0 & 0 & 1 & 0 \end{bmatrix}$ so $x = 0, y = 0, z = 0$ (origin).

(c) $\begin{bmatrix} 1 & 6 & 2 & 0 \\ 3 & 3 & -1 & 0 \\ -1 & 9 & 5 & 0 \end{bmatrix} \rightarrow \begin{bmatrix} 1 & 6 & 2 & 0 \\ 0 & -15 & -7 & 0 \\ 0 & 15 & 7 & 0 \end{bmatrix} \rightarrow \begin{bmatrix} 1 & 0 & -4/5 & 0 \\ 0 & 1 & 7/15 & 0 \\ 0 & 0 & 0 & 0 \end{bmatrix}$ so $z = t, y = \frac{-7}{15}t, x = \frac{4}{5}t$ (line).

10. (a) The equation $c_1(1, 2, 8) + c_2(3, 0, 1) = (-1, 4, 15)$

is equivalent to $\begin{bmatrix} 1 & 3 \\ 2 & 0 \\ 8 & 1 \end{bmatrix} \begin{bmatrix} c_1 \\ c_2 \end{bmatrix} = \begin{bmatrix} -1 \\ 4 \\ 15 \end{bmatrix}$.

$\begin{bmatrix} 1 & 3 & -1 \\ 2 & 0 & 4 \\ 8 & 1 & 15 \end{bmatrix} \rightarrow \begin{bmatrix} 1 & 3 & -1 \\ 0 & -6 & 6 \\ 0 & -23 & 23 \end{bmatrix} \rightarrow \begin{bmatrix} 1 & 0 & 2 \\ 0 & 1 & -1 \\ 0 & 0 & 0 \end{bmatrix}$ so $c_1 = 2, c_2 = -1$.

74

(b) The equation $c_1(1, 2, 3) + c_2(3, 1, 2) + c_3(4, 1, 0) = (4, 5, 10)$

is equivalent to $\begin{bmatrix} 1 & 3 & 4 \\ 2 & 1 & 1 \\ 3 & 2 & 0 \end{bmatrix} \begin{bmatrix} c_1 \\ c_2 \\ c_3 \end{bmatrix} = \begin{bmatrix} 4 \\ 5 \\ 10 \end{bmatrix}.$

$$\begin{bmatrix} 1 & 3 & 4 & 4 \\ 2 & 1 & 1 & 5 \\ 3 & 2 & 0 & 10 \end{bmatrix} \rightarrow \begin{bmatrix} 1 & 3 & 4 & 4 \\ 0 & -5 & -7 & -3 \\ 0 & -7 & -12 & -2 \end{bmatrix} \rightarrow \begin{bmatrix} 1 & 3 & 4 & 4 \\ 0 & 1 & 7/5 & 3/5 \\ 0 & 0 & -11/5 & 11/5 \end{bmatrix} \rightarrow \begin{bmatrix} 1 & 3 & 4 & 4 \\ 0 & 1 & 7/5 & 3/5 \\ 0 & 0 & 1 & -1 \end{bmatrix}$$

$$\rightarrow \begin{bmatrix} 1 & 0 & -1/5 & 11/5 \\ 0 & 1 & 7/5 & 3/5 \\ 0 & 0 & 1 & -1 \end{bmatrix} \rightarrow \begin{bmatrix} 1 & 0 & 0 & 2 \\ 0 & 1 & 0 & 2 \\ 0 & 0 & 1 & -1 \end{bmatrix}$$ so $c_1 = 2, c_2 = 2, c_3 = -1$.

(c) The equation $c_1(1 - x) + c_2(2 + x + 3x^2) = 1 + x^2$

is equivalent to $\begin{bmatrix} 1 & 2 \\ -1 & 1 \\ 0 & 3 \end{bmatrix} \begin{bmatrix} c_1 \\ c_2 \end{bmatrix} = \begin{bmatrix} 1 \\ 0 \\ 1 \end{bmatrix}.$

$$\begin{bmatrix} 1 & 2 & 1 \\ -1 & 1 & 0 \\ 0 & 3 & 1 \end{bmatrix} \rightarrow \begin{bmatrix} 1 & 2 & 1 \\ 0 & 3 & 1 \\ 0 & 3 & 1 \end{bmatrix} \rightarrow \begin{bmatrix} 1 & 0 & 1/3 \\ 0 & 1 & 1/3 \\ 0 & 0 & 0 \end{bmatrix}$$ so $c_1 = 1/3, c_2 = 1/3$.

(d) The equation $c_1(1 + x + x^2) + c_2(-2 + 2x + 3x^2) + c_3(1 + 5x + 6x^2) = 4x + 6x^2$
is equivalent to

$$\begin{bmatrix} 1 & -2 & 1 \\ 1 & 2 & 5 \\ 1 & 3 & 6 \end{bmatrix} \begin{bmatrix} c_1 \\ c_2 \\ c_3 \end{bmatrix} = \begin{bmatrix} 0 \\ 4 \\ 6 \end{bmatrix}.$$

$$\begin{bmatrix} 1 & -2 & 1 & 0 \\ 1 & 2 & 5 & 4 \\ 1 & 3 & 6 & 6 \end{bmatrix} \rightarrow \begin{bmatrix} 1 & -2 & 1 & 0 \\ 0 & 4 & 4 & 4 \\ 0 & 5 & 5 & 6 \end{bmatrix} \rightarrow \begin{bmatrix} 1 & -2 & 1 & 0 \\ 0 & 1 & 1 & 1 \\ 0 & 0 & 0 & 1 \end{bmatrix}$$ is inconsistent,

so **w** is not in the span.

(e) The equation $c_1 \begin{bmatrix} 1 & 2 \\ -1 & 0 \end{bmatrix} + c_2 \begin{bmatrix} 3 & 1 \\ 1 & 1 \end{bmatrix} = \begin{bmatrix} 0 & 5 \\ -4 & -1 \end{bmatrix}$

is equivalent to $\begin{bmatrix} 1 & 3 \\ 2 & 1 \\ -1 & 1 \\ 0 & 1 \end{bmatrix} \begin{bmatrix} c_1 \\ c_2 \end{bmatrix} = \begin{bmatrix} 0 \\ 5 \\ -4 \\ -1 \end{bmatrix}.$

$$\begin{bmatrix} 1 & 3 & 0 \\ 2 & 1 & 5 \\ -1 & 1 & -4 \\ 0 & 1 & -1 \end{bmatrix} \rightarrow \begin{bmatrix} 1 & 3 & 0 \\ 0 & -5 & 5 \\ 0 & 4 & -4 \\ 0 & 1 & -1 \end{bmatrix} \rightarrow \begin{bmatrix} 1 & 0 & 3 \\ 0 & 1 & -1 \\ 0 & 0 & 0 \\ 0 & 0 & 0 \end{bmatrix}$$ so $c_1 = 3, c_2 = -1$.

(f) The equation $c_1 \begin{bmatrix} 2 & 4 \\ 0 & 2 \end{bmatrix} + c_2 \begin{bmatrix} 3 & 1 \\ 3 & 2 \end{bmatrix} + c_3 \begin{bmatrix} 0 & 10 \\ -6 & 2 \end{bmatrix} = \begin{bmatrix} 7 & 19 \\ -3 & 8 \end{bmatrix}$

is equivalent to $\begin{bmatrix} 2 & 3 & 0 \\ 4 & 1 & 10 \\ 0 & 3 & -6 \\ 2 & 2 & 2 \end{bmatrix} \begin{bmatrix} c_1 \\ c_2 \\ c_3 \end{bmatrix} = \begin{bmatrix} 7 \\ 19 \\ -3 \\ 8 \end{bmatrix}.$

$$\begin{bmatrix} 2 & 3 & 0 & 7 \\ 4 & 1 & 10 & 19 \\ 0 & 3 & -6 & -3 \\ 2 & 2 & 2 & 8 \end{bmatrix} \rightarrow \begin{bmatrix} 2 & 2 & 2 & 8 \\ 2 & 3 & 0 & 7 \\ 4 & 1 & 10 & 19 \\ 0 & 3 & -6 & -3 \end{bmatrix} \rightarrow \begin{bmatrix} 1 & 1 & 1 & 4 \\ 0 & 1 & -2 & -1 \\ 0 & -3 & 6 & 3 \\ 0 & 3 & -6 & -3 \end{bmatrix} \rightarrow \begin{bmatrix} 1 & 0 & 3 & 5 \\ 0 & 1 & 2 & -1 \\ 0 & 0 & 0 & 0 \\ 0 & 0 & 0 & 0 \end{bmatrix}$$

so there are infinitely many solutions, all of the form

$$\begin{aligned} c_1 &= 5 - 3t \\ c_2 &= -1 - 2t \\ c_3 &= t \end{aligned}$$

For example, $c_1 = 5, c_2 = -1, c_3 = 0$.

11. (a) The equation $c_1(1,3,4) + c_2(2,0,1) + c_3(2,1,0) = (b_1, b_2, b_3)$

is equivalent to $\begin{bmatrix} 1 & 2 & 2 \\ 3 & 0 & 1 \\ 4 & 1 & 0 \end{bmatrix} \begin{bmatrix} c_1 \\ c_2 \\ c_3 \end{bmatrix} = \begin{bmatrix} b_1 \\ b_2 \\ b_3 \end{bmatrix}$

and since $\begin{vmatrix} 1 & 2 & 2 \\ 3 & 0 & 1 \\ 4 & 1 & 0 \end{vmatrix} = 3(2) + 1(7) = 13 \neq 0$, this is consistent for all b_1, b_2, b_3.

Thus, the set spans R^3.

(b) The equation $c_1(2,0,2) + c_2(3,1,1) + c_3(-3,5,5) = (b_1, b_2, b_3)$

is equivalent to $\begin{bmatrix} 2 & 3 & -3 \\ 0 & 1 & 5 \\ 2 & 1 & 5 \end{bmatrix} \begin{bmatrix} c_1 \\ c_2 \\ c_3 \end{bmatrix} = \begin{bmatrix} b_1 \\ b_2 \\ b_3 \end{bmatrix}$

and since $\begin{vmatrix} 2 & 3 & -3 \\ 0 & 1 & 5 \\ 2 & 1 & 5 \end{vmatrix} = 2(0) + 2(18) = 36 \neq 0$, this is consistent for all b_1, b_2, b_3.

Thus, the set spans R^3.

(c) The equation $c_1(1,5,1) + c_2(2,6,1) + c_3(3,3,0) + c_4(4,6,2) = (b_1, b_2, b_3)$

is equivalent to $\begin{bmatrix} 1 & 2 & 3 & 4 \\ 5 & 6 & 3 & 6 \\ 1 & 1 & 0 & 2 \end{bmatrix} \begin{bmatrix} c_1 \\ c_2 \\ c_3 \end{bmatrix} = \begin{bmatrix} b_1 \\ b_2 \\ b_3 \end{bmatrix}$

$$\begin{bmatrix} 1 & 2 & 3 & 4 \\ 5 & 6 & 3 & 6 \\ 1 & 1 & 0 & 2 \end{bmatrix} \rightarrow \begin{bmatrix} 1 & 2 & 3 & 4 \\ 0 & -4 & -12 & -14 \\ 0 & -1 & -3 & -2 \end{bmatrix} \rightarrow \begin{bmatrix} 1 & 2 & 3 & 4 \\ 0 & 1 & 3 & 7/2 \\ 0 & 0 & 0 & 3/2 \end{bmatrix} \rightarrow \begin{bmatrix} 1 & 2 & 3 & 4 \\ 0 & 1 & 3 & 7/2 \\ 0 & 0 & 0 & 1 \end{bmatrix}$$

and since no rows are all zeroes, the equation is consistent for all b_1, b_2, b_3.

Thus, the set spans R^3.

12. (a) The equation $c_1(2 + 5x + 6x^2) + c_2(1 + x^2) + c_3(1 - x^2) = b_0 + b_1x + b_2x^2$

is equivalent to $\begin{bmatrix} 2 & 1 & 1 \\ 5 & 0 & 0 \\ 6 & 1 & -1 \end{bmatrix} \begin{bmatrix} c_1 \\ c_2 \\ c_3 \end{bmatrix} = \begin{bmatrix} b_0 \\ b_1 \\ b_2 \end{bmatrix}$

and since $\begin{vmatrix} 2 & 1 & 1 \\ 5 & 0 & 0 \\ 6 & 1 & -1 \end{vmatrix} = 5(2) = 10 \neq 0$, this is consistent for all b_0, b_1, b_2.

Thus, the set spans P_2.

(b) The equation $c_1(7 - x + x^2) + c_2(1 + x + x^2) + c_3(2 + 3x + 5x^2) = b_0 + b_1x + b_2x^2$

is equivalent to $\begin{bmatrix} 7 & 1 & 2 \\ -1 & 1 & 3 \\ 1 & 1 & 5 \end{bmatrix} \begin{bmatrix} c_1 \\ c_2 \\ c_3 \end{bmatrix} = \begin{bmatrix} b_0 \\ b_1 \\ b_2 \end{bmatrix}$

and since $\begin{vmatrix} 7 & 1 & 2 \\ -1 & 1 & 3 \\ 1 & 1 & 5 \end{vmatrix} = 7(2) + 1(8) + 2(-2) = 18 \neq 0$, this is consistent for all b_0, b_1, b_2.

Thus, the set spans P_2.

(c) The equation $c_1(1 + 4x - x^2) + c_2(2 + 5x + 3x^2) + c_3(3x - 5x^2) + c_4(3 + 15x - 8x^2) = b_0 + b_1 x + b_2 x^2$

is equivalent to $\begin{bmatrix} 1 & 2 & 0 & 3 \\ 4 & 5 & 3 & 15 \\ -1 & 3 & -5 & -8 \end{bmatrix} \begin{bmatrix} c_1 \\ c_2 \\ c_3 \end{bmatrix} = \begin{bmatrix} b_0 \\ b_1 \\ b_2 \end{bmatrix}$

$$\begin{bmatrix} 1 & 2 & 0 & 3 \\ 4 & 5 & 3 & 15 \\ -1 & 3 & -5 & -8 \end{bmatrix} \to \begin{bmatrix} 1 & 2 & 0 & 3 \\ 0 & -3 & 3 & 3 \\ 0 & 5 & -5 & -5 \end{bmatrix} \to \begin{bmatrix} 1 & 2 & 0 & 3 \\ 0 & 1 & -1 & -1 \\ 0 & 0 & 0 & 0 \end{bmatrix}$$

and since a row is all zeroes, the equation is not consistent for all b_0, b_1, b_2.

Thus, the set does not span P_2.

SECTION 5.3 LINEAR INDEPENDENCE

13. (a) By inspection, the first vector is a scalar multiple of the second, so the set is dependent.

(b) The equation $c_1(1, -4, 2) + c_2(2, 0, 1) + c_3(3, 2, 2) = (0, 0, 0)$

is equivalent to $\begin{bmatrix} 1 & 2 & 3 \\ -4 & 0 & 2 \\ 2 & 1 & 2 \end{bmatrix} \begin{bmatrix} c_1 \\ c_2 \\ c_3 \end{bmatrix} = \begin{bmatrix} 0 \\ 0 \\ 0 \end{bmatrix}$

and since $\begin{vmatrix} 1 & 2 & 3 \\ -4 & 0 & 2 \\ 2 & 1 & 2 \end{vmatrix} = -4(-1) + 2(3) = 10 \neq 0$, the only solution is $c_1 = c_2 = c_3 = 0$.

Thus, the set is independent.

(c) Every set of 4 3-tuples is dependent.

Indeed, the equation $c_1(1, 1, 1) + c_2(1, 1, 0) + c_3(1, 0, 0) + c_4(1, 0, 1) = (0, 0, 0)$

is equivalent to $\begin{bmatrix} 1 & 1 & 1 & 1 \\ 1 & 1 & 0 & 0 \\ 1 & 0 & 0 & 1 \end{bmatrix} \begin{bmatrix} c_1 \\ c_2 \\ c_3 \end{bmatrix} = \begin{bmatrix} 0 \\ 0 \\ 0 \end{bmatrix}$

$$\begin{bmatrix} 1 & 1 & 1 & 1 & 0 \\ 1 & 1 & 0 & 0 & 0 \\ 1 & 0 & 0 & 1 & 0 \end{bmatrix} \to \begin{bmatrix} 1 & 1 & 1 & 1 & 0 \\ 0 & 0 & -1 & -1 & 0 \\ 0 & -1 & -1 & 0 & 0 \end{bmatrix} \to \begin{bmatrix} 1 & 1 & 1 & 1 & 0 \\ 0 & -1 & -1 & 0 & 0 \\ 0 & 0 & -1 & -1 & 0 \end{bmatrix} \to$$

$$\begin{bmatrix} 1 & 1 & 1 & 1 & 0 \\ 0 & 1 & 1 & 0 & 0 \\ 0 & 0 & 1 & 1 & 0 \end{bmatrix}$$ has infinitely many solutions. Thus, the set is dependent.

14. (a) The equation $c_1(1, 2, -4, -3) + c_2(1, 1, 0, 1) + c_3(2, 1, 1, 3) = (0, 0, 0, 0)$

is equivalent to $\begin{bmatrix} 1 & 1 & 2 \\ 2 & 1 & 1 \\ 4 & 0 & 1 \\ -3 & 1 & 3 \end{bmatrix} \begin{bmatrix} c_1 \\ c_2 \\ c_3 \end{bmatrix} = \begin{bmatrix} 0 \\ 0 \\ 0 \\ 0 \end{bmatrix}$

$$\begin{bmatrix} 1 & 1 & 2 & 0 \\ 2 & 1 & 1 & 0 \\ 4 & 0 & 1 & 0 \\ -3 & 1 & 3 & 0 \end{bmatrix} \rightarrow \begin{bmatrix} 1 & 1 & 2 & 0 \\ 0 & -1 & -3 & 0 \\ 0 & -4 & -7 & 0 \\ 0 & 4 & 9 & 0 \end{bmatrix} \rightarrow \begin{bmatrix} 1 & 1 & 2 & 0 \\ 0 & 1 & 3 & 0 \\ 0 & 0 & 5 & 0 \\ 0 & 0 & -3 & 0 \end{bmatrix} \rightarrow \begin{bmatrix} 1 & 1 & 2 & 0 \\ 0 & 1 & 3 & 0 \\ 0 & 0 & 1 & 0 \\ 0 & 0 & 0 & 0 \end{bmatrix}$$

has only the solution $c_1 = c_2 = c_3 = 0$. Thus, the set is independent.

(b) The equation $c_1(3,2,2,2) + c_2(12,5,2,2) + c_3(6,2,5,2) + c_4(3,2,2,5) = (0,0,0,0)$

is equivalent to
$$\begin{bmatrix} 3 & 12 & 6 & 3 \\ 2 & 5 & 2 & 2 \\ 2 & 2 & 5 & 2 \\ 2 & 2 & 2 & 5 \end{bmatrix} \begin{bmatrix} c_1 \\ c_2 \\ c_3 \\ c_4 \end{bmatrix} = \begin{bmatrix} 0 \\ 0 \\ 0 \\ 0 \end{bmatrix}$$

$$\begin{bmatrix} 3 & 12 & 6 & 3 & 0 \\ 2 & 5 & 2 & 2 & 0 \\ 2 & 2 & 5 & 2 & 0 \\ 2 & 2 & 2 & 5 & 0 \end{bmatrix} \rightarrow \begin{bmatrix} 1 & 4 & 2 & 1 & 0 \\ 0 & -3 & -2 & 0 & 0 \\ 0 & -6 & 1 & 0 & 0 \\ 0 & -6 & -2 & 3 & 0 \end{bmatrix} \rightarrow$$

$$\begin{bmatrix} 1 & 4 & 2 & 1 & 0 \\ 0 & 1 & 2/3 & 0 & 0 \\ 0 & 0 & 5 & 0 & 0 \\ 0 & 0 & 2 & 3 & 0 \end{bmatrix} \rightarrow \begin{bmatrix} 1 & 4 & 2 & 1 & 0 \\ 0 & 1 & 2/3 & 0 & 0 \\ 0 & 0 & 1 & 0 & 0 \\ 0 & 0 & 0 & 3 & 0 \end{bmatrix} \rightarrow \begin{bmatrix} 1 & 4 & 2 & 1 & 0 \\ 0 & 1 & 2/3 & 0 & 0 \\ 0 & 0 & 1 & 0 & 0 \\ 0 & 0 & 0 & 1 & 0 \end{bmatrix}$$

has only the solution $c_1 = c_2 = c_3 = c_4 = 0$. Thus, the set is independent.

(Alternatively, det $A = -135 \neq 0$, so the set is independent).

(c) The equation $c_1(1,a,0,0) + c_2(0,1,a,0) + c_3(0,0,1,a) + c_4(0,0,0,1) = (0,0,0,0)$

is equivalent to
$$\begin{bmatrix} 1 & 0 & 0 & 0 \\ a & 1 & 0 & 0 \\ 0 & a & 1 & 0 \\ 0 & 0 & a & 1 \end{bmatrix} \begin{bmatrix} c_1 \\ c_2 \\ c_3 \\ c_4 \end{bmatrix} = \begin{bmatrix} 0 \\ 0 \\ 0 \\ 0 \end{bmatrix}$$

$$\begin{bmatrix} 1 & 0 & 0 & 0 & 0 \\ a & 1 & 0 & 0 & 0 \\ 0 & a & 1 & 0 & 0 \\ 0 & 0 & a & 1 & 0 \end{bmatrix} \rightarrow \begin{bmatrix} 1 & 0 & 0 & 0 & 0 \\ 0 & 1 & 0 & 0 & 0 \\ 0 & a & 1 & 0 & 0 \\ 0 & 0 & a & 1 & 0 \end{bmatrix} \rightarrow \begin{bmatrix} 1 & 0 & 0 & 0 & 0 \\ 0 & 1 & 0 & 0 & 0 \\ 0 & 0 & 1 & 0 & 0 \\ 0 & 0 & a & 1 & 0 \end{bmatrix} \rightarrow \begin{bmatrix} 1 & 0 & 0 & 0 & 0 \\ 0 & 1 & 0 & 0 & 0 \\ 0 & 0 & 1 & 0 & 0 \\ 0 & 0 & 0 & 1 & 0 \end{bmatrix}$$

has only the solution $c_1 = c_2 = c_3 = c_4 = 0$. Thus, the set is independent for all a.
(Alternatively, det $A = 1 \neq 0$, so the set is independent).

15. (a) By inspection the two vectors are not scalar multiples of one another, so the set is independent.

(b) The equation $c_1(1 + 5x + 6x^2) + c_2(3 + x + x^2) + c_3(5x - 7x^2) = 0$

is equivalent to
$$\begin{bmatrix} 1 & 3 & 0 \\ 5 & 1 & 5 \\ 6 & 1 & -7 \end{bmatrix} \begin{bmatrix} c_1 \\ c_2 \\ c_3 \end{bmatrix} = \begin{bmatrix} 0 \\ 0 \\ 0 \end{bmatrix}$$

and since $\begin{vmatrix} 1 & 3 & 0 \\ 5 & 1 & 5 \\ 6 & 1 & -7 \end{vmatrix} = 1(-12) + 3(65) = 183 \neq 0$, the only solution is $c_1 = c_2 = c_3 = 0$.

Thus, the set is independent.

(c) The equation $c_1(\pi + x + 2x^2) + c_2(\pi + 3x) + c_3(\pi) = 0$

is equivalent to
$$\begin{bmatrix} \pi & \pi & \pi \\ 1 & 3 & 0 \\ 2 & 0 & 0 \end{bmatrix} \begin{bmatrix} c_1 \\ c_2 \\ c_3 \end{bmatrix} = \begin{bmatrix} 0 \\ 0 \\ 0 \end{bmatrix}$$

and since $\begin{vmatrix} \pi & \pi & \pi \\ 1 & 3 & 0 \\ 2 & 0 & 0 \end{vmatrix} = -2 \cdot 3 \cdot \pi = -6\pi \neq 0$, the only solution is $c_1 = c_2 = c_3 = 0$.

Thus, the set is independent.

16. (a) $\begin{vmatrix} 5 & 2 & 0 \\ -1 & 4 & 1 \\ 6 & 1 & 1 \end{vmatrix} = 5(3) + 2(7) = 29 \neq 0$, so the vectors are independent, hence noncoplanar.

(b) $\begin{vmatrix} 1 & 2 & 1 \\ 1 & 0 & -3 \\ 3 & 5 & 1 \end{vmatrix} = 1(3) + -3(1) = 0$, so the vectors are dependent, hence coplanar.

(c) $\begin{vmatrix} 2 & 0 & 6 \\ 5 & 2 & 6 \\ 7 & 0 & 1 \end{vmatrix} = 2(-40) = -80 \neq 0$, so the vectors are independent, hence noncoplanar.

17. (a) $\begin{bmatrix} 1 & -7 & 4 \\ 2 & -14 & 8 \\ -3 & 21 & -12 \end{bmatrix} \rightarrow \begin{bmatrix} 1 & -7 & 4 \\ 0 & 0 & 0 \\ 0 & 0 & 0 \end{bmatrix}$, so the vectors are scalar multiples, hence collinear.

(b) $\begin{bmatrix} 1 & 6 & 5 \\ 2 & 12 & 11 \\ 3 & 18 & 15 \end{bmatrix} \rightarrow \begin{bmatrix} 1 & 6 & 5 \\ 0 & 0 & 1 \\ 0 & 0 & 0 \end{bmatrix}$, so the vectors are not all scalar multiples, hence noncollinear.

(c) $\begin{bmatrix} 2/3 & 1/3 & -5/3 \\ -2/5 & -1/5 & 1 \\ 1/2 & 1/4 & -5/4 \end{bmatrix} \rightarrow \begin{bmatrix} 1 & 1/2 & -5/2 \\ 0 & 0 & 0 \\ 0 & 0 & 0 \end{bmatrix}$, so the vectors are scalar multiples, hence collinear.

18. (a) $W(x) = \begin{vmatrix} x & x^2 & x^3 \\ 1 & 2x & 3x^2 \\ 0 & 2 & 6x \end{vmatrix} = x(6x^2) + 1(-4x^3) = 2x^3$, so independent.

(b) $W(x) = \begin{vmatrix} x & e^x & xe^x \\ 1 & e^x & (x+1)e^x \\ 0 & e^x & (x+2)e^x \end{vmatrix} = x(e^{2x}) + 1(-2e^{2x}) = (x-2)e^{2x}$, so independent.

(c) $W(x) = \begin{vmatrix} \sin x & \cos x & \sin 2x \\ \cos x & -\sin x & 2\cos 2x \\ -\sin x & -\cos x & -4\sin 2x \end{vmatrix}$

$= (\sin 2x)(-\cos^2 x - \sin^2 x) + (2\cos 2x)(0) + (-4\sin 2x)(-\sin^2 x - \cos^2 x)$

$= -\sin 2x + 4\sin 2x$

$= 3\sin 2x$, so independent.

SECTION 5.4 BASIS AND DIMENSION

19. (a) $\begin{vmatrix} 1 & 0 \\ 3 & -2 \end{vmatrix} = -2 - 0 = -2 \neq 0$, so it's a basis.

(b) $\begin{vmatrix} 7 & 6 \\ 1 & 1 \end{vmatrix} = 7 - 6 = 1 \neq 0$, so it's a basis.

(c) $\begin{vmatrix} 10 & -8 \\ -15 & 12 \end{vmatrix} = 120 - 120 = 0$, so it's not a basis.

(d) $\begin{vmatrix} 3/5 & -4/5 \\ 4/5 & 3/5 \end{vmatrix} = 9/25 - (-16/25) = 1 \neq 0$, so it's a basis.

20. (a) $\begin{vmatrix} 1 & 2 & 3 \\ 1 & 2 & 0 \\ 1 & 0 & 0 \end{vmatrix} = 3(-2) = -6 \neq 0$, so it's a basis.

(b) $\begin{vmatrix} 0 & 1 & 2 \\ 17 & 7 & -3 \\ 8 & 5 & 2 \end{vmatrix} = 1(-58) + 2(29) = 0$, so it's not a basis.

(c) $\begin{vmatrix} 2 & 1 & 0 \\ 5 & -1 & 1 \\ 2 & 3 & 1 \end{vmatrix} = 2(-4) + 1(-3) = -11 \neq 0$, so it's a basis.

(d) $\begin{vmatrix} \sqrt{2} & \sqrt{3} & 0 \\ 0 & 0 & -\sqrt{6} \\ \sqrt{2} & \sqrt{6} & \sqrt{3} \end{vmatrix} = -\sqrt{6}(\sqrt{6} - \sqrt{12}) \neq 0$, so it's a basis.

21. (a) $\begin{vmatrix} 1 & 1 & 1 \\ 0 & 1 & 1 \\ 0 & 0 & 1 \end{vmatrix} = 1 \neq 0$, so it's a basis.

(b) $\begin{vmatrix} 1 & 1 & 1 \\ -1 & 1 & 0 \\ 0 & 0 & -1 \end{vmatrix} = -1(2) = -2 \neq 0$, so it's a basis.

(c) $\begin{vmatrix} 3 & 1 & 5 \\ 1 & -1 & 1 \\ -2 & -1 & 0 \end{vmatrix} = -2(6) + -1(2) = 14 \neq 0$, so it's a basis.

(d) $\begin{vmatrix} 1 & 1 & 5 \\ 1 & 3 & 3 \\ 1 & 5 & 1 \end{vmatrix} = 1(-12) + 1(24) + 1(-12) = 0$, so it's not a basis.

22. (a) $\begin{vmatrix} 1 & 0 & 2 & 0 \\ 0 & -1 & 2 & 3 \\ 0 & -1 & 2 & 3 \\ 1 & 0 & 0 & 3 \end{vmatrix} = 1(3 \cdot 0) + 1(-2 \cdot 0) = 0$, so it's not a basis.

(b) $\begin{vmatrix} 1 & 1 & 1 & 0 \\ 1 & 1 & 0 & 1 \\ 1 & 0 & 1 & 1 \\ 0 & 1 & 1 & 1 \end{vmatrix} = 1 \cdot (1 \cdot 0 + 1 \cdot -1) + 1 \cdot -(1 \cdot 0 + 1 \cdot 1) + 1 \cdot (1 \cdot -1 + 1 \cdot 0) = -3 \neq 0$, so it's a basis.

(c) $\begin{vmatrix} 1 & 0 & 0 & 0 \\ 7 & 0 & 5 & 1 \\ 0 & 2 & 5 & 4 \\ 0 & -3 & 0 & 4 \end{vmatrix} = 1 \cdot (5 \cdot -20 + 1 \cdot 15) = -85 \neq 0$, so it's a basis.

(d) $\begin{vmatrix} 1/2 & 1/2 & 1/2 & 1/2 \\ 1/2 & -5/6 & 1/6 & 1/6 \\ 1/2 & 1/6 & 1/6 & -5/6 \\ 1/2 & 1/6 & -5/6 & 1/6 \end{vmatrix} = \frac{1}{6^4} \begin{vmatrix} 3 & 3 & 3 & 3 \\ 3 & -5 & 1 & 1 \\ 3 & 1 & 1 & -5 \\ 3 & 1 & -5 & 1 \end{vmatrix} = \frac{3}{6^4} \begin{vmatrix} 1 & 1 & 1 & 1 \\ 0 & -8 & -2 & -2 \\ 0 & -2 & -2 & -8 \\ 0 & -2 & -8 & -2 \end{vmatrix}$

$= \frac{-24}{6^4} \begin{vmatrix} 4 & 1 & 1 \\ 1 & 1 & 4 \\ 1 & 4 & 1 \end{vmatrix}$

$= \frac{-24}{6^4}(4 \cdot -15 + 1 \cdot 3 + 1 \cdot 3)$

$= \frac{-24}{6^4}(-54) \neq 0$, so it's a basis

80

$$= 1$$

23. (a) By inspection $(\mathbf{w})_S = (4, 5)$.

(b) $\begin{bmatrix} 1 & 1 \\ 4 & 5 \end{bmatrix}^{-1} \begin{bmatrix} 7 \\ -3 \end{bmatrix} = \begin{bmatrix} 5 & -1 \\ -4 & 1 \end{bmatrix} \begin{bmatrix} 7 \\ -3 \end{bmatrix} = \begin{bmatrix} 38 \\ -31 \end{bmatrix}$, so $(\mathbf{w})_S = (38, -31)$.

(c) $\begin{bmatrix} 2 & 3 \\ 0 & -1 \end{bmatrix}^{-1} \begin{bmatrix} 6 \\ 5 \end{bmatrix} = \frac{-1}{2} \begin{bmatrix} -1 & -3 \\ 0 & 2 \end{bmatrix} \begin{bmatrix} 6 \\ 5 \end{bmatrix} = \frac{-1}{2} \begin{bmatrix} -21 \\ 10 \end{bmatrix}$, so $(\mathbf{w})_S = \left(\frac{21}{2}, -5 \right)$.

24. (a)
$$\begin{bmatrix} 1 & 1 & 2 \\ 1 & 5 & 2 \\ 1 & -3 & 1 \end{bmatrix}^{-1} \begin{bmatrix} 8 \\ -4 \\ -12 \end{bmatrix} = \frac{1}{-4} \begin{bmatrix} 11 & 1 & -8 \\ -7 & -1 & 4 \\ -8 & 0 & 4 \end{bmatrix}^{T} \begin{bmatrix} 8 \\ -4 \\ -12 \end{bmatrix}$$
$$= \begin{bmatrix} 11 & -7 & -8 \\ 1 & -1 & 0 \\ -8 & 4 & 4 \end{bmatrix} \begin{bmatrix} -2 \\ 1 \\ 3 \end{bmatrix}$$
$$= \begin{bmatrix} -53 \\ -3 \\ 32 \end{bmatrix}, \text{ so } (\mathbf{w})_S = (-53, -3, 32).$$

(b)
$$\begin{bmatrix} 2 & 1 & 0 \\ 0 & 1 & 1 \\ -1 & 0 & 0 \end{bmatrix}^{-1} \begin{bmatrix} 7 \\ 1 \\ -3 \end{bmatrix} = \frac{1}{-1} \begin{bmatrix} 0 & -1 & 1 \\ 0 & 0 & -1 \\ 1 & -2 & 2 \end{bmatrix}^{T} \begin{bmatrix} 7 \\ 1 \\ -3 \end{bmatrix}$$
$$= \begin{bmatrix} 0 & 0 & -1 \\ 1 & 0 & 2 \\ -1 & 1 & -2 \end{bmatrix} \begin{bmatrix} 7 \\ 1 \\ -3 \end{bmatrix}$$
$$= \begin{bmatrix} 3 \\ 1 \\ 0 \end{bmatrix}, \text{ so } (\mathbf{w})_S = (3, 1, 0).$$

(c)
$$\begin{bmatrix} 3 & -1 & 1 \\ 4 & 1 & 1 \\ 5 & 8 & 0 \end{bmatrix}^{-1} \begin{bmatrix} 1 \\ 1 \\ 1 \end{bmatrix} = \frac{1}{-2} \begin{bmatrix} -8 & 5 & 27 \\ 8 & -5 & -29 \\ -2 & 1 & 7 \end{bmatrix}^{T} \begin{bmatrix} 1 \\ 1 \\ 1 \end{bmatrix}$$
$$= \frac{1}{-2} \begin{bmatrix} -8 & 8 & -2 \\ 5 & -5 & 1 \\ 27 & -29 & 7 \end{bmatrix} \begin{bmatrix} 1 \\ 1 \\ 1 \end{bmatrix}$$
$$= \frac{1}{-2} \begin{bmatrix} -2 \\ 1 \\ 5 \end{bmatrix}$$
$$= \begin{bmatrix} 1 \\ -1/2 \\ -5/2 \end{bmatrix}, \text{ so } (\mathbf{w})_S = (1, -1/2, -5/2).$$

25. (a)
$$\begin{bmatrix} 1 & 0 & 0 \\ -1 & 1 & 0 \\ 0 & -1 & 1 \end{bmatrix}^{-1} \begin{bmatrix} 6 \\ 2 \\ 3 \end{bmatrix} = \frac{1}{1} \begin{bmatrix} 1 & 1 & 1 \\ 0 & 1 & 1 \\ 0 & 0 & 1 \end{bmatrix}^{T} \begin{bmatrix} 6 \\ 2 \\ 3 \end{bmatrix}$$
$$= \begin{bmatrix} 1 & 0 & 0 \\ 1 & 1 & 0 \\ 1 & 1 & 1 \end{bmatrix} \begin{bmatrix} 6 \\ 2 \\ 3 \end{bmatrix}$$
$$= \begin{bmatrix} 6 \\ 8 \\ 11 \end{bmatrix}, \text{ so } (\mathbf{p})_S = (6, 8, 11).$$

(b) $\begin{bmatrix} 1 & 0 & -3 \\ 0 & 3 & 1 \\ 1 & 1 & 0 \end{bmatrix}^{-1} \begin{bmatrix} 0 \\ 1 \\ 0 \end{bmatrix} = \frac{1}{8} \begin{bmatrix} -1 & 1 & -3 \\ -3 & 3 & -1 \\ 9 & -1 & 3 \end{bmatrix}^T \begin{bmatrix} 0 \\ 1 \\ 0 \end{bmatrix}$

$\qquad = \frac{1}{8} \begin{bmatrix} -1 & -3 & 9 \\ 1 & 3 & -1 \\ -3 & -1 & 3 \end{bmatrix} \begin{bmatrix} 0 \\ 1 \\ 0 \end{bmatrix}$

$\qquad = \frac{1}{8} \begin{bmatrix} -3 \\ 3 \\ -1 \end{bmatrix}$, so $(\mathbf{p})_S = (-3/8, 3/8, -1/8)$.

(c) $\begin{bmatrix} 1 & 1 & 1 \\ 0 & 0 & 1 \\ -1 & 1 & 1 \end{bmatrix}^{-1} \begin{bmatrix} -2 \\ 0 \\ 4 \end{bmatrix} = \frac{1}{-2} \begin{bmatrix} -1 & -1 & 0 \\ 0 & 2 & -2 \\ 1 & -1 & 0 \end{bmatrix}^T \begin{bmatrix} -2 \\ 0 \\ 4 \end{bmatrix}$

$\qquad = \begin{bmatrix} -1 & 0 & 1 \\ -1 & 2 & -1 \\ 0 & -2 & 0 \end{bmatrix} \begin{bmatrix} 1 \\ 0 \\ -2 \end{bmatrix}$

$\qquad = \begin{bmatrix} -3 \\ 1 \\ 0 \end{bmatrix}$, so $(\mathbf{p})_S = (-3, 1, 0)$.

26. (a) $\begin{bmatrix} 1 & 0 & 0 & 1 \\ 0 & 0 & 2 & 1 \\ 0 & 3 & 0 & 1 \\ 0 & 0 & 2 & 0 \end{bmatrix}^{-1} \begin{bmatrix} 1 \\ 2 \\ 0 \\ -1 \end{bmatrix} = \frac{1}{6} \begin{bmatrix} 6 & 0 & 0 & 0 \\ -6 & -2 & 0 & 6 \\ 0 & 2 & 0 & 0 \\ 6 & 2 & 3 & -6 \end{bmatrix}^T \begin{bmatrix} 1 \\ 2 \\ 0 \\ -1 \end{bmatrix}$

$\qquad = \frac{1}{6} \begin{bmatrix} 6 & -6 & 0 & 6 \\ 0 & -2 & 2 & 2 \\ 0 & 0 & 0 & 3 \\ 0 & 6 & 0 & -6 \end{bmatrix} \begin{bmatrix} 1 \\ 2 \\ 0 \\ -1 \end{bmatrix}$

$\qquad = \frac{1}{6} \begin{bmatrix} -12 \\ -6 \\ -3 \\ 18 \end{bmatrix}$

$\qquad = \begin{bmatrix} -2 \\ -1 \\ -1/2 \\ 3 \end{bmatrix}$, so $(A)_S = (-2, -1, -1/2, 3)$.

(b) $\begin{bmatrix} 1 & 0 & 1 & 0 \\ -2 & 0 & 0 & 0 \\ 1 & 1 & 0 & 0 \\ 0 & 1 & 0 & 1 \end{bmatrix}^{-1} \begin{bmatrix} 1 \\ 2 \\ -1 \\ 3 \end{bmatrix} = \frac{1}{-2} \begin{bmatrix} 0 & 0 & -2 & 0 \\ 1 & -1 & -1 & 1 \\ 0 & -2 & 0 & 2 \\ 0 & 0 & 0 & -2 \end{bmatrix}^T \begin{bmatrix} 1 \\ 2 \\ -1 \\ 3 \end{bmatrix}$

$\qquad = \frac{-1}{2} \begin{bmatrix} 0 & 1 & 0 & 0 \\ 0 & -1 & -2 & 0 \\ -2 & -1 & 0 & 0 \\ 0 & 1 & 2 & -2 \end{bmatrix} \begin{bmatrix} 1 \\ 2 \\ -1 \\ 3 \end{bmatrix}$

$\qquad = \frac{-1}{2} \begin{bmatrix} 2 \\ 0 \\ -4 \\ -6 \end{bmatrix}$

$\qquad = \begin{bmatrix} -1 \\ 0 \\ 2 \\ 3 \end{bmatrix}$, so $(A)_S = (-1, 0, 2, 3)$.

26. (c) $\begin{bmatrix} 0 & 2 & -1 & 3 \\ 3 & 6 & 1 & 0 \\ 2 & -2 & 1 & 4 \\ 5 & 0 & 3 & 3 \end{bmatrix}^{-1} \begin{bmatrix} 1 \\ 0 \\ 0 \\ 0 \end{bmatrix} = \frac{1}{2} \begin{bmatrix} -48 & 13 & 66 & 14 \\ 42 & -11 & -58 & -12 \\ 78 & -21 & -108 & -22 \\ -56 & 15 & 78 & 16 \end{bmatrix}^T \begin{bmatrix} 1 \\ 0 \\ 0 \\ 0 \end{bmatrix}$

$= \frac{1}{2} \begin{bmatrix} -48 & 42 & 78 & -56 \\ 13 & -11 & -21 & 15 \\ 66 & -58 & -108 & 78 \\ 14 & -12 & -22 & 16 \end{bmatrix} \begin{bmatrix} 1 \\ 0 \\ 0 \\ 0 \end{bmatrix}$

$= \frac{1}{2} \begin{bmatrix} -48 \\ 13 \\ 66 \\ 14 \end{bmatrix}$, so $(A)_S = (-24, 13/2, 33, 7)$.

27. $\begin{bmatrix} 1 & 3 & -1 & 0 \\ 2 & -1 & 1 & 0 \end{bmatrix} \rightarrow \begin{bmatrix} 1 & 3 & -1 & 0 \\ 0 & -7 & 3 & 0 \end{bmatrix} \rightarrow \begin{bmatrix} 1 & 0 & 2/7 & 0 \\ 0 & 1 & -3/7 & 0 \end{bmatrix}$

Let $x_3 = t$, $x_2 = 3/7\,t$, $x_1 = -2/7\,t$

so $(x_1, x_2, x_3) = (-2/7\,t, 3/7\,t, t) = t(-2/7, 3/7, 1)$.

Basis: $(-2/7, 3/7, 1)$; dimension $= 1$.

28. $\begin{bmatrix} 1 & 1 & 3 & 0 & 0 \\ 2 & 1 & 5 & -3 & 0 \end{bmatrix} \rightarrow \begin{bmatrix} 1 & 1 & 3 & 0 & 0 \\ 0 & -1 & -1 & -3 & 0 \end{bmatrix} \rightarrow \begin{bmatrix} 1 & 0 & 2 & -3 & 0 \\ 0 & 1 & 1 & 3 & 0 \end{bmatrix}$

Let $x_4 = t$, $x_3 = s$, $x_2 = -s - 3t$, $x_1 = -2s + 3t$

so $(x_1, x_2, x_3, x_4) = (-2s + 3t, -s - 3t, s, t) = s(-2, -1, 1, 0) + t(3, -3, 0, 1)$.

Basis: $(-2, -1, 1, 0)$, $(3, -3, 0, 1)$; dimension $= 2$.

29. $\begin{bmatrix} 2 & 5 & 1 & 0 \\ 1 & 3 & 2 & 0 \\ 3 & 4 & -9 & 0 \end{bmatrix} \rightarrow \begin{bmatrix} 1 & 3 & 2 & 0 \\ 2 & 5 & 1 & 0 \\ 3 & 4 & -9 & 0 \end{bmatrix} \rightarrow \begin{bmatrix} 1 & 3 & 2 & 0 \\ 0 & -1 & -3 & 0 \\ 0 & -5 & -15 & 0 \end{bmatrix} \rightarrow \begin{bmatrix} 1 & 0 & -7 & 0 \\ 0 & 1 & 3 & 0 \\ 0 & 0 & 0 & 0 \end{bmatrix}$

Let $x_3 = t$, $x_2 = -3t$, $x_1 = 7t$

so $(x_1, x_2, x_3) = (7t, -3t, t) = t(7, -3, 1)$.

Basis: $(7, -3, 1)$; dimension $= 1$.

30. $\begin{bmatrix} 1 & 1 & -1 & 0 \\ 2 & 1 & 0 & 0 \\ 2 & 0 & 1 & 0 \\ -1 & 3 & 0 & 0 \end{bmatrix} \rightarrow \begin{bmatrix} 1 & 1 & -1 & 0 \\ 0 & -1 & 2 & 0 \\ 0 & -2 & 3 & 0 \\ 0 & 4 & -1 & 0 \end{bmatrix} \rightarrow \begin{bmatrix} 1 & 1 & -1 & 0 \\ 0 & 1 & -2 & 0 \\ 0 & 0 & -1 & 0 \\ 0 & 0 & 7 & 0 \end{bmatrix} \rightarrow \begin{bmatrix} 1 & 1 & -1 & 0 \\ 0 & 1 & -2 & 0 \\ 0 & 0 & 1 & 0 \\ 0 & 0 & 0 & 0 \end{bmatrix}$

so $(x_1, x_2, x_3) = (0, 0, 0)$.

Basis: none; dimension $= 0$.

31. (a) Basis: $(1, 0, 0)$, $(0, 1, 0)$, $(0, 0, 1)$; dimension $= 3$.

(b) Basis: $1, x, x^2, x^3$; dimension $= 4$.

(c) Basis: $\begin{bmatrix} 1 & 0 & 0 \\ 0 & 0 & 0 \end{bmatrix}$, $\begin{bmatrix} 0 & 1 & 0 \\ 0 & 0 & 0 \end{bmatrix}$, $\begin{bmatrix} 0 & 0 & 1 \\ 0 & 0 & 0 \end{bmatrix}$, $\begin{bmatrix} 0 & 0 & 0 \\ 1 & 0 & 0 \end{bmatrix}$, $\begin{bmatrix} 0 & 0 & 0 \\ 0 & 1 & 0 \end{bmatrix}$, $\begin{bmatrix} 0 & 0 & 0 \\ 0 & 0 & 1 \end{bmatrix}$; dimension $= 6$.

(d) $(x, y, z) = (t, 7t, -3t) = t(1, 7, -3)$.
Basis: $(1, 7, -3)$; dimension $= 1$.

(e) $[5 \ 3 \ -2 \ 0] \to [1 \ 3/5 \ -2/5 \ 0]$

Let $z = t, y = s, x = -3/5\,s + 2/5\,t$

so $(x, y, z) = (\frac{-3}{5}s + \frac{2}{5}t, s, t) = s\left(\frac{-3}{5}, 1, 0\right) + t\left(\frac{2}{5}, 0, 1\right)$.

Basis: $\left(\frac{-3}{5}, 1, 0\right), \left(\frac{2}{5}, 0, 1\right)$; dimension $= 2$.

(f) Let $a = r, b = s, c = t, d = r + s + t$

so $(a, b, c, d) = (r, s, t, r + s + t) = r(1, 0, 0, 1) + s(0, 1, 0, 1) + t(0, 0, 1, 1)$

Basis: $(1, 0, 0, 1), (0, 1, 0, 1), (0, 0, 1, 1)$; dimension $= 3$

(g) Let $a_0 = r, a_1 = s, a_2 = t, a_3 = -r$

so $(a_0, a_1, a_2, a_3) = (r, s, t, -r) = r(1, 0, 0, -1) + s(0, 1, 0, 0) + t(0, 0, 1, 0)$.

Basis: $1 - x^3, x, x^2$; dimension $= 3$.

SECTION 5.5   ROW SPACE, COLUMN SPACE, AND NULLSPACE

32. (a) $3\begin{bmatrix} 1 \\ 2 \end{bmatrix} + 4\begin{bmatrix} 7 \\ -3 \end{bmatrix}$ (b) $4\begin{bmatrix} 2 \\ 1 \\ 3 \end{bmatrix} + 4\begin{bmatrix} -2 \\ 0 \\ 5 \end{bmatrix} + 1\begin{bmatrix} 1 \\ 3 \\ -1 \end{bmatrix}$ (c) $1\begin{bmatrix} 2 \\ 6 \\ 5 \end{bmatrix} + 1\begin{bmatrix} 3 \\ 1 \\ 5 \end{bmatrix} + 1\begin{bmatrix} 0 \\ -6 \\ 0 \end{bmatrix} + 1\begin{bmatrix} 1 \\ 6 \\ -1 \end{bmatrix}$

33. (a) $\begin{bmatrix} -1 & 6 & 19 \\ 2 & 5 & 13 \end{bmatrix} \to \begin{bmatrix} 1 & -6 & -19 \\ 0 & 17 & 51 \end{bmatrix} \to \begin{bmatrix} 1 & -6 & -19 \\ 0 & 1 & 3 \end{bmatrix} \to \begin{bmatrix} 1 & 0 & -1 \\ 0 & 1 & 3 \end{bmatrix}$

so $\begin{bmatrix} 19 \\ 13 \end{bmatrix} = -1\begin{bmatrix} -1 \\ 2 \end{bmatrix} + 3\begin{bmatrix} 6 \\ 5 \end{bmatrix}$.

(b) $\begin{bmatrix} 1 & 7 & 2 & -1 \\ 2 & 4 & -6 & 3 \\ 3 & 19 & 4 & -4 \end{bmatrix} \to \begin{bmatrix} 1 & 7 & 2 & -1 \\ 0 & -10 & -10 & 5 \\ 0 & -2 & -2 & -1 \end{bmatrix} \to \begin{bmatrix} 1 & 7 & 2 & -1 \\ 0 & 1 & 1 & -1/2 \\ 0 & 0 & 0 & -2 \end{bmatrix}$

and the inconsistency means **b** is not in the column space.

(c) $\begin{bmatrix} 3 & -9 & -6 & -20 \\ 3 & -10 & -6 & -19 \\ 0 & 1 & 0 & -1 \\ -3 & 11 & 8 & 28 \end{bmatrix} \to \begin{bmatrix} 1 & -3 & -2 & -20/3 \\ 0 & -1 & 0 & 1 \\ 0 & 1 & 0 & -1 \\ 0 & 2 & 2 & 8 \end{bmatrix} \to \begin{bmatrix} 1 & -3 & -2 & -20/3 \\ 0 & 1 & 0 & -1 \\ 0 & 0 & 0 & 0 \\ 0 & 0 & 2 & 10 \end{bmatrix}$

$\to \begin{bmatrix} 1 & -3 & -2 & -20/3 \\ 0 & 1 & 0 & -1 \\ 0 & 0 & 1 & 5 \\ 0 & 0 & 0 & 0 \end{bmatrix} \to \begin{bmatrix} 1 & 0 & -2 & -29/3 \\ 0 & 1 & 0 & -1 \\ 0 & 0 & 1 & 5 \\ 0 & 0 & 0 & 0 \end{bmatrix} \to \begin{bmatrix} 1 & 0 & 0 & 1/3 \\ 0 & 1 & 0 & -1 \\ 0 & 0 & 1 & 5 \\ 0 & 0 & 0 & 0 \end{bmatrix}$

so $\begin{bmatrix} -20 \\ -19 \\ -1 \\ 28 \end{bmatrix} = \frac{1}{3}\begin{bmatrix} 3 \\ 3 \\ 0 \\ -3 \end{bmatrix} + -1\begin{bmatrix} -9 \\ -10 \\ 1 \\ 11 \end{bmatrix} + 5\begin{bmatrix} -6 \\ -6 \\ 0 \\ 8 \end{bmatrix}$

34. (a) $\begin{bmatrix} 3 & 9 & -6 \\ -2 & -6 & 4 \end{bmatrix} \to \begin{bmatrix} 1 & 3 & -2 \\ 0 & 0 & 0 \end{bmatrix}$

Let $x_2 = t$, $x_1 = -2 - 3t$. Then the general solution is

$$\begin{bmatrix} x_1 \\ x_2 \end{bmatrix} = \begin{bmatrix} -2 - 3t \\ t \end{bmatrix} = \begin{bmatrix} -2 \\ 0 \end{bmatrix} + t\begin{bmatrix} -3 \\ 1 \end{bmatrix}$$

and the associated homogeneous solution is

$$\begin{bmatrix} x_1 \\ x_2 \end{bmatrix} = t\begin{bmatrix} -3 \\ 1 \end{bmatrix}.$$

84

(b) $\begin{bmatrix} 2 & 2 & 2 & 2 \\ 3 & 5 & 5 & 11 \\ 4 & 3 & 3 & 0 \end{bmatrix} \rightarrow \begin{bmatrix} 1 & 1 & 1 & 1 \\ 0 & 2 & 2 & 8 \\ 0 & -1 & -1 & -4 \end{bmatrix} \rightarrow \begin{bmatrix} 1 & 0 & 0 & -3 \\ 0 & 1 & 1 & 4 \\ 0 & 0 & 0 & 0 \end{bmatrix}$

Let $x_3 = t$, $x_2 = 4 - t$, $x_1 = -3$. Then the general solution is

$$\begin{bmatrix} x_1 \\ x_2 \\ x_3 \end{bmatrix} = \begin{bmatrix} -3 \\ 4 - t \\ t \end{bmatrix} = \begin{bmatrix} -3 \\ 4 \\ 0 \end{bmatrix} + t \begin{bmatrix} 0 \\ -1 \\ 1 \end{bmatrix}$$

and the associated homogeneous solution is

$$\begin{bmatrix} x_1 \\ x_2 \\ x_3 \end{bmatrix} = t \begin{bmatrix} 0 \\ -1 \\ 1 \end{bmatrix}.$$

(c) $\begin{bmatrix} 1 & 2 & -2 & 8 & 0 \\ 1 & 2 & 0 & 2 & 4 \\ 1 & 2 & -1 & 5 & 2 \\ 2 & 4 & -2 & 10 & 4 \end{bmatrix} \rightarrow \begin{bmatrix} 1 & 2 & -2 & 8 & 0 \\ 0 & 0 & 2 & -6 & 4 \\ 0 & 0 & 1 & -3 & 2 \\ 0 & 0 & 2 & -6 & 4 \end{bmatrix} \rightarrow \begin{bmatrix} 1 & 2 & 0 & 2 & 4 \\ 0 & 0 & 1 & -3 & 2 \\ 0 & 0 & 0 & 0 & 0 \\ 0 & 0 & 0 & 0 & 0 \end{bmatrix}$

Let $x_4 = t$, $x_2 = s$, $x_3 = 2 + 3t$, $x_1 = 4 - 2s - 2t$. Then the general solution is

$$\begin{bmatrix} x_1 \\ x_2 \\ x_3 \\ x_4 \end{bmatrix} = \begin{bmatrix} 4 - 2s - 2t \\ s \\ 2 + 3t \\ t \end{bmatrix} = \begin{bmatrix} 4 \\ 0 \\ 2 \\ 0 \end{bmatrix} + s \begin{bmatrix} -2 \\ 1 \\ 0 \\ 0 \end{bmatrix} + t \begin{bmatrix} -2 \\ 0 \\ 3 \\ 1 \end{bmatrix}$$

and the associated homogeneous solution is

$$\begin{bmatrix} x_1 \\ x_2 \\ x_3 \\ x_4 \end{bmatrix} = s \begin{bmatrix} -2 \\ 1 \\ 0 \\ 0 \end{bmatrix} + t \begin{bmatrix} -2 \\ 0 \\ 3 \\ 1 \end{bmatrix}.$$

35. (a) $\begin{bmatrix} 1 & -3 & 3 & 0 \\ 2 & -6 & 8 & 0 \\ 3 & -9 & 11 & 0 \end{bmatrix} \rightarrow \begin{bmatrix} 1 & -3 & 3 & 0 \\ 0 & 0 & 2 & 0 \\ 0 & 0 & 2 & 0 \end{bmatrix} \rightarrow \begin{bmatrix} 1 & -3 & 0 & 0 \\ 0 & 0 & 1 & 0 \\ 0 & 0 & 0 & 0 \end{bmatrix}$

Let $x_2 = t, x_1 = 3t, x_3 = 0$. Then

$$\begin{bmatrix} x_1 \\ x_2 \\ x_3 \end{bmatrix} = \begin{bmatrix} 3t \\ t \\ 0 \end{bmatrix} = t \begin{bmatrix} 3 \\ 1 \\ 0 \end{bmatrix}$$

so a basis for the nullspace is $(3, 1, 0)$
and a basis for the row space is $(1, -3, 0), (0, 0, 1)$
and a basis for the column space is $(1, 2, 3), (3, 8, 11)$.

(b) $\begin{bmatrix} 5 & -5 & -1 & 0 & 0 \\ 5 & 0 & 3 & 10 & 0 \\ 10 & -5 & 2 & 10 & 0 \end{bmatrix} \rightarrow \begin{bmatrix} 1 & -1 & -1/5 & 0 & 0 \\ 0 & 5 & 4 & 10 & 0 \\ 0 & 5 & 4 & 10 & 0 \end{bmatrix} \rightarrow \begin{bmatrix} 1 & 0 & 3/5 & 2 & 0 \\ 0 & 1 & 4/5 & 2 & 0 \\ 0 & 0 & 0 & 0 & 0 \end{bmatrix}$

Let $x_4 = t, x_3 = s, x_2 = -4/5s - 2t, x_1 = -3/5s - 2t$. Then

$$\begin{bmatrix} x_1 \\ x_2 \\ x_3 \\ x_4 \end{bmatrix} = \begin{bmatrix} -\frac{3}{5}s - 2t \\ -\frac{4}{5}s - 2t \\ s \\ t \end{bmatrix} = s \begin{bmatrix} -3/5 \\ -4/5 \\ 1 \\ 0 \end{bmatrix} + t \begin{bmatrix} -2 \\ -2 \\ 0 \\ 1 \end{bmatrix}$$

so a basis for the nullspace is $(-3/5, -4/5, 1, 0), (-2, -2, 0, 1)$
and a basis for the row space is $(1, 0, 3/5, 2), (0, 1, 4/5, 2)$
and a basis for the column space is $(5, 5, 10), (-5, 0, -5)$.

(c) $\begin{bmatrix} 1 & 0 & 0 & 3 & 0 \\ 1 & 0 & 1 & 4 & 0 \\ 1 & 0 & -1 & 2 & 0 \\ 1 & 1 & 2 & 7 & 0 \end{bmatrix} \rightarrow \begin{bmatrix} 1 & 0 & 0 & 3 & 0 \\ 0 & 0 & 1 & 1 & 0 \\ 0 & 0 & -1 & -1 & 0 \\ 0 & 1 & 2 & 4 & 0 \end{bmatrix} \rightarrow \begin{bmatrix} 1 & 0 & 0 & 3 & 0 \\ 0 & 1 & 2 & 4 & 0 \\ 0 & 0 & 1 & 1 & 0 \\ 0 & 0 & -1 & -1 & 0 \end{bmatrix} \rightarrow \begin{bmatrix} 1 & 0 & 0 & 3 & 0 \\ 0 & 1 & 0 & 2 & 0 \\ 0 & 0 & 1 & 1 & 0 \\ 0 & 0 & 0 & 0 & 0 \end{bmatrix}$

Let $x_4 = t, x_3 = -t, x_2 = -2t, x_1 = -3t$. Then

$$\begin{bmatrix} x_1 \\ x_2 \\ x_3 \\ x_4 \end{bmatrix} = \begin{bmatrix} -3t \\ -2t \\ -t \\ t \end{bmatrix} = t \begin{bmatrix} -3 \\ -2 \\ -1 \\ 1 \end{bmatrix}$$

so a basis for the nullspace is $(-3, -2, -1, 1)$
and a basis for the row space is $(1, 0, 0, 3), (0, 1, 0, 2), (0, 0, 1, 1)$
and a basis for the column space is $(1, 1, 1, 1), (0, 0, 0, 1), (0, 1, -1, 2)$.

36. (a) $\begin{bmatrix} 1 & 3 & 2 \\ 1 & -5 & 5 \\ 3 & 1 & 9 \end{bmatrix} \rightarrow \begin{bmatrix} 1 & 3 & 2 \\ 0 & -8 & 3 \\ 0 & -8 & 3 \end{bmatrix} \rightarrow \begin{bmatrix} 1 & 3 & 2 \\ 0 & 1 & -3/8 \\ 0 & 0 & 0 \end{bmatrix}$ so a basis is $(1, 3, 2), (0, 1, -3/8)$.

(b) $\begin{bmatrix} -1 & 2 & 2 & 3 \\ 2 & 1 & 1 & 5 \\ 7 & -4 & -4 & 1 \end{bmatrix} \rightarrow \begin{bmatrix} 1 & -2 & -2 & -3 \\ 0 & 5 & 5 & 11 \\ 0 & 10 & 10 & 22 \end{bmatrix} \rightarrow \begin{bmatrix} 1 & -2 & -2 & -3 \\ 0 & 1 & 1 & 11/5 \\ 0 & 0 & 0 & 0 \end{bmatrix}$ so a basis is $(1, -2, -2, -3), (0, 1, 1, 11/$

(c) $\begin{bmatrix} 1 & 0 & 2 & -1 \\ 3 & 3 & 0 & 1 \\ 0 & -3 & 6 & -4 \\ 1 & 3 & -4 & 3 \end{bmatrix} \rightarrow \begin{bmatrix} 1 & 0 & 2 & -1 \\ 0 & 3 & -6 & 4 \\ 0 & -3 & 6 & -4 \\ 0 & 3 & -6 & 4 \end{bmatrix} \rightarrow \begin{bmatrix} 1 & 0 & 2 & -1 \\ 0 & 1 & -2 & 4/3 \\ 0 & 0 & 0 & 0 \\ 0 & 0 & 0 & 0 \end{bmatrix}$ so a basis is $(1, 0, 2, -1), (0, 1, -2, 4/3)$.

37. (a) $\begin{bmatrix} 1 & 1 & 1 & 5 \\ 1 & 0 & -2 & 3 \\ -1 & 1 & 5 & 2 \end{bmatrix} \rightarrow \begin{bmatrix} 1 & 1 & 1 & 5 \\ 0 & -1 & -3 & -2 \\ 0 & 2 & 6 & 7 \end{bmatrix} \rightarrow \begin{bmatrix} 1 & 1 & 1 & 5 \\ 0 & 1 & 3 & 2 \\ 0 & 0 & 0 & 3 \end{bmatrix} \rightarrow \begin{bmatrix} 1 & 1 & 1 & 5 \\ 0 & 1 & 3 & 2 \\ 0 & 0 & 0 & 1 \end{bmatrix}$

$\rightarrow \begin{bmatrix} 1 & 0 & -2 & 3 \\ 0 & 1 & 3 & 2 \\ 0 & 0 & 0 & 1 \end{bmatrix} \rightarrow \begin{bmatrix} 1 & 0 & -2 & 0 \\ 0 & 1 & 3 & 0 \\ 0 & 0 & 0 & 1 \end{bmatrix}$

Basis $B = \{v_1, v_2, v_4\}$ and $v_3 = -2v_1 + 3v_2$.

(b) $\begin{bmatrix} 1 & 3 & 2 & 3 \\ 2 & 6 & 1 & 0 \\ 1 & 3 & 3 & 5 \\ 2 & 6 & 3 & 4 \end{bmatrix} \rightarrow \begin{bmatrix} 1 & 3 & 2 & 3 \\ 0 & 0 & -3 & -6 \\ 0 & 0 & 1 & 2 \\ 0 & 0 & -1 & -2 \end{bmatrix} \rightarrow \begin{bmatrix} 1 & 3 & 2 & 3 \\ 0 & 0 & 1 & 2 \\ 0 & 0 & 0 & 0 \\ 0 & 0 & 0 & 0 \end{bmatrix} \rightarrow \begin{bmatrix} 1 & 3 & 0 & -1 \\ 0 & 0 & 1 & 2 \\ 0 & 0 & 0 & 0 \\ 0 & 0 & 0 & 0 \end{bmatrix}$

Basis $B = \{v_1, v_3\}$ and $v_2 = 3v_1, v_4 = -v_1 + 2v_3$.

(c) $\begin{bmatrix} 1 & 1 & 3 & 6 & 8 \\ 1 & -1 & -5 & 2 & 2 \\ -1 & 1 & 5 & -3 & -4 \\ 2 & 1 & 2 & 8 & 9 \end{bmatrix} \rightarrow \begin{bmatrix} 1 & 1 & 3 & 6 & 8 \\ 0 & -2 & -8 & -4 & -6 \\ 0 & 2 & 8 & 3 & 4 \\ 0 & -1 & -4 & -4 & -7 \end{bmatrix} \rightarrow \begin{bmatrix} 1 & 1 & 3 & 6 & 8 \\ 0 & 1 & 4 & 2 & 3 \\ 0 & 0 & 0 & -1 & -2 \\ 0 & 0 & 0 & -2 & -4 \end{bmatrix}$

$\rightarrow \begin{bmatrix} 1 & 1 & 3 & 6 & 8 \\ 0 & 1 & 4 & 2 & 3 \\ 0 & 0 & 0 & 1 & 2 \\ 0 & 0 & 0 & 0 & 0 \end{bmatrix} \rightarrow \begin{bmatrix} 1 & 0 & -1 & 4 & 5 \\ 0 & 1 & 4 & 2 & 3 \\ 0 & 0 & 0 & 1 & 2 \\ 0 & 0 & 0 & 0 & 0 \end{bmatrix} \rightarrow \begin{bmatrix} 1 & 0 & -1 & 0 & -3 \\ 0 & 1 & 4 & 0 & -1 \\ 0 & 0 & 0 & 1 & 2 \\ 0 & 0 & 0 & 0 & 0 \end{bmatrix}$

Basis $B = \{v_1, v_2, v_4\}$ and $v_3 = -v_1 + 4v_2, v_5 = -3v_1 - v_2 + 2v_4$.

SECTION 5.6 RANK AND NULLITY

38. (a) $\begin{bmatrix} 1 & 1 & 7 \\ 1 & 2 & 0 \\ 2 & 3 & 10 \end{bmatrix} \rightarrow \begin{bmatrix} 1 & 1 & 7 \\ 0 & 1 & -7 \\ 0 & 1 & -4 \end{bmatrix} \rightarrow \begin{bmatrix} 1 & 1 & 7 \\ 0 & 1 & -7 \\ 0 & 0 & 3 \end{bmatrix} \rightarrow \begin{bmatrix} 1 & 1 & 7 \\ 0 & 1 & -7 \\ 0 & 0 & 1 \end{bmatrix}$

rank = number of leading ones = 3
nullity = number of columns − rank = 3 − 3 = 0

86

(b) $\begin{bmatrix} 1 & -4 & 5 & 1 \\ 2 & -8 & 9 & 0 \\ 1 & -4 & 3 & -3 \\ -1 & 4 & -2 & 5 \end{bmatrix} \rightarrow \begin{bmatrix} 1 & -4 & 5 & 1 \\ 0 & 0 & -1 & -2 \\ 0 & 0 & -2 & -4 \\ 0 & 0 & 3 & 6 \end{bmatrix} \rightarrow \begin{bmatrix} 1 & -4 & 5 & 1 \\ 0 & 0 & 1 & 2 \\ 0 & 0 & 0 & 0 \\ 0 & 0 & 0 & 0 \end{bmatrix}$

rank = number of leading ones = 2

nullity = number of columns − rank = 4 − 2 = 2

(c) $\begin{bmatrix} 1 & -2 & 0 & 1 & 0 \\ 2 & -4 & 2 & 4 & 6 \\ 3 & -6 & 1 & 4 & 1 \\ 1 & -2 & -2 & -1 & -3 \end{bmatrix} \rightarrow \begin{bmatrix} 1 & -2 & 0 & 1 & 0 \\ 0 & 0 & 2 & 2 & 6 \\ 0 & 0 & 1 & 1 & 1 \\ 0 & 0 & -2 & -2 & -3 \end{bmatrix} \rightarrow \begin{bmatrix} 1 & -2 & 0 & 1 & 0 \\ 0 & 0 & 1 & 1 & 3 \\ 0 & 0 & 0 & 0 & -2 \\ 0 & 0 & 0 & 0 & 3 \end{bmatrix} \rightarrow \begin{bmatrix} 1 & -2 & 0 & 1 & 0 \\ 0 & 0 & 1 & 1 & 3 \\ 0 & 0 & 0 & 0 & 1 \\ 0 & 0 & 0 & 0 & 0 \end{bmatrix}$

rank = number of leading ones = 3

nullity = number of columns − rank = 5 − 3 = 2

39. (a) dim rowspace(A) = dim colspace(A) = rank (A) = 2

dim nullspace(A) = no. cols - rank(A) = 3 − 2 = 1

dim nullspace(A^T) = no. rows - rank(A) = 3 − 2 = 1

(b) dim rowspace(A) = dim colspace(A) = rank (A) = 1

dim nullspace(A) = no. cols - rank(A) = 4 − 1 = 3

dim nullspace(A^T) = no. rows - rank(A) = 4 − 1 = 3

(c) dim rowspace(A) = dim colspace(A) = rank (A) = 3

dim nullspace(A) = no. cols - rank(A) = 5 − 3 = 2

dim nullspace(A^T) = no. rows - rank(A) = 3 − 3 = 0

(d) dim rowspace(A) = dim colspace(A) = rank (A) = 3

dim nullspace(A) = no. cols - rank(A) = 3 − 3 = 0

dim nullspace(A^T) = no. rows - rank(A) = 5 − 3 = 2

(e) dim rowspace(A) = dim colspace(A) = rank (A) = 3

dim nullspace(A) = no. cols - rank(A) = 6 − 3 = 3

dim nullspace(A^T) = no. rows - rank(A) = 4 − 3 = 1

(f) dim rowspace(A) = dim colspace(A) = rank (A) = 0

dim nullspace(A) = no. cols - rank(A) = 5 − 0 = 5

dim nullspace(A^T) = no. rows - rank(A) = 7 − 0 = 7

40. (a) rank[A|$\mathbf{b}$] > rank(A) so inconsistent

(b) rank[A|$\mathbf{b}$] = rank(A) so consistent;

and no. parameters = nullity(A) = no.cols − rank(A) = 4 − 3 = 1

(c) rank[A|$\mathbf{b}$] > rank(A) so inconsistent

(d) rank[A|$\mathbf{b}$] = rank(A) so consistent;

and no. parameters = nullity(A) = no.cols − rank(A) = 3 − 3 = 0

(e) rank[A|$\mathbf{b}$] = rank(A) so consistent;

and no. parameters = nullity(A) = no.cols − rank(A) = 9 − 5 = 4

(f) rank[A|$\mathbf{b}$] > rank(A) so inconsistent

CHAPTER 6: INNER PRODUCT SPACES

1. Let $\mathbf{u} = (u_1, u_2)$ and $\mathbf{v} = (v_1, v_2)$. Show whether the given function is an inner product on R^2.

   (a) $\langle \mathbf{u}, \mathbf{v} \rangle = u_1 v_1 + 2u_2 v_2$

   (b) $\langle \mathbf{u}, \mathbf{v} \rangle = u_1 v_2 + u_2 v_1$

   (c) $\langle \mathbf{u}, \mathbf{v} \rangle = 3u_1 v_1 - 2u_2 v_2$

2. Let $\mathbf{u} = (u_1, u_2, u_3)$ and $\mathbf{v} = (v_1, v_2, v_3)$. Show whether the given function is an inner product on R^3.

   (a) $\langle \mathbf{u}, \mathbf{v} \rangle = 2u_1 v_1 + 3u_2 v_2$

   (b) $\langle \mathbf{u}, \mathbf{v} \rangle = u_1 v_1 + u_2 v_2 + u_3 v_3 + u_1 u_2 v_3$

   (c) $\langle \mathbf{u}, \mathbf{v} \rangle = 2u_1 v_1 + 5u_2 v_2 + u_3 v_3 - u_2 v_3 - u_3 v_2$

3. Let $\mathbf{u} = (1, 3, -1)$ and $\mathbf{v} = (2, 0, 5)$. Use the Euclidean inner product on R^3 to compute the following.

   (a) $\langle \mathbf{u}, \mathbf{v} \rangle$ (b) $\|\mathbf{u}\|$ (c) $\|\mathbf{v}\|$ (d) $d(\mathbf{u}, \mathbf{v})$

4. Let $\mathbf{u} = (2\sqrt{3}, 2)$ and $\mathbf{v} = (-3/2, 3/2\sqrt{3})$. Use the Euclidean inner product on R^2 to compute the following.

   (a) $\langle \mathbf{u}, \mathbf{v} \rangle$ (b) $\|\mathbf{u}\|$ (c) $\|\mathbf{v}\|$ (d) $d(\mathbf{u}, \mathbf{v})$

5. Let $\mathbf{u} = (1, -3)$ and $\mathbf{v} = (5, 1)$. Use the inner product $\langle \mathbf{u}, \mathbf{v} \rangle = 3u_1 v_1 + 5u_2 v_2$ to compute the following.

   (a) $\langle \mathbf{u}, \mathbf{v} \rangle$ (b) $\|\mathbf{u}\|$ (c) $\|\mathbf{v}\|$ (d) $d(\mathbf{u}, \mathbf{v})$

6. Let $A = \begin{bmatrix} 1 & 3 \\ -2 & 4 \end{bmatrix}$ and $B = \begin{bmatrix} 2 & -1 \\ 2 & 0 \end{bmatrix}$. Use the inner product

$$\left\langle \begin{bmatrix} a_{11} & a_{12} \\ a_{21} & a_{22} \end{bmatrix}, \begin{bmatrix} b_{11} & b_{12} \\ b_{21} & b_{22} \end{bmatrix} \right\rangle = a_{11}b_{11} + a_{12}b_{12} + a_{21}b_{21} + a_{22}b_{22} \quad \text{on} \quad M_{22}$$

to compute the following.

   (a) $\langle A, B \rangle$ (b) $\|A\|$ (c) $\|B\|$ (d) $d(A, B)$

7. Let $\mathbf{p} = 1 + x^2$ and $\mathbf{q} = 1 - x^2$. Use the inner product $\langle \mathbf{p}, \mathbf{q} \rangle = p_0 q_0 + p_1 q_1 + p_2 q_2$ on P_2 to compute the following.

   (a) $\langle \mathbf{p}, \mathbf{q} \rangle$ (b) $\|\mathbf{p}\|$ (c) $\|\mathbf{q}\|$ (d) $d(\mathbf{p}, \mathbf{q})$

8. Let $\mathbf{u} = \begin{bmatrix} 5 \\ 2 \end{bmatrix}$ and $\mathbf{v} = \begin{bmatrix} 11 \\ 6 \end{bmatrix}$. Use the inner product on R^2 generated by the matrix $\begin{bmatrix} 1 & -1 \\ 0 & 2 \end{bmatrix}$ to compute the following.

   (a) $\langle \mathbf{u}, \mathbf{v} \rangle$ (b) $\|\mathbf{u}\|$ (c) $\|\mathbf{v}\|$ (d) $d(\mathbf{u}, \mathbf{v})$

9. Let $f(x) = x$ and $g(x) = e^x$. Use the inner product $\langle f, g \rangle = \int_0^1 f(x)g(x)dx$ on $C[0,1]$ to compute the following.

   (a) $\langle f, g \rangle$ (b) $\|f\|$ (c) $\|g\|$ (d) $d(f, g)$

10. Suppose that u, v and w are vectors such that $\langle u, v \rangle = 3$, $\langle v, w \rangle = -1$, $\langle u, w \rangle = 2$, $\|u\| = 5$, $\|v\| = 3$, $\|w\| = 4$. Evaluate the expression.

    (a) $\langle u - v, u + v \rangle$ (b) $\|3u + v\|$ (c) $\|2v - 3w\|$ (d) $\langle u - v + 3w, 2u + v + w \rangle$

11. Let $u = (1, 4, -5)$, $v = (2, 3, 2)$, $w = (3, -1, -3/2)$. Use the Euclidean inner product on R^3 to compute the cosine of the angle between the indicated pair of vectors.

    (a) u and v (b) v and w (c) u and w

12. Let $u = (3, 4)$, $v = (4, 5)$, $w = (5, 6)$. Use the Euclidean inner product on R^2 to compute the cosine of the angle between the indicated pair of vectors.

    (a) u and v (b) v and w (c) u and w

13. Let $u = (7, -1)$, $v = (2, 3)$, $w = (10, -4)$. Use the inner product $\langle u, v \rangle = 3u_1 v_1 + 5u_2 v_2$ to compute the cosine of the angle between the indicated pair of vectors.

    (a) u and v (b) v and w (c) u and w

14. Let $A = \begin{bmatrix} 1 & 0 \\ 0 & 1 \end{bmatrix}$, $B = \begin{bmatrix} 1 & 0 \\ 1 & 0 \end{bmatrix}$, $C = \begin{bmatrix} -1 & 0 \\ 0 & 0 \end{bmatrix}$. Use the inner product

$$\left\langle \begin{bmatrix} a_{11} & a_{12} \\ a_{21} & a_{22} \end{bmatrix}, \begin{bmatrix} b_{11} & b_{12} \\ b_{21} & b_{22} \end{bmatrix} \right\rangle = a_{11}b_{11} + a_{12}b_{12} + a_{21}b_{21} + a_{22}b_{22} \quad \text{on} \quad M_{22} \text{ to compute the cosine}$$

of the angle between the indicated pair of vectors.

    (a) A and B (b) B and C (c) A and C

15. Let $p = 1 - x^2$, $q = 3 + 12x - 4x^2$, $r = 12 - 9x - 8x^2$. Use the inner product $\langle p, q \rangle = p_0 q_0 + p_1 q_1 + p_2 q_2$ on P_2 to compute the cosine of the angle between the indicated pair of vectors.

    (a) p and q (b) q and r (c) p and r

16. Let $u = \begin{bmatrix} 1 \\ 0 \end{bmatrix}$, $v = \begin{bmatrix} 3 \\ 2 \end{bmatrix}$, $w = \begin{bmatrix} -5 \\ -1 \end{bmatrix}$. Use the inner product on R^2 generated by the matrix $A = \begin{bmatrix} 1 & -1 \\ -1 & 2 \end{bmatrix}$ to compute the cosine of the angle between the indicated pair of vectors.

    (a) u and v (b) v and w (c) u and w

17. Let $f(x) = \frac{1}{3} + x^4$, $g(x) = 6x$, $h(x) = \frac{1}{3} - x^4$. Use the inner product $\langle f, g \rangle = \int_0^1 f(x)g(x)dx$ on $C[0,1]$ to compute the cosine of the angle between the indicated pair of vectors.

(a) **f and g** (b) **g and h** (c) **f and h**

18. Consider the unit cube in R^4, whose diagonal extends from $(0,0,0,0)$ to $(1,1,1,1)$. Under the Euclidean inner product, compute the following.

    (a)   the length of the diagonal

    (b)   the angle between the diagonal and each face.

19. Let W be the line in R^2 with equation $y = -3x$. Find an equation for $W^{\perp}$.

20. Let W be the line in R^3 with parametic equations $x = 3t$, $y = t$, $z = -2t$ for $-\infty < t < \infty$. Find an equation for $W^{\perp}$.

21. Let W be the plane in R^3 with equation $3x + 2y - 2z = 0$. Find parametric equations for $W^{\perp}$.

22. In each part, find a basis for $W^{\perp}$, where W is the subspace of R^n spanned by the given vectors.

    (a) $\mathbf{v}_1 = (4, -6)$, $\mathbf{v}_2 = (-6, 9)$

    (b) $\mathbf{v}_1 = (1, 2, 1)$, $\mathbf{v}_2 = (3, 1, -2)$, $\mathbf{v}_3 = (-1, 3, 4)$

    (c) $\mathbf{v}_1 = (3, 1, 7)$, $\mathbf{v}_2 = (2, 4, -2)$, $\mathbf{v}_3 = (-2, -1, 0)$

    (d) $\mathbf{v}_1 = (1, 2, 3, 4)$, $\mathbf{v}_2 = (1, 1, 1, 0)$, $\mathbf{v}_3 = (1, 4, 7, 12)$

23. Let $\mathbf{u} = \left(\frac{4}{5}, \frac{-3}{5}\right)$, $\mathbf{v} = \left(\frac{3}{5}, \frac{4}{5}\right)$. Using the Euclidean inner product for R^2, determine whether the set $\{\mathbf{u}, \mathbf{v}\}$ is orthonormal, orthogonal only, normal only, or neither.

24. Let $\mathbf{u} = \left(\frac{1}{3}, \frac{2}{3}, \frac{2}{3}\right)$, $\mathbf{v} = \left(\frac{2}{\sqrt{6}}, \frac{-1}{\sqrt{6}}, \frac{-1}{\sqrt{6}}\right)$, $\mathbf{w} = \left(0, \frac{1}{\sqrt{2}}, \frac{-1}{\sqrt{2}}\right)$. Using the Euclidean inner product for R^3, determine whether the set $\{\mathbf{u}, \mathbf{v}, \mathbf{w}\}$ is orthonormal, orthogonal only, normal only, or neither.

25. Let $\mathbf{u} = \left(\frac{1}{\sqrt{8}}, \frac{1}{\sqrt{8}}\right)$, $\mathbf{v} = \left(\frac{1}{2}, \frac{-1}{4}\right)$. Using the inner product $\langle \mathbf{u}, \mathbf{v} \rangle = 3u_1 v_1 + 5u_2 v_2$, determine whether the set $\{u, v\}$ is orthonormal, orthogonal only, normal only, or neither.

26. Let $f(x) = \sin x$, $g(x) = \cos x$. Using the inner product $\langle f, g \rangle = \int_0^{\pi} f(x)g(x)dx$, determine whether the set $\{f, g\}$ is orthonormal, orthogonal only, normal only, or neither.

27. For each vector given, compute its coördinate vector relative to the orthonormal basis
$B = \left\{ \left(\frac{-1}{\sqrt{2}}, \frac{1}{\sqrt{2}}, 0 \right), \left\{ \left(\frac{-1}{\sqrt{6}}, \frac{-1}{\sqrt{6}}, \frac{2}{\sqrt{6}} \right), \frac{1}{\sqrt{3}}, \frac{1}{\sqrt{3}}, \frac{1}{\sqrt{3}} \right) \right\}$ under the Euclidean inner product for R^3.

    (a) $(1, 1, 1)$ (b) $(1, 0, -1)$ (c) $(0, 0, 1)$

28. For each vector given, compute its coördinate vector relative to the orthonormal basis
$B = \left\{ \left(\frac{1}{\sqrt{3}}, 0 \right), \left(0, \frac{1}{\sqrt{5}} \right) \right\}$ under the inner product $\langle \mathbf{u}, \mathbf{v} \rangle = 3u_1 v_1 + 5u_2 v_2$ for R^2.

    (a) $(3, 5)$ (b) $(1, 1)$ (c) $(5, 3)$

29. For each vector given, compute its coördinate vector relative to the orthonormal basis
$B = \left\{ 1, \sqrt{3}(2x - 1), \sqrt{5}(6x^2 - 6x + 1) \right\}$ under the inner product $\langle p, q \rangle = \int_0^1 p(x)q(x)dx$ for P_2.

(a) x (b) x^2 (c) $1 - x + x^2$

30. Consider R^2 with the Euclidean inner product. In each part, use the Gram–Schmidt process to transform the given basis into an orthonormal basis.

(a) $\mathbf{u}_1 = (1,1)$, $\mathbf{u}_2 = (1,2)$ (b) $\mathbf{u}_1 = (3,-1)$, $\mathbf{u}_2 = (0,1)$

31. Consider R^3 with the Euclidean inner product. In each part, use the Gram–Schmidt process to transform the given basis into an orthonormal basis.

(a) $\mathbf{u}_1 = (1,1,1)$, $\mathbf{u}_2 = (1,1,0)$, $\mathbf{u}_3 = (1,0,0)$

(b) $\mathbf{u}_1 = (1,2,-1)$, $\mathbf{u}_2 = (1,3,0)$, $\mathbf{u}_3 = (4,1,0)$

32. Consider R^2 with the inner product $\langle \mathbf{u}, \mathbf{v} \rangle = 3u_1v_1 + 5u_2v_2$. In each part, use Gram–Schmidt process to transform the given basis into an orthonormal basis.

(a) $\mathbf{u}_1 = (2,-1)$, $\mathbf{u}_2 = (1,1)$ (b) $\mathbf{u}_2 = (1,1)$, $\mathbf{u}_2 = (1,0)$

33. Consider P_2 with the inner product $\langle p, q \rangle = \int_{-1}^{1} p(x)q(x)dx$. In each part, use the Gram–Schmidt process to transform the given basis into an orthonormal basis.

(a) $\mathbf{u}_1 = 1 + x^2$, $\mathbf{u}_2 = 1 - x^2$, $\mathbf{u}_3 = x$

(b) $\mathbf{u}_1 = 2$, $\mathbf{u}_2 = 3x$, $\mathbf{u}_3 = 4x^2$

34. Find the QR–decomposition of A under the Euclidena inner product.

(a) $A = \begin{bmatrix} 1 & 1 \\ 1 & -2 \end{bmatrix}$ (b) $A = \begin{bmatrix} 1 & 2 \\ 0 & 1 \\ 1 & 0 \end{bmatrix}$ (c) $A = \begin{bmatrix} 2 & 0 & 2 \\ 2 & 2 & -1 \\ 1 & -1 & -2 \end{bmatrix}$

35. Use $\det(A^T A)$ to determine whether the column vectors of A are linearly independent.

(a) $A = \begin{bmatrix} 1 & 2 & 1 \\ 0 & 1 & -1 \\ 1 & -1 & 0 \end{bmatrix}$ (b) $A = \begin{bmatrix} 3 & 1 & 2 \\ 0 & -2 & 1 \\ 0 & 1 & 1 \\ 5 & 0 & 2 \end{bmatrix}$ (c) $A = \begin{bmatrix} 2 & 3 & -1 \\ 3 & 4 & 1 \\ 0 & 1 & -5 \\ 1 & 2 & -3 \\ -1 & 0 & -7 \end{bmatrix}$

36. In each part, determine the least squares solution of the linear system $A\mathbf{x} = \mathbf{b}$, as well as the projection of $\mathbf{b}$ on the column space of A.

(a) $A = \begin{bmatrix} 2 & 1 \\ 1 & 0 \\ 2 & 3 \end{bmatrix}$, $\mathbf{b} = \begin{bmatrix} 26 \\ -13 \\ 0 \end{bmatrix}$ (b) $A = \begin{bmatrix} 7 & 6 \\ 0 & 3 \\ -2 & 1 \end{bmatrix}$, $\mathbf{b} = \begin{bmatrix} 3 \\ 12 \\ 10 \end{bmatrix}$

(c) $A = \begin{bmatrix} 2 & 1 \\ 0 & 1 \\ -1 & 1 \\ 3 & 0 \end{bmatrix}$, $\mathbf{b} = \begin{bmatrix} 1 \\ 3 \\ 3 \\ -3 \end{bmatrix}$ (d) $A = \begin{bmatrix} 1 & 0 & 1 \\ 0 & 1 & -2 \\ 1 & 0 & 0 \\ 1 & 0 & 1 \end{bmatrix}$, $\mathbf{b} = \begin{bmatrix} 6 \\ -6 \\ 2 \\ 4 \end{bmatrix}$

37. Find the orthogonal projection of $\mathbf{u}$ on span $\{\mathbf{v}_1, \mathbf{v}_2\}$.

    (a) $\mathbf{u} = (1, 3, -2)$, $\mathbf{v}_1 = (1, 0, 3)$, $\mathbf{v}_2 = (1, 1, 2)$

    (b) $\mathbf{u} = (1, 1, 1, 1)$, $\mathbf{v}_1 = (2, 1, 0, 1)$, $\mathbf{v}_2 = (2, 0, -1, 0)$

38. Find the orthogonal projection of $\mathbf{u}$ on nullspace A.

    (a) $\mathbf{u} = (-1, 2, 3, 4)$, $A = \begin{bmatrix} 1 & -1 & 2 & 0 \\ 1 & 1 & 0 & 2 \end{bmatrix}$

    (b) $\mathbf{u} = (0, 2, 1, -1, 1)$, $A = \begin{bmatrix} 1 & 1 & 1 & 0 & 1 \\ 2 & 3 & 1 & 1 & 1 \\ 1 & -1 & 3 & -2 & 3 \end{bmatrix}$

39. Let W be the plane with equation $2x + y - 3z = 0$.

    (a)   Find a basis for W.

    (b)   Find the stnadard matrix $[P] = A(A^T A)^{-1} A^T$ for the orthogonal projection on W.

    (c)   Use your answer to part (b) to find the distance between $P(0, 4, -1)$ and W.

40. Let W be the line with parametric equations $x = 3t$, $y = 4t$, $z = -t$ where $-\infty < t < \infty$.

    (a)   Find a basis for W.

    (b)   Find the standard matrix $[P] = A(A^T A)^{-1} A^T$ for the orthogonal projection on W.

    (c)   Use your answer to part (b) to find the distance between $P(2, 2, 1)$ and W.

41. Show whether the matrix A is orthogonal.

    (a) $A = \begin{bmatrix} 4/5 & 3/5 \\ -3/5 & 4/5 \end{bmatrix}$ (b) $A = \begin{bmatrix} 1/3 & 2/3 & 2/3 \\ 2/3 & 1/3 & -2/3 \\ 2/3 & -2/3 & 1/3 \end{bmatrix}$ (c) $A = \begin{bmatrix} 1/\sqrt{3} & -1/\sqrt{6} & 3/\sqrt{14} \\ 1/\sqrt{3} & 2/\sqrt{6} & -2/\sqrt{14} \\ 1/\sqrt{3} & -1/\sqrt{6} & -1/\sqrt{14} \end{bmatrix}$

    (d) $\begin{bmatrix} 2/3 & -1/3 & 2/3 \\ 1/\sqrt{2} & 0 & -1/\sqrt{2} \\ 1/\sqrt{18} & 4/\sqrt{18} & 1/\sqrt{18} \end{bmatrix}$

42. Consider the bases $B = \{\mathbf{u}_1, \mathbf{u}_2\}$ and $B' = \{\mathbf{v}_1, \mathbf{v}_2\}$ for R^2, where

$$\mathbf{u}_1 = \begin{bmatrix} 1 \\ 2 \end{bmatrix}, \qquad \mathbf{u}_2 = \begin{bmatrix} 3 \\ 5 \end{bmatrix}, \qquad \mathbf{v}_1 = \begin{bmatrix} 1 \\ 1 \end{bmatrix}, \qquad \mathbf{v}_2 = \begin{bmatrix} 0 \\ 1 \end{bmatrix}.$$

    (a)   Find the transition matrix $P_{B',B}$ from B to B'.

    (b)   Find the transition matrix $P_{B,B'}$ from B' to B.

    (c)   Compute the coördinate matrix $[\mathbf{w}]_{B'}$ where $\mathbf{w} = \begin{bmatrix} 4 \\ 7 \end{bmatrix}$.

    (d)   Use your answers to parts (b) and (c) to compute $[\mathbf{w}]_B$.

43. Consider the bases $\quad B = \{u_1, u_2\}$ and $\quad B' = \{v_1, v_2\}$ for R^2, where

$$u_1 = \begin{bmatrix} 3 \\ 3 \end{bmatrix}, \qquad u_2 = \begin{bmatrix} -2 \\ 1 \end{bmatrix}, \qquad v_1 = \begin{bmatrix} 2 \\ 5 \end{bmatrix}, \qquad v_2 = \begin{bmatrix} 3 \\ 7 \end{bmatrix}.$$

(a) Find the transition matrix $P_{B',B}$ from B to B'.

(b) Find the transition matrix $P_{B,B'}$ from B' to B.

(c) Compute the coördinate matrix $[w]_{B'}$ where $w = \begin{bmatrix} 4 \\ 7 \end{bmatrix}$.

(d) Use your answers to parts (b) and (c) to compute $[w]_B$.

44. Consider the bases $\quad B = \{u_1, u_2, u_3\}$ and $\quad B' = \{v_1, v_2, v_3\}$ for R^3, where

$$u_1 = \begin{bmatrix} 1 \\ 0 \\ 3 \end{bmatrix}, \quad u_2 = \begin{bmatrix} 0 \\ 1 \\ 0 \end{bmatrix}, \quad u_3 = \begin{bmatrix} -2 \\ 5 \\ 1 \end{bmatrix}, \quad v_1 = \begin{bmatrix} -2 \\ 1 \\ 1 \end{bmatrix}, \quad v_2 = \begin{bmatrix} 0 \\ 1 \\ -1 \end{bmatrix}, \quad v_3 = \begin{bmatrix} 1 \\ 0 \\ 0 \end{bmatrix}.$$

(a) Find the transition matrix $P_{B',B}$ from B to B'.

(b) Find the transition matrix $P_{B,B'}$ from B' to B.

(c) Compute the coördinate matrix $[w]_{B'}$ where $w = \begin{bmatrix} 2 \\ 3 \\ -1 \end{bmatrix}$.

(d) Use your answers to parts (b) and (c) to compute $[w]_B$.

45. Consider the bases $\quad B = \{u_1, u_2, u_3\}$ and $\quad B' = \{v_1, v_2, v_3\}$ for R^3, where

$$u_1 = \begin{bmatrix} 1 \\ 0 \\ 0 \end{bmatrix}, \quad u_2 = \begin{bmatrix} 3 \\ 3 \\ 0 \end{bmatrix}, \quad u_3 = \begin{bmatrix} 5 \\ 5 \\ 5 \end{bmatrix}, \quad v_1 = \begin{bmatrix} 0 \\ 2 \\ 2 \end{bmatrix}, \quad v_2 = \begin{bmatrix} 2 \\ 4 \\ 0 \end{bmatrix}, \quad v_3 = \begin{bmatrix} 4 \\ 4 \\ 4 \end{bmatrix}.$$

(a) Find the transition matrix $P_{B',B}$ from B to B'.

(b) Find the transition matrix $P_{B,B'}$ from B' to B.

(c) Compute the coördinate matrix $[w]_{B'}$ where $w = \begin{bmatrix} 2 \\ 3 \\ -1 \end{bmatrix}$.

(d) Use your answers to parts (b) and (c) to compute $[w]_B$.

46. Consider the bases $\quad B = \{p_1, p_2\}$ and $\quad B' = \{q_1, q_2\}$ for P_1, where

$$p_1 = 1 + 2x, \qquad p_2 = 3 - 3x, \qquad q_1 = x, \qquad q_2 = 4 + x.$$

(a) Find the transition matrix $P_{B,B'}$ from B' to B.

(b) Find the transition matrix $P_{B',B}$ from B to B'.

(c) Compute the coördinate matrix $[p]_B$ where $p = 1 + x$.

(d) Use your answers to parts (b) and (c) to compute $[p]_{B'}$.

47. Consider the bases $\quad B = \{f_1, f_2\}$ and $\quad B' = \{g_1, g_2\}$ for span $\{e^x, xe^x\}$, where $f_1 = 3e^x - xe^x$, $\quad f_2 = 2e^x$, $\quad g_1 = 4e^x - 2xe^x$, $\quad g_2 = -e^x + 3xe^x$.

94

(a) Find the transition matrix $P_{B,B'}$ from B' to B.

(b) Find the transition matrix $P_{B',B}$ from B to B'.

(c) Compute the coördinate matrix $[\mathbf{h}]_B$ where $\mathbf{h} = 5e^x + xe^x$.

(d) Use your answers to parts (b) and (c) to compute $[\mathbf{h}]_{B'}$.

48. Suppose a rectangular $x'y'$–coördinate system is obtained by rotating a rectangular xy–coördinate system counterclockwise about the origin through the angle $\theta = \frac{\pi}{6}$.

(a) Compute the $x'y'$–coördinates of the point whose xy–coördinates are $(12, -4)$.

(b) Compute the xy–coördinates of the point whose $x'y'$–coördinates are (a, b).

49. Suppose a rectangular $x'y'z'$–coördinate system is obtained by rotating a rectangular xyz–coördinate system counterclockwise about the z–axis (looking down the z–axis) through the angle $\theta = \frac{2}{3}\pi$.

(a) Compute the $x'y'z'$–coördinates of the point whose xyz–coördinates are $(2, 4, 6)$.

(b) Compute the xyz–coördinates of the point whose $x'y'z'$–coördinates are (a, b, c).

50. Suppose a rectangular $x''y''z''$–coördinate system is obtained by first rotating a rectangular xyz–coördinate system counterclockwise about the x–axis (looking along the positive x–axis toward the origin) through the angle $\theta = \frac{\pi}{4}$ to obtain an $x'y'z'$–coördinate system, and then rotating the $x'y'z$–coördinate system counterclockwise about the y'–axis (looking along the positive y'–axis toward the origin) through the angle $\theta = \frac{\pi}{3}$.

(a) Compute the $x''y''z''$–coördinates of the point whose xyz–coördinates are $(-4, 12, 8)$.

(b) Compute the xyz–coördinates of the point whose $x''y''z''$–coördinates are (a, b, c).

WRITING QUESTIONS

51. Explain in what way a vector space acquires a "geometry" when it is given an inner product.

52. What advantages do orthonormal bases have over other bases?

53. Without using any numerals or symbols, summarize the goal of the Gram–Schmidt process and how that goal is achieved.

54. What is a QR–decomposition?

55. What is the purpose of a transition matrix from basis B to B'? Isn't it easier to just compute co-ordinates in B' directly and not worry about B?

56. If you were writing your own text in linear algebra, would you include the discussion of transition matrices within the chapter on inner product spaces? Why or why not?

SECTION 6.1 *INNER PRODUCTS*

1.(a)   symmetry: $\langle \mathbf{u}, \mathbf{v} \rangle = \langle \mathbf{v}, \mathbf{u} \rangle$

$$
\begin{aligned}
\langle (u_1, u_2), (v_1, v_2) \rangle &= \langle (v_1, v_2), (u_1, u_2) \rangle \\
u_1 v_1 + 2u_2 v_2 &= v_1 u_1 + 2v_2 u_2 \\
&= u_1 v_1 + 2u_2 v_2
\end{aligned}
$$

additivity: $\langle \mathbf{u} + \mathbf{v}, \mathbf{w} \rangle = \langle \mathbf{u}, \mathbf{w} \rangle + \langle \mathbf{v}, \mathbf{w} \rangle$

$$
\begin{aligned}
\langle (u_1, u_2) + (v_1, v_2), (w_1, w_2) \rangle &= \langle (u_1, u_2), (w_1, w_2) \rangle + \langle (v_1, v_2), (w_1, w_2) \rangle \\
\langle (u_1 + v_1, u_2 + v_2), (w_1, w_2) \rangle &= (u_1 w_1 + 2u_2 w_2) + (v_1 w_1 + 2v_2 w_2) \\
(u_1 + v_1) w_1 + 2(u_2 + v_2) w_2 &= (u_1 w_1 + v_1 w_1) + (2u_2 w_2 + 2v_2 w_2) \\
(u_1 w_1 + v_1 w_1) + (2u_2 w_2 + 2v_2 w_2) &=
\end{aligned}
$$

homogeneity: $\langle k\mathbf{u}, \mathbf{v} \rangle = k\langle \mathbf{u}, \mathbf{v} \rangle$

$$
\begin{aligned}
\langle k(u_1, u_2), (v_1, v_2) \rangle &= k\langle (u_1, u_2), (v_1, v_2) \rangle \\
\langle (ku_1, ku_2), (v_1, v_2) \rangle &= k(u_1 v_1 + 2u_2 v_2) \\
(ku_1) v_1 + 2(ku_2) v_2 &= k(u_1 v_1) + 2k(u_2 v_2) \\
&= (ku_1) v_1 + 2(ku_2) v_2
\end{aligned}
$$

positivity:
$$
\begin{aligned}
\langle \mathbf{v}, \mathbf{v} \rangle &= \langle (v_1, v_2), (v_1, v_2) \rangle \\
&= v_1 v_1 + 2v_2 v_2 \\
&= v_1^2 + 2v_2^2
\end{aligned}
$$

so $\langle \mathbf{v}, \mathbf{v} \rangle \geq 0$,

and $\langle \mathbf{v}, \mathbf{v} \rangle = 0$ implies
$$
\begin{aligned}
v_1 + 2v_2^2 &= 0 \\
v_1^2 &= 2v_2^2 = 0 \\
v_1 &= v_2 = 0 \\
(v_1, v_2) &= (0, 0) \\
\mathbf{v} &= \mathbf{0}.
\end{aligned}
$$

The function is an inner product.

1. (b)   symmetry: $\langle \mathbf{u}, \mathbf{v} \rangle = \langle \mathbf{v}, \mathbf{u} \rangle$

$$
\begin{aligned}
\langle (u_1, u_2), (v_1, v_2) \rangle &= \langle (v_1, v_2), (u_1, u_2) \rangle \\
u_1 v_2 + u_2 v_1 &= v_1 u_2 + v_2 u_1 \\
&= u_2 v_1 + u_1 v_2 \\
&= u_1 v_2 + u_2 v_1
\end{aligned}
$$

additivity: $\langle \mathbf{u} + \mathbf{v}, \mathbf{w} \rangle = \langle \mathbf{u}, \mathbf{w} \rangle + \langle \mathbf{v}, \mathbf{w} \rangle$

$$
\begin{aligned}
\langle (u_1, u_2) + (v_1, v_2), (w_1, w_2) \rangle &= \langle (u_1, u_2), (w_1, w_2) \rangle + \langle (v_1, v_2), (w_1, w_2) \rangle \\
\langle (u_1 + v_1, u_2 + v_2), (w_1, w_2) \rangle &= (u_1 w_2 + u_2 w_1) + (v_1 w_2 + v_2 w_1) \\
(u_1 + v_1) w_2 + (u_2 + v_2) w_1 &= (u_1 w_2 + v_1 w_2) + (u_2 w_1 + v_2 w_1) \\
(u_1 w_2 + v_1 w_2) + (u_2 w_1 + v_2 w_1) &=
\end{aligned}
$$

homogeneity: $\langle k\mathbf{u}, \mathbf{v} \rangle = k\langle \mathbf{u}, \mathbf{v} \rangle$

$$\langle k(u_1, u_2), (v_1, v_2) \rangle = k\langle (u_1, u_2), (v_1, v_2) \rangle$$
$$\langle (ku_1, ku_2), (v_1, v_2) \rangle = k(u_1 v_2 + u_2 v_1)$$
$$(ku_1)v_2 + (ku_2)v_1 = k(u_1 v_2) + k(u_2 v_1)$$
$$= (ku_1)v_2 + (ku_2)v_1$$

positivity: $\langle \mathbf{v}, \mathbf{v} \rangle = \langle (v_1, v_2), (v_1, v_2) \rangle$
$$= v_1 v_2 + v_2 v_1$$
$$= 2 v_1 v_2$$

so $\quad \langle \mathbf{v}, \mathbf{v} \rangle \geq 0 \quad$ is false;

for example, $\quad \langle (1, -1,), (1, -1) \rangle = 1(-1) + (-1)(1) = -2$

Since the positivity axiom fails, this is not an inner product.

1. (c) symmetry: $\langle \mathbf{u}, \mathbf{v} \rangle = \langle \mathbf{v}, \mathbf{u} \rangle$
$$\langle (u_1, u_2), (v_1, v_2) \rangle = \langle (v_1, v_2), (u_1, u_2) \rangle$$
$$3 u_1 v_1 - 2 u_2 v_2 = 3 v_1 u_1 - 2 v_2 u_2$$
$$= 3 u_1 v_1 - 2 u_2 v_2$$

additivity: $\langle \mathbf{u} + \mathbf{v}, \mathbf{w} \rangle = \langle \mathbf{u}, \mathbf{w} \rangle + \langle \mathbf{v}, \mathbf{w} \rangle$
$$\langle (u_1, u_2) + (v_1, v_2), (w_1, w_2) \rangle = \langle (u_1, u_2), (w_1, w_2) \rangle + \langle (v_1, v_2), (w_1, w_2) \rangle$$
$$\langle (u_1 + v_1, u_2 + v_2), (w_1, w_2) \rangle = (3 u_1 w_1 - 2 u_2 w_2) + (3 v_1 w_1 - 2 v_2 w_2)$$
$$3(u_1 + v_1)w_1 - 2(u_2 + v_2)w_2 = (3 u_1 w_1 + 3 v_1 w_1) + (-2 u_2 w_2 + -2 v_2 w_2)$$
$$(3 u_1 w_1 + 3 v_1 w_1) - (2 u_2 w_2 + 2 v_2 w_2) = (3 u_1 w_1 + 3 v_1 w_1) - (2 u_2 w_2 + 2 v_2 w_2)$$

homogeneity: $\langle k\mathbf{u}, \mathbf{v} \rangle = k\langle \mathbf{u}, \mathbf{v} \rangle$
$$\langle k(u_1, u_2), (v_1, v_2) \rangle = k\langle (u_1, u_2), (v_1, v_2) \rangle$$
$$\langle (ku_1, ku_2), (v_1, v_2) \rangle = k(3 u_1 v_1 - 2 u_2 v_2)$$
$$3(ku_1)v_1 - 2(ku_2)v_2 = 3(ku_1)v_1 - 2(ku_2)v_2$$

positivity: $\langle \mathbf{v}, \mathbf{v} \rangle = \langle (v_1, v_2), (v_1, v_2) \rangle$
$$= 3 v_1 v_1 - 2 v_2 v_2$$
$$= 3 v_1^2 - 2 v_2^2$$

so $\quad \langle \mathbf{v}, \mathbf{v} \rangle \geq 0 \quad$ is false;

for example, $\quad \langle (1, 2), (1, 2) \rangle = 3(1)(1) - 2(2)(2) = -5$

Since the positivity axiom fails, this is not an inner product.

2.(a) symmetry: $\langle \mathbf{u}, \mathbf{v} \rangle = \langle \mathbf{v}, \mathbf{u} \rangle$
$$\langle (u_1, u_2, u_3), (v_1, v_2, v_3) \rangle = \langle (v_1, v_2, v_3), (u_1, u_2, u_3) \rangle$$
$$2 u_1 v_1 + 3 u_2 v_2 = 2 v_1 u_1 + 3 v_2 u_2$$
$$= 2 u_1 v_1 + 3 u_2 v_2$$

additivity: $\langle \mathbf{u} + \mathbf{v}, \mathbf{w} \rangle = \langle \mathbf{u}, \mathbf{w} \rangle + \langle \mathbf{v}, \mathbf{w} \rangle$

But $\quad \langle \mathbf{u} + \mathbf{v}, \mathbf{w} \rangle = \langle (u_1, u_2, u_3) + (v_1, v_2, v_3), (w_1, w_2, w_3) \rangle$
$$= \langle (u_1 + v_1, u_2 + v_2, u_3 + v_3), (w_1, w_2, w_3) \rangle$$
$$= 2(u_1 + v_1)w_1 + 3(u_2 + v_2)w_2$$
$$= (2 u_1 w_1 + 2 v_1 w_1) + (3 u_2 w_2 + 3 v_2 w_2)$$

and $\quad \langle \mathbf{u}, \mathbf{w} \rangle + \langle \mathbf{v}, \mathbf{w} \rangle = \langle (u_1, u_2, u_3), (w_1, w_2, w_3) \rangle + \langle (v_1, v_2, v_3), (w_1, w_2, w_3) \rangle$
$$= (2 u_1 w_1 + 3 u_2 w_2) + (2 v_1 w_1 + 3 v_2 w_2)$$
$$= (2 u_1 w_1 + 2 v_1 w_1) + (3 u_2 w_2 + 3 v_2 w_2)$$

homogeneity: $\langle k\mathbf{u}, \mathbf{v}\rangle = k\langle \mathbf{u}, \mathbf{v}\rangle$

$$
\begin{aligned}
\langle k(u_1, u_2, u_3), (v_1, v_2, v_3)\rangle &= k\langle (u_1, u_2, u_3), (v_1, v_2, v_3)\rangle \\
\langle (ku_1, ku_2, ku_3), (v_1, v_2, v_3)\rangle &= k(2u_1 v_1 + 3u_2 v_2) \\
2(ku_1)v_1 + 3(ku_2)v_2 &= 2(ku_1)v_1 + 3(ku_2)v_2
\end{aligned}
$$

positivity:
$$
\begin{aligned}
\langle \mathbf{v}, \mathbf{v}\rangle &= \langle (v_1, v_2, v_3), (v_1, v_2, v_3)\rangle \\
&= 2v_1 v_1 + 3v_2 v_2 \\
&= 2v_1^2 + 3v_2^2
\end{aligned}
$$

so $\quad \langle \mathbf{v}, \mathbf{v}\rangle \geq 0$,

and $\quad \langle \mathbf{v}, \mathbf{v}\rangle = 0 \qquad$ implies $\qquad 2v_1^2 + 3v_2^2 = 0$

$$2v_1^2 = 3v_2^2 = 0$$

$$v_1 = v_2 = 0$$

but not $\qquad v_3 = 0;$

for example, $\quad \langle (0,0,1), (0,0,1)\rangle = 2(0)(0) + 3(0)(0) = 0.$

Since the positivity axiom fails, this is not an inner product.

(b) symmetry: $\langle \mathbf{u}, \mathbf{v}\rangle = \langle \mathbf{v}, \mathbf{u}\rangle$

$$
\begin{aligned}
\langle (u_1, u_2, u_3), (v_1, v_2, v_3)\rangle &= \langle (v_1, v_2, v_3), (u_1, u_2, u_3)\rangle \\
u_1 v_1 + u_2 v_2 + u_3 v_3 + u_1 u_2 v_3 &= v_1 u_1 + v_2 u_2 + v_3 u_3 + v_1 v_2 u_3, \qquad \text{false.}
\end{aligned}
$$

Since the symmetry axiom fails, this is not an inner product.

(c) symmetry: $\langle \mathbf{u}, \mathbf{v}\rangle = \langle \mathbf{v}, \mathbf{u}\rangle$

$$
\begin{aligned}
\text{But} \quad \langle \mathbf{u}, \mathbf{v}\rangle &= \langle (u_1, u_2, u_3) + (v_1, v_2, v_3)\rangle \\
&= 2u_1 v_1 + 5u_2 v_2 + u_3 v_3 - u_2 v_3 - u_3 v_2
\end{aligned}
$$

$$
\begin{aligned}
\text{and} \quad \langle \mathbf{v}, \mathbf{u}\rangle &= \langle (v_1, v_2, v_3), (u_1, u_2, u_3)\rangle \\
&= 2v_1 u_1 + 5v_2 u_2 + v_3 u_3 - v_2 u_3 - v_3 u_2 \\
&= 2u_1 v_1 + 5u_2 v_2 + u_3 v_3 - u_3 v_2 - u_2 v_3 \\
&= 2u_1 v_1 + 5u_2 v_2 + u_3 v_3 - u_2 v_3 - u_3 v_2
\end{aligned}
$$

additivity: $\langle \mathbf{u} + \mathbf{v}, \mathbf{w}\rangle = \langle \mathbf{u}, \mathbf{w}\rangle + \langle \mathbf{v}, \mathbf{w}\rangle$

$$
\begin{aligned}
\text{But} \quad \langle \mathbf{u} + \mathbf{v}, \mathbf{w}\rangle &= \langle (u_1, u_2, u_3) + (v_1, v_2, v_3), (w_1, w_2, w_3)\rangle \\
&= \langle (u_1 + v_1, u_2 + v_2, u_3 + v_3), (w_1, w_2, w_3)\rangle \\
&= 2(u_1 + v_1)w_1 + 5(u_2 + v_2)w_2 + (u_3 + v_3)w_3 - (u_2 + v_2)w_3 \\
&\quad - (u_3 + v_3)w_2 \\
&= 2u_1 w_1 + 2v_1 w_1 + 5u_2 w_2 + 5v_2 w_2 + u_3 w_3 + v_3 w_3 - u_2 w_3 \\
&\quad - v_2 w_3 - u_3 w_2 - v_3 w_2
\end{aligned}
$$

$$
\begin{aligned}
\text{and} \quad \langle \mathbf{u}, \mathbf{w}\rangle + \langle \mathbf{v}, \mathbf{w}\rangle &= 2u_1 w_1 + 5u_2 w_2 + u_3 w_3 - u_2 w_3 - u_3 w_2 \\
&\quad + 2v_1 w_1 + 5v_2 w_2 + v_3 w_3 - v_2 w_3 - v_3 w_2 \\
&= 2u_1 w_1 + 2v_1 w_1 + 5u_2 w_2 + 5v_2 w_2 + u_3 w_3 + v_3 w_3 - u_2 w_3 \\
&\quad - v_2 w_3 - u_3 w_2 - v_3 w_2
\end{aligned}
$$

homogeneity: $\langle k\mathbf{u}, \mathbf{v}\rangle = k\langle \mathbf{u}, \mathbf{v}\rangle$

But $\langle k\mathbf{u}, \mathbf{v} \rangle = \langle k(u_1, u_2, u_3), (v_1, v_2, v_3) \rangle$
$$= \langle (ku_1, ku_2, ku_3), (v_1, v_2, v_3) \rangle$$
$$= 2(ku_1)v_1 + 5(ku_2)v_2 + (ku_3)v_3 - (ku_2)v_3 - (ku_3)v_2$$

and $k\langle \mathbf{u}, \mathbf{v} \rangle = k\langle (u_1, u_2, u_3), (v_1, v_2, v_3) \rangle$
$$= k(2u_1v_1 + 5u_2v_2 + u_3v_3 - u_2v_3 - u_3v_2)$$
$$= 2(ku_1)v_1 + 5(ku_2)v_2 + (ku_3)v_3 - (ku_2)v_3 - (ku_3)v_2$$

positivity: $\langle \mathbf{v}, \mathbf{v} \rangle = \langle (v_1, v_2, v_3), (v_1, v_2, v_3) \rangle$
$$= 2v_1v_1 + 5v_2v_2 + v_3v_3 - v_2v_3 - v_3v_2$$
$$= 2v_1^2 + 5v_2^2 + v_3^2 - 2v_2v_3$$
$$= 2v_1^2 + 4v_2^2 + v_2^2 + v_3^2 - 2v_2v_3$$
$$= 2v_1^2 + 4v_2^2 + (v_2 - v_3)^2$$

so $\langle \mathbf{v}, \mathbf{v} \rangle \geq 0,$
and $\langle \mathbf{v}, \mathbf{v} \rangle = 0$ implies
$$2v_1^2 + 4v_2^2 + (v_2 - v_3)^2 = 0$$
$$2v_1 = 4v_2^2 = (v_2 - v_3)^2 = 0$$
$$v_1 = v_2 = v_2 - v_3 = 0$$
$$v_1 = v_2 = v_3 = 0$$
$$(v_1, v_2, v_3) = (0, 0, 0)$$
$$\mathbf{v} = 0.$$

The function is an inner product.

3.   (a) $\langle \mathbf{u}, \mathbf{v} \rangle = \langle (1, 3, -1), (2, 0, 5) \rangle$

$$= (1)(2) + (3)(0) + (-1)(5)$$

$$= -3$$

(b) $\|\mathbf{u}\| = \langle \mathbf{u}, \mathbf{u} \rangle^{1/2}$

$$= \langle (1, 3, -1), (1, 3, -1) \rangle^{1/2}$$

$$= [(1)(1) + (3)(3) + (-1)(-1)]^{1/2}$$

$$= \sqrt{11}$$

(c) $\|\mathbf{v}\| = \langle \mathbf{v}, \mathbf{v} \rangle^{1/2}$

$$= \langle (2, 0, 5), (2, 0, 5) \rangle^{1/2}$$

$$= [(2)(2) + (0)(0) + (5)(5)]^{1/2}$$

$$= \sqrt{29}$$

(d) $d(\mathbf{u}, \mathbf{v}) = \|\mathbf{u}, \mathbf{v}\|$

$$= \langle \mathbf{u} - \mathbf{v}, \mathbf{u} - \mathbf{v} \rangle^{1/2}$$

$$= \langle (-1, 3, -6), (-1, 3, -6) \rangle^{1/2}$$

$$= [(-1)(-1) + (3)(3) + (-6)(-6)]^{1/2}$$

$$= \sqrt{46}$$

4. (a) $\langle \mathbf{u}, \mathbf{v} \rangle = \langle (2\sqrt{3}, 2), (-3/2, 3/2\sqrt{3}) \rangle$

$= (2\sqrt{3})(-3/2) + (2)(3/2\sqrt{3})$

$= 0$

(b) $\|\mathbf{u}\| = \langle \mathbf{u}, \mathbf{u} \rangle^{1/2}$

$= \langle (2\sqrt{3}, 2), (2\sqrt{3}, 2) \rangle^{1/2}$

$= [(2\sqrt{3})(2\sqrt{3}) + (2)(2)]^{1/2}$

$= \sqrt{16} = 4$

(c) $\|\mathbf{v}\| = \langle \mathbf{v}, \mathbf{v} \rangle^{1/2}$

$= \langle (-3/2, 3/2\sqrt{3}), (-3/2, 3/2\sqrt{3}) \rangle^{1/2}$

$= [(-3/2)(-3/2) + (3/2\sqrt{3})(3/2\sqrt{3})]^{1/2}$

$= \sqrt{9} = 3$

(d) $d(\mathbf{u}, \mathbf{v}) = \|\mathbf{u} - \mathbf{v}\|$

$= \langle \mathbf{u} - \mathbf{v}, \mathbf{u} - \mathbf{v} \rangle^{1/2}$

$= \langle (2\sqrt{3} + 3/2, 2 - 3/2\sqrt{3}), (2\sqrt{3} + 3/2, 2 - 3/2\sqrt{3}) \rangle^{1/2}$

$= [(2\sqrt{3} + 3/2)^2 + (2 - 3/2\sqrt{3})^2]^{1/2}$

$= [(12 + 3\sqrt{3} + 9/4) + (4 - 3\sqrt{3} + 27/4)]^{1/2}$

$= \sqrt{25} = 5$

5. (a) $\langle \mathbf{u}, \mathbf{v} \rangle = \langle (1, -3), (5, 1) \rangle$

$= 3(1)(5) + 5(-3)(1)$

$= 0$

(b) $\|\mathbf{u}\| = \langle \mathbf{u}, \mathbf{u} \rangle^{1/2}$

$= \langle (1, -3), (1, -3) \rangle^{1/2}$

$= [3(1)(1) + 5(-3)(-3)]^{1/2}$

$= \sqrt{48} = 4\sqrt{3}$

(c) $\|\mathbf{v}\| = \langle \mathbf{v}, \mathbf{v} \rangle^{1/2}$

$= \langle (5, 1), (5, 1) \rangle^{1/2}$

$= [3(5)(5) + 5(1)(1)]^{1/2}$

$= \sqrt{80} = 4\sqrt{5}$

(d) $d(\mathbf{u}, \mathbf{v}) = \|\mathbf{u} - \mathbf{v}\|$

$= \langle \mathbf{u} - \mathbf{v}, \mathbf{u} - \mathbf{v} \rangle^{1/2}$

$= \langle (-4, -4), (-4, -4) \rangle^{1/2}$

$= [3(-4)(-4) + 5(-4)(-4)]^{1/2}$

$= \sqrt{128} = 8\sqrt{2}$

6.   (a) $\langle A, B \rangle = \left\langle \begin{bmatrix} 1 & 3 \\ -2 & 4 \end{bmatrix}, \begin{bmatrix} 2 & -1 \\ 2 & 0 \end{bmatrix} \right\rangle$

$$= (1)(2) + (3)(-1) + (-2)(2) + (4)(0)$$
$$= -5$$

(b) $\|A\| = \langle A, A \rangle^{1/2}$

$$= \left\langle \begin{bmatrix} 1 & 3 \\ -2 & 4 \end{bmatrix}, \begin{bmatrix} 1 & 3 \\ -2 & 4 \end{bmatrix} \right\rangle^{1/2}$$
$$= [(1)(1) + (3)(3) + (-2)(-2) + (4)(4)]^{1/2}$$
$$= \sqrt{30}$$

(c) $\|B\| = \langle B, B \rangle^{1/2}$

$$= \left\langle \begin{bmatrix} 2 & -1 \\ 2 & 0 \end{bmatrix}, \begin{bmatrix} 2 & -1 \\ 2 & 0 \end{bmatrix} \right\rangle^{1/2}$$
$$= [(2)(2) + (-1)(-1) + (2)(2) + (0)(0)]^{1/2}$$
$$= \sqrt{9} = 3$$

(d) $d(A, B) = \|A - B\|$

$$= \langle A - B, A - B \rangle^{1/2}$$
$$= \left\langle \begin{bmatrix} -1 & 4 \\ -4 & 4 \end{bmatrix}, \begin{bmatrix} -1 & 4 \\ -4 & 4 \end{bmatrix} \right\rangle^{1/2}$$
$$= [(-1)(-1) + (4)(4) + (-4)(-4) + (4)(4)]^{1/2}$$
$$= \sqrt{49} = 7$$

7.   (a) $\langle \mathbf{p}, \mathbf{q} \rangle = \langle 1 + x^2, 1 - x^2 \rangle$

$$= (1)(1) + (0)(0) + (1)(-1)$$
$$= 0$$

(b) $\|\mathbf{p}\| = \langle \mathbf{p}, \mathbf{p} \rangle^{1/2}$

$$= \langle 1 + x^2, 1 + x^2 \rangle$$
$$= [(1)(1) + (0)(0) + (1)(1)]^{1/2}$$
$$= \sqrt{2}$$

(c) $\|\mathbf{q}\| = \langle \mathbf{q}, \mathbf{q} \rangle^{1/2}$

$$= \langle 1 - x^2, 1 - x^2 \rangle^{1/2}$$
$$= [(1)(1) + (0)(0) + (-1)(-1)]^{1/2}$$
$$= \sqrt{2}$$

(d) $d(\mathbf{p}, \mathbf{q}) = \|\mathbf{p} - \mathbf{q}\|$

$\qquad = \langle \mathbf{p} - \mathbf{q}, \mathbf{p} - \mathbf{q} \rangle^{1/2}$

$\qquad = \langle 2x^2, 2x^2 \rangle^{1/2}$

$\qquad = [(0)(0) + (0)(0) + (2)(2)]^{1/2}$

$\qquad = \sqrt{4} = 2$

8.   (a) $\langle \mathbf{u}, \mathbf{v} \rangle = A\mathbf{u} \cdot A\mathbf{v}$

$$= \begin{bmatrix} 1 & -1 \\ 0 & 2 \end{bmatrix} \begin{bmatrix} 5 \\ 2 \end{bmatrix} \cdot \begin{bmatrix} 1 & -1 \\ 0 & 2 \end{bmatrix} \begin{bmatrix} 11 \\ 6 \end{bmatrix}$$

$$= \begin{bmatrix} 3 \\ 4 \end{bmatrix} \cdot \begin{bmatrix} 5 \\ 12 \end{bmatrix}$$

$$= (3)(5) + (4)(12)$$

$$= 63$$

(b) $\|\mathbf{u}\| = \langle \mathbf{u}, \mathbf{u} \rangle^{1/2}$

$\qquad = [A\mathbf{u} \cdot A\mathbf{u}]^{1/2}$

$$= \left[\begin{bmatrix} 3 \\ 4 \end{bmatrix} \cdot \begin{bmatrix} 3 \\ 4 \end{bmatrix} \right]^{1/2}$$

$$= [(3)(3) + (4)(4)]^{1/2}$$

$$= \sqrt{25} = 5$$

(c) $\|\mathbf{v}\| = \langle \mathbf{v}, \mathbf{v} \rangle^{1/2}$

$\qquad = [A\mathbf{v} \cdot A\mathbf{v}]^{1/2}$

$$= \left[\begin{bmatrix} 5 \\ 12 \end{bmatrix} \cdot \begin{bmatrix} 5 \\ 12 \end{bmatrix} \right]^{1/2}$$

$$= [(5)(5) + (12)(12)]^{1/2}$$

$$= \sqrt{169} = 13$$

(d) $d(\mathbf{u}, \mathbf{v}) = \|\mathbf{u} - \mathbf{v}\|$

$\qquad = \langle \mathbf{u} - \mathbf{v}, \mathbf{u} - \mathbf{v} \rangle^{1/2}$

$$= \left\langle \begin{bmatrix} -6 \\ -4 \end{bmatrix}, \begin{bmatrix} -6 \\ -4 \end{bmatrix} \right\rangle^{1/2}$$

$$= \left[\begin{bmatrix} 1 & -1 \\ 0 & 2 \end{bmatrix} \begin{bmatrix} -6 \\ -4 \end{bmatrix} \cdot \begin{bmatrix} 1 & -1 \\ 0 & 2 \end{bmatrix} \begin{bmatrix} -6 \\ -4 \end{bmatrix} \right]^{1/2}$$

$$= \left[\begin{bmatrix} -2 \\ -8 \end{bmatrix} \cdot \begin{bmatrix} -2 \\ -8 \end{bmatrix} \right]^{1/2}$$

$$= [(-2)(-2) + (-8)(-8)]^{1/2}$$

$$= \sqrt{68} = 2\sqrt{17}$$

9. (a) $\langle \mathbf{f}, \mathbf{g} \rangle = \int_0^1 x e^x \, dx$

$$= \left[(x-1)e^x \right]_0^1$$
$$= (0)e^1 - (-1)e^0$$
$$= 1$$

(b) $\|\mathbf{f}\| = \langle \mathbf{f}, \mathbf{f} \rangle^{1/2}$

$$= \left[\int_0^1 x \cdot x \, dx \right]^{1/2}$$
$$= \left(\left[\frac{1}{3} x^3 \right]_0^1 \right)^{1/2}$$
$$= \left(\frac{1}{3} - 0 \right)^{1/2}$$
$$= \sqrt{\frac{1}{3}} = \frac{1}{3} \sqrt{3}$$

(c) $\|\mathbf{g}\| = \langle \mathbf{g}, \mathbf{g} \rangle^{1/2}$

$$= \left[\int_0^1 e^x \cdot e^x \, dx \right]^{1/2}$$
$$= \left(\left[\frac{1}{2} e^{2x} \right]_0^1 \right)^{1/2}$$
$$= \left(\frac{1}{2} e^2 - \frac{1}{2} e^0 \right)^{1/2}$$
$$= \sqrt{\frac{1}{2}(e^2 - 1)} = \frac{1}{2} \sqrt{2(e^2 - 1)}$$

(d) $d(\mathbf{f}, \mathbf{g}) = \|\mathbf{f} - \mathbf{g}\|$

$$= \langle \mathbf{f} - \mathbf{g}, \mathbf{f} - \mathbf{g} \rangle^{1/2}$$
$$= \left[\int_0^1 (x - e^x) \cdot (x - e^x) \, dx \right]^{1/2}$$
$$= \left[\int_0^1 (x^2 - 2x e^x + e^{2x}) \, dx \right]^{1/2}$$
$$= \left(\left[\frac{1}{3} x^3 - 2(x-1)e^x + \frac{1}{2} e^{2x} \right]_0^1 \right)^{1/2}$$
$$= \left[\left(\frac{1}{3} - 0 + \frac{1}{2} e^2 \right) - \left(0 + 2 + \frac{1}{2} \right) \right]^{1/2}$$
$$= \left[\frac{1}{2} e^2 - \frac{13}{6} \right]^{1/2}$$
$$= \sqrt{\frac{1}{6}(3e^2 - 13)} = \frac{1}{6} \sqrt{6(3e^2 - 13)}$$

10. (a) $\langle \mathbf{u} - \mathbf{v}, \mathbf{u} + \mathbf{v} \rangle = \langle \mathbf{u}, \mathbf{u} \rangle + \langle \mathbf{u}, \mathbf{v} \rangle - \langle \mathbf{v}, \mathbf{u} \rangle - \langle \mathbf{v}, \mathbf{v} \rangle$

$$= \langle \mathbf{u}, \mathbf{u} \rangle + \langle \mathbf{u}, \mathbf{v} \rangle - \langle \mathbf{u}, \mathbf{v} \rangle - \langle \mathbf{v}, \mathbf{v} \rangle$$
$$= \langle \mathbf{u}, \mathbf{u} \rangle - \langle \mathbf{v}, \mathbf{v} \rangle$$
$$= \|\mathbf{u}\|^2 - \|\mathbf{v}\|^2$$
$$= 5^2 - 3^2$$
$$= 16$$

(b) $\|3\mathbf{u} + \mathbf{v}\| = \langle 3\mathbf{u} + \mathbf{v}, 3\mathbf{u} + \mathbf{v} \rangle^{1/2}$

$$= [\langle 3\mathbf{u}, 3\mathbf{u} \rangle + \langle 3\mathbf{u}, \mathbf{v} \rangle + \langle \mathbf{v}, 3\mathbf{u} \rangle + \langle \mathbf{v}, \mathbf{v} \rangle]^{1/2}$$
$$= [9\langle \mathbf{u}, \mathbf{u} \rangle + 3\langle \mathbf{u}, \mathbf{v} \rangle + 3\langle \mathbf{v}, \mathbf{u} \rangle + \langle \mathbf{v}, \mathbf{v} \rangle]^{1/2}$$
$$= [9\langle \mathbf{u}, \mathbf{u} \rangle + 6\langle \mathbf{u}, \mathbf{v} \rangle + \langle \mathbf{v}, \mathbf{v} \rangle]^{1/2}$$
$$= [9 \cdot 5^2 + 6 \cdot 3 + 3^2]^{1/2}$$
$$= \sqrt{252} = 6\sqrt{7}$$

(c) $\|2\mathbf{v} - 3\mathbf{w}\| = \langle 2\mathbf{v} - 3\mathbf{w}, 2\mathbf{v} - 3\mathbf{w} \rangle^{1/2}$

$$= [\langle 2\mathbf{v}, 2\mathbf{v} \rangle - \langle 2\mathbf{v}, 3\mathbf{w} \rangle - \langle 3\mathbf{w}, 2\mathbf{v} \rangle + \langle 3\mathbf{w}, 3\mathbf{w} \rangle]^{1/2}$$
$$= [4\langle \mathbf{v}, \mathbf{v} \rangle - 6\langle \mathbf{v}, \mathbf{w} \rangle - 6\langle \mathbf{w}, \mathbf{v} \rangle + 9\langle \mathbf{w}, \mathbf{w} \rangle]^{1/2}$$
$$= [4\langle \mathbf{v}, \mathbf{v} \rangle - 12\langle \mathbf{v}, \mathbf{w} \rangle + 9\langle \mathbf{w}, \mathbf{w} \rangle]^{1/2}$$
$$= [4 \cdot 3^2 - 12 \cdot -1 + 9 \cdot 4^2]^{1/2}$$
$$= \sqrt{192} = 8\sqrt{3}$$

(d) $\langle \mathbf{u} - \mathbf{v} + 3\mathbf{w}, 2\mathbf{u} + \mathbf{v} + \mathbf{w} \rangle$

$$= \langle \mathbf{u}, 2\mathbf{u} \rangle + \langle \mathbf{u}, \mathbf{v} \rangle + \langle \mathbf{u}, \mathbf{w} \rangle - \langle \mathbf{v}, 2\mathbf{u} \rangle - \langle \mathbf{v}, \mathbf{v} \rangle - \langle \mathbf{v}, \mathbf{w} \rangle + $$
$$\langle 3\mathbf{w}, 2\mathbf{u} \rangle + \langle 3\mathbf{w}, \mathbf{v} \rangle + \langle 3\mathbf{w}, \mathbf{w} \rangle$$
$$= 2\langle \mathbf{u}, \mathbf{u} \rangle + \langle \mathbf{u}, \mathbf{v} \rangle + \langle \mathbf{u}, \mathbf{w} \rangle - 2\langle \mathbf{u}, \mathbf{v} \rangle - \langle \mathbf{v}, \mathbf{v} \rangle - \langle \mathbf{v}, \mathbf{w} \rangle + 6\langle \mathbf{u}, \mathbf{w} \rangle + $$
$$3\langle \mathbf{v}, \mathbf{w} \rangle + 3\langle \mathbf{w}, \mathbf{w} \rangle$$
$$= 2\langle \mathbf{u}, \mathbf{u} \rangle + \langle \mathbf{u}, \mathbf{v} \rangle + \langle \mathbf{u}, \mathbf{w} \rangle - 2\langle \mathbf{u}, \mathbf{v} \rangle - \langle \mathbf{v}, \mathbf{v} \rangle - \langle \mathbf{v}, \mathbf{w} \rangle + $$
$$6\langle \mathbf{u}, \mathbf{w} \rangle + 3\langle \mathbf{v}, \mathbf{w} \rangle + 3\langle \mathbf{w}, \mathbf{w} \rangle$$
$$= 2\langle \mathbf{u}, \mathbf{u} \rangle - \langle \mathbf{u}, \mathbf{v} \rangle + 7\langle \mathbf{u}, \mathbf{w} \rangle - \langle \mathbf{v}, \mathbf{v} \rangle + 2\langle \mathbf{v}, \mathbf{w} \rangle + 3\langle \mathbf{w}, \mathbf{w} \rangle$$
$$= 2 \cdot 5^2 - 3 + 7 \cdot 2 - 3^2 + 2 \cdot -1 + 3 \cdot 4^2$$
$$= 98$$

11. (a) $\cos\theta = \dfrac{\langle(1,4,-5),(2,3,2)\rangle}{\|(1,4,-5)\|\|(2,3,2)\|} = \dfrac{(1)(2)+(4)(3)+(-5)(2)}{[(1)(1)+(4)(4)+(-5)(-5)]^{1/2}[(2)(2)+(3)(3)+(2)(2)]^{1/2}}$

$\qquad = \dfrac{4}{\sqrt{42}\sqrt{17}}$

(b) $\cos\theta = \dfrac{\langle(2,3,2),(3,-1,\frac{3}{2})\rangle}{\|(2,3,2)\|\|(3,-1,\frac{3}{2})\|} = \dfrac{(2)(3)+(3)(-1)+(2)(\frac{3}{2})}{[(2)(2)+(3)(3)+(2)(2)]^{1/2}[(3)(3)+(-1)(-1)+(\frac{3}{2})(\frac{3}{2})]^{1/2}}$

$\qquad = \dfrac{0}{\sqrt{17}\sqrt{\frac{49}{4}}} = 0$

(c) $\cos\theta = \dfrac{\langle(1,4,-5),(3,-1,\frac{-3}{2})\rangle}{\|(1,4,-5)\|\|(3,-1,\frac{-3}{2})\|} =$

$\qquad \dfrac{(1)(3)+(4)(-1)+(-5)(\frac{-3}{2})}{[(1)(1)+(4)(4)+(-5)(-5)]^{1/2}[(3)(3)+(-1)(-1)+(\frac{-3}{2})(\frac{-3}{2})]^{1/2}}$

$\qquad = \dfrac{\frac{13}{2}}{\sqrt{42}\sqrt{\frac{49}{4}}} = \dfrac{\frac{13}{2}}{\sqrt{42}\frac{7}{2}} = \dfrac{13}{7\sqrt{42}}$

12. (a) $\cos\theta = \dfrac{\langle(3,4),(4,5)\rangle}{\|(3,4)\|\|(4,5)\|} = \dfrac{(3)(4)+(4)(5)}{[(3)(3)+(4)(4)]^{1/2}[(4)(4)+(5)(5)]^{1/2}}$

$\qquad = \dfrac{32}{\sqrt{25}\sqrt{41}} = \dfrac{32}{5\sqrt{41}}$

(b) $\cos\theta = \dfrac{\langle(4,5),(5,6)\rangle}{\|(4,5)\|\|(5,6)\|} = \dfrac{(4)(5)+(5)(6)}{[(4)(4)+(5)(5)]^{1/2}[(5)(5)+(6)(6)]^{1/2}}$

$\qquad = \dfrac{50}{\sqrt{41}\sqrt{61}}$

(c) $\cos\theta = \dfrac{\langle(3,4),(5,6)\rangle}{\|(3,4)\|\|(5,6)\|} = \dfrac{(3)(5)+(4)(6)}{[(3)(3)+(4)(4)]^{1/2}[(5)(5)+(6)(6)]^{1/2}}$

$\qquad = \dfrac{39}{\sqrt{25}\sqrt{61}} = \dfrac{39}{5\sqrt{61}}$

13. (a) $\cos\theta = \dfrac{\langle(7,-1),(2,3)\rangle}{\|(7,-1)\|\|(2,3)\|} = \dfrac{3(7)(2)+5(-1)(3)}{[3(7)(7)+5(-1)(-1)]^{1/2}[3(2)(2)+5(3)(3)]^{1/2}}$

$\qquad = \dfrac{27}{\sqrt{152}\sqrt{57}} = \dfrac{27}{38\sqrt{6}}$

(b) $\cos\theta = \dfrac{\langle(2,3),(10,-4)\rangle}{\|(2,3)\|\|(10,-4)\|} = \dfrac{3(2)(10)+5(3)(-4)}{[3(2)(2)+5(3)(3)]^{1/2}[3(10)(10)+5(-4)(-4)]^{1/2}}$

$\qquad = \dfrac{0}{\sqrt{57}\sqrt{380}} = 0$

(c) $\cos\theta = \dfrac{\langle(7,-1),(10,-4)\rangle}{\|(7,-1)\|\|(10,-4)\|} = \dfrac{3(7)(10)+5(-1)(-4)}{[3(7)(7)+5(-1)(-1)]^{1/2}[3(10)(10)+5(-4)(-4)]^{1/2}}$

$\qquad = \dfrac{230}{\sqrt{152}\sqrt{380}} = \dfrac{115}{38\sqrt{10}}$

14. (a) $\cos\theta = \dfrac{\left\langle \begin{bmatrix} 1 & 0 \\ 0 & 1 \end{bmatrix}, \begin{bmatrix} 1 & 0 \\ 1 & 0 \end{bmatrix} \right\rangle}{\left\| \begin{bmatrix} 1 & 0 \\ 0 & 1 \end{bmatrix} \right\| \left\| \begin{bmatrix} 1 & 0 \\ 1 & 0 \end{bmatrix} \right\|} =$

$$\dfrac{(1)(1)+(0)(0)+(0)(1)+(1)(0)}{[(1)(1)+(0)(0)+(0)(0)+(1)(1)]^{1/2}[(1)(1)+(0)(0)+(1)(1)+(0)(0)]^{1/2}}$$

$\qquad = \dfrac{1}{\sqrt{2}\sqrt{2}} = \dfrac{1}{2}$

(b) $\cos\theta = \dfrac{\left\langle \begin{bmatrix} 1 & 0 \\ 1 & 0 \end{bmatrix}, \begin{bmatrix} -1 & 1 \\ 0 & 0 \end{bmatrix} \right\rangle}{\left\| \begin{bmatrix} 1 & 0 \\ 1 & 0 \end{bmatrix} \right\| \left\| \begin{bmatrix} -1 & 1 \\ 0 & 0 \end{bmatrix} \right\|} =$

$$\dfrac{(1)(-1)+(0)(1)+(1)(0)+(0)(0)}{[(1)(1)+(0)(0)+(1)(1)+(0)(0)]^{1/2}[(-1)(-1)+(1)(1)+(0)(0)+(0)(0)]^{1/2}}$$

$\qquad = \dfrac{-1}{\sqrt{2}\sqrt{2}} = \dfrac{-1}{2}$

(c) $\cos\theta = \dfrac{\left\langle \begin{bmatrix} 1 & 0 \\ 0 & 1 \end{bmatrix}, \begin{bmatrix} -1 & 1 \\ 0 & 0 \end{bmatrix} \right\rangle}{\left\| \begin{bmatrix} 1 & 0 \\ 0 & 1 \end{bmatrix} \right\| \left\| \begin{bmatrix} -1 & 1 \\ 0 & 0 \end{bmatrix} \right\|} =$

$$\dfrac{(1)(-1)+(0)(1)+(0)(0)+(1)(0)}{[(1)(1)+(0)(0)+(0)(0)+(1)(1)]^{1/2}[(-1)(-1)+(1)(1)+(0)(0)+(0)(0)]^{1/2}}$$

$\qquad = \dfrac{-1}{\sqrt{2}\sqrt{2}} = \dfrac{-1}{2}$

15. (a) $\cos\theta = \dfrac{\langle 1 - x^2, 3 + 12x - 4x^2 \rangle}{\|1 - x^2\|\|3 + 12x - 4x^2\|} =$

$$\dfrac{(1)(3) + (0)(12) + (-1)(-4)}{[(1)(1) + (0)(0) + (-1)(-1)]^{1/2}[(3)(3) + (12)(12) + (-4)(-4)]^{1/2}}$$

$$= \dfrac{7}{\sqrt{2}\sqrt{169}} = \dfrac{7}{13\sqrt{2}}$$

(b) $\cos\theta = \dfrac{\langle 3 + 12x - 4x^2, 12 - 9x - 8x^2 \rangle}{\|3 + 12x - 4x^2\|\|12 - 9x - 8x^2\|} =$

$$\dfrac{(3)(12) + (12)(-9) + (-4)(-8)}{[(3)(3) + (12)(12) + (-4)(-4)]^{1/2}[(12)(12) + (-9)(-9) + (-8)(-8)]^{1/2}}$$

$$= \dfrac{-40}{\sqrt{169}\sqrt{289}} = \dfrac{-40}{221}$$

(c) $\cos\theta = \dfrac{\langle (1 - x^2, 12 - 9x - 8x^2 \rangle}{\|1 - x^2\|\|12 - 9x - 8x^2\|} =$

$$\dfrac{(1)(12) + (0)(-9) + (-1)(-8)}{[(1)(1) + (0)(0) + (-1)(-1)]^{1/2}[(12)(12) + (-9)(-9) + (-8)(-8)]^{1/2}}$$

$$= \dfrac{20}{\sqrt{2}\sqrt{289}} = \dfrac{20}{17\sqrt{2}}$$

16. Note $A\mathbf{u} = \begin{bmatrix} 1 & -1 \\ -1 & 2 \end{bmatrix} \begin{bmatrix} 1 \\ 0 \end{bmatrix} = \begin{bmatrix} 1 \\ -1 \end{bmatrix}$,

$$A\mathbf{v} = \begin{bmatrix} 1 & -1 \\ -1 & 2 \end{bmatrix} \begin{bmatrix} 3 \\ 2 \end{bmatrix} = \begin{bmatrix} 1 \\ 1 \end{bmatrix},$$

$$A\mathbf{w} = \begin{bmatrix} 1 & -1 \\ -1 & 2 \end{bmatrix} \begin{bmatrix} -5 \\ -1 \end{bmatrix} = \begin{bmatrix} -4 \\ 3 \end{bmatrix}.$$

(a) $\cos\theta = \dfrac{(1,-1)\cdot(1,1)}{\|(1,-1)\|\|(1,1)\|} = \dfrac{0}{\sqrt{2}\sqrt{2}} = 0$

(b) $\cos\theta = \dfrac{(1,1)\cdot(-4,3)}{\|(1,1)\|\|(-4,3)\|} = \dfrac{-1}{\sqrt{2}\sqrt{25}} = \dfrac{-1}{5\sqrt{2}}$

(c) $\cos\theta = \dfrac{(1,-1)\cdot(-4,3)}{\|(1,-1)\|\|(-4,3)\|} = \dfrac{-7}{\sqrt{2}\sqrt{25}} = \dfrac{-7}{5\sqrt{2}}$

17. (a) $\cos\theta = \dfrac{\langle \frac{1}{3}+x^4, 6x\rangle}{\|\frac{1}{3}+x^4\|\|6x\|} = \dfrac{\displaystyle\int_0^1 (\frac{1}{3}+x^4)(6x)\,dx}{\left[\displaystyle\int_0^1 (\frac{1}{3}+x^4)(\frac{1}{3}+x^4)\,dx\right]^{1/2}\left[\displaystyle\int_0^1 (6x)(6x)\,dx\right]^{1/2}}$

$$= \dfrac{\displaystyle\int_0^1 (2x+6x^5)\,dx}{\left[\displaystyle\int_0^1 (\frac{1}{9}+\frac{2}{3}x^4+x^8)\,dx\right]^{1/2}\left[\displaystyle\int_0^1 36x^2\,dx\right]^{1/2}}$$

$$= \dfrac{\left[x^2+x^6\right]_0^1}{\left(\left[\frac{1}{9}x+\frac{2}{15}x^5+\frac{1}{9}x^9\right]_0^1\right)^{1/2}\left(\left[12x^3\right]_0^1\right)^{1/2}}$$

$$= \dfrac{2}{\left(\frac{1}{9}+\frac{2}{15}+\frac{1}{9}\right)^{1/2}(12)^{1/2}} = \dfrac{2}{\sqrt{\frac{16}{45}}\sqrt{12}} = \dfrac{\sqrt{15}}{4}$$

(b) $\cos\theta = \dfrac{\langle 6x, \frac{1}{3}-x^4\rangle}{\|6x\|\|\frac{1}{3}-x^4\|} = \dfrac{\displaystyle\int_0^1 (6x)(\frac{1}{3}-x^4)\,dx}{\left[\displaystyle\int_0^1 (6x)(6x)\,dx\right]^{1/2}\left[\displaystyle\int_0^1 (\frac{1}{3}-x^4)(\frac{1}{3}-x^4)\,dx\right]^{1/2}}$

$$= \dfrac{\displaystyle\int_0^1 (2x-6x^5)\,dx}{\left[\displaystyle\int_0^1 36x^2\,dx\right]^{1/2}\left[\displaystyle\int_0^1 (\frac{1}{9}-\frac{2}{3}x^4+x^8)\,dx\right]^{1/2}}$$

$$= \dfrac{\left[x^2-x^6\right]_0^1}{\left(\left[12x^3\right]_0^1\right)^{1/2}\left(\left[\frac{1}{9}x-\frac{2}{15}x^5+\frac{1}{9}x^9\right]_0^1\right)^{1/2}}$$

$$= \dfrac{0}{\sqrt{12}\sqrt{\frac{4}{45}}} = 0$$

(c) $\cos\theta = \dfrac{\langle \frac{1}{3}+x^4, \frac{1}{3}-x^4\rangle}{\|\frac{1}{3}+x^4\|\|\frac{1}{3}-x^4\|} = \dfrac{\displaystyle\int_0^1 (\frac{1}{3}+x^4)(\frac{1}{3}-x^4)\,dx}{\left[\displaystyle\int_0^1 (\frac{1}{3}+x^4)(\frac{1}{3}+x^4)\,dx\right]^{1/2}\left[\displaystyle\int_0^1 (\frac{1}{3}-x^4)(\frac{1}{3}-x^4)\,dx\right]^{1/2}}$

$\qquad\qquad = \dfrac{\displaystyle\int_0^1 (\frac{1}{9}-x^8)\,dx}{\left[\displaystyle\int_0^1 (\frac{1}{9}+\frac{2}{3}x^4+x^8)\,dx\right]^{1/2}\left[\displaystyle\int_0^1 (\frac{1}{9}-\frac{2}{3}x^4+x^8)\,dx\right]^{1/2}}$

$\qquad\qquad = \dfrac{\left[\frac{1}{9}x-\frac{1}{9}x^9\right]_0^1}{\left(\left[\frac{1}{9}x+\frac{2}{15}x^5+\frac{1}{9}x^9\right]_0^1\right)^{1/2}\left(\left[\frac{1}{9}x-\frac{2}{15}x^5+\frac{1}{9}x^9\right]_0^1\right)^{1/2}}$

$\qquad\qquad = \dfrac{0}{(\frac{1}{9}+\frac{2}{15}+\frac{1}{9})^{1/2}(\frac{1}{9}-\frac{2}{15}+\frac{1}{9})^{1/2}} = 0$

18. Let $\quad \mathbf{u} = $ diagonal of cube $= (1,1,1,1)$

and $\quad \mathbf{v} = $ diagonal of base face $= (1,1,1,0)$.

(a) $\quad \|\mathbf{u}\| = [(1,1,1,1)\cdot(1,1,1,1)]^{1/2} = [(1)(1)+(1)(1)+(1)(1)+(1)(1)]^{1/2} = \sqrt{4} = 2$.

(b) $\quad \cos\theta = \dfrac{\mathbf{u}\cdot\mathbf{v}}{\|\mathbf{u}\|\|\mathbf{v}\|} = \dfrac{(1,1,1,1)\cdot(1,1,1,0)}{\|(1,1,1,1)\|\|(1,1,1,0)\|}$

$\qquad\qquad = \dfrac{(1)(1)+(1)(1)+(1)(1)+(1)(0)}{[(1)(1)+(1)(1)+(1)(1)+(1)(1)]^{1/2}[(1)(1)+(1)(1)+(1)(1)+(0)(0)]^{1/2}}$

$\qquad\qquad = \dfrac{3}{\sqrt{4}\sqrt{3}} = \dfrac{\sqrt{3}}{2}$, so $\quad \theta = \dfrac{\pi}{6}$ or $30°$.

19. $W = \{(x,y) : y = -3x\} = \{(x,-3x)\} = \{x(1,-3)\} = \text{span }\{(1,-3)\}$.

$W^\perp = \text{nullspace }[1\ -3]$;

$\qquad [1\ -3\ 0] :$ Let $y = t$

$\qquad\qquad$ so $x - 3y = 0$ i.e., $x = 3y = 3t$

$\qquad\qquad$ so $\begin{bmatrix} x \\ y \end{bmatrix} = \begin{bmatrix} 3t \\ t \end{bmatrix} = t\begin{bmatrix} 3 \\ 1 \end{bmatrix}$

Thus $W^\perp = \text{nullspace }[1\ -3] = \text{span }\left\{\begin{bmatrix} 3 \\ 1 \end{bmatrix}\right\} = \left\{\begin{bmatrix} x \\ y \end{bmatrix} : x = 3y\right\} = \left\{\begin{bmatrix} x \\ y \end{bmatrix} : y = \frac{1}{3}x\right\}$

20. $W = \{(x,y,z) : x = 3t, y = t, z = -2t\} = \{(3t,t,-2t)\} = \{t(3,1,-2)\} = \text{span }\{(3,1,-2)\}$.

$W^\perp = \text{nullspace }[3\ 1\ -2] = \{(x,y,z) : 3x+y-2z = 0\}$.

21. $W = \{(x, y, z) : 3x + 2y - 2z = 0\} = \text{nullspace } [3 \; 1 \; -2]$

$$W^\perp = \text{colspace } [3 \; 1 \; -2]^T = \text{colspace } \begin{bmatrix} 3 \\ 1 \\ -2 \end{bmatrix} = \text{span } \begin{bmatrix} 3 \\ 1 \\ -2 \end{bmatrix}$$

$$= \left\{ t \begin{bmatrix} 3 \\ 1 \\ -2 \end{bmatrix} \right\} = \left\{ \begin{bmatrix} x \\ y \\ z \end{bmatrix} : x = 3t, y = t, z = -2t \right\}$$

22. (a) $W = \text{span } \{(4, -6), (-6, 9)\} = \text{rowspace } \begin{bmatrix} 4 & -6 \\ -6 & 9 \end{bmatrix}$.

$$W^\perp = \text{nullspace } \begin{bmatrix} 4 & -6 \\ -6 & 9 \end{bmatrix};$$

$$\begin{bmatrix} 4 & -6 & 0 \\ -6 & 9 & 0 \end{bmatrix} \longrightarrow \begin{bmatrix} 1 & -3/2 & 0 \\ 0 & 0 & 0 \end{bmatrix} : \text{Let } y = t$$

$$\text{so } x - \frac{3}{2}y = 0 \quad \text{i.e.,} \quad x = \frac{3}{2}t$$

$$\text{so } \begin{bmatrix} x \\ y \end{bmatrix} = \begin{bmatrix} (3/2)t \\ t \end{bmatrix} = t \begin{bmatrix} 3/2 \\ 1 \end{bmatrix}.$$

Thus $W^\perp = \text{nullspace } \begin{bmatrix} 4 & -6 \\ -6 & 9 \end{bmatrix} = \text{span } \left\{ \begin{bmatrix} 3/2 \\ 1 \end{bmatrix} \right\} = \text{span } \left\{ \begin{bmatrix} 3 \\ 2 \end{bmatrix} \right\}.$

(b) $W = \text{span } \{(1, 2, 1), (3, 1, -2), (-1, 3, 4)\} = \text{rowspace } \begin{bmatrix} 1 & 2 & 1 \\ 3 & 1 & -2 \\ -1 & 3 & 4 \end{bmatrix}.$

$$W^\perp = \text{nullspace } \begin{bmatrix} 1 & 2 & 1 \\ 3 & 1 & -2 \\ -1 & 3 & 4 \end{bmatrix};$$

$$\begin{bmatrix} 1 & 2 & 1 & 0 \\ 3 & 1 & -2 & 0 \\ -1 & 3 & 4 & 0 \end{bmatrix} \longrightarrow \begin{bmatrix} 1 & 2 & 1 & 0 \\ 0 & -5 & -5 & 0 \\ 0 & 5 & 5 & 0 \end{bmatrix} \longrightarrow \begin{bmatrix} 1 & 0 & -1 & 0 \\ 0 & 1 & 1 & 0 \\ 0 & 0 & 0 & 0 \end{bmatrix}$$

Let $z = t$

so $y + z = 0$ i.e., $y = -t$

and $x - z = 0$ i.e., $x = t$

$$\text{so } \begin{bmatrix} x \\ y \\ z \end{bmatrix} = \begin{bmatrix} t \\ -t \\ t \end{bmatrix} = t \begin{bmatrix} 1 \\ -1 \\ 1 \end{bmatrix}$$

Thus $W^\perp = \text{span } \left\{ \begin{bmatrix} 1 \\ -1 \\ 1 \end{bmatrix} \right\}.$

(c) $W = \text{span } \{(3,1,7),(2,4,-2),(-2,-1,0)\} = \text{rowspace} \begin{bmatrix} 3 & 1 & 7 \\ 2 & 4 & -2 \\ -2 & -1 & 0 \end{bmatrix}.$

$W^\perp = \text{nullspace} \begin{bmatrix} 3 & 1 & 7 \\ 2 & 4 & -2 \\ -2 & -1 & 0 \end{bmatrix};$

$$\begin{bmatrix} 3 & 1 & 7 & 0 \\ 2 & 4 & -2 & 0 \\ -2 & -1 & 0 & 0 \end{bmatrix} \longrightarrow \begin{bmatrix} 1 & 1/3 & 7/3 & 0 \\ 0 & 10/3 & -20/3 & 0 \\ 0 & -1/3 & 14/3 & 0 \end{bmatrix} \longrightarrow \begin{bmatrix} 1 & 1/3 & 7/3 & 0 \\ 0 & 1 & -2 & 0 \\ 0 & 0 & 4 & 0 \end{bmatrix} \longrightarrow$$

$$\begin{bmatrix} 1 & 1/3 & 7/3 & 0 \\ 0 & 1 & -2 & 0 \\ 0 & 0 & 1 & 0 \end{bmatrix}$$

Thus $z = 0$ so $y = 0$ so $x = 0$,   i.e., $W^\perp = \{(0,0,0)\}$

(d) $W = \text{span } \{(1,2,3,4),(1,1,1,0),(1,4,7,12)\} = \text{rowspace} \begin{bmatrix} 1 & 2 & 3 & 4 \\ 1 & 1 & 1 & 0 \\ 1 & 4 & 7 & 12 \end{bmatrix}.$

$W^\perp = \text{nullspace} \begin{bmatrix} 1 & 2 & 3 & 4 \\ 1 & 1 & 1 & 0 \\ 1 & 4 & 7 & 12 \end{bmatrix};$

$$\begin{bmatrix} 1 & 2 & 3 & 4 & 0 \\ 1 & 1 & 1 & 0 & 0 \\ 1 & 4 & 7 & 12 & 0 \end{bmatrix} \longrightarrow \begin{bmatrix} 1 & 2 & 3 & 4 & 0 \\ 0 & -1 & -2 & -4 & 0 \\ 0 & 2 & 4 & 8 & 0 \end{bmatrix} \longrightarrow \begin{bmatrix} 1 & 0 & -1 & -4 & 0 \\ 0 & 1 & 2 & 4 & 0 \\ 0 & 0 & 0 & 0 & 0 \end{bmatrix}$$

Let $x_4 = t$ and $x_3 = s$;

then $x_2 + 2x_3 + 4x_4 = 0$ i.e., $x_2 = -2s - 4t$

and $x_1 - x_3 - 4x_4 = 0$ i.e., $x_1 = s + 4t$

so $\begin{bmatrix} x_1 \\ x_2 \\ x_3 \\ x_4 \end{bmatrix} = \begin{bmatrix} s + 4t \\ -2s - 4t \\ s \\ t \end{bmatrix} = s \begin{bmatrix} 1 \\ -2 \\ 1 \\ 0 \end{bmatrix} + t \begin{bmatrix} 4 \\ -4 \\ 0 \\ 1 \end{bmatrix}$

Thus $W^\perp = \text{span} \left\{ \begin{bmatrix} 1 \\ -2 \\ 1 \\ 0 \end{bmatrix}, \begin{bmatrix} 4 \\ -4 \\ 0 \\ 1 \end{bmatrix} \right\}.$

SECTION 6.3   *ORTHONORMAL BASES; GRAM–SCHMIDT PROCESS; Q–R DECOMPOSITION*

23. $\langle \mathbf{u}, \mathbf{u} \rangle = \left(\dfrac{4}{5}, \dfrac{-3}{5} \right) \cdot \left(\dfrac{4}{5}, \dfrac{-3}{5} \right) = \dfrac{16}{25} + \dfrac{9}{25} = 1$

$\langle \mathbf{v}, \mathbf{v} \rangle = \left(\dfrac{3}{5}, \dfrac{4}{5} \right) \cdot \left(\dfrac{3}{5}, \dfrac{4}{5} \right) = \dfrac{9}{25} + \dfrac{16}{25} = 1$

$\langle \mathbf{u}, \mathbf{v} \rangle = \left(\dfrac{4}{5}, \dfrac{-3}{5} \right) \cdot \left(\dfrac{3}{5}, \dfrac{4}{5} \right) = \dfrac{12}{25} + \dfrac{-12}{25} = 0$,   orthonormal.

24. $\langle \mathbf{u}, \mathbf{u} \rangle = \left(\frac{1}{3}, \frac{2}{3}, \frac{2}{3}\right) \cdot \left(\frac{1}{3}, \frac{2}{3}, \frac{2}{3}\right) = \frac{1}{9} + \frac{4}{9} + \frac{4}{9} = 1$

$\langle \mathbf{v}, \mathbf{v} \rangle = \left(\frac{2}{\sqrt{6}}, \frac{-1}{\sqrt{6}}, \frac{-1}{\sqrt{6}}\right) \cdot \left(\frac{2}{\sqrt{6}}, \frac{-1}{\sqrt{6}}, \frac{-1}{\sqrt{6}}\right) = \frac{4}{6} + \frac{1}{6} + \frac{1}{6} = 1$

$\langle \mathbf{w}, \mathbf{w} \rangle = \left(0, \frac{1}{\sqrt{2}}, \frac{-1}{\sqrt{2}}\right) \cdot \left(0, \frac{1}{\sqrt{2}}, \frac{-1}{\sqrt{2}}\right) = 0 + \frac{1}{2} + \frac{1}{2} = 1$

$\langle \mathbf{u}, \mathbf{v} \rangle = \left(\frac{1}{3}, \frac{2}{3}, \frac{2}{3}\right) \cdot \left(\frac{2}{\sqrt{6}}, \frac{-1}{\sqrt{6}}, \frac{-1}{\sqrt{6}}\right) = \frac{2}{3\sqrt{6}} + \frac{-2}{3\sqrt{6}} + \frac{-2}{3\sqrt{6}} = \frac{-2}{3\sqrt{6}} \neq 0$

$\langle \mathbf{v}, \mathbf{w} \rangle = \left(\frac{2}{\sqrt{6}}, \frac{-1}{\sqrt{6}}, \frac{-1}{\sqrt{6}}\right) \cdot \left(0, \frac{1}{\sqrt{2}}, \frac{-1}{\sqrt{2}}\right) = 0 + \frac{-1}{\sqrt{12}} + \frac{1}{\sqrt{12}} = 0$

$\langle \mathbf{u}, \mathbf{w} \rangle = \left(\frac{1}{3}, \frac{2}{3}, \frac{2}{3}\right) \cdot \left(0, \frac{1}{\sqrt{2}}, \frac{-1}{\sqrt{2}}\right) = 0 + \frac{2}{3\sqrt{2}} + \frac{-2}{3\sqrt{2}} = 0$, normal only.

25. $\langle \mathbf{u}, \mathbf{u} \rangle = 3\left(\frac{1}{\sqrt{8}}\right)\left(\frac{1}{\sqrt{8}}\right) + 5\left(\frac{1}{\sqrt{8}}\right)\left(\frac{1}{\sqrt{8}}\right) = \frac{3}{8} + \frac{5}{8} = 1$

$\langle \mathbf{v}, \mathbf{v} \rangle = 3\left(\frac{1}{2}\right)\left(\frac{1}{2}\right) + 5\left(\frac{-1}{4}\right)\left(\frac{-1}{4}\right) = \frac{3}{4} + \frac{5}{16} = \frac{17}{16} \neq 1$

$\langle \mathbf{u}, \mathbf{v} \rangle = 3\left(\frac{1}{\sqrt{8}}\right)\left(\frac{1}{2}\right) + 5\left(\frac{1}{\sqrt{8}}\right)\left(\frac{-1}{4}\right) = \frac{3}{2\sqrt{8}} + \frac{-5}{4\sqrt{8}} = \frac{1}{4\sqrt{8}} \neq 0$, neither.

26. $\langle \mathbf{f}, \mathbf{f} \rangle = \int_0^\pi (\sin x)(\sin x)dx = \frac{1}{2}\int_0^\pi (1 - \cos 2x)dx = \frac{1}{2}\left[x - \frac{1}{2}\sin 2x\right]_0^\pi = \frac{1}{2}(\pi) \neq 1$

$\langle \mathbf{g}, \mathbf{g} \rangle = \int_0^\pi (\cos x)(\cos x)dx = \frac{1}{2}\int_0^\pi (1 + \cos 2x)dx = \frac{1}{2}\left[x + \frac{1}{2}\sin 2x\right]_0^\pi = \frac{1}{2}(\pi) \neq 1$

$\langle \mathbf{f}, \mathbf{g} \rangle = \int_0^\pi (\sin x)(\cos x)dx = \frac{1}{2}\left[\sin^2 x\right]_0^\pi = \frac{1}{2}(0) = 0$, orthogonal only.

27. (a) $(1,1,1) \cdot \left(\frac{-1}{\sqrt{2}}, \frac{1}{\sqrt{2}}, 0\right) = 0$

$(1,1,1) \cdot \left(\frac{-1}{\sqrt{6}}, \frac{-1}{\sqrt{6}}, \frac{2}{\sqrt{6}}\right) = 0$

$(1,1,1) \cdot \left(\frac{1}{\sqrt{3}}, \frac{1}{\sqrt{3}}, \frac{1}{\sqrt{3}}\right) = \frac{3}{\sqrt{3}} = \sqrt{3}$

$(1,1,1)_B = \left(0, 0, \sqrt{3}\right)$

(b) $(1,0,-1) \cdot \left(\frac{-1}{\sqrt{2}}, \frac{1}{\sqrt{2}}, 0\right) = \frac{-1}{\sqrt{2}}$

$(1,0,-1) \cdot \left(\frac{-1}{\sqrt{6}}, \frac{-1}{\sqrt{6}}, \frac{2}{\sqrt{6}}\right) = \frac{-3}{\sqrt{6}}$

$(1,0,-1) \cdot \left(\frac{1}{\sqrt{3}}, \frac{1}{\sqrt{3}}, \frac{1}{\sqrt{3}}\right) = 0$

$(1,0,-1)_B = \left(\frac{-1}{\sqrt{2}}, \frac{-3}{\sqrt{6}}, 0\right)$

(c) $(0,0,1)\cdot\left(\frac{-1}{\sqrt{2}},\frac{1}{\sqrt{2}},0\right) = 0$

$(0,0,1)\cdot\left(\frac{-1}{\sqrt{6}},\frac{-1}{\sqrt{6}},\frac{2}{\sqrt{6}}\right) = \frac{2}{\sqrt{6}}$

$(0,0,1)\cdot\left(\frac{1}{\sqrt{3}},\frac{1}{\sqrt{3}},\frac{1}{\sqrt{3}}\right) = \frac{1}{\sqrt{3}}$

$(0,0,1)_B = \left(0,\frac{2}{\sqrt{6}},\frac{1}{\sqrt{3}}\right)$

28. (a) $\langle(3,5),\left(\frac{1}{\sqrt{3}},0\right)\rangle = 3(3)\left(\frac{1}{\sqrt{3}}\right) + 5(5)(0) = \frac{9}{\sqrt{3}} = 3\sqrt{3}$

$\langle(3,5),\left(0,\frac{1}{\sqrt{5}}\right)\rangle = 3(3)(0) + 5(5)\left(\frac{1}{\sqrt{5}}\right) = \frac{25}{\sqrt{5}} = 5\sqrt{5}$

$(3,5)_B = (3\sqrt{3},5\sqrt{5})$

(b) $\langle(1,1),\left(\frac{1}{\sqrt{3}},0\right)\rangle = 3(1)\left(\frac{1}{\sqrt{3}}\right) + 5(1)(0) = \frac{3}{\sqrt{3}} = \sqrt{3}$

$\langle(1,1),\left(0,\frac{1}{\sqrt{5}}\right)\rangle = 3(1)(0) + 5(1)\left(\frac{1}{\sqrt{5}}\right) = \frac{5}{\sqrt{5}} = \sqrt{5}$

$(1,1)_B = (\sqrt{3},\sqrt{5})$

(c) $\langle(5,3),\left(\frac{1}{\sqrt{3}},0\right)\rangle = 3(5)\left(\frac{1}{\sqrt{3}}\right) + 5(3)(0) = \frac{15}{\sqrt{3}} = 5\sqrt{3}$

$\langle(5,3),\left(0,\frac{1}{\sqrt{5}}\right)\rangle = 3(5)(0) + 5(3)\left(\frac{1}{\sqrt{5}}\right) = \frac{15}{\sqrt{5}} = 3\sqrt{5}$

$(5,3)_B = (5\sqrt{3},3\sqrt{5})$

29. (a) $\langle x,1\rangle = \int_0^1 (x)(1)dx = \int_0^1 xdx = \left[\frac{1}{2}x^2\right]_0^1 = \frac{1}{2}$

$\langle x,\sqrt{3}(2x-1)\rangle = \int_0^1 x\sqrt{3}(2x-1)dx = \sqrt{3}\int_0^1 (2x^2-x)dx$

$= \sqrt{3}\left[\frac{2}{3}x^3 - \frac{1}{2}x^2\right]_0^1 = \sqrt{3}\left(\frac{1}{6}\right) = \frac{1}{6}\sqrt{3}$

$\langle x,\sqrt{5}(6x^2-6x+1)\rangle = \int_0^1 x\sqrt{5}(6x^2-6x+1)dx = \sqrt{5}\int_0^1 (6x^3-6x^2+x)dx$

$= \sqrt{5}\left[\frac{3}{2}x^4 - 2x^3 + \frac{1}{2}x^2\right]_0^1 = \sqrt{5}(0) = 0$

$(x)_B = \left(\frac{1}{2},\frac{1}{6}\sqrt{3},0\right)$

(b) $\quad \langle x^2, 1 \rangle = \int_0^1 (x^2)(1)dx = \int_0^1 x^2 dx = \left[\frac{1}{3}x^3\right]_0^1 = \frac{1}{3}$

$$\langle x^2, \sqrt{3}(2x-1) \rangle = \int_0^1 x^2 \sqrt{3}(2x-1)dx = \sqrt{3}\int_0^1 (2x^3 - x^2)dx$$

$$= \sqrt{3}\left[\frac{1}{2}x^4 - \frac{1}{3}x^3\right]_0^1 = \sqrt{3}\left(\frac{1}{6}\right) = \frac{1}{6}\sqrt{3}$$

$$\langle x^2, \sqrt{5}(6x^2 - 6x + 1) \rangle = \int_0^1 x^2 \sqrt{5}(6x^2 - 6x + 1)dx = \sqrt{5}\int_0^1 (6x^4 - 6x^3 + x^2)dx$$

$$= \sqrt{5}\left[\frac{6}{5}x^5 - \frac{3}{2}x^4 + \frac{1}{3}x^3\right]_0^1 = \sqrt{5}\left(\frac{1}{30}\right) = \frac{1}{30}\sqrt{5}$$

$$(x^2)_B = \left(\frac{1}{3}, \frac{1}{6}\sqrt{3}, \frac{1}{30}\sqrt{5}\right)$$

(c) $\quad \langle 1 - x + x^2, 1 \rangle = \int_0^1 (1 - x + x^2)(1)dx = \int_0^1 (1 - x + x^2)dx = \left[x - \frac{1}{2}x^2 + \frac{1}{3}x^3\right]_0^1 = \frac{5}{6}$

$$\langle 1 - x + x^2, \sqrt{3}(2x-1) \rangle = \int_0^1 (1 - x + x^2)\sqrt{3}(2x-1)dx = \sqrt{3}\int_0^1 (2x^3 - 3x^2 + 3x - 1)dx$$

$$= \sqrt{3}\left[\frac{1}{2}x^4 - x^3 + \frac{3}{2}x^2 - 0\right]_0^1 = \sqrt{3}(0) = 0$$

$$\langle 1 - x + x^2, \sqrt{5}(6x^2 - 6x + 1) \rangle = \int_0^1 (1 - x + x^2)\sqrt{5}(6x^2 - 6x + 1)dx$$

$$= \sqrt{5}\int_0^1 (6x^4 - 12x^3 + 13x^2 - 7x + 1)dx$$

$$= \sqrt{5}\left[\frac{6}{5}x^5 - 3x^4 + \frac{13}{3}x^3 - \frac{7}{2}x^2 + x\right]_0^1 = \sqrt{5}\left(\frac{1}{30}\right) = \frac{1}{30}\sqrt{5}$$

$$(1 - x + x^2)_B = \left(\frac{5}{6}, 0, \frac{1}{30}\sqrt{5}\right)$$

Shortcut: $\quad (1 - x + x^2)_B = (1)_B - (x)_B + (x^2)_B$

$$= (1, 0, 0) - \left(\frac{1}{2}, \frac{1}{6}\sqrt{3}, 0\right) + \left(\frac{1}{3}, \frac{1}{6}\sqrt{3}, \frac{1}{30}\sqrt{5}\right) \quad \text{from parts (a), (b)}$$

$$= \left(\frac{5}{6}, 0, \frac{1}{30}\sqrt{5}\right)$$

30. (a) $\quad \mathbf{v}_1 = (1, 1)$

$$\mathbf{v}_2 = (1, 2) - \frac{(1,2) \cdot (1,1)}{(1,1) \cdot (1,1)}(1,1) = (1,2) - \frac{3}{2}(1,1) = \left(\frac{-1}{2}, \frac{1}{2}\right)$$

$$\mathbf{w}_1 = \frac{(1,1)}{\|(1,1)\|} = \frac{(1,1)}{[(1,1) \cdot (1,1)]^{1/2}} = \frac{(1,1)}{\sqrt{2}} = \frac{1}{\sqrt{2}}(1,1)$$

$$\mathbf{w}_2 = \frac{\left(\frac{-1}{2}, \frac{1}{2}\right)}{\|\left(\frac{-1}{2}, \frac{1}{2}\right)\|} = \frac{(-1,1)}{\|(-1,1)\|} = \frac{(-1,1)}{[(-1,1) \cdot (-1,1)]^{1/2}} = \frac{(-1,1)}{\sqrt{2}} = \frac{1}{\sqrt{2}}(-1,1)$$

115

(b) $\mathbf{v}_1 = (3,-1)$

$$\mathbf{v}_2 = (0,1) - \frac{(0,1)\cdot(3,-1)}{(3,-1)\cdot(3,-1)}(3,-1) = (0,1) - \frac{-1}{10}(3,-1) = \left(\frac{3}{10},\frac{9}{10}\right)$$

$$\mathbf{w}_1 = \frac{(3,-1)}{\|(3,-1)\|} = \frac{(3,-1)}{[(3,-1)\cdot(3,-1)]^{1/2}} = \frac{(3,-1)}{\sqrt{10}} = \frac{1}{\sqrt{10}}(3,-1)$$

$$\mathbf{w}_2 = \frac{\left(\frac{3}{10},\frac{9}{10}\right)}{\left\|\left(\frac{3}{10},\frac{9}{10}\right)\right\|} = \frac{(1,3)}{\|(1,3)\|} = \frac{(1,3)}{[(1,3)\cdot(1,3)]^{1/2}} = \frac{(1,3)}{\sqrt{10}} = \frac{1}{\sqrt{10}}(1,3)$$

31. (a) $\mathbf{v}_1 = (1,1,1)$

$$\mathbf{v}_2 = (1,1,0) - \frac{(1,1,0)\cdot(1,1,1)}{(1,1,1)\cdot(1,1,1)}(1,1,1) = (1,1,0) - \frac{2}{3}(1,1,1) = \left(\frac{1}{3},\frac{1}{3},\frac{-2}{3}\right)$$

$$\mathbf{v}_3 = (1,0,0) - \frac{(1,0,0)\cdot(1,1,1)}{(1,1,1)\cdot(1,1,1)}(1,1,1) - \frac{(1,0,0)\cdot\left(\frac{1}{3},\frac{1}{3},\frac{-2}{3}\right)}{\left(\frac{1}{3},\frac{1}{3},\frac{-2}{3}\right)\cdot\left(\frac{1}{3},\frac{1}{3},\frac{-2}{3}\right)}\left(\frac{1}{3},\frac{1}{3},\frac{-2}{3}\right)$$

$$= (1,0,0) - \frac{1}{3}(1,1,1) - \frac{1}{2}\left(\frac{1}{3},\frac{1}{3},\frac{-2}{3}\right) = \left(\frac{1}{2},\frac{-1}{2},0\right)$$

$$\mathbf{w}_1 = \frac{(1,1,1)}{\|(1,1,1)\|} = \frac{(1,1,1)}{[(1,1,1)\cdot(1,1,1)]^{1/2}} = \frac{(1,1,1)}{\sqrt{3}} = \frac{1}{\sqrt{3}}(1,1,1)$$

$$\mathbf{w}_2 = \frac{\left(\frac{1}{3},\frac{1}{3},\frac{-2}{3}\right)}{\left\|\left(\frac{1}{3},\frac{1}{3},\frac{-2}{3}\right)\right\|} = \frac{(1,1,-2)}{\|(1,1,-2)\|} = \frac{(1,1,-2)}{[(1,1,-2)\cdot(1,1,-2)]^{1/2}} = \frac{(1,1,-2)}{\sqrt{6}} = \frac{1}{\sqrt{6}}(1,1,-2)$$

$$\mathbf{w}_3 = \frac{\left(\frac{1}{2},\frac{-1}{2},0\right)}{\left\|\left(\frac{1}{2},\frac{-1}{2},0\right)\right\|} = \frac{(1,-1,0)}{\|(1,-1,0)\|} = \frac{(1,-1,0)}{[(1,-1,0)\cdot(1,-1,0)]^{1/2}} = \frac{(1,-1,0)}{\sqrt{2}} = \frac{1}{\sqrt{2}}(1,-1,0)$$

(b) $\mathbf{v}_1 = (1,2,-1)$

$$\mathbf{v}_2 = (1,3,0) - \frac{(1,3,0)\cdot(1,2,-1)}{(1,2,-1)\cdot(1,2,-1)}(1,2,-1) = (1,3,0) - \frac{7}{6}(1,2,-1) = \left(\frac{-1}{6},\frac{4}{6},\frac{7}{6}\right)$$

$$\mathbf{v}_3 = (4,1,0) - \frac{(4,1,0)\cdot(1,2,-1)}{(1,2,-1)\cdot(1,2,-1)}(1,2,-1) - \frac{(4,1,0)\cdot\left(\frac{-1}{6},\frac{4}{6},\frac{7}{6}\right)}{\left(\frac{-1}{6},\frac{4}{6},\frac{7}{6}\right)\cdot\left(\frac{-1}{6},\frac{4}{6},\frac{7}{6}\right)}\left(\frac{-1}{6},\frac{4}{6},\frac{7}{6}\right)$$

$$= (4,1,0) - \frac{6}{6}(1,2,-1) - 0\left(\frac{-1}{6},\frac{4}{6},\frac{7}{6}\right) = (3,-1,1)$$

$$\mathbf{w}_1 = \frac{(1,2,-1)}{\|(1,2,-1)\|} = \frac{(1,2,-1)}{[(1,2,-1)\cdot(1,2,-1)]^{1/2}} = \frac{(1,2,-1)}{\sqrt{6}} = \frac{1}{\sqrt{6}}(1,2,-1)$$

$$\mathbf{w}_2 = \frac{\left(\frac{-1}{6},\frac{4}{6},\frac{7}{6}\right)}{\left\|\left(\frac{-1}{6},\frac{4}{6},\frac{7}{6}\right)\right\|} = \frac{(-1,4,7)}{\|(-1,4,7)\|} = \frac{(-1,4,7)}{[(-1,4,7)\cdot(-1,4,7)]^{1/2}} = \frac{(-1,4,7)}{\sqrt{66}} = \frac{1}{\sqrt{66}}(-1,4,7)$$

$$\mathbf{w}_3 = \frac{(3,-1,1)}{\|(3,-1,1)\|} = \frac{(3,-1,1)}{[(3,-1,1)\cdot(3,-1,1)]^{1/2}} = \frac{(3,-1,1)}{\sqrt{11}} = \frac{1}{\sqrt{11}}(3,-1,1)$$

32. (a) $\mathbf{v}_1 = (2, -1)$

$$\mathbf{v}_2 = (1,1) - \frac{\langle (1,1),(2,-1) \rangle}{\langle (2,-1),(2,-1) \rangle}(2,-1) = (1,1) - \frac{3(1)(2)+5(1)(-1)}{3(2)(2)+5(-1)(-1)}(2,-1)$$

$$= (1,1) - \frac{1}{17}(2,-1) = \left(\frac{15}{17}, \frac{18}{17}\right)$$

$$\mathbf{w}_1 = \frac{(2,-1)}{\|(2,-1)\|} = \frac{(2,-1)}{[\langle (2,-1),(2,-1) \rangle]^{1/2}} = \frac{(2,-1)}{[3(2)(2)+5(-1)(-1)]^{1/2}} = \frac{(2,-1)}{\sqrt{17}} = \frac{1}{\sqrt{17}}(2,-1)$$

$$\mathbf{w}_1 = \frac{\left(\frac{15}{17},\frac{18}{17}\right)}{\left\|\left(\frac{15}{17},\frac{18}{17}\right)\right\|} = \frac{(5,6)}{\|(5,6)\|} = \frac{(5,6)}{[\langle (5,6),(5,6) \rangle]^{1/2}} = \frac{(5,6)}{[3(5)(5)+5(6)(6)]^{1/2}} = \frac{(5,6)}{\sqrt{255}} =$$

$$\frac{1}{\sqrt{255}}(5,6)$$

(b) $\mathbf{v}_1 = (1,1)$

$$\mathbf{v}_2 = (1,0) - \frac{\langle (1,0),(1,1) \rangle}{\langle (1,1),(1,1) \rangle}(1,1)$$

$$= (1,0) - \frac{3(1)(1)+5(0)(1)}{3(1)(1)+5(1)(1)}(1,1)$$

$$= (1,0) - \frac{3}{8}(1,1) = \left(\frac{5}{8}, \frac{-3}{8}\right)$$

$$\mathbf{w}_1 = \frac{(1,1)}{\|(1,1)\|} = \frac{(1,1)}{[\langle (1,1),(1,1) \rangle]^{1/2}} = \frac{(1,1)}{[3(1)(1)+5(1)(1)]^{1/2}}$$

$$= \frac{(1,1)}{\sqrt{8}} = \frac{1}{\sqrt{8}}(1,1)$$

$$\mathbf{w}_1 = \frac{\left(\frac{5}{8},\frac{-3}{8}\right)}{\left\|\left(\frac{5}{8},\frac{-3}{8}\right)\right\|} = \frac{(5,-3)}{\|(5,-3)\|} = \frac{(5,-3)}{[\langle (5,-3),(5,-3) \rangle]^{1/2}} = \frac{(5,-3)}{[3(5)(5)+5(-3)(-3)]^{1/2}}$$

$$= \frac{(5,-3)}{\sqrt{120}} = \frac{1}{\sqrt{120}}(5,3)$$

33. (a) $\mathbf{v}_1 = 1 + x^2$

$$\mathbf{v}_2 = (1-x^2) - \frac{\langle 1-x^2, 1+x^2 \rangle}{\langle 1+x^2, 1+x^2 \rangle}(1+x^2) = (1-x^2) - \frac{\displaystyle\int_{-1}^{1}(1-x^4)dx}{\displaystyle\int_{-1}^{1}(1+2x^2+x^4)dx}(1+x^2)$$

$$= (1-x^2) - \frac{\left[x - \frac{1}{5}x^5\right]_{-1}^{1}}{\left[x + \frac{2}{3}x^3 + \frac{1}{5}x^5\right]_{-1}^{1}}(1+x^2) = (1-x^2) - \frac{8/5}{56/15}(1+x^2)$$

$$= (1-x^2) - \frac{3}{7}(1+x^2) = \frac{4}{7} - \frac{10}{7}x^2$$

$$\mathbf{v}_3 = x - \frac{\langle x, 1+x^2 \rangle}{\langle 1+x^2, 1+x^2 \rangle}(1+x^2) - \frac{\langle x, \frac{4}{7} - \frac{10}{7}x^2 \rangle}{\langle \frac{4}{7} - \frac{10}{7}x^2, \frac{4}{7} - \frac{10}{7}x^2 \rangle}\left(\frac{4}{7} - \frac{10}{7}x^2\right)$$

117

$$= x - \frac{\int_{-1}^{1}(x+x^3)dx}{\int_{-1}^{1}(1+2x^2+x^4)dx}(1+x^2) - \frac{\int_{-1}^{1}\left(\frac{4}{7}x-\frac{10}{7}x^3\right)dx}{\int_{-1}^{1}\left(\frac{4}{7}-\frac{10}{7}x^2\right)^2 dx}\left(\frac{4}{7}-\frac{10}{7}x^2\right)$$

$$= x - \frac{\left[\frac{1}{2}x^2+\frac{1}{4}x^4\right]_{-1}^{1}}{\int_{-1}^{1}(1+2x^2+x^4)dx}(1+x^2) - \frac{\left[\frac{2}{7}x^2-\frac{5}{14}x^4\right]_{-1}^{1}}{\int_{-1}^{1}\left(\frac{4}{7}-\frac{10}{7}x^2\right)^2 dx}\left(\frac{4}{7}-\frac{10}{7}x^2\right)$$

$$= x - 0(1+x^2) - 0\left(\frac{4}{7}-\frac{10}{7}x^2\right) = x$$

$$\mathbf{w}_1 = \frac{1+x^2}{\|1+x^2\|} = \frac{1+x^2}{[\langle 1+x^2, 1+x^2\rangle]^{1/2}} = \frac{1+x^2}{\left[\int_{-1}^{1}(1+2x^2+x^4)dx\right]^{1/2}}$$

$$= \frac{1+x^2}{\left(\left[x+\frac{2}{3}x^3+\frac{1}{5}x^5\right]_{-1}^{1}\right)^{1/2}} = \frac{1+x^2}{\sqrt{\frac{56}{15}}} = \sqrt{\frac{15}{56}}(1+x^2)$$

$$\mathbf{w}_2 = \frac{\frac{4}{7}-\frac{10}{7}x^2}{\left\|\frac{4}{7}-\frac{10}{7}x^2\right\|} = \frac{2-5x^2}{\|2-5x^2\|} = \frac{2-5x^2}{[\langle 2-5x^2, 2-5x^2\rangle]^{1/2}}$$

$$= \frac{2-5x^2}{\left[\int_{-1}^{1}(4-20x^2+25x^4)dx\right]^{1/2}} = \frac{2-5x^2}{\left(\left[4x-\frac{20}{3}x^3+5x^5\right]_{-1}^{1}\right)^{1/2}} = \frac{2-5x^2}{\sqrt{\frac{14}{3}}} = \sqrt{\frac{3}{14}}(2-5x^2)$$

$$= \frac{x}{\|x\|} = \frac{x}{[\langle x,x\rangle]^{1/2}} = \frac{x}{\left[\int_{-1}^{1}x^2 dx\right]^{1/2}} = \frac{x}{\left(\left[\frac{1}{3}x^3\right]_{-1}^{1}\right)^{1/2}} = \frac{x}{\sqrt{\frac{2}{3}}} = \sqrt{\frac{3}{2}}x$$

(b) $\mathbf{v}_1 = 1$

$$\mathbf{v}_2 = 3x - \frac{\langle 3x, 2\rangle}{\langle 2, 2\rangle}2 = 3x - \frac{\int_{-1}^{1}6x\,dx}{\int_{-1}^{1}4\,dx}2$$

$$= 3x - \frac{\left[3x^2\right]_{-1}^{1}}{\left[4x\right]_{-1}^{1}}2 = 3x - 0(2) = 3x$$

$$\mathbf{v}_3 = 4x^2 - \frac{\langle 4x^2, 2\rangle}{\langle 2, 2\rangle}2 - \frac{\langle 4x^2, 3x\rangle}{\langle 3x, 3x\rangle}3x$$

$$= 4x^2 - \frac{\int_{-1}^{1}8x^2 dx}{\int_{-1}^{1}4\,dx}2 - \frac{\int_{-1}^{1}12x^3 dx}{\int_{-1}^{1}9x^2 dx}3x$$

$$= 4x^2 - \frac{\left[\frac{8}{3}x^3\right]_{-1}^1}{\left[4x\right]_{-1}^1}2 - \frac{\left[3x^4\right]_{-1}^1}{\left[3x^3\right]_{-1}^1}3x = 4x^2 - \frac{\frac{16}{3}}{8}2 - 0(3x) = 4x^2 - \frac{4}{3}$$

$$\mathbf{w}_1 = \frac{2}{\|2\|} = \frac{2}{[\langle 2,2\rangle]^{1/2}} = \frac{2}{\left[\int_{-1}^1 4dx\right]^{1/2}} = \frac{2}{\left(\left[4x\right]_{-1}^1\right)^{1/2}} = \frac{2}{\sqrt{8}} = \frac{\sqrt{2}}{2}$$

$$\mathbf{w}_2 = \frac{3x}{\|3x\|} = \frac{3x}{[\langle 3x,3x\rangle]^{1/2}} = \frac{3x}{\left[\int_{-1}^1 9x^2dx\right]^{1/2}} = \frac{3x}{\left(\left[3x^3\right]_{-1}^1\right)^{1/2}} = \frac{3x}{\sqrt{6}} = \frac{\sqrt{6}}{2}x$$

$$\mathbf{w}_3 = \frac{4x^2 - \frac{4}{3}}{\|4x^2 - \frac{4}{3}\|} = \frac{4x^2 - \frac{4}{3}}{[\langle 4x^2 - \frac{4}{3}, 4x^2 - \frac{4}{3}\rangle]^{1/2}} = \frac{4x^2 - \frac{4}{3}}{\left[\int_{-1}^1 \left(16x^4 - \frac{32}{3}x^2 + \frac{16}{9}\right)dx\right]^{1/2}}$$

$$= \frac{4x^2 - \frac{4}{3}}{\left(\left[\frac{16}{5}x^5 - \frac{32}{9}x^3 + \frac{16}{9}x\right]_{-1}^1\right)^{1/2}} = \frac{4x^2 - \frac{4}{3}}{\sqrt{\frac{128}{45}}} = \sqrt{\frac{45}{128}}\left(4x^2 - \frac{4}{3}\right) = \sqrt{\frac{5}{8}}(3x^2 - 1)$$

34. (a) $\mathbf{u}_1 = (1,1)$

$\mathbf{u}_2 = (1,-2)$

$\mathbf{v}_1 = (1,1)$

$$\mathbf{v}_2 = (1,-2) - \frac{(1,-2)\cdot(1,1)}{(1,1)\cdot(1,1)}(1,1) = (1,-2) - \frac{-1}{2}(1,1) = \left(\frac{3}{2}, \frac{-3}{2}\right)$$

$$\mathbf{w}_1 = \frac{(1,1)}{\|(1,1)\|} = \frac{(1,1)}{\sqrt{2}} = \left(\frac{1}{\sqrt{2}}, \frac{1}{\sqrt{2}}\right)$$

$$\mathbf{w}_2 = \frac{\left(\frac{3}{2}, \frac{-3}{2}\right)}{\|\left(\frac{3}{2}, \frac{-3}{2}\right)\|} = \frac{(1,-1)}{\|(1,-1)\|} = \frac{(1,-1)}{\sqrt{2}} = \left(\frac{1}{\sqrt{2}}, \frac{-1}{\sqrt{2}}\right)$$

$$\mathbf{u}_1\cdot\mathbf{w}_1 = (1,1)\cdot\left(\frac{1}{\sqrt{2}}, \frac{1}{\sqrt{2}}\right) = \frac{2}{\sqrt{2}} = \sqrt{2}$$

$$\mathbf{u}_2\cdot\mathbf{w}_1 = (1,-2)\cdot\left(\frac{1}{\sqrt{2}}, \frac{1}{\sqrt{2}}\right) = \frac{-1}{\sqrt{2}}$$

$$\mathbf{u}_2\cdot\mathbf{w}_2 = (1,-2)\cdot\left(\frac{1}{\sqrt{2}}, \frac{-1}{\sqrt{2}}\right) = \frac{3}{\sqrt{2}}$$

$$R = \begin{bmatrix} \sqrt{2} & \frac{-1}{\sqrt{2}} \\ 0 & \frac{3}{\sqrt{2}} \end{bmatrix}, \quad Q = \begin{bmatrix} \frac{1}{\sqrt{2}} & \frac{1}{\sqrt{2}} \\ \frac{1}{\sqrt{2}} & \frac{-1}{\sqrt{2}} \end{bmatrix}.$$

(b) $\mathbf{u}_1 = (1, 0, 1)$

$\mathbf{u}_2 = (2, 1, 0)$

$\mathbf{v}_1 = (1, 0, 1)$

$\mathbf{v}_2 = (2, 1, 0) - \dfrac{(2,1,0)\cdot(1,0,1)}{(1,0,1)\cdot(1,0,1)}(1, 0, 1) = (2, 1, 0) - \dfrac{2}{2}(1, 0, 1) = (1, 1, -1)$

$\mathbf{w}_1 = \dfrac{(1,0,1)}{\|(1,0,1)\|} = \dfrac{(1,0,1)}{\sqrt{2}} = \left(\dfrac{1}{\sqrt{2}}, 0, \dfrac{1}{\sqrt{2}}\right)$

$\mathbf{w}_2 = \dfrac{(1,1,-1)}{\|(1,1,-1)\|} = \dfrac{(1,1,-1)}{\sqrt{3}} = \left(\dfrac{1}{\sqrt{3}}, \dfrac{1}{\sqrt{3}}, \dfrac{-1}{\sqrt{3}}\right)$

$\mathbf{u}_1\cdot\mathbf{w}_1 = (1,0,1)\cdot\left(\dfrac{1}{\sqrt{2}}, 0, \dfrac{1}{\sqrt{2}}\right) = \dfrac{2}{\sqrt{2}} = \sqrt{2}$

$\mathbf{u}_2\cdot\mathbf{w}_1 = (2,1,0)\cdot\left(\dfrac{1}{\sqrt{2}}, 0, \dfrac{1}{\sqrt{2}}\right) = \dfrac{2}{\sqrt{2}} = \sqrt{2}$

$\mathbf{u}_2\cdot\mathbf{w}_2 = (2,1,0)\cdot\left(\dfrac{1}{\sqrt{3}}, \dfrac{1}{\sqrt{3}}, \dfrac{1}{\sqrt{3}}\right) = \dfrac{3}{\sqrt{3}} = \sqrt{3}$

$$R = \begin{bmatrix} \sqrt{2} & \sqrt{2} \\ 0 & \sqrt{3} \end{bmatrix} \quad , \quad Q = \begin{bmatrix} \dfrac{1}{\sqrt{2}} & \dfrac{1}{\sqrt{3}} \\ 0 & \dfrac{1}{\sqrt{3}} \\ \dfrac{1}{\sqrt{2}} & \dfrac{-1}{\sqrt{3}} \end{bmatrix}.$$

(c) $\mathbf{u}_1 = (2, 2, 1)$

$\mathbf{u}_2 = (0, 2, -1)$

$\mathbf{u}_3 = (2, -1, -2)$

$\mathbf{v}_1 = (2, 2, 1)$

$\mathbf{v}_2 = (0, 2, -1) - \dfrac{(0,2,-1)\cdot(2,2,1)}{(2,2,1)\cdot(2,2,1)}(2, 2, 1) = (0, 2, -1) - \dfrac{3}{9}(2, 2, 1) = \left(\dfrac{-2}{3}, \dfrac{4}{3}, \dfrac{-4}{3}\right)$

$\mathbf{v}_3 = (2, -1, -2) - \dfrac{(2,-1,-2)\cdot(2,2,1)}{(2,2,1)\cdot(2,2,1)}(2, 2, 1) - \dfrac{(2,-1,-2)\cdot\left(\frac{-2}{3},\frac{4}{3},\frac{-4}{3}\right)}{\left(\frac{-2}{3},\frac{4}{3},\frac{-4}{3}\right)\cdot\left(\frac{-2}{3},\frac{4}{3},\frac{-4}{3}\right)}\left(\dfrac{-2}{3}, \dfrac{4}{3}, \dfrac{-4}{3}\right)$

$= (2, -1, -2) - 0(2, 2, 1) - 0\left(\dfrac{-2}{3}, \dfrac{4}{3}, \dfrac{-4}{3}\right) = (2, -1, -2)$

$\mathbf{w}_1 = \dfrac{(2,2,1)}{\|(2,2,1)\|} = \dfrac{(2,2,1)}{\sqrt{9}} = \left(\dfrac{2}{3}, \dfrac{2}{3}, \dfrac{1}{3}\right)$

$\mathbf{w}_2 = \dfrac{\left(\frac{-2}{3}, \frac{4}{3}, \frac{-4}{3}\right)}{\left\|\left(\frac{-2}{3}, \frac{4}{3}, \frac{-4}{3}\right)\right\|} = \dfrac{(1,-2,2)}{\|(1,-2,2)\|} = \dfrac{(1,-2,2)}{\sqrt{9}} = \left(\dfrac{1}{3}, \dfrac{-2}{3}, \dfrac{2}{3}\right)$

$\mathbf{w}_3 = \dfrac{(2,-1,-2)}{\|(2,-1,-2)\|} = \dfrac{(2,-1,-2)}{\sqrt{9}} = \left(\dfrac{2}{3}, \dfrac{-1}{3}, \dfrac{-2}{3}\right)$

$$\mathbf{u_1 \cdot w_1} = (2,2,1) \cdot \left(\frac{2}{3}, \frac{2}{3}, \frac{1}{3}\right) = \frac{9}{3} = 3$$

$$\mathbf{u_2 \cdot w_1} = (0,2,-1) \cdot \left(\frac{2}{3}, \frac{2}{3}, \frac{1}{3}\right) = \frac{3}{3} = 1$$

$$\mathbf{u_3 \cdot w_1} = (2,-1,-2) \cdot \left(\frac{2}{3}, \frac{2}{3}, \frac{1}{3}\right) = \frac{0}{3} = 0$$

$$\mathbf{u_2 \cdot w_2} = (0,2,-1) \cdot \left(\frac{1}{3}, \frac{-2}{3}, \frac{2}{3}\right) = \frac{-6}{3} = -2$$

$$\mathbf{u_3 \cdot w_2} = (2,-1,-2) \cdot \left(\frac{1}{3}, \frac{-2}{3}, \frac{2}{3}\right) = \frac{0}{3} = 0$$

$$\mathbf{u_3 \cdot w_3} = (2,-1,-2) \cdot \left(\frac{2}{3}, \frac{-1}{3}, \frac{-2}{3}\right) = \frac{9}{3} = 3$$

$$R = \begin{bmatrix} 3 & 1 & 0 \\ 0 & -2 & 0 \\ 0 & 0 & 3 \end{bmatrix} \quad , \quad Q = \begin{bmatrix} \frac{2}{3} & \frac{1}{3} & \frac{2}{3} \\ \frac{2}{3} & \frac{-2}{3} & \frac{-1}{3} \\ \frac{1}{3} & \frac{2}{3} & \frac{-2}{3} \end{bmatrix} .$$

35. (a) $A^T A = \begin{bmatrix} 1 & 0 & 1 \\ 2 & 1 & -1 \\ 1 & -1 & 0 \end{bmatrix} \begin{bmatrix} 1 & 2 & 1 \\ 0 & 1 & -1 \\ 1 & -1 & 0 \end{bmatrix} = \begin{bmatrix} 2 & 1 & 1 \\ 1 & 6 & 1 \\ 1 & 1 & 2 \end{bmatrix}$

$\det(A^T A) = 2(11) + 1(-1) + 1(-5) = 16 \neq 0$,   so columns of A are independent.

(b) $A^T A = \begin{bmatrix} 3 & 0 & 0 & 5 \\ 1 & -2 & 1 & 0 \\ 2 & 1 & 1 & 2 \end{bmatrix} \begin{bmatrix} 3 & 1 & 2 \\ 0 & -2 & 1 \\ 0 & 1 & 1 \\ 5 & 0 & 2 \end{bmatrix} = \begin{bmatrix} 34 & 3 & 16 \\ 3 & 6 & 1 \\ 16 & 1 & 10 \end{bmatrix}$

$\det(A^T A) = 3(-14) + 6(84) + 1(14) = 476 \neq 0$,   so columns of A are independent.

(c) $A^T A = \begin{bmatrix} 2 & 3 & 0 & 1 & -1 \\ 3 & 4 & 1 & 2 & 0 \\ -1 & 1 & -5 & -3 & -7 \end{bmatrix} \begin{bmatrix} 2 & 3 & -1 \\ 3 & 4 & 1 \\ 0 & 1 & -5 \\ 1 & 2 & -3 \\ -1 & 0 & -7 \end{bmatrix} = \begin{bmatrix} 15 & 20 & 5 \\ 20 & 30 & -10 \\ 5 & -10 & 85 \end{bmatrix} = 5 \begin{bmatrix} 3 & 4 & 1 \\ 4 & 6 & -2 \\ 1 & -2 & 17 \end{bmatrix}$

$\det(A^T A) = 5^3 \det \begin{bmatrix} 3 & 4 & 1 \\ 4 & 6 & -2 \\ 1 & -2 & 17 \end{bmatrix} = 5^3 [3(98) + 4(-70) + 1(-14)] = 5^3(0) = 0$,

so columns of A are dependent.

36. (a) $A^T A = \begin{bmatrix} 2 & 1 & 2 \\ 1 & 0 & 3 \end{bmatrix} \begin{bmatrix} 2 & 1 \\ 1 & 0 \\ 2 & 3 \end{bmatrix} = \begin{bmatrix} 9 & 8 \\ 8 & 10 \end{bmatrix}$, $(A^T A)^{-1} = \frac{1}{26} \begin{bmatrix} 10 & -8 \\ -8 & 9 \end{bmatrix}$.

$\mathbf{x} = (A^T A)^{-1} A^T \mathbf{b} = \frac{1}{26} \begin{bmatrix} 10 & -8 \\ -8 & 9 \end{bmatrix} \begin{bmatrix} 2 & 1 & 2 \\ 1 & 0 & 3 \end{bmatrix} \begin{bmatrix} 26 \\ -13 \\ 0 \end{bmatrix}$

$= \frac{1}{26} \begin{bmatrix} 12 & 10 & -4 \\ -7 & -8 & 11 \end{bmatrix} \begin{bmatrix} 26 \\ -13 \\ 0 \end{bmatrix} = \begin{bmatrix} 12 & 10 & -4 \\ -7 & -8 & 11 \end{bmatrix} \begin{bmatrix} 1 \\ -1/2 \\ 0 \end{bmatrix} = \begin{bmatrix} 7 \\ -3 \end{bmatrix}$.

The projection is $A\mathbf{x} = \begin{bmatrix} 2 & 1 \\ 1 & 0 \\ 2 & 3 \end{bmatrix} \begin{bmatrix} 7 \\ -3 \end{bmatrix} = \begin{bmatrix} 11 \\ 7 \\ 5 \end{bmatrix}$.

(b) $\quad A^T A = \begin{bmatrix} 7 & 0 & -2 \\ 6 & 3 & 1 \end{bmatrix} \begin{bmatrix} 7 & 6 \\ 0 & 3 \\ -2 & 1 \end{bmatrix} = \begin{bmatrix} 53 & 40 \\ 40 & 46 \end{bmatrix}$, $\quad (A^T A)^{-1} = \dfrac{1}{838} \begin{bmatrix} 46 & -40 \\ -40 & 53 \end{bmatrix}$.

$$\mathbf{x} = (A^T A)^{-1} A^T \mathbf{b} = \frac{1}{838} \begin{bmatrix} 46 & -40 \\ -40 & 53 \end{bmatrix} \begin{bmatrix} 7 & 0 & -2 \\ 6 & 3 & 1 \end{bmatrix} \begin{bmatrix} 3 \\ 12 \\ 10 \end{bmatrix}$$

$$= \frac{1}{838} \begin{bmatrix} 46 & -40 \\ -40 & 53 \end{bmatrix} \begin{bmatrix} 1 \\ 64 \end{bmatrix} = \frac{1}{838} \begin{bmatrix} -2514 \\ 3352 \end{bmatrix} = \begin{bmatrix} -3 \\ 4 \end{bmatrix}$$

The projection is $\quad A\mathbf{x} = \begin{bmatrix} 7 & 6 \\ 0 & 3 \\ -2 & 1 \end{bmatrix} \begin{bmatrix} -3 \\ 4 \end{bmatrix} = \begin{bmatrix} 3 \\ 12 \\ 10 \end{bmatrix} = \mathbf{b}.$

(c) $\quad A^T A = \begin{bmatrix} 2 & 0 & -1 & 3 \\ 1 & 1 & 1 & 0 \end{bmatrix} \begin{bmatrix} 2 & 1 \\ 0 & 1 \\ -1 & 1 \\ 3 & 0 \end{bmatrix} = \begin{bmatrix} 14 & 1 \\ 1 & 3 \end{bmatrix}$, $\quad (A^T A)^{-1} = \dfrac{1}{41} \begin{bmatrix} 3 & -1 \\ -1 & 14 \end{bmatrix}$.

$$\mathbf{x} = (A^T A)^{-1} A^T \mathbf{b} = \frac{1}{41} \begin{bmatrix} 3 & -1 \\ -1 & 14 \end{bmatrix} \begin{bmatrix} 2 & 0 & -1 & 3 \\ 1 & 1 & 1 & 0 \end{bmatrix} \begin{bmatrix} 1 \\ 3 \\ 3 \\ -3 \end{bmatrix}$$

$$= \frac{1}{41} \begin{bmatrix} 3 & -1 \\ -1 & 14 \end{bmatrix} \begin{bmatrix} -10 \\ 7 \end{bmatrix} = \frac{1}{41} \begin{bmatrix} -37 \\ 108 \end{bmatrix}.$$

The projection is $\quad A\mathbf{x} = \dfrac{1}{41} \begin{bmatrix} 2 & 1 \\ 0 & 1 \\ -1 & 1 \\ 3 & 0 \end{bmatrix} \begin{bmatrix} -37 \\ 108 \end{bmatrix} = \dfrac{1}{41} \begin{bmatrix} 34 \\ 108 \\ 145 \\ 111 \end{bmatrix}.$

(d) $\quad A^T A = \begin{bmatrix} 1 & 0 & 1 & 1 \\ 0 & 1 & 0 & 0 \\ 1 & -2 & 0 & 1 \end{bmatrix} \begin{bmatrix} 1 & 0 & 1 \\ 0 & 1 & -2 \\ 1 & 0 & 0 \\ 1 & 0 & 1 \end{bmatrix} = \begin{bmatrix} 3 & 0 & 2 \\ 0 & 1 & -2 \\ 2 & -2 & 6 \end{bmatrix}$

$$(A^T A)^{-1} = \frac{1}{2} \begin{bmatrix} 2 & -4 & -2 \\ -4 & 14 & 6 \\ -2 & 6 & 3 \end{bmatrix}^T = \frac{1}{2} \begin{bmatrix} 2 & -4 & -2 \\ -4 & 14 & 6 \\ -2 & 6 & 3 \end{bmatrix}$$

$$\mathbf{x} = (A^T A)^{-1} A^T \mathbf{b} = \frac{1}{2} \begin{bmatrix} 2 & -4 & -2 \\ -4 & 14 & 6 \\ -2 & 6 & 3 \end{bmatrix} \begin{bmatrix} 1 & 0 & 1 & 1 \\ 0 & 1 & 0 & 0 \\ 1 & -2 & 0 & 1 \end{bmatrix} \begin{bmatrix} 6 \\ -6 \\ 2 \\ 4 \end{bmatrix}$$

$$= \begin{bmatrix} 2 & -4 & -2 \\ -4 & 14 & 6 \\ -2 & 6 & 3 \end{bmatrix} \begin{bmatrix} 1 & 0 & 1 & 1 \\ 0 & 1 & 0 & 0 \\ 1 & -2 & 0 & 1 \end{bmatrix} \begin{bmatrix} 3 \\ -3 \\ 1 \\ 2 \end{bmatrix} = \begin{bmatrix} 2 & -4 & -2 \\ -4 & 14 & 6 \\ -2 & 6 & 3 \end{bmatrix} \begin{bmatrix} 6 \\ -3 \\ 11 \end{bmatrix} = \begin{bmatrix} 2 \\ 0 \\ 3 \end{bmatrix}.$$

The projection is $\quad A\mathbf{x} = \begin{bmatrix} 1 & 0 & 1 \\ 0 & 1 & -2 \\ 1 & 0 & 0 \\ 1 & 0 & 1 \end{bmatrix} \begin{bmatrix} 2 \\ 0 \\ 3 \end{bmatrix} = \begin{bmatrix} 5 \\ -6 \\ 2 \\ 5 \end{bmatrix}.$

37. (a) $A^T A = \begin{bmatrix} 1 & 0 & 3 \\ 1 & 1 & 2 \end{bmatrix} \begin{bmatrix} 1 & 1 \\ 0 & 1 \\ 3 & 2 \end{bmatrix} = \begin{bmatrix} 10 & 7 \\ 7 & 6 \end{bmatrix}$, $(A^T A)^{-1} = \frac{1}{11} \begin{bmatrix} 6 & -7 \\ -7 & 10 \end{bmatrix}$.

$$\mathbf{x} = (A^T A)^{-1} A^T \mathbf{u} = \frac{1}{11} \begin{bmatrix} 6 & -7 \\ -7 & 10 \end{bmatrix} \begin{bmatrix} 1 & 0 & 3 \\ 1 & 1 & 2 \end{bmatrix} \begin{bmatrix} 1 \\ 3 \\ -1 \end{bmatrix}$$

$$= \frac{1}{11} \begin{bmatrix} 6 & -7 \\ -7 & 10 \end{bmatrix} \begin{bmatrix} -2 \\ 2 \end{bmatrix} = \frac{1}{11} \begin{bmatrix} -26 \\ 34 \end{bmatrix}$$

$A\mathbf{x} = \frac{1}{11} \begin{bmatrix} 1 & 1 \\ 0 & 1 \\ 3 & 2 \end{bmatrix} \begin{bmatrix} -26 \\ 34 \end{bmatrix} = \frac{1}{11} \begin{bmatrix} 8 \\ 34 \\ -10 \end{bmatrix}$ so the projection is $\left(\frac{8}{11}, \frac{34}{11}, \frac{-10}{11} \right)$.

(b) $A^T A = \begin{bmatrix} 2 & 1 & 0 & 1 \\ 2 & 0 & -1 & 0 \end{bmatrix} \begin{bmatrix} 2 & 2 \\ 1 & 0 \\ 0 & -1 \\ 1 & 0 \end{bmatrix} = \begin{bmatrix} 6 & 4 \\ 4 & 5 \end{bmatrix}$, $(A^T A)^{-1} = \frac{1}{14} \begin{bmatrix} 5 & -4 \\ -4 & 6 \end{bmatrix}$.

$$\mathbf{x} = (A^T A)^{-1} A^T \mathbf{u} = \frac{1}{14} \begin{bmatrix} 5 & -4 \\ -4 & 6 \end{bmatrix} \begin{bmatrix} 2 & 1 & 0 & 1 \\ 2 & 0 & -1 & 0 \end{bmatrix} \begin{bmatrix} 1 \\ 1 \\ 1 \\ 1 \end{bmatrix}$$

$$= \frac{1}{14} \begin{bmatrix} 5 & -4 \\ -4 & 6 \end{bmatrix} \begin{bmatrix} 4 \\ 1 \end{bmatrix} = \frac{1}{14} \begin{bmatrix} 16 \\ -10 \end{bmatrix} = \frac{1}{7} \begin{bmatrix} 8 \\ -5 \end{bmatrix}$$

$A\mathbf{x} = \frac{1}{7} \begin{bmatrix} 2 & 2 \\ 1 & 0 \\ 0 & -1 \\ 1 & 0 \end{bmatrix} \begin{bmatrix} 8 \\ -5 \end{bmatrix} = \frac{1}{7} \begin{bmatrix} 6 \\ 8 \\ 5 \\ 8 \end{bmatrix}$ so the projection is $\left(\frac{6}{7}, \frac{8}{7}, \frac{5}{7}, \frac{8}{7} \right)$.

38. (a) $\begin{bmatrix} 1 & -1 & 2 & 0 & 0 \\ 1 & 1 & 0 & 2 & 0 \end{bmatrix} \longrightarrow \begin{bmatrix} 1 & -1 & 2 & 0 & 0 \\ 0 & 2 & -2 & 2 & 0 \end{bmatrix} \longrightarrow \begin{bmatrix} 1 & 0 & 1 & 1 & 0 \\ 0 & 1 & -1 & 1 & 0 \end{bmatrix}$

Let $x_4 = t$, $x_3 = s$;

then $x_2 - x_3 + x_4 = 0$ i.e., $x_2 = s - t$

and $x_1 + x_3 + x_4 = 0$ i.e., $x_1 = -s - t$

so $\begin{bmatrix} x_1 \\ x_2 \\ x_3 \\ x_4 \end{bmatrix} = \begin{bmatrix} -s - t \\ s - t \\ s \\ t \end{bmatrix} = s \begin{bmatrix} -1 \\ 1 \\ 1 \\ 0 \end{bmatrix} + t \begin{bmatrix} -1 \\ -1 \\ 0 \\ 1 \end{bmatrix}$.

Let $B = \begin{bmatrix} -1 & -1 \\ 1 & -1 \\ 1 & 0 \\ 0 & 1 \end{bmatrix}$ so $B^T B = \begin{bmatrix} -1 & 1 & 1 & 0 \\ -1 & -1 & 0 & 1 \end{bmatrix} \begin{bmatrix} -1 & -1 \\ 1 & -1 \\ 1 & 0 \\ 0 & 1 \end{bmatrix} = \begin{bmatrix} 3 & 0 \\ 0 & 3 \end{bmatrix}$.

$$(B^TB)^{-1} = \begin{bmatrix} 1/3 & 0 \\ 0 & 1/3 \end{bmatrix} \quad , \quad (B^TB)^{-1}B^T\mathbf{u} = \begin{bmatrix} 1/3 & 0 \\ 0 & 1/3 \end{bmatrix} \begin{bmatrix} -1 & 1 & 1 & 0 \\ -1 & -1 & 0 & 1 \end{bmatrix} \begin{bmatrix} -1 \\ 2 \\ 3 \\ 4 \end{bmatrix}$$

$$= \begin{bmatrix} 1/3 & 0 \\ 0 & 1/3 \end{bmatrix} \begin{bmatrix} 6 \\ 3 \end{bmatrix} = \begin{bmatrix} 2 \\ 1 \end{bmatrix}.$$

The projection is $\begin{bmatrix} -1 & -1 \\ 1 & -1 \\ 1 & 0 \\ 0 & 1 \end{bmatrix} \begin{bmatrix} 2 \\ 1 \end{bmatrix} = \begin{bmatrix} -3 \\ 1 \\ 2 \\ 1 \end{bmatrix}.$

(b) $\begin{bmatrix} 1 & 1 & 1 & 0 & 1 & 0 \\ 2 & 3 & 1 & 1 & 1 & 0 \\ 1 & -1 & 3 & -2 & 3 & 0 \end{bmatrix} \longrightarrow \begin{bmatrix} 1 & 1 & 1 & 0 & 1 & 0 \\ 0 & 1 & -1 & 1 & -1 & 0 \\ 0 & -2 & 2 & -2 & 2 & 0 \end{bmatrix} \longrightarrow \begin{bmatrix} 1 & 0 & 2 & -1 & 2 & 0 \\ 0 & 1 & -1 & 1 & -1 & 0 \\ 0 & 0 & 0 & 0 & 0 & 0 \end{bmatrix}$

Let $x_5 = t$, $x_4 = s$, $x_3 = r$;

then $x_2 - x_3 + x_4 - x_5 = 0$ i.e., $x_2 = r - s + t$

and $x_1 + 2x_3 - x_4 + 2x_5 = 0$ i.e., $x_1 = -2r + s - 2t$

so $\begin{bmatrix} x_1 \\ x_2 \\ x_3 \\ x_4 \\ x_5 \end{bmatrix} = \begin{bmatrix} -2r + s - 2t \\ r - s + t \\ r \\ s \\ t \end{bmatrix} = r\begin{bmatrix} -2 \\ 1 \\ 1 \\ 0 \\ 0 \end{bmatrix} + s\begin{bmatrix} 1 \\ -1 \\ 0 \\ 1 \\ 0 \end{bmatrix} + t\begin{bmatrix} -2 \\ 1 \\ 0 \\ 0 \\ 1 \end{bmatrix}.$

Let $B = \begin{bmatrix} -2 & 1 & -2 \\ 1 & -1 & 1 \\ 1 & 0 & 0 \\ 0 & 1 & 0 \\ 0 & 0 & 1 \end{bmatrix}$ so $B^TB = \begin{bmatrix} -2 & 1 & 1 & 0 & 0 \\ 1 & -1 & 0 & 1 & 0 \\ -2 & 1 & 0 & 0 & 1 \end{bmatrix} \begin{bmatrix} -2 & 1 & -2 \\ 1 & -1 & 1 \\ 1 & 0 & 0 \\ 0 & 1 & 0 \\ 0 & 0 & 1 \end{bmatrix}$

$$= \begin{bmatrix} 6 & -3 & 5 \\ -3 & 3 & -3 \\ 5 & -3 & 6 \end{bmatrix}.$$

$$(B^TB)^{-1} = \frac{1}{15}\begin{bmatrix} 9 & 3 & -6 \\ 3 & 11 & 3 \\ -6 & 3 & 9 \end{bmatrix}^T = \frac{1}{15}\begin{bmatrix} 9 & 3 & -6 \\ 3 & 11 & 3 \\ -6 & 3 & 9 \end{bmatrix}$$

$$(B^TB)^{-1}B^T\mathbf{u} = \frac{1}{15}\begin{bmatrix} 9 & 3 & -6 \\ 3 & 11 & 3 \\ -6 & 3 & 9 \end{bmatrix} \begin{bmatrix} -2 & 1 & 1 & 0 & 0 \\ 1 & -1 & 0 & 1 & 0 \\ -2 & 1 & 0 & 0 & 1 \end{bmatrix} \begin{bmatrix} 0 \\ 2 \\ 1 \\ -1 \\ 1 \end{bmatrix}$$

$$= \frac{1}{15}\begin{bmatrix} 9 & 3 & -6 \\ 3 & 11 & 3 \\ -6 & 3 & 9 \end{bmatrix} \begin{bmatrix} 3 \\ -3 \\ 3 \end{bmatrix} = \frac{1}{15}\begin{bmatrix} 0 \\ -15 \\ 0 \end{bmatrix} = \begin{bmatrix} 0 \\ -1 \\ 0 \end{bmatrix}$$

The projection is $\begin{bmatrix} -2 & 1 & -2 \\ 1 & -1 & 1 \\ 1 & 0 & 0 \\ 0 & 1 & 0 \\ 0 & 0 & 1 \end{bmatrix} \begin{bmatrix} 0 \\ -1 \\ 0 \end{bmatrix} = \begin{bmatrix} -1 \\ 1 \\ 0 \\ -1 \\ 0 \end{bmatrix}.$

39. (a) $[2 \; 1 \; -3 \; 0] \longrightarrow [1 \; 1/2 \; -3/2 \; 0]$

Let $z = t$, $y = s$;

then $x + \dfrac{1}{2}y - \dfrac{3}{2}z = 0$ i.e., $x = \dfrac{-1}{2}s + \dfrac{3}{2}t$

so $\begin{bmatrix} x \\ y \\ z \end{bmatrix} = \begin{bmatrix} (-1/2)s + (3/2)t \\ s \\ t \end{bmatrix} = s\begin{bmatrix} -1/2 \\ 1 \\ 0 \end{bmatrix} + t\begin{bmatrix} 3/2 \\ 0 \\ 1 \end{bmatrix}$.   Let $B = \left\{ \begin{bmatrix} -1 \\ 2 \\ 0 \end{bmatrix}, \begin{bmatrix} 3 \\ 0 \\ 2 \end{bmatrix} \right\}$.

(b) $A = \begin{bmatrix} -1 & 3 \\ 2 & 0 \\ 0 & 2 \end{bmatrix}$, $A^T A = \begin{bmatrix} -1 & 2 & 0 \\ 3 & 0 & 2 \end{bmatrix} \begin{bmatrix} -1 & 3 \\ 2 & 0 \\ 0 & 2 \end{bmatrix} = \begin{bmatrix} 5 & -3 \\ -3 & 13 \end{bmatrix}$,

$(A^T A)^{-1} = \dfrac{1}{56} \begin{bmatrix} 13 & 3 \\ 3 & 5 \end{bmatrix}$,

$[P] = \dfrac{1}{56} \begin{bmatrix} -1 & 3 \\ 2 & 0 \\ 0 & 2 \end{bmatrix} \begin{bmatrix} 13 & 3 \\ 3 & 5 \end{bmatrix} \begin{bmatrix} -1 & 2 & 0 \\ 3 & 0 & 2 \end{bmatrix} = \dfrac{1}{56} \begin{bmatrix} -1 & 3 \\ 2 & 0 \\ 0 & 2 \end{bmatrix} \begin{bmatrix} -4 & 26 & 6 \\ 12 & 6 & 10 \end{bmatrix}$

$= \dfrac{1}{56} \begin{bmatrix} 40 & -8 & 24 \\ -8 & 52 & 12 \\ 24 & 12 & 20 \end{bmatrix} = \dfrac{1}{14} \begin{bmatrix} 10 & -2 & 6 \\ -2 & 13 & 3 \\ 6 & 3 & 5 \end{bmatrix}$.

(c) The projction of P on W is $Q = [P]P = \dfrac{1}{14} \begin{bmatrix} 10 & -2 & 6 \\ -2 & 13 & 3 \\ 6 & 3 & 5 \end{bmatrix} \begin{bmatrix} 0 \\ 4 \\ -1 \end{bmatrix} = \dfrac{1}{14} \begin{bmatrix} -14 \\ 49 \\ 7 \end{bmatrix} = \begin{bmatrix} -1 \\ 7/2 \\ 1/2 \end{bmatrix}$

$d(P, W) = d(P, Q) = \|P - Q\| = \|(0, 4, -1) - (-1, 7/2, 1/2)\| = \|(1, 1/2, -3/2)\|$

$= \|1/2(2, 1, -3)\| = \dfrac{1}{2}\|(2, 1, -3)\| = \dfrac{1}{2}\sqrt{4 + 1 + 9} = \dfrac{1}{2}\sqrt{14}$.

40. (a) $\begin{bmatrix} x \\ y \\ z \end{bmatrix} = \begin{bmatrix} 3t \\ 4t \\ -t \end{bmatrix} = t\begin{bmatrix} 3 \\ 4 \\ -1 \end{bmatrix}$.   Let $B = \left\{ \begin{bmatrix} 3 \\ 4 \\ -1 \end{bmatrix} \right\}$.

(b) $A = \begin{bmatrix} 3 \\ 4 \\ -1 \end{bmatrix}$, $A^T A = [3 \; 4 \; -1] \begin{bmatrix} 3 \\ 4 \\ -1 \end{bmatrix} = [26]$, $(A^T A)^{-1} = \left[\dfrac{1}{26} \right]$,

$[P] = \begin{bmatrix} 3 \\ 4 \\ -1 \end{bmatrix} \left[\dfrac{1}{26} \right] [3 \; 4 \; -1] = \dfrac{1}{26} \begin{bmatrix} 3 \\ 4 \\ -1 \end{bmatrix} [3 \; 4 \; -1] = \dfrac{1}{26} \begin{bmatrix} 9 & 12 & -3 \\ 12 & 16 & -4 \\ -3 & -4 & 1 \end{bmatrix}$.

(c) The projction of P on W is $Q = [P]P = \dfrac{1}{26} \begin{bmatrix} 9 & 12 & -3 \\ 12 & 16 & -4 \\ -3 & -4 & 1 \end{bmatrix} \begin{bmatrix} 2 \\ 2 \\ 1 \end{bmatrix} = \dfrac{1}{26} \begin{bmatrix} 39 \\ 52 \\ -13 \end{bmatrix} = \begin{bmatrix} 3/2 \\ 2 \\ -1/2 \end{bmatrix}$.

$d(P, W) = d(P, Q) = \|P - Q\| = \|(2, 2, 1) - (3/2, 2, -1/2)\| = \|(1/2, 0, 3/2)\|$

$= \|1/2(1, 0, 3)\| = \dfrac{1}{2}\|(1, 0, 3)\| = \dfrac{1}{2}\sqrt{1 + 0 + 9} = \dfrac{1}{2}\sqrt{10}$.

41. (a) $A^T A = \begin{bmatrix} 4/5 & -3/5 \\ 3/5 & 4/5 \end{bmatrix} \begin{bmatrix} 4/5 & 3/5 \\ -3/5 & 4/5 \end{bmatrix} = \begin{bmatrix} 1 & 0 \\ 0 & 1 \end{bmatrix} = I$ so A is orthogonal.

(b) $A^T A = \begin{bmatrix} 1/3 & 2/3 & 2/3 \\ 2/3 & 1/3 & -2/3 \\ 2/3 & -2/3 & 1/3 \end{bmatrix} \begin{bmatrix} 1/3 & 2/3 & 2/3 \\ 2/3 & 1/3 & -2/3 \\ 2/3 & -2/3 & 1/3 \end{bmatrix} = \begin{bmatrix} 1 & 0 & 0 \\ 0 & 1 & 0 \\ 0 & 0 & 1 \end{bmatrix} = I$ so A is orthogonal.

(c) $A^T A = \begin{bmatrix} 1/\sqrt{3} & 1/\sqrt{3} & 1/\sqrt{3} \\ -1/\sqrt{6} & 2/\sqrt{6} & -1/\sqrt{6} \\ 3/\sqrt{14} & -2/\sqrt{14} & -1/\sqrt{14} \end{bmatrix} \begin{bmatrix} 1/\sqrt{3} & -1/\sqrt{6} & 3/\sqrt{14} \\ 1/\sqrt{3} & 2/\sqrt{6} & -2/\sqrt{14} \\ 1/\sqrt{3} & -1/\sqrt{6} & -1/\sqrt{14} \end{bmatrix}$

$= \begin{bmatrix} 1 & 0 & 0 \\ 0 & 1 & -\sqrt{3/7} \\ 0 & -\sqrt{3/7} & 1 \end{bmatrix} \neq I$ so A is not orthogonal.

(d) $A^T A = \begin{bmatrix} 2/3 & 1/\sqrt{2} & 1/\sqrt{18} \\ -1/3 & 0 & 4/\sqrt{18} \\ 2/3 & -1/\sqrt{2} & 1/\sqrt{18} \end{bmatrix} \begin{bmatrix} 2/3 & -1/3 & 2/3 \\ 1/\sqrt{2} & 0 & -1/\sqrt{2} \\ 1/\sqrt{18} & 4/\sqrt{18} & 1/\sqrt{18} \end{bmatrix}$

$= \begin{bmatrix} 1 & 0 & 0 \\ 0 & 1 & 0 \\ 0 & 0 & 1 \end{bmatrix} = I$ so A is orthogonal.

42. (a) $P_{B',B} = \left[\left[\mathbf{u}_1\right]_{B'} \vdots \left[\mathbf{u}_2\right]_{B'} \right] = \left[\left[\begin{smallmatrix}1\\2\end{smallmatrix}\right]_{B'} \vdots \left[\begin{smallmatrix}3\\5\end{smallmatrix}\right]_{B'} \right]$

$= \left[\begin{bmatrix}1 & 0\\1 & 1\end{bmatrix}^{-1} \begin{bmatrix}1\\2\end{bmatrix} \vdots \begin{bmatrix}1 & 0\\1 & 1\end{bmatrix}^{-1} \begin{bmatrix}3\\5\end{bmatrix} \right] = \begin{bmatrix}1 & 0\\1 & 1\end{bmatrix}^{-1} \begin{bmatrix}1 & 3\\2 & 5\end{bmatrix}$

$= \begin{bmatrix}1 & 0\\-1 & 1\end{bmatrix} \begin{bmatrix}1 & 3\\2 & 5\end{bmatrix} = \begin{bmatrix}1 & 3\\1 & 2\end{bmatrix}.$

(b) $P_{B,B'} = P_{B',B}^{-1} = \begin{bmatrix}1 & 3\\1 & 2\end{bmatrix}^{-1} = \frac{1}{-1} \begin{bmatrix}2 & -3\\-1 & 1\end{bmatrix} = \begin{bmatrix}-2 & 3\\1 & -1\end{bmatrix}.$

(c) $[\mathbf{w}]_{B'} = \begin{bmatrix}4\\7\end{bmatrix}_{B'} = \begin{bmatrix}1 & 0\\1 & 1\end{bmatrix}^{-1} \begin{bmatrix}4\\7\end{bmatrix} = \begin{bmatrix}1 & 0\\-1 & 1\end{bmatrix} \begin{bmatrix}4\\7\end{bmatrix} = \begin{bmatrix}4\\3\end{bmatrix}.$

(d) $[\mathbf{w}]_B = P_{B,B'}[\mathbf{w}]_{B'} = \begin{bmatrix}-2 & 3\\1 & -1\end{bmatrix} \begin{bmatrix}4\\3\end{bmatrix} = \begin{bmatrix}1\\1\end{bmatrix}.$

43. (a) $P_{B',B} = \left[\left[\mathbf{u}_1\right]_{B'} \vdots \left[\mathbf{u}_2\right]_{B'} \right] = \left[\left[\begin{smallmatrix}3\\3\end{smallmatrix}\right]_{B'} \vdots \left[\begin{smallmatrix}-2\\1\end{smallmatrix}\right]_{B'} \right]$

$= \left[\begin{bmatrix}2 & 3\\5 & 7\end{bmatrix}^{-1} \begin{bmatrix}3\\3\end{bmatrix} \vdots \begin{bmatrix}2 & 3\\5 & 7\end{bmatrix}^{-1} \begin{bmatrix}-2\\1\end{bmatrix} \right] = \begin{bmatrix}2 & 3\\5 & 7\end{bmatrix}^{-1} \begin{bmatrix}3 & -2\\3 & 1\end{bmatrix}$

$= \frac{1}{-1} \begin{bmatrix}7 & -3\\-5 & 2\end{bmatrix} \begin{bmatrix}3 & -2\\3 & 1\end{bmatrix} = \begin{bmatrix}-12 & 17\\9 & -12\end{bmatrix}.$

(b) $P_{B,B'} = P_{B',B}^{-1} = \begin{bmatrix}-12 & 17\\9 & -12\end{bmatrix}^{-1} = \frac{1}{-9} \begin{bmatrix}-12 & -17\\-9 & -12\end{bmatrix} = \frac{1}{9} \begin{bmatrix}12 & 17\\9 & 12\end{bmatrix}.$

(c) $[\mathbf{w}]_{B'} = \begin{bmatrix} 4 \\ 7 \end{bmatrix}_{B'} = \begin{bmatrix} 2 & 3 \\ 5 & 7 \end{bmatrix}^{-1} \begin{bmatrix} 4 \\ 7 \end{bmatrix} = \begin{bmatrix} -7 & 3 \\ 5 & -2 \end{bmatrix} \begin{bmatrix} 4 \\ 7 \end{bmatrix} = \begin{bmatrix} -7 \\ 6 \end{bmatrix}.$

(d) $[\mathbf{w}]_B = P_{B,B'} [\mathbf{w}]_{B'} = \dfrac{1}{9} \begin{bmatrix} 12 & 17 \\ 9 & 12 \end{bmatrix} \begin{bmatrix} -7 \\ 6 \end{bmatrix} = \dfrac{1}{9} \begin{bmatrix} 18 \\ 9 \end{bmatrix} = \begin{bmatrix} 2 \\ 1 \end{bmatrix}.$

44. (a) $P_{B',B} = \left[[\mathbf{u_1}]_{B'} \vdots [\mathbf{u_2}]_{B'} \vdots [\mathbf{u_3}]_{B'} \right] = \left[\begin{bmatrix} 1 \\ 0 \\ 3 \end{bmatrix}_{B'} \vdots \begin{bmatrix} 0 \\ 1 \\ 0 \end{bmatrix}_{B'} \vdots \begin{bmatrix} -2 \\ 5 \\ 1 \end{bmatrix}_{B'} \right]$

$= \begin{bmatrix} -2 & 0 & 1 \\ 1 & 1 & 0 \\ 1 & -1 & 0 \end{bmatrix}^{-1} \begin{bmatrix} 1 & 0 & -2 \\ 0 & 1 & 5 \\ 3 & 0 & 1 \end{bmatrix} = \dfrac{1}{-2} \begin{bmatrix} 0 & 0 & -2 \\ -1 & -1 & -2 \\ -1 & 1 & -2 \end{bmatrix}^T \begin{bmatrix} 1 & 0 & -2 \\ 0 & 1 & 5 \\ 3 & 0 & 1 \end{bmatrix}$

$= \dfrac{-1}{2} \begin{bmatrix} 0 & -1 & -1 \\ 0 & -1 & 1 \\ -2 & -2 & -2 \end{bmatrix} \begin{bmatrix} 1 & 0 & -2 \\ 0 & 1 & 5 \\ 3 & 0 & 1 \end{bmatrix} = \dfrac{-1}{2} \begin{bmatrix} -3 & -1 & -6 \\ 3 & -1 & -4 \\ -8 & -2 & -8 \end{bmatrix} = \dfrac{1}{2} \begin{bmatrix} 3 & 1 & 6 \\ -3 & 1 & 4 \\ 8 & 2 & 8 \end{bmatrix}$

(b) $P_{B,B'} = P_{B',B}^{-1} = \left(\dfrac{1}{2} \begin{bmatrix} 3 & 1 & 6 \\ -3 & 1 & 4 \\ 8 & 2 & 8 \end{bmatrix} \right)^{-1} = 2 \begin{bmatrix} 3 & 1 & 6 \\ -3 & 1 & 4 \\ 8 & 2 & 8 \end{bmatrix}^{-1}$

$= 2 \cdot \dfrac{1}{-28} \begin{bmatrix} 0 & 56 & -14 \\ 4 & -24 & 2 \\ -2 & -30 & 6 \end{bmatrix}^T = \dfrac{-1}{7} \begin{bmatrix} 0 & 2 & -1 \\ 28 & -12 & -15 \\ -7 & 1 & 3 \end{bmatrix}$

(c) $[\mathbf{w}]_{B'} = \begin{bmatrix} 2 \\ 3 \\ -1 \end{bmatrix}_{B'} = \begin{bmatrix} -2 & 0 & 1 \\ 1 & 1 & 0 \\ 1 & -1 & 0 \end{bmatrix}^{-1} \begin{bmatrix} 2 \\ 3 \\ -1 \end{bmatrix} = \dfrac{-1}{2} \begin{bmatrix} 0 & -1 & -1 \\ 0 & -1 & 1 \\ -2 & -2 & -2 \end{bmatrix} \begin{bmatrix} 2 \\ 3 \\ -1 \end{bmatrix} = \begin{bmatrix} 1 \\ 2 \\ 4 \end{bmatrix}.$

(d) $[\mathbf{w}]_B = P_{B,B'} [\mathbf{w}]_{B'} = \dfrac{-1}{7} \begin{bmatrix} 0 & 2 & -1 \\ 28 & -12 & -15 \\ -7 & 1 & 3 \end{bmatrix} \begin{bmatrix} 1 \\ 2 \\ 4 \end{bmatrix} = \begin{bmatrix} 0 \\ 8 \\ -1 \end{bmatrix}.$

45. (a) $P_{B',B} = \left[[\mathbf{u_1}]_{B'} \vdots [\mathbf{u_2}]_{B'} \vdots [\mathbf{u_3}]_{B'} \right] = \left[\begin{bmatrix} 1 \\ 0 \\ 0 \end{bmatrix}_{B'} \vdots \begin{bmatrix} 3 \\ 3 \\ 0 \end{bmatrix}_{B'} \vdots \begin{bmatrix} 5 \\ 5 \\ 5 \end{bmatrix}_{B'} \right]$

$= \begin{bmatrix} 0 & 2 & 4 \\ 2 & 4 & 4 \\ 2 & 0 & 4 \end{bmatrix}^{-1} \begin{bmatrix} 1 & 3 & 5 \\ 0 & 3 & 5 \\ 0 & 0 & 5 \end{bmatrix} = \dfrac{1}{-32} \begin{bmatrix} 16 & 0 & -8 \\ -8 & -8 & 4 \\ -8 & 8 & -4 \end{bmatrix}^T \begin{bmatrix} 1 & 3 & 5 \\ 0 & 3 & 5 \\ 0 & 0 & 5 \end{bmatrix}$

$= \dfrac{-1}{32} \begin{bmatrix} 16 & -8 & -8 \\ 0 & -8 & 8 \\ -8 & 4 & -4 \end{bmatrix} \begin{bmatrix} 1 & 3 & 5 \\ 0 & 3 & 5 \\ 0 & 0 & 5 \end{bmatrix} = \dfrac{1}{8} \begin{bmatrix} -4 & 2 & 2 \\ 0 & 2 & -2 \\ 2 & -1 & 1 \end{bmatrix} \begin{bmatrix} 1 & 3 & 5 \\ 0 & 3 & 5 \\ 0 & 0 & 5 \end{bmatrix}$

$= \dfrac{1}{8} \begin{bmatrix} -4 & -6 & 0 \\ 0 & 6 & 0 \\ 2 & 3 & 10 \end{bmatrix}.$

(b) $P_{B,B'} = P_{B',B}^{-1} = \left(\dfrac{1}{8} \begin{bmatrix} -4 & -6 & 0 \\ 0 & 6 & 0 \\ 2 & 3 & 10 \end{bmatrix} \right)^{-1} = 8 \begin{bmatrix} -4 & -6 & 0 \\ 0 & 6 & 0 \\ 2 & 3 & 10 \end{bmatrix}^{-1}$

$= 8 \cdot \dfrac{1}{-240} \begin{bmatrix} 60 & 0 & -12 \\ 60 & -40 & 0 \\ 0 & 0 & -24 \end{bmatrix}^T = \dfrac{-1}{30} \begin{bmatrix} 60 & 60 & 0 \\ 0 & -40 & 0 \\ -12 & 0 & -24 \end{bmatrix} = \dfrac{-2}{15} \begin{bmatrix} 15 & 15 & 0 \\ 0 & -10 & 0 \\ -3 & 0 & -6 \end{bmatrix}$

128

(c) $[\mathbf{w}]_{B'} = \begin{bmatrix} 2 \\ 3 \\ -1 \end{bmatrix}_{B'} = \begin{bmatrix} 0 & 2 & 4 \\ 2 & 4 & 4 \\ 2 & 0 & 4 \end{bmatrix}^{-1} \begin{bmatrix} 2 \\ 3 \\ -1 \end{bmatrix} = \frac{1}{8} \begin{bmatrix} -4 & 2 & 2 \\ 0 & 2 & -2 \\ 2 & -1 & 1 \end{bmatrix} \begin{bmatrix} 2 \\ 3 \\ -1 \end{bmatrix}$

$= \frac{1}{8} \begin{bmatrix} -4 \\ 8 \\ 0 \end{bmatrix} = \frac{1}{2} \begin{bmatrix} -1 \\ 2 \\ 0 \end{bmatrix}.$

(d) $[\mathbf{w}]_B = P_{B,B'}[\mathbf{w}]_{B'} = \frac{-2}{15} \begin{bmatrix} 15 & 15 & 0 \\ 0 & -10 & 0 \\ -3 & 0 & -6 \end{bmatrix} \frac{1}{2} \begin{bmatrix} -1 \\ 2 \\ 0 \end{bmatrix} = \frac{-1}{15} \begin{bmatrix} 15 \\ -20 \\ 3 \end{bmatrix}.$

46. (a) $P_{B,B'} = \left[[\mathbf{q}_1]_B \vdots [\mathbf{q}_2]_B \right] = \left[[x]_B \vdots [4+x]_B \right]$

$= \begin{bmatrix} 1 & 3 \\ 2 & -3 \end{bmatrix}^{-1} \begin{bmatrix} 0 & 4 \\ 1 & 1 \end{bmatrix} = \frac{-1}{9} \begin{bmatrix} -3 & -3 \\ -2 & 1 \end{bmatrix} \begin{bmatrix} 0 & 4 \\ 1 & 1 \end{bmatrix} = \frac{-1}{9} \begin{bmatrix} -3 & -15 \\ 1 & -7 \end{bmatrix} = \frac{1}{9} \begin{bmatrix} 3 & 15 \\ -1 & 7 \end{bmatrix}.$

(b) $P_{B',B} = P_{B,B'}^{-1} = \left(\frac{1}{9} \begin{bmatrix} 3 & 15 \\ -1 & 7 \end{bmatrix} \right)^{-1} = 9 \begin{bmatrix} 3 & 15 \\ -1 & 7 \end{bmatrix}^{-1} = 9 \cdot \frac{1}{36} \begin{bmatrix} 7 & -15 \\ 1 & 3 \end{bmatrix} = \frac{1}{4} \begin{bmatrix} 7 & -15 \\ 1 & 3 \end{bmatrix}.$

(c) $[\mathbf{p}]_B = [1+x]_B \begin{bmatrix} 1 & 3 \\ 2 & -3 \end{bmatrix}^{-1} \begin{bmatrix} 1 \\ 1 \end{bmatrix} = \frac{-1}{9} \begin{bmatrix} -3 & -3 \\ -2 & 1 \end{bmatrix} \begin{bmatrix} 1 \\ 1 \end{bmatrix} = \frac{-1}{9} \begin{bmatrix} -6 \\ -1 \end{bmatrix} = \frac{1}{9} \begin{bmatrix} 6 \\ 1 \end{bmatrix}.$

(d) $[\mathbf{p}]_{B'} = P_{B',B}[\mathbf{p}]_B = \frac{1}{4} \begin{bmatrix} 7 & -15 \\ 1 & 3 \end{bmatrix} \frac{1}{9} \begin{bmatrix} 6 \\ 1 \end{bmatrix} = \frac{1}{36} \begin{bmatrix} 27 \\ 9 \end{bmatrix} = \frac{1}{4} \begin{bmatrix} 3 \\ 1 \end{bmatrix}.$

47. (a) $P_{B,B'} = \left[[\mathbf{g}_1]_B \vdots [\mathbf{g}_2]_B \right] = \left[[4e^x - 2xe^x]_B \vdots [-e^x + 3xe^x]_B \right]$

$= \begin{bmatrix} 3 & 2 \\ -1 & 0 \end{bmatrix}^{-1} \begin{bmatrix} 4 & -1 \\ -2 & 3 \end{bmatrix} = \frac{1}{2} \begin{bmatrix} 0 & -2 \\ 1 & 3 \end{bmatrix} \begin{bmatrix} 4 & -1 \\ -2 & 3 \end{bmatrix} = \frac{1}{2} \begin{bmatrix} 4 & -6 \\ -2 & 8 \end{bmatrix} = \begin{bmatrix} 2 & -3 \\ -1 & 4 \end{bmatrix}.$

(b) $P_{B',B} = P_{B,B'}^{-1} = \begin{bmatrix} 2 & -3 \\ -1 & 4 \end{bmatrix}^{-1} = \frac{1}{5} \begin{bmatrix} 4 & 3 \\ 1 & 2 \end{bmatrix}.$

(c) $[\mathbf{h}]_B = [5e^x + xe^x]_B = \begin{bmatrix} 3 & 2 \\ -1 & 0 \end{bmatrix}^{-1} \begin{bmatrix} 5 \\ 1 \end{bmatrix} = \frac{1}{2} \begin{bmatrix} 0 & -2 \\ 1 & 3 \end{bmatrix} \begin{bmatrix} 5 \\ 1 \end{bmatrix} = \frac{1}{2} \begin{bmatrix} -2 \\ 8 \end{bmatrix} = \begin{bmatrix} -1 \\ 4 \end{bmatrix}.$

(d) $[\mathbf{h}]_{B'} = P_{B',B}[\mathbf{h}]_B = \frac{1}{5} \begin{bmatrix} 4 & 3 \\ 1 & 2 \end{bmatrix} \begin{bmatrix} -1 \\ 4 \end{bmatrix} = \frac{1}{5} \begin{bmatrix} 8 \\ 7 \end{bmatrix}.$

48. (a) The transition matrix is $P = \begin{bmatrix} \cos\theta & -\sin\theta \\ \sin\theta & \cos\theta \end{bmatrix} = \begin{bmatrix} \cos\frac{\pi}{6} & -\sin\frac{\pi}{6} \\ \sin\frac{\pi}{6} & \cos\pi \end{bmatrix} = \begin{bmatrix} \frac{\sqrt{3}}{2} & \frac{-1}{2} \\ \frac{1}{2} & \frac{\sqrt{3}}{2} \end{bmatrix}$,

so

$$P^{-1} \begin{bmatrix} 12 \\ -4 \end{bmatrix} = \begin{bmatrix} \frac{\sqrt{3}}{2} & \frac{-1}{2} \\ \frac{1}{2} & \frac{\sqrt{3}}{2} \end{bmatrix}^T \begin{bmatrix} 12 \\ -4 \end{bmatrix}$$

$$= \begin{bmatrix} \frac{\sqrt{3}}{2} & \frac{1}{2} \\ \frac{-1}{2} & \frac{\sqrt{3}}{2} \end{bmatrix} \begin{bmatrix} 12 \\ -4 \end{bmatrix} = \begin{bmatrix} 6\sqrt{3} - 2 \\ -6 - 2\sqrt{3} \end{bmatrix}.$$

so the $x'y'$–coördinates are $(6\sqrt{3} - 2, -6 - 2\sqrt{3})$.

(b) $P \begin{bmatrix} a \\ b \end{bmatrix} = \begin{bmatrix} \frac{\sqrt{3}}{2} & \frac{-1}{2} \\ \frac{1}{2} & \frac{\sqrt{3}}{2} \end{bmatrix} \begin{bmatrix} a \\ b \end{bmatrix} = \begin{bmatrix} \frac{\sqrt{3}}{2}a - \frac{1}{2}b \\ \frac{1}{2}a + \frac{\sqrt{3}}{2}b \end{bmatrix}$

so the xy–coördinates are $\left(\frac{\sqrt{3}}{2}a - \frac{1}{2}b, \frac{1}{2}a + \frac{\sqrt{3}}{2}b \right)$.

49. (a) The transition matrix is $P = \begin{bmatrix} \cos\theta & -\sin\theta & 0 \\ \sin\theta & \cos\theta & 0 \\ 0 & 0 & 1 \end{bmatrix} = \begin{bmatrix} \cos\frac{2}{3}\pi & -\sin\frac{2}{3}\pi & 0 \\ \sin\frac{2}{3}\pi & \cos\frac{2}{3}\pi & 0 \\ 0 & 0 & 1 \end{bmatrix}$

$$= \begin{bmatrix} \frac{-1}{2} & \frac{-\sqrt{3}}{2} & 0 \\ \frac{\sqrt{3}}{2} & \frac{-1}{2} & 0 \\ 0 & 0 & 1 \end{bmatrix},$$

so $P^{-1} \begin{bmatrix} 2 \\ 4 \\ 6 \end{bmatrix} = \begin{bmatrix} \frac{-1}{2} & \frac{-\sqrt{3}}{2} & 0 \\ \frac{\sqrt{3}}{2} & \frac{-1}{2} & 0 \\ 0 & 0 & 1 \end{bmatrix}^T \begin{bmatrix} 2 \\ 4 \\ 6 \end{bmatrix} = \begin{bmatrix} \frac{-1}{2} & \frac{\sqrt{3}}{2} & 0 \\ \frac{-\sqrt{3}}{2} & \frac{-1}{2} & 0 \\ 0 & 0 & 1 \end{bmatrix} \begin{bmatrix} 2 \\ 4 \\ 6 \end{bmatrix} = \begin{bmatrix} -1 + 2\sqrt{3} \\ -\sqrt{3} - 2 \\ 6 \end{bmatrix}.$

so the $x'y'z'$–coördinates are $(-1 + 2\sqrt{3}, -2 - \sqrt{3}, 6)$.

(b) $P \begin{bmatrix} a \\ b \\ c \end{bmatrix} = \begin{bmatrix} \frac{-1}{2} & \frac{-\sqrt{3}}{2} & 0 \\ \frac{\sqrt{3}}{2} & \frac{-1}{2} & 0 \\ 0 & 0 & 1 \end{bmatrix} \begin{bmatrix} a \\ b \\ c \end{bmatrix} = \begin{bmatrix} \frac{-1}{2}a - \frac{\sqrt{3}}{2}b \\ \frac{\sqrt{3}}{2}a - \frac{1}{2}b \\ c \end{bmatrix}$

so the xyz–coördinates are $\left(\frac{-1}{2}a - \frac{\sqrt{3}}{2}b, \frac{\sqrt{3}}{2}a - \frac{1}{2}b, c \right)$.

50. (a) The first transition matrix is $P_1 = \begin{bmatrix} 1 & 0 & 0 \\ 0 & \cos\theta & -\sin\theta \\ 0 & \sin\theta & \cos\theta \end{bmatrix} = \begin{bmatrix} 1 & 0 & 0 \\ 0 & \cos\frac{\pi}{4} & -\sin\frac{\pi}{4} \\ 0 & \sin\frac{\pi}{4} & \cos\frac{\pi}{4} \end{bmatrix}$

$$= \begin{bmatrix} 1 & 0 & 0 \\ 0 & \frac{\sqrt{2}}{2} & \frac{-\sqrt{2}}{2} \\ 0 & \frac{\sqrt{2}}{2} & \frac{\sqrt{2}}{2} \end{bmatrix},$$

and the second transition matrix is $P_2 = \begin{bmatrix} -\sin\theta & 0 & \cos\theta \\ 0 & 1 & 0 \\ \cos\theta & 0 & \sin\theta \end{bmatrix} = \begin{bmatrix} -\sin\frac{\pi}{3} & 0 & \cos\frac{\pi}{3} \\ 0 & 1 & 0 \\ \cos\frac{\pi}{3} & 0 & \sin\frac{\pi}{3} \end{bmatrix}$

$$= \begin{bmatrix} \frac{-\sqrt{3}}{2} & 0 & \frac{1}{2} \\ 0 & 1 & 0 \\ \frac{1}{2} & 0 & \frac{\sqrt{3}}{2} \end{bmatrix}$$

so $\quad P_1^{-1} P_2^{-1} \begin{bmatrix} -4 \\ 12 \\ 8 \end{bmatrix} = \begin{bmatrix} 1 & 0 & 0 \\ 0 & \frac{\sqrt{2}}{2} & \frac{-\sqrt{2}}{2} \\ 0 & \frac{\sqrt{2}}{2} & \frac{\sqrt{2}}{2} \end{bmatrix}^T \begin{bmatrix} \frac{-\sqrt{3}}{2} & 0 & \frac{1}{2} \\ 0 & 1 & 0 \\ \frac{1}{2} & 0 & \frac{\sqrt{3}}{2} \end{bmatrix}^T \begin{bmatrix} -4 \\ 12 \\ 8 \end{bmatrix}$

$$= \begin{bmatrix} 1 & 0 & 0 \\ 0 & \frac{\sqrt{2}}{2} & \frac{\sqrt{2}}{2} \\ 0 & \frac{-\sqrt{2}}{2} & \frac{\sqrt{2}}{2} \end{bmatrix} \begin{bmatrix} \frac{-\sqrt{3}}{2} & 0 & \frac{1}{2} \\ 0 & 1 & 0 \\ \frac{1}{2} & 0 & \frac{\sqrt{3}}{2} \end{bmatrix} \begin{bmatrix} -4 \\ 12 \\ 8 \end{bmatrix}$$

$$= \begin{bmatrix} 1 & 0 & 0 \\ 0 & \frac{\sqrt{2}}{2} & \frac{\sqrt{2}}{2} \\ 0 & \frac{-\sqrt{2}}{2} & \frac{\sqrt{2}}{2} \end{bmatrix} \begin{bmatrix} 2\sqrt{3}+4 \\ 12 \\ -2+4\sqrt{3} \end{bmatrix}$$

$$= \begin{bmatrix} 2\sqrt{3}+4 \\ 5\sqrt{2}+2\sqrt{6} \\ -7\sqrt{2}+2\sqrt{6} \end{bmatrix}$$

so the $x''y''z''$–coördinates are $\left(4+2\sqrt{3}, 5\sqrt{2}+2\sqrt{6}, -7\sqrt{2}+2\sqrt{6}\right).$

(b) $P_2 P_1 \begin{bmatrix} a \\ b \\ c \end{bmatrix} = \begin{bmatrix} \frac{-\sqrt{3}}{2} & 0 & \frac{1}{2} \\ 0 & 1 & 0 \\ \frac{1}{2} & 0 & \frac{\sqrt{3}}{2} \end{bmatrix} \begin{bmatrix} 1 & 0 & 0 \\ 0 & \frac{\sqrt{2}}{2} & \frac{-\sqrt{2}}{2} \\ 0 & \frac{\sqrt{2}}{2} & \frac{\sqrt{2}}{2} \end{bmatrix} \begin{bmatrix} a \\ b \\ c \end{bmatrix} = \begin{bmatrix} \frac{-\sqrt{3}}{2} & \frac{\sqrt{2}}{4} & \frac{\sqrt{2}}{4} \\ 0 & \frac{\sqrt{2}}{2} & \frac{-\sqrt{2}}{2} \\ \frac{1}{2} & \frac{\sqrt{6}}{4} & \frac{\sqrt{6}}{4} \end{bmatrix} \begin{bmatrix} a \\ b \\ c \end{bmatrix}$

$$= \begin{bmatrix} \frac{-\sqrt{3}}{2}a + \frac{\sqrt{2}}{4}b + \frac{\sqrt{2}}{4}c \\ \frac{\sqrt{2}}{2}b - \frac{\sqrt{2}}{2}c \\ \frac{1}{2}a + \frac{\sqrt{6}}{4}b + \frac{\sqrt{6}}{4}c \end{bmatrix}$$

so the xyz–coördinates are $\left(\dfrac{-\sqrt{3}}{2}a + \dfrac{\sqrt{2}}{4}b + \dfrac{\sqrt{2}}{4}c, \dfrac{\sqrt{2}}{2}b - \dfrac{\sqrt{2}}{2}c, \dfrac{1}{2}a + \dfrac{\sqrt{6}}{4}b + \dfrac{\sqrt{6}}{4}c\right).$

In questions 1–14,

    (a) Find the characteristic equation of the matrix A.

    (b) Find the eigenvalues of the matrix A.

    (c) Find a basis for each eigenspace of the matrix A.

1. $A = \begin{bmatrix} 3 & 0 \\ 1 & 9 \end{bmatrix}$

2. $A = \begin{bmatrix} 5 & -3 \\ 1 & 1 \end{bmatrix}$

3. $A = \begin{bmatrix} 4 & -5 \\ -3 & 2 \end{bmatrix}$

4. $A = \begin{bmatrix} 4 & -12 \\ -6 & 3 \end{bmatrix}$

5. $A = \begin{bmatrix} 2 & 1 \\ 1 & 0 \end{bmatrix}$

6. $A = \begin{bmatrix} 2 & 0 \\ k^2 & k \end{bmatrix}$

7. $A = \begin{bmatrix} 0 & 0 & 0 \\ 0 & 3 & 2 \\ 0 & -1 & 0 \end{bmatrix}$

8. $A = \begin{bmatrix} -7 & -9 & 3 \\ 2 & 4 & -2 \\ -3 & -3 & -1 \end{bmatrix}$

9. $A = \begin{bmatrix} -9 & -6 & -22 \\ 1 & 2 & 2 \\ 4 & 2 & 10 \end{bmatrix}$

10. $A = \begin{bmatrix} 2 & 0 & 0 \\ \frac{1}{2} & 3 & 1 \\ 0 & 0 & 2 \end{bmatrix}$

11. $A = \begin{bmatrix} 2 & 0 & 1 \\ 0 & 1 & 0 \\ 2 & 0 & 0 \end{bmatrix}$

12. $A = \begin{bmatrix} 0 & 2k & 0 \\ 0 & -k & -2k^2 \\ -1 & -2 & 0 \end{bmatrix}$

13. $A = \begin{bmatrix} 0 & -1 & 1 & -1 \\ 0 & 1 & 0 & 0 \\ -2 & -2 & 3 & -1 \\ 0 & 0 & 0 & 2 \end{bmatrix}$

14. $A = \begin{bmatrix} 3 & -2 & 0 & 0 \\ 4 & -3 & 0 & 0 \\ 0 & 0 & -2 & 3 \\ 0 & 0 & 1 & 0 \end{bmatrix}$

In questions 15–17, find the eigenvalues of the triangular matrix A.

15. $A = \begin{bmatrix} 3 & 0 & 0 \\ 0 & 7 & 0 \\ 0 & 0 & 3 \end{bmatrix}$

16. $A = \begin{bmatrix} 1 & k & k^2 \\ 0 & -1 & -k^3 \\ 0 & 0 & 0 \end{bmatrix}$

17. $A = \begin{bmatrix} \sqrt{2} & 0 & 0 & 0 \\ \sqrt{6} & \sqrt{3} & 0 & 0 \\ \sqrt{10} & \sqrt{15} & \sqrt{5} & 0 \\ \sqrt{14} & \sqrt{21} & \sqrt{35} & \sqrt{7} \end{bmatrix}$

18. Find the eigenvalues and bases for the eigenspaces of A^{15} for

$$A = \begin{bmatrix} 4 & -3 \\ 5 & -4 \end{bmatrix}$$

19. Find the eigenvalues and bases for the eigenspaces of A^{10} for

$$A = \begin{bmatrix} 5 & 3 & -7 \\ -1 & 1 & 1 \\ 3 & 3 & -5 \end{bmatrix}$$

20. Find the eigenvalues and bases for the eigenspaces of A^5 for

$$A = \begin{bmatrix} 0 & -2 & 1 & 2 \\ 0 & -2 & 0 & 5 \\ 0 & -2 & -1 & 2 \\ 0 & 0 & 0 & 3 \end{bmatrix}$$

21. Let A be a 3×3 matrix with characteristic equation $(\lambda + 1)(\lambda + 2)^2 = 0$. What are the possible dimensions for eigenspaces of A?

22. Let A be a 4×4 matrix with characteristic equation $(\lambda + 2)^2(\lambda - 2)^2 = 0$. What are the possible dimensions for eigenspaces of A?

23. Let A be a 5×5 matrix with characteristic equation $\lambda^2(\lambda + 3)^2(\lambda - 7) = 0$. What are the possible dimensions for eigenspaces of A?

24. Let A be a 6×6 matrix with characteristic equation $(\lambda - 1)(\lambda - 3)^2(\lambda - 5)^3 = 0$. What are the possible dimensions for eigenspaces of A?

In questions 25–28, show whether the matrix A is diagonalizable.

25. $A = \begin{bmatrix} -9 & -6 & -22 \\ 1 & 2 & 2 \\ 4 & 2 & 10 \end{bmatrix}$

26. $A = \begin{bmatrix} 1 & 2 & -1 \\ 0 & 1 & 0 \\ 0 & -2 & 3 \end{bmatrix}$

27. $A = \begin{bmatrix} -1 & 1 & 0 & 1 \\ 0 & 3 & -3 & 0 \\ 1 & 2 & -3 & -1 \\ 0 & -3 & 3 & 0 \end{bmatrix}$

28. $A = \begin{bmatrix} 3 & -2 & 0 & 0 \\ 4 & -3 & 0 & 0 \\ 0 & 0 & -2 & 3 \\ 0 & 0 & 1 & 0 \end{bmatrix}$

In questions 29–34, find a matrix P that diagonalizes A, and determine $P^{-1}AP$.

29. $A = \begin{bmatrix} 3 & 0 \\ 1 & 9 \end{bmatrix}$

30. $A = \begin{bmatrix} 4 & -12 \\ -6 & 3 \end{bmatrix}$

31. $A = \begin{bmatrix} 0 & 0 & 0 \\ 0 & 3 & 2 \\ 0 & -1 & 0 \end{bmatrix}$

32. $A = \begin{bmatrix} -7 & -9 & 3 \\ 2 & 4 & -2 \\ -3 & -3 & -1 \end{bmatrix}$

33. $A = \begin{bmatrix} 2 & 0 & 0 \\ \frac{1}{2} & 3 & 1 \\ 0 & 0 & 2 \end{bmatrix}$

34. $A = \begin{bmatrix} 0 & -1 & 1 & -1 \\ 0 & 1 & 0 & 0 \\ -2 & -2 & 3 & -1 \\ 0 & 0 & 0 & 2 \end{bmatrix}$

35. Use diagonalization to compute A^{15} for $A = \begin{bmatrix} 4 & -3 \\ 5 & -4 \end{bmatrix}$.

36. Use diagonalization to compute A^{10} for $A = \begin{bmatrix} 5 & 3 & -7 \\ -1 & 1 & 1 \\ 3 & 3 & -5 \end{bmatrix}$.

37. Use diagonalization to compute A^5 for $A = \begin{bmatrix} 0 & -2 & 1 & 2 \\ 0 & -2 & 0 & 5 \\ 0 & -2 & -1 & 2 \\ 0 & 0 & 0 & 3 \end{bmatrix}$.

38. Use diagonalization to compute A^n if n is a positive integer and $A = \begin{bmatrix} 4 & -5 \\ -3 & 2 \end{bmatrix}$.

In questions 39–42, find the characteristic equation of the symmetric matrix A, and state the dimensions of the eigenspaces of A.

39. $A = \begin{bmatrix} 4 & 3 \\ 3 & -4 \end{bmatrix}$

40. $A = \begin{bmatrix} -1 & 0 & 2 \\ 0 & 1 & 2 \\ 2 & 2 & 0 \end{bmatrix}$

41. $A = \begin{bmatrix} 5 & -2 & 4 \\ -2 & 8 & 2 \\ 4 & 2 & 5 \end{bmatrix}$

42. $A = \begin{bmatrix} 2 & 0 & 0 & 0 \\ 0 & 2 & 0 & 0 \\ 0 & 0 & 2 & 2 \\ 0 & 0 & 2 & 3 \end{bmatrix}$

In questions 43–51, find a matrix P that orthogonally diagonalizes A, and determine $P^{-1}AP$.

43. $A = \begin{bmatrix} 3 & 4 \\ 4 & -3 \end{bmatrix}$

44. $A = \begin{bmatrix} 5 & 2 \\ 2 & 2 \end{bmatrix}$

45. $A = \begin{bmatrix} 13 & -5 \\ -5 & 13 \end{bmatrix}$

46. $A = \begin{bmatrix} -1 & 2 & 0 \\ 2 & 0 & 2 \\ 0 & 2 & 1 \end{bmatrix}$

47. $A = \begin{bmatrix} 1 & 1 & 1 \\ 1 & 1 & 1 \\ 1 & 1 & 1 \end{bmatrix}$

48. $A = \begin{bmatrix} 0 & 2 & 2 \\ 2 & 0 & 2 \\ 2 & 2 & 0 \end{bmatrix}$

49. $A = \begin{bmatrix} 1 & 1 & 0 & 0 \\ 1 & 1 & 0 & 0 \\ 0 & 0 & 1 & 2 \\ 0 & 0 & 2 & 1 \end{bmatrix}$

50. $A = \begin{bmatrix} 2 & 1 & 0 & 0 \\ 1 & 2 & 0 & 0 \\ 0 & 0 & 2 & 3 \\ 0 & 0 & 3 & 2 \end{bmatrix}$

51. $A = \begin{bmatrix} 1 & 2 & 0 & 0 \\ 2 & 1 & 0 & 0 \\ 0 & 0 & 2 & 1 \\ 0 & 0 & 1 & 2 \end{bmatrix}$

WRITING QUESTIONS

52. The word "eigen" means "characteristic" in German. Explain how the eigenvalues "characterize" multiplication by a matrix.

53. Re–trace where the zero comes from that always appears on the right–hand–side of a characteristic equation.

54. This chapter defined a procedure that can be used to compute all of the eigenvalues of an arbitrary square matrix. Discuss the problems one would need to resolve in order to computerize this procedure.

55. Suppose you were appointed to a "reparations committee" charged with awarding Nobel Prizes for the ten greatest achievements in the history of mathematics. Would you award a prize for Gaussian elimination? Justify your answer.

56. Under what conditions will a matrix be diagonalizable? Are there any cases where one can tell at a glance whether a matrix is diagonalizable?

135

57. Refute the following: "When you diagonalize a matrix, you can stop as soon as you know the eigenvalues; you line them up along a diagonal matrix D, and the transition matrix P isn't important."

58. Suppose a 10×10 symmetric matrix has 5 different eigenvalues. In orthogonally diagonalizing the matrix, what is the largest set of basis vectors that might need to be orthonormalized using the Gram–Schmidt process? Explain your answer.

SECTION 7.1   *EIGENVALUES AND EIGENVECTORS*

1.   a) $0 = |\lambda I - A| = \begin{vmatrix} \lambda - 3 & 0 \\ -1 & \lambda - 9 \end{vmatrix} = (\lambda - 3)(\lambda - 9)$

   b) $\lambda = 3, 9$

   c) $\lambda_1 = 3 \longrightarrow \begin{bmatrix} 0 & 0 & 0 \\ -1 & -6 & 0 \end{bmatrix} \longrightarrow \begin{bmatrix} 1 & 6 & 0 \\ 0 & 0 & 0 \end{bmatrix}$

   Let $x_2 = s$;

   then $x_1 + 6x_2 = 0$,   i.e., $x_1 = -6x_2 = -6s$

   so $\begin{bmatrix} x_1 \\ x_2 \end{bmatrix} = \begin{bmatrix} -6s \\ s \end{bmatrix} = s \begin{bmatrix} -6 \\ 1 \end{bmatrix}$,   i.e., $B_1 = \left\{ \begin{bmatrix} -6 \\ 1 \end{bmatrix} \right\}$.

   $\lambda_2 = 9 \longrightarrow \begin{bmatrix} 6 & 0 & 0 \\ -1 & 0 & 0 \end{bmatrix} \longrightarrow \begin{bmatrix} 1 & 0 & 0 \\ 0 & 0 & 0 \end{bmatrix}$

   Let $x_2 = t$;

   then $x_1 = 0$

   so $\begin{bmatrix} x_1 \\ x_2 \end{bmatrix} = \begin{bmatrix} 0 \\ t \end{bmatrix} = t \begin{bmatrix} 0 \\ 1 \end{bmatrix}$,   i.e., $B_2 = \left\{ \begin{bmatrix} 0 \\ 1 \end{bmatrix} \right\}$.

2.   a) $0 = |\lambda I - A| = \begin{vmatrix} \lambda - 5 & 3 \\ -1 & \lambda - 1 \end{vmatrix} = (\lambda - 5)(\lambda - 1) - (-1)(3)$

   $= (\lambda^2 - 6\lambda + 5) + 3 = \lambda^2 - 6\lambda + 8$

   b) $\lambda^2 - 6\lambda + 8 = (\lambda - 2)(\lambda - 4)$ so $\lambda = 2, 4$

   c) $\lambda_1 = 2 \longrightarrow \begin{bmatrix} -3 & 3 & 0 \\ -1 & 1 & 0 \end{bmatrix} \longrightarrow \begin{bmatrix} 1 & -1 & 0 \\ 0 & 0 & 0 \end{bmatrix}$

   Let $x_2 = s$;

   then $x_1 - x_2 = 0$,   i.e., $x_1 = x_2 = s$

   so $\begin{bmatrix} x_1 \\ x_2 \end{bmatrix} = \begin{bmatrix} s \\ s \end{bmatrix} = s \begin{bmatrix} 1 \\ 1 \end{bmatrix}$,   i.e., $B_1 = \left\{ \begin{bmatrix} 1 \\ 1 \end{bmatrix} \right\}$.

   $\lambda_2 = 4 \longrightarrow \begin{bmatrix} -1 & 3 & 0 \\ -1 & 3 & 0 \end{bmatrix} \longrightarrow \begin{bmatrix} 1 & -3 & 0 \\ 0 & 0 & 0 \end{bmatrix}$

Let $x_2 = t$;

then $x_1 - 3x_2 = 0$, i.e., $x_1 = 3x_2 = 3t$

so $\begin{bmatrix} x_1 \\ x_2 \end{bmatrix} = \begin{bmatrix} 3t \\ t \end{bmatrix} = t \begin{bmatrix} 3 \\ 1 \end{bmatrix}$, i.e., $B_2 = \left\{ \begin{bmatrix} 3 \\ 1 \end{bmatrix} \right\}$.

3. a) $0 = |\lambda I - A| = \begin{vmatrix} \lambda - 4 & 5 \\ 3 & \lambda - 2 \end{vmatrix} = (\lambda - 4)(\lambda - 2) - (3)(5)$

$\qquad = (\lambda^2 - 6\lambda + 8) - 15 = \lambda^2 - 6\lambda - 7$

b) $\lambda^2 - 6\lambda - 7 = (\lambda - 7)(\lambda + 1)$ so $\lambda = 7, -1$

c) $\lambda_1 = 7 \longrightarrow \begin{bmatrix} 3 & 5 & 0 \\ 3 & 5 & 0 \end{bmatrix} \longrightarrow \begin{bmatrix} 1 & \frac{5}{3} & 0 \\ 0 & 0 & 0 \end{bmatrix}$

Let $x_2 = s$;

then $x_1 + \frac{5}{3}x_2 = 0$, i.e., $x_1 = \frac{-5}{3}x_2 = \frac{-5}{3}s$

so $\begin{bmatrix} x_1 \\ x_2 \end{bmatrix} = \begin{bmatrix} \frac{-5}{3}s \\ s \end{bmatrix} = s \begin{bmatrix} \frac{-5}{3} \\ 1 \end{bmatrix} = \frac{1}{3}s \begin{bmatrix} -5 \\ 3 \end{bmatrix}$, i.e., $B_1 = \left\{ \begin{bmatrix} -5 \\ 3 \end{bmatrix} \right\}$.

$\lambda_2 = -1 \longrightarrow \begin{bmatrix} -5 & 5 & 0 \\ 3 & -3 & 0 \end{bmatrix} \longrightarrow \begin{bmatrix} 1 & -1 & 0 \\ 0 & 0 & 0 \end{bmatrix}$

Let $x_2 = t$;

then $x_1 - x_2 = 0$, i.e., $x_1 = x_2 = t$

so $\begin{bmatrix} x_1 \\ x_2 \end{bmatrix} = \begin{bmatrix} t \\ t \end{bmatrix} = t \begin{bmatrix} 1 \\ 1 \end{bmatrix}$, i.e., $B_2 = \left\{ \begin{bmatrix} 1 \\ 1 \end{bmatrix} \right\}$.

4. a) $0 = |\lambda I - A| = \begin{vmatrix} \lambda - 4 & 12 \\ 6 & \lambda - 3 \end{vmatrix} = (\lambda - 4)(\lambda - 3) - (6)(12)$

$\qquad = (\lambda^2 - 7\lambda + 12) - 72 = \lambda^2 - 7\lambda - 60$

b) $\lambda^2 - 7\lambda - 60 = (\lambda - 12)(\lambda + 5)$ so $\lambda = 12, -5$

c) $\lambda_1 = 12 \longrightarrow \begin{bmatrix} 8 & 12 & 0 \\ 6 & 9 & 0 \end{bmatrix} \longrightarrow \begin{bmatrix} 1 & \frac{3}{2} & 0 \\ 0 & 0 & 0 \end{bmatrix}$

Let $x_2 = s$;

then $x_1 + \frac{3}{2}x_2 = 0$, i.e., $x_1 = \frac{-3}{2}x_2 = \frac{-3}{2}s$

so $\begin{bmatrix} x_1 \\ x_2 \end{bmatrix} = \begin{bmatrix} \frac{-3}{2}s \\ s \end{bmatrix} = s \begin{bmatrix} \frac{-3}{2} \\ 1 \end{bmatrix} = \frac{1}{2}s \begin{bmatrix} -3 \\ 2 \end{bmatrix}$, i.e., $B_1 = \left\{ \begin{bmatrix} -3 \\ 2 \end{bmatrix} \right\}$.

$$\lambda_2 = -5 \longrightarrow \begin{bmatrix} -9 & 12 & 0 \\ 6 & -8 & 0 \end{bmatrix} \longrightarrow \begin{bmatrix} 1 & \frac{-4}{3} & 0 \\ 0 & 0 & 0 \end{bmatrix}$$

Let $x_2 = t$;

then $x_1 - \frac{4}{3}x_2 = 0$, i.e., $x_1 = \frac{4}{3}x_2 = \frac{4}{3}t$

so $\begin{bmatrix} x_1 \\ x_2 \end{bmatrix} = \begin{bmatrix} \frac{4}{3}t \\ t \end{bmatrix} = t\begin{bmatrix} \frac{4}{3} \\ 1 \end{bmatrix} = \frac{1}{3}t\begin{bmatrix} 4 \\ 3 \end{bmatrix}$, i.e., $B_2 = \left\{ \begin{bmatrix} 4 \\ 3 \end{bmatrix} \right\}$.

5. a) $0 = |\lambda I - A| = \begin{vmatrix} \lambda - 2 & -1 \\ -1 & \lambda \end{vmatrix} = (\lambda - 2)\lambda - (-1)(-1) = \lambda^2 - 2\lambda - 1$

b) $\lambda = \frac{2 \pm \sqrt{4 - (4)(-1)}}{2} = \frac{2 \pm \sqrt{8}}{2} = \frac{2 \pm 2\sqrt{2}}{2} = 1 \pm \sqrt{2}$

c) $\lambda_1 = 1 + \sqrt{2} \longrightarrow \begin{bmatrix} -1 + \sqrt{2} & -1 & 0 \\ -1 & 1 + \sqrt{2} & 0 \end{bmatrix} \longrightarrow \begin{bmatrix} 1 & -1 - \sqrt{2} & 0 \\ 0 & 0 & 0 \end{bmatrix}$

Let $x_2 = s$;

then $x_1 + (-1 - \sqrt{2})x_2 = 0$, i.e., $x_1 = (1 + \sqrt{2})x_2 = (1 + \sqrt{2})s$

so $\begin{bmatrix} x_1 \\ x_2 \end{bmatrix} = \begin{bmatrix} (1 + \sqrt{2})s \\ s \end{bmatrix} = s\begin{bmatrix} 1 + \sqrt{2} \\ 1 \end{bmatrix}$, i.e., $B_1 = \left\{ \begin{bmatrix} 1 + \sqrt{2} \\ 1 \end{bmatrix} \right\}$.

$$\lambda_2 = 1 - \sqrt{2} \longrightarrow \begin{bmatrix} -1 - \sqrt{2} & -1 & 0 \\ -1 & 1 - \sqrt{2} & 0 \end{bmatrix} \longrightarrow \begin{bmatrix} 1 & -1 + \sqrt{2} & 0 \\ 0 & 0 & 0 \end{bmatrix}$$

Let $x_2 = t$;

then $x_1 + (-1 + \sqrt{2})x_2 = 0$, i.e., $x_1 = (1 - \sqrt{2})x_2 = (1 - \sqrt{2})t$

so $\begin{bmatrix} x_1 \\ x_2 \end{bmatrix} = \begin{bmatrix} (1 - \sqrt{2})t \\ t \end{bmatrix} = t\begin{bmatrix} 1 - \sqrt{2} \\ 1 \end{bmatrix}$, i.e., $B_2 = \left\{ \begin{bmatrix} 1 - \sqrt{2} \\ 1 \end{bmatrix} \right\}$.

6. a) $0 = |\lambda I - A| = \begin{vmatrix} \lambda - 2 & 0 \\ -k^2 & \lambda - k \end{vmatrix} = (\lambda - 2)(\lambda - k)$

b) $\lambda = 2, k$

c) $\lambda_1 = 2 \longrightarrow \begin{bmatrix} 0 & 0 & 0 \\ -k^2 & 2 - k & 0 \end{bmatrix} \longrightarrow \begin{bmatrix} k^2 & k - 2 & 0 \\ 0 & 0 & 0 \end{bmatrix}$

Let $x_2 = s$;

then $k^2 x_1 + (k - 2)x_2 = 0$, i.e., $k^2 x_1 = (2 - k)x_2 = (2 - k)s$

so $\begin{bmatrix} k^2 x_1 \\ k^2 x_2 \end{bmatrix} = \begin{bmatrix} (2 - k)s \\ k^2 s \end{bmatrix} = s\begin{bmatrix} 2 - k \\ k^2 \end{bmatrix}$, i.e., $B_1 = \left\{ \begin{bmatrix} 2 - k \\ k^2 \end{bmatrix} \right\}$.

$$\lambda_2 = k \neq 2 \longrightarrow \begin{bmatrix} k-2 & 0 & 0 \\ -k^2 & 0 & 0 \end{bmatrix} \longrightarrow \begin{bmatrix} 1 & 0 & 0 \\ 0 & 0 & 0 \end{bmatrix}$$

Let $x_2 = t$;

then $x_1 = 0$

so $\begin{bmatrix} x_1 \\ x_2 \end{bmatrix} = \begin{bmatrix} 0 \\ t \end{bmatrix} = t \begin{bmatrix} 0 \\ 1 \end{bmatrix}$, i.e., $B_2 = \left\{ \begin{bmatrix} 0 \\ 1 \end{bmatrix} \right\}$.

7. a) $0 = |\lambda I - A| = \begin{vmatrix} \lambda & 0 & 0 \\ 0 & \lambda-3 & -2 \\ 0 & 1 & \lambda \end{vmatrix} = \lambda[(\lambda-3)\lambda - (1)(-2)]$

$\qquad = \lambda(\lambda^2 - 3\lambda + 2)$

b) $\lambda(\lambda^2 - 3\lambda + 2) = \lambda(\lambda - 1)(\lambda - 2)$ so $\lambda = 0, 1, 2$

c) $\lambda_1 = 0 \longrightarrow \begin{bmatrix} 0 & 0 & 0 & 0 \\ 0 & -3 & -2 & 0 \\ 0 & 1 & 0 & 0 \end{bmatrix} \longrightarrow \begin{bmatrix} 0 & 1 & 0 & 0 \\ 0 & 0 & -2 & 0 \\ 0 & 0 & 0 & 0 \end{bmatrix} \longrightarrow \begin{bmatrix} 0 & 1 & 0 & 0 \\ 0 & 0 & 1 & 0 \\ 0 & 0 & 0 & 0 \end{bmatrix}$

Let $x_1 = r$;

then $x_2 = 0$ and $x_3 = 0$

so $\begin{bmatrix} x_1 \\ x_2 \\ x_3 \end{bmatrix} = \begin{bmatrix} r \\ 0 \\ 0 \end{bmatrix} = r \begin{bmatrix} 1 \\ 0 \\ 0 \end{bmatrix}$, i.e., $B_1 = \left\{ \begin{bmatrix} 1 \\ 0 \\ 0 \end{bmatrix} \right\}$.

$$\lambda_2 = 1 \longrightarrow \begin{bmatrix} 1 & 0 & 0 & 0 \\ 0 & -2 & -2 & 0 \\ 0 & 1 & 1 & 0 \end{bmatrix} \longrightarrow \begin{bmatrix} 1 & 0 & 0 & 0 \\ 0 & 1 & 1 & 0 \\ 0 & 0 & 0 & 0 \end{bmatrix}$$

Let $x_3 = s$;

then $x_2 + x_3 = 0$, i.e., $x_2 = -x_3 = -s$

and $x_1 = 0$

so $\begin{bmatrix} x_1 \\ x_2 \\ x_3 \end{bmatrix} = \begin{bmatrix} 0 \\ -s \\ s \end{bmatrix} = s \begin{bmatrix} 0 \\ -1 \\ 1 \end{bmatrix}$, i.e., $B_2 = \left\{ \begin{bmatrix} 0 \\ -1 \\ 1 \end{bmatrix} \right\}$.

$$\lambda_3 = 2 \longrightarrow \begin{bmatrix} 2 & 0 & 0 & 0 \\ 0 & -1 & -2 & 0 \\ 0 & 1 & 2 & 0 \end{bmatrix} \longrightarrow \begin{bmatrix} 1 & 0 & 0 & 0 \\ 0 & 1 & 2 & 0 \\ 0 & 0 & 0 & 0 \end{bmatrix}$$

Let $x_3 = t$;

then $x_2 + 2x_3 = 0$, i.e., $x_2 = -2x_3 = -2t$

and $x_1 = 0$

so $\begin{bmatrix} x_1 \\ x_2 \\ x_3 \end{bmatrix} = \begin{bmatrix} 0 \\ -2t \\ t \end{bmatrix} = t \begin{bmatrix} 0 \\ -2 \\ 1 \end{bmatrix}$, i.e., $B_3 = \left\{ \begin{bmatrix} 0 \\ -2 \\ 1 \end{bmatrix} \right\}$.

8. a) $0 = |\lambda I - A| = \begin{vmatrix} \lambda + 7 & 9 & -3 \\ -2 & \lambda - 4 & 2 \\ 3 & 3 & \lambda + 1 \end{vmatrix}$

$= (\lambda + 7)[(\lambda - 4)(\lambda + 1) - (3)(2)] - 9[-2(\lambda + 1) - (3)(2)] - 3[(-2)(3) - (3)(\lambda - 4)]$

$= (\lambda + 7)(\lambda^2 - 3\lambda - 10) - 9(-2\lambda - 8) - 3(-3\lambda + 6)$

$= (\lambda^3 + 4\lambda^2 - 31\lambda - 70) + (18\lambda + 72) + (9\lambda - 18)$

$= \lambda^3 + 4\lambda^2 - 4\lambda - 16$

b) $\lambda^3 + 4\lambda^2 - 4\lambda - 16 = (\lambda^3 + 4\lambda^2) + (-4\lambda - 16) = \lambda^2(\lambda + 4) - 4(\lambda + 4)$

$= (\lambda^2 - 4)(\lambda + 4) = (\lambda - 2)(\lambda + 2)(\lambda + 4)$

so $\lambda = 2, -2, -4$

c) $\lambda_1 = 2 \longrightarrow \begin{bmatrix} 9 & 9 & -3 & 0 \\ -2 & -2 & 2 & 0 \\ 3 & 3 & 3 & 0 \end{bmatrix} \longrightarrow \begin{bmatrix} 1 & 1 & -1 & 0 \\ 0 & 0 & 6 & 0 \\ 0 & 0 & 6 & 0 \end{bmatrix} \longrightarrow \begin{bmatrix} 1 & 1 & 0 & 0 \\ 0 & 0 & 1 & 0 \\ 0 & 0 & 0 & 0 \end{bmatrix}$

Let $x_2 = r$;

then $x_1 + x_2 = 0$, i.e., $x_1 = -x_2 = -r$

and $x_3 = 0$

so $\begin{bmatrix} x_1 \\ x_2 \\ x_3 \end{bmatrix} = \begin{bmatrix} r \\ -r \\ 0 \end{bmatrix} = r \begin{bmatrix} 1 \\ -1 \\ 0 \end{bmatrix}$, i.e., $B_1 = \left\{ \begin{bmatrix} 1 \\ -1 \\ 0 \end{bmatrix} \right\}$.

$\lambda_2 = -2 \longrightarrow \begin{bmatrix} 5 & 9 & -3 & 0 \\ -2 & -6 & 2 & 0 \\ 3 & 3 & -1 & 0 \end{bmatrix} \longrightarrow \begin{bmatrix} 1 & 3 & -1 & 0 \\ 0 & -6 & 2 & 0 \\ 0 & -6 & 2 & 0 \end{bmatrix} \longrightarrow \begin{bmatrix} 1 & 0 & 0 & 0 \\ 0 & 1 & -1/3 & 0 \\ 0 & 0 & 0 & 0 \end{bmatrix}$

Let $x_3 = s$;

then $x_2 - \dfrac{1}{3}x_3 = 0$, i.e., $x_2 = \dfrac{1}{3}x_3 = \dfrac{1}{3}s$

and $x_1 = 0$

so $\begin{bmatrix} x_1 \\ x_2 \\ x_3 \end{bmatrix} = \begin{bmatrix} 0 \\ \frac{1}{3}s \\ s \end{bmatrix} = s \begin{bmatrix} 0 \\ \frac{1}{3} \\ 1 \end{bmatrix} = \dfrac{1}{3}s \begin{bmatrix} 0 \\ 1 \\ 3 \end{bmatrix}$, i.e., $B_2 = \left\{ \begin{bmatrix} 0 \\ 1 \\ 3 \end{bmatrix} \right\}$.

141

$$\lambda_3 = -4 \longrightarrow \begin{bmatrix} 3 & 9 & -3 & 0 \\ -2 & -8 & 2 & 0 \\ 3 & 3 & -3 & 0 \end{bmatrix} \longrightarrow \begin{bmatrix} 1 & 3 & -1 & 0 \\ 0 & -2 & 0 & 0 \\ 0 & -6 & 0 & 0 \end{bmatrix} \longrightarrow \begin{bmatrix} 1 & 0 & -1 & 0 \\ 0 & 1 & 0 & 0 \\ 0 & 0 & 0 & 0 \end{bmatrix}$$

Let $x_3 = t$;

then $x_1 - x_3 = 0$, i.e., $x_1 = x_3 = t$

and $x_2 = 0$

so $\begin{bmatrix} x_1 \\ x_2 \\ x_3 \end{bmatrix} = \begin{bmatrix} t \\ 0 \\ t \end{bmatrix} = t \begin{bmatrix} 1 \\ 0 \\ 1 \end{bmatrix}$, i.e., $B_3 = \left\{ \begin{bmatrix} 1 \\ 0 \\ 1 \end{bmatrix} \right\}.$

9. a) $0 = |\lambda I - A| = \begin{vmatrix} \lambda + 9 & 6 & 22 \\ -1 & \lambda - 2 & -2 \\ -4 & -2 & \lambda - 10 \end{vmatrix}$

$= (\lambda + 9)[(\lambda - 2)(\lambda - 10) - (-2)(-2)] - 6[(-1)(\lambda - 10) - (-4)(-2)]$
$\qquad + 22[(-1)(-2) - (-4)(\lambda - 2)]$

$= (\lambda + 9)(\lambda^2 - 12\lambda + 16) - 6(-\lambda + 2) + 22(4\lambda - 6)$

$= (\lambda^3 - 3\lambda^2 - 92\lambda + 144) + (6\lambda - 12) + (88\lambda - 132)$

$= \lambda^3 - 3\lambda^2 + 2\lambda$

b) $\lambda^3 - 3\lambda^2 + 2\lambda = \lambda(\lambda^2 - 3\lambda + 2) = \lambda(\lambda - 1)(\lambda - 2)$ so $\lambda = 0, 1, 2$

c) $\lambda_1 = 0 \longrightarrow \begin{bmatrix} 9 & 6 & 22 & 0 \\ -1 & -2 & -2 & 0 \\ -4 & -2 & -10 & 0 \end{bmatrix} \longrightarrow \begin{bmatrix} 1 & 2 & 2 & 0 \\ 0 & -12 & 4 & 0 \\ 0 & 6 & -2 & 0 \end{bmatrix} \longrightarrow \begin{bmatrix} 1 & 0 & 8/3 & 0 \\ 0 & 1 & -1/3 & 0 \\ 0 & 0 & 0 & 0 \end{bmatrix}$

Let $x_3 = r$;

then $x_2 - \dfrac{1}{3} x_3 = 0$, i.e., $x_2 = \dfrac{1}{3} x_3 = \dfrac{1}{3} r$

and $x_1 + \dfrac{8}{3} x_3 = 0$, i.e., $x_1 = \dfrac{-8}{3} x_3 = \dfrac{-8}{3} r$

so $\begin{bmatrix} x_1 \\ x_2 \\ x_3 \end{bmatrix} = \begin{bmatrix} (-8/3)r \\ (1/3)r \\ r \end{bmatrix} = r \begin{bmatrix} -8/3 \\ 1/3 \\ 1 \end{bmatrix} = \dfrac{1}{3} r \begin{bmatrix} -8 \\ 1 \\ 3 \end{bmatrix}$, i.e., $B_1 = \left\{ \begin{bmatrix} -8 \\ 1 \\ 3 \end{bmatrix} \right\}.$

$\lambda_2 = 1 \longrightarrow \begin{bmatrix} 10 & 6 & 22 & 0 \\ -1 & -1 & -2 & 0 \\ -4 & -2 & -9 & 0 \end{bmatrix} \longrightarrow \begin{bmatrix} 1 & 1 & 2 & 0 \\ 0 & -4 & 2 & 0 \\ 0 & 2 & -1 & 0 \end{bmatrix} \longrightarrow \begin{bmatrix} 1 & 0 & 5/2 & 0 \\ 0 & 1 & -1/2 & 0 \\ 0 & 0 & 0 & 0 \end{bmatrix}$

Let $x_3 = s$;

then $x_2 - \frac{1}{2}x_3 = 0$, i.e., $x_2 = \frac{1}{2}x_3 = \frac{1}{2}s$

and $x_1 + \frac{5}{2}x_3 = 0$, i.e., $x_1 = \frac{-5}{2}x_3 = \frac{-5}{2}s$

so $\begin{bmatrix} x_1 \\ x_2 \\ x_3 \end{bmatrix} = \begin{bmatrix} (-5/2)s \\ (1/2)s \\ s \end{bmatrix} = s\begin{bmatrix} -5/2 \\ 1/2 \\ 1 \end{bmatrix} = \frac{1}{2}s\begin{bmatrix} -5 \\ 1 \\ 2 \end{bmatrix}$, i.e., $B_2 = \left\{ \begin{bmatrix} -5 \\ 1 \\ 2 \end{bmatrix} \right\}$.

$\lambda_3 = 2 \longrightarrow \begin{bmatrix} 11 & 6 & 22 & 0 \\ -1 & 0 & -2 & 0 \\ -4 & -2 & -8 & 0 \end{bmatrix} \longrightarrow \begin{bmatrix} 1 & 0 & 2 & 0 \\ 0 & 6 & 0 & 0 \\ 0 & -2 & 0 & 0 \end{bmatrix} \longrightarrow \begin{bmatrix} 1 & 0 & 2 & 0 \\ 0 & 1 & 0 & 0 \\ 0 & 0 & 0 & 0 \end{bmatrix}$

Let $x_3 = t$;

then $x_1 + 2x_3 = 0$, i.e., $x_1 = -2x_3 = -2t$

and $x_2 = 0$

so $\begin{bmatrix} x_1 \\ x_2 \\ x_3 \end{bmatrix} = \begin{bmatrix} -2t \\ 0 \\ t \end{bmatrix} = t\begin{bmatrix} -2 \\ 0 \\ 1 \end{bmatrix} =$, i.e., $B_3 = \left\{ \begin{bmatrix} -2 \\ 0 \\ 1 \end{bmatrix} \right\}$.

10. a) $0 = |\lambda I - A| = \begin{vmatrix} \lambda - 2 & 0 & 0 \\ -1/2 & \lambda - 3 & -1 \\ 0 & 0 & \lambda - 2 \end{vmatrix} = (\lambda - 2)(\lambda - 3)(\lambda - 2)$

b) $\lambda = 2, 2, 3$

c) $\lambda_1 = 2 \longrightarrow \begin{bmatrix} 0 & 0 & 0 & 0 \\ -1/2 & -1 & -1 & 0 \\ 0 & 0 & 0 & 0 \end{bmatrix} \longrightarrow \begin{bmatrix} 1 & 2 & 2 & 0 \\ 0 & 0 & 0 & 0 \\ 0 & 0 & 0 & 0 \end{bmatrix}$

Let $x_3 = r$ and $x_2 = s$;

then $x_1 + 2x_2 + 2x_3 = 0$, i.e., $x_1 = -2x_2 - 2x_3 = -2s - 2r$

so $\begin{bmatrix} x_1 \\ x_2 \\ x_3 \end{bmatrix} = \begin{bmatrix} -2s - 2r \\ s \\ r \end{bmatrix} = \begin{bmatrix} -2s \\ s \\ 0 \end{bmatrix} + \begin{bmatrix} -2r \\ 0 \\ r \end{bmatrix} = s\begin{bmatrix} -2 \\ 1 \\ 0 \end{bmatrix} + r\begin{bmatrix} -2 \\ 0 \\ 1 \end{bmatrix}$,

i.e., $B_1 = \left\{ \begin{bmatrix} -2 \\ 1 \\ 0 \end{bmatrix} , \begin{bmatrix} -2 \\ 0 \\ 1 \end{bmatrix} \right\}$.

$\lambda_3 = 3 \longrightarrow \begin{bmatrix} 1 & 0 & 0 & 0 \\ -1/2 & 0 & -1 & 0 \\ 0 & 0 & 1 & 0 \end{bmatrix} \longrightarrow \begin{bmatrix} 1 & 0 & 0 & 0 \\ 0 & 0 & -1 & 0 \\ 0 & 0 & 1 & 0 \end{bmatrix} \longrightarrow \begin{bmatrix} 1 & 0 & 0 & 0 \\ 0 & 0 & 1 & 0 \\ 0 & 0 & 0 & 0 \end{bmatrix}$

Let $x_2 = t$;

then $x_1 = 0$ and $x_3 = 0$

so $\begin{bmatrix} x_1 \\ x_2 \\ x_3 \end{bmatrix} = \begin{bmatrix} 0 \\ t \\ 0 \end{bmatrix} = t \begin{bmatrix} 0 \\ 1 \\ 0 \end{bmatrix}$, i.e., $B_2 = \left\{ \begin{bmatrix} 0 \\ 1 \\ 0 \end{bmatrix} \right\}$.

11. a) $0 = |\lambda I - A| = \begin{vmatrix} \lambda - 2 & 0 & -1 \\ 0 & \lambda - 1 & 0 \\ -2 & 0 & \lambda \end{vmatrix} = (\lambda - 2)(\lambda - 1)(\lambda) - (-1)(\lambda - 1)(-2)$

$= (\lambda - 1)(\lambda^2 - 2\lambda - 2)$

b) $\lambda = 1$ or $\lambda = \frac{2 \pm \sqrt{4 - 4(-2)}}{2} = \frac{2 \pm \sqrt{12}}{2} = \frac{2 \pm 2\sqrt{3}}{2} = 1 \pm \sqrt{3}$

c) $\lambda_1 = 1 \longrightarrow \begin{bmatrix} -1 & 0 & -1 & 0 \\ 0 & 0 & 0 & 0 \\ -2 & 0 & 1 & 0 \end{bmatrix} \longrightarrow \begin{bmatrix} 1 & 0 & 1 & 0 \\ 0 & 0 & 3 & 0 \\ 0 & 0 & 0 & 0 \end{bmatrix} \longrightarrow \begin{bmatrix} 1 & 0 & 0 & 0 \\ 0 & 0 & 1 & 0 \\ 0 & 0 & 0 & 0 \end{bmatrix}$

Let $x_2 = r$;

then $x_1 = 0$ and $x_3 = 0$

so $\begin{bmatrix} x_1 \\ x_2 \\ x_3 \end{bmatrix} = \begin{bmatrix} 0 \\ r \\ 0 \end{bmatrix} = r \begin{bmatrix} 0 \\ 1 \\ 0 \end{bmatrix}$, i.e., $B_1 = \left\{ \begin{bmatrix} 0 \\ 1 \\ 0 \end{bmatrix} \right\}$.

$\lambda_2 = 1 + \sqrt{3} \longrightarrow \begin{bmatrix} -1 + \sqrt{3} & 0 & -1 & 0 \\ 0 & \sqrt{3} & 0 & 0 \\ -2 & 0 & 1 + \sqrt{3} & 0 \end{bmatrix} \longrightarrow \begin{bmatrix} -1 + \sqrt{3} & 0 & -1 & 0 \\ 0 & 1 & 0 & 0 \\ 0 & 0 & 0 & 0 \end{bmatrix}$

Let $x_1 = s$;

then $(-1 + \sqrt{3})x_1 - x_3 = 0$, i.e., $x_3 = (-1 + \sqrt{3})x_1 = (-1 + \sqrt{3})s$
and $x_2 = 0$

so $\begin{bmatrix} x_1 \\ x_2 \\ x_3 \end{bmatrix} = \begin{bmatrix} s \\ 0 \\ (-1 + \sqrt{3})s \end{bmatrix} = s \begin{bmatrix} 1 \\ 0 \\ -1 + \sqrt{3} \end{bmatrix}$, i.e., $B_2 = \left\{ \begin{bmatrix} 1 \\ 0 \\ -1 + \sqrt{3} \end{bmatrix} \right\}$.

$\lambda_3 = 1 - \sqrt{3} \longrightarrow \begin{bmatrix} -1 - \sqrt{3} & 0 & -1 & 0 \\ 0 & -\sqrt{3} & 0 & 0 \\ -2 & 0 & 1 - \sqrt{3} & 0 \end{bmatrix} \longrightarrow \begin{bmatrix} 1 + \sqrt{3} & 0 & 1 & 0 \\ 0 & 1 & 0 & 0 \\ 0 & 0 & 0 & 0 \end{bmatrix}$

Let $x_1 = t$;

then $(1 + \sqrt{3})x_1 + x_3 = 0$, i.e., $x_3 = -(1 + \sqrt{3})x_1 = -(1 + \sqrt{3})t$

and $x_2 = 0$

$$\text{so} \quad \begin{bmatrix} x_1 \\ x_2 \\ x_3 \end{bmatrix} = \begin{bmatrix} t \\ 0 \\ -(1 + \sqrt{3})t \end{bmatrix} = t \begin{bmatrix} 1 \\ 0 \\ -1 - \sqrt{3} \end{bmatrix} \quad , \quad \text{i.e.,} \quad B_3 = \left\{ \begin{bmatrix} 1 \\ 0 \\ -1 - \sqrt{3} \end{bmatrix} \right\}.$$

12. a) $\quad 0 = |\lambda I - A| = \begin{vmatrix} \lambda & -2k & 0 \\ 0 & \lambda + k & 2k^2 \\ 1 & 2 & \lambda \end{vmatrix}$

$\qquad = \lambda[(\lambda + k)\lambda - (2)(2k^2)] + 2k[0 - (1)(2k^2)]$

$\qquad = \lambda(\lambda^2 + k\lambda - 4k^2) - 4k^3 = \lambda^3 + k\lambda^2 - 4k^2\lambda - 4k^3$

b) $\quad \lambda^3 + k\lambda^2 - 4k^2\lambda - 4k^3 = (\lambda^3 + k\lambda^2) - (4k^2\lambda + 4k^3)$

$\qquad\qquad\qquad\qquad\qquad\quad = \lambda^2(\lambda + k) - 4k^2(\lambda + k)$

$\qquad\qquad\qquad\qquad\qquad\quad = (\lambda^2 - 4k^2)(\lambda + k) \quad \text{so} \quad \lambda = 2k, -2k, -k$

c) If $\quad k = 0, \quad$ then the only eigenvalue is $\quad \lambda = 0$

$$\text{and} \quad \begin{bmatrix} 0 & 0 & 0 & 0 \\ 0 & 0 & 0 & 0 \\ 1 & 2 & 0 & 0 \end{bmatrix} \longrightarrow \begin{bmatrix} 1 & 2 & 0 & 0 \\ 0 & 0 & 0 & 0 \\ 0 & 0 & 0 & 0 \end{bmatrix}$$

Let $\quad x_3 = r \quad$ and $\quad x_2 = s$;

then $\quad x_1 + 2x_2 = 0 \quad$ i.e., $\quad x_1 = -2x_2 = -2s$

$$\text{so} \quad \begin{bmatrix} x_1 \\ x_2 \\ x_3 \end{bmatrix} = \begin{bmatrix} -2s \\ s \\ r \end{bmatrix} = \begin{bmatrix} -2s \\ s \\ 0 \end{bmatrix} + \begin{bmatrix} 0 \\ 0 \\ r \end{bmatrix} = s \begin{bmatrix} -2 \\ 1 \\ 0 \end{bmatrix} + r \begin{bmatrix} 0 \\ 0 \\ 0 \end{bmatrix}$$

$$\text{i.e.,} \quad B = \left\{ \begin{bmatrix} -2 \\ 1 \\ 0 \end{bmatrix}, \begin{bmatrix} 0 \\ 0 \\ 1 \end{bmatrix} \right\}.$$

If $\quad k \neq 0, \quad$ then

$$\lambda_1 = 2k \longrightarrow \begin{bmatrix} 2k & -2k & 0 & 0 \\ 0 & 3k & 2k^2 & 0 \\ 1 & 2 & 2k & 0 \end{bmatrix} \longrightarrow \begin{bmatrix} 1 & 2 & 2k & 0 \\ 0 & -6k & -4k^2 & 0 \\ 0 & 3k & 2k^2 & 0 \end{bmatrix} \longrightarrow \begin{bmatrix} 1 & 0 & (2/3)k & 0 \\ 0 & 1 & (2/3)k & 0 \\ 0 & 0 & 0 & 0 \end{bmatrix}$$

Let $x_3 = r$;

then $x_2 + \dfrac{2}{3}kx_3 = 0$, i.e., $x_2 = \dfrac{-2}{3}kx_3 = \dfrac{-2}{3}kr$

and $x_1 + \dfrac{2}{3}kx_3 = 0$, i.e., $x_1 = \dfrac{-2}{3}kx_3 = \dfrac{-2}{3}kr$

so $\begin{bmatrix} x_1 \\ x_2 \\ x_3 \end{bmatrix} = \begin{bmatrix} (-2/3)kr \\ (-2/3)kr \\ r \end{bmatrix} = r\begin{bmatrix} (-2/3)k \\ (-2/3)k \\ 1 \end{bmatrix} = \dfrac{1}{3}r\begin{bmatrix} -2k \\ -2k \\ 3 \end{bmatrix}$, i.e., $B_1 = \left\{ \begin{bmatrix} -2k \\ -2k \\ 3 \end{bmatrix} \right\}$.

$\lambda_2 = -2k \longrightarrow \begin{bmatrix} -2k & -2k & 0 & 0 \\ 0 & -k & 2k^2 & 0 \\ 1 & 2 & -2k & 0 \end{bmatrix} \longrightarrow \begin{bmatrix} 1 & 2 & -2k & 0 \\ 0 & 2k & -4k^2 & 0 \\ 0 & -k & 2k^2 & 0 \end{bmatrix} \longrightarrow \begin{bmatrix} 1 & 0 & 2k & 0 \\ 0 & 1 & -2k & 0 \\ 0 & 0 & 0 & 0 \end{bmatrix}$

Let $x_3 = s$;

then $x_2 - 2kx_3 = 0$, i.e., $x_2 = 2kx_3 = 2ks$

and $x_1 + 2kx_3 = 0$, i.e., $x_1 = -2kx_3 = -2ks$

so $\begin{bmatrix} x_1 \\ x_2 \\ x_3 \end{bmatrix} = \begin{bmatrix} -2ks \\ 2ks \\ s \end{bmatrix} = s\begin{bmatrix} -2k \\ 2k \\ 1 \end{bmatrix}$, i.e., $B_2 = \left\{ \begin{bmatrix} -2k \\ 2k \\ 1 \end{bmatrix} \right\}$.

$\lambda_3 = -k \longrightarrow \begin{bmatrix} -k & -2k & 0 & 0 \\ 0 & 0 & 2k^2 & 0 \\ 1 & 2 & -k & 0 \end{bmatrix} \longrightarrow \begin{bmatrix} 1 & 2 & -k & 0 \\ 0 & 0 & -k^2 & 0 \\ 0 & 0 & 2k^2 & 0 \end{bmatrix} \longrightarrow \begin{bmatrix} 1 & 2 & 0 & 0 \\ 0 & 0 & 1 & 0 \\ 0 & 0 & 0 & 0 \end{bmatrix}$

Let $x_2 = t$;

then $x_1 + 2x_2 = 0$, i.e., $x_1 = -2x_2 = -2t$

and $x_3 = 0$

so $\begin{bmatrix} x_1 \\ x_2 \\ x_3 \end{bmatrix} = \begin{bmatrix} -2t \\ t \\ 0 \end{bmatrix} = t\begin{bmatrix} -2 \\ 1 \\ 0 \end{bmatrix}$, i.e., $B_3 = \left\{ \begin{bmatrix} -2 \\ 1 \\ 0 \end{bmatrix} \right\}$.

13. a) $0 = |\lambda I - A| = \begin{vmatrix} \lambda & 1 & -1 & 1 \\ 0 & \lambda-1 & 0 & 0 \\ -2 & 2 & \lambda-3 & 1 \\ 0 & 0 & 0 & \lambda-2 \end{vmatrix} = (\lambda-2)\begin{vmatrix} \lambda & 1 & -1 \\ 0 & \lambda-1 & 0 \\ 2 & 2 & \lambda-3 \end{vmatrix}$

$= (\lambda-2)(\lambda-1)[(\lambda)(\lambda-3) - (2)(-1)] = (\lambda-2)(\lambda-1)(\lambda^2 - 3\lambda + 2)$

b) $(\lambda-2)(\lambda-1)(\lambda^2 - 3\lambda + 2) = (\lambda-2)(\lambda-1)(\lambda-1)(\lambda-2) = (\lambda-1)^2(\lambda-2)^2$ so $\lambda = 1, 1, 2, 2$.

c) $\lambda_1 = 1 \longrightarrow \begin{bmatrix} 1 & 1 & -1 & 1 & 0 \\ 0 & 0 & 0 & 0 & 0 \\ 2 & 2 & -2 & 1 & 0 \\ 0 & 0 & 0 & -1 & 0 \end{bmatrix} \longrightarrow \begin{bmatrix} 1 & 1 & -1 & 1 & 0 \\ 0 & 0 & 0 & -1 & 0 \\ 0 & 0 & 0 & 0 & 0 \\ 0 & 0 & 0 & 0 & 0 \end{bmatrix} \longrightarrow \begin{bmatrix} 1 & 1 & -1 & 0 & 0 \\ 0 & 0 & 0 & 1 & 0 \\ 0 & 0 & 0 & 0 & 0 \\ 0 & 0 & 0 & 0 & 0 \end{bmatrix}$

Let $x_3 = r$ and $x_2 = q$;

then $x_1 + x_2 - x_3 = 0$ i.e., $x_1 = -x_2 + x_3 = -q + r$

and $x_4 = 0$

so $\begin{bmatrix} x_1 \\ x_2 \\ x_3 \\ x_4 \end{bmatrix} = \begin{bmatrix} -q+r \\ q \\ r \\ 0 \end{bmatrix} = \begin{bmatrix} -q \\ q \\ 0 \\ 0 \end{bmatrix} + \begin{bmatrix} r \\ 0 \\ r \\ 0 \end{bmatrix} = q\begin{bmatrix} -1 \\ 1 \\ 0 \\ 0 \end{bmatrix} + r\begin{bmatrix} 1 \\ 0 \\ 1 \\ 0 \end{bmatrix},$

i.e., $B_1 = \left\{ \begin{bmatrix} -1 \\ 1 \\ 0 \\ 0 \end{bmatrix}, \begin{bmatrix} 1 \\ 0 \\ 1 \\ 0 \end{bmatrix} \right\}.$

$\lambda_2 = 2 \longrightarrow \begin{bmatrix} 2 & 1 & -1 & 1 & 0 \\ 0 & 1 & 0 & 0 & 0 \\ 2 & 2 & -1 & 1 & 0 \\ 0 & 0 & 0 & 0 & 0 \end{bmatrix} \longrightarrow \begin{bmatrix} 1 & 1/2 & -1/2 & 1/2 & 0 \\ 0 & 1 & 0 & 0 & 0 \\ 0 & 1 & 0 & 0 & 0 \\ 0 & 0 & 0 & 0 & 0 \end{bmatrix} \longrightarrow \begin{bmatrix} 1 & 0 & -1/2 & 1/2 & 0 \\ 0 & 1 & 0 & 0 & 0 \\ 0 & 0 & 0 & 0 & 0 \\ 0 & 0 & 0 & 0 & 0 \end{bmatrix}$

Let $x_4 = t$ and $x_3 = 3$;

then $x_1 - \frac{1}{2}x_3 + \frac{1}{2}x_4 = 0$, i.e., $x_1 = \frac{1}{2}x_3 - \frac{1}{2}x_4 = \frac{1}{2}s - \frac{1}{2}t$

and $x_2 = 0$

so $\begin{bmatrix} x_1 \\ x_2 \\ x_3 \\ x_4 \end{bmatrix} = \begin{bmatrix} (1/2)s - (1/2)t \\ 0 \\ s \\ t \end{bmatrix} = \begin{bmatrix} (1/2)s \\ 0 \\ s \\ 0 \end{bmatrix} + \begin{bmatrix} (-1/2)t \\ 0 \\ 0 \\ t \end{bmatrix} = s\begin{bmatrix} (1/2) \\ 0 \\ 1 \\ 0 \end{bmatrix} + t\begin{bmatrix} (-1/2) \\ 0 \\ 0 \\ 1 \end{bmatrix}$

$= \frac{1}{2}s\begin{bmatrix} 1 \\ 0 \\ 2 \\ 0 \end{bmatrix} + \frac{1}{2}t\begin{bmatrix} -1 \\ 0 \\ 0 \\ 2 \end{bmatrix}$, i.e., $B_2 = \left\{ \begin{bmatrix} 1 \\ 0 \\ 2 \\ 0 \end{bmatrix}, \begin{bmatrix} -1 \\ 0 \\ 0 \\ 2 \end{bmatrix} \right\}.$

14. a) $0 = |\lambda I - A| = \begin{vmatrix} \lambda - 3 & 2 & 0 & 0 \\ -4 & \lambda + 3 & 0 & 0 \\ 0 & 0 & \lambda + 2 & -3 \\ 0 & 0 & -1 & \lambda \end{vmatrix}$

$= [(\lambda - 3)(\lambda + 3) - (-4)(2)][(\lambda + 2)(\lambda) - (-1)(-3)]$

$= (\lambda^2 - 9 + 8)(\lambda^2 + 2\lambda - 3) = (\lambda^2 - 1)(\lambda^2 + 2\lambda - 3)$

b) $(\lambda^2 - 1)(\lambda^2 + 2\lambda - 3) = (\lambda - 1)(\lambda + 1)(\lambda - 1)(\lambda + 3) = (\lambda - 1)^2(\lambda + 1)(\lambda + 3)$ so $\lambda = 1, 1, -1, -3.$

c) $\lambda_1 = 1 \longrightarrow \begin{bmatrix} -2 & 2 & 0 & 0 & 0 \\ -4 & 4 & 0 & 0 & 0 \\ 0 & 0 & 3 & -3 & 0 \\ 0 & 0 & -1 & 1 & 0 \end{bmatrix} \longrightarrow \begin{bmatrix} 1 & -1 & 0 & 0 & 0 \\ 0 & 0 & 0 & 0 & 0 \\ 0 & 0 & 3 & -3 & 0 \\ 0 & 0 & -1 & 1 & 0 \end{bmatrix} \longrightarrow \begin{bmatrix} 1 & -1 & 0 & 0 & 0 \\ 0 & 0 & 1 & -1 & 0 \\ 0 & 0 & 0 & 0 & 0 \\ 0 & 0 & 0 & 0 & 0 \end{bmatrix}$

Let $x_4 = r$ and $x_2 = q$;

then $x_3 - x_4 = 0$ i.e., $x_3 = x_4 = r$

and $x_1 - x_2 = 0$ i.e., $x_1 = x_2 = q$

so $\begin{bmatrix} x_1 \\ x_2 \\ x_3 \\ x_4 \end{bmatrix} = \begin{bmatrix} q \\ q \\ r \\ r \end{bmatrix} = \begin{bmatrix} q \\ q \\ 0 \\ 0 \end{bmatrix} + \begin{bmatrix} 0 \\ 0 \\ r \\ r \end{bmatrix} = q\begin{bmatrix} 1 \\ 1 \\ 0 \\ 0 \end{bmatrix} + r\begin{bmatrix} 0 \\ 0 \\ 1 \\ 1 \end{bmatrix}$, i.e., $B_1 = \left\{ \begin{bmatrix} 1 \\ 1 \\ 0 \\ 0 \end{bmatrix}, \begin{bmatrix} 0 \\ 0 \\ 1 \\ 1 \end{bmatrix} \right\}$.

$\lambda_2 = -1 \longrightarrow \begin{bmatrix} -4 & 2 & 0 & 0 & 0 \\ -4 & 2 & 0 & 0 & 0 \\ 0 & 0 & 1 & -3 & 0 \\ 0 & 0 & -1 & -1 & 0 \end{bmatrix} \longrightarrow \begin{bmatrix} 1 & -1/2 & 0 & 0 & 0 \\ 0 & 0 & 0 & 0 & 0 \\ 0 & 0 & 1 & -3 & 0 \\ 0 & 0 & -1 & -1 & 0 \end{bmatrix} \longrightarrow$

$\begin{bmatrix} 1 & -1/2 & 0 & 0 & 0 \\ 0 & 0 & 1 & -3 & 0 \\ 0 & 0 & 0 & -4 & 0 \\ 0 & 0 & 0 & 0 & 0 \end{bmatrix} \longrightarrow \begin{bmatrix} 1 & -1/2 & 0 & 0 & 0 \\ 0 & 0 & 1 & 0 & 0 \\ 0 & 0 & 0 & 1 & 0 \\ 0 & 0 & 0 & 0 & 0 \end{bmatrix}$

Let $x_2 = s$;

then $x_1 - \frac{1}{2}x_2 = 0$, i.e., $x_1 = \frac{1}{2}x_2 = \frac{1}{2}s$

and $x_3 = 0$

and $x_4 = 0$

so $\begin{bmatrix} x_1 \\ x_2 \\ x_3 \\ x_4 \end{bmatrix} = \begin{bmatrix} (1/2)s \\ s \\ 0 \\ 0 \end{bmatrix} = s\begin{bmatrix} 1/2 \\ 1 \\ 0 \\ 0 \end{bmatrix} = \frac{1}{2}s\begin{bmatrix} 1 \\ 2 \\ 0 \\ 0 \end{bmatrix} = s$, i.e., $B_2 = \left\{ \begin{bmatrix} 1 \\ 2 \\ 0 \\ 0 \end{bmatrix} \right\}$.

$\lambda_3 = -3 \longrightarrow \begin{bmatrix} -6 & 2 & 0 & 0 & 0 \\ -4 & 0 & 0 & 0 & 0 \\ 0 & 0 & -1 & -3 & 0 \\ 0 & 0 & -1 & -3 & 0 \end{bmatrix} \longrightarrow \begin{bmatrix} 1 & -1/3 & 0 & 0 & 0 \\ 0 & -4/3 & 0 & 0 & 0 \\ 0 & 0 & -1 & -3 & 0 \\ 0 & 0 & -1 & -3 & 0 \end{bmatrix} \longrightarrow$

$\begin{bmatrix} 1 & -1/3 & 0 & 0 & 0 \\ 0 & 1 & 0 & 0 & 0 \\ 0 & 0 & 1 & 3 & 0 \\ 0 & 0 & 0 & 0 & 0 \end{bmatrix} \longrightarrow \begin{bmatrix} 1 & 0 & 0 & 0 & 0 \\ 0 & 1 & 0 & 0 & 0 \\ 0 & 0 & 1 & 3 & 0 \\ 0 & 0 & 0 & 0 & 0 \end{bmatrix}$

Let $x_4 = t$;

then $x_3 + 3x_4 = 0$, i.e., $x_3 = -3x_4 = -3t$

and $x_1 = 0$

and $x_2 = 0$

so $\begin{bmatrix} x_1 \\ x_2 \\ x_3 \\ x_4 \end{bmatrix} = \begin{bmatrix} 0 \\ 0 \\ -3t \\ t \end{bmatrix} = t\begin{bmatrix} 0 \\ 0 \\ -3 \\ 1 \end{bmatrix}$, i.e., $B_3 = \left\{ \begin{bmatrix} 0 \\ 0 \\ -3 \\ 1 \end{bmatrix} \right\}$.

15. $\lambda = 3, 3, 7$

16. $\lambda = 0, 1, -1$

17. $\lambda = \sqrt{2}, \sqrt{3}, \sqrt{5}, \sqrt{7}$

18. $0 = |\lambda I - A| = \begin{vmatrix} \lambda - 4 & 3 \\ -5 & \lambda + 4 \end{vmatrix} = (\lambda - 4)(\lambda + 4) - (-5)(3)$

$$= \lambda^2 - 16 + 15 = \lambda^2 - 1 = (\lambda - 1)(\lambda + 1)$$

Thus, the eigenvalues of A are 1 and -1,
so the eigenvalues of A^{15} are $(1)^{15} = 1$ and $(-1)^{15} = -1$.

$$\lambda = 1 \longrightarrow \begin{bmatrix} -3 & 3 & 0 \\ -5 & 5 & 0 \end{bmatrix} \longrightarrow \begin{bmatrix} 1 & -1 & 0 \\ 0 & 0 & 0 \end{bmatrix}$$

Let $x_2 = s$;

then $x_1 - x_2 = 0$, i.e., $x_1 = x_2 = s$

so $\begin{bmatrix} x_1 \\ x_2 \end{bmatrix} = \begin{bmatrix} s \\ s \end{bmatrix} = s \begin{bmatrix} 1 \\ 1 \end{bmatrix}$, i.e., $B_1 = \left\{ \begin{bmatrix} 1 \\ 1 \end{bmatrix} \right\}$.

$$\lambda = -1 \longrightarrow \begin{bmatrix} -5 & 3 & 0 \\ -5 & 3 & 0 \end{bmatrix} \longrightarrow \begin{bmatrix} 1 & -3/5 & 0 \\ 0 & 0 & 0 \end{bmatrix}$$

Let $x_2 = t$;

then $x_1 - \dfrac{3}{5}x_2 = 0$, i.e., $x_1 = \dfrac{3}{5}x_2 = \dfrac{3}{5}t$

so $\begin{bmatrix} x_1 \\ x_2 \end{bmatrix} = \begin{bmatrix} (3/5)t \\ t \end{bmatrix} = t \begin{bmatrix} 3/5 \\ 1 \end{bmatrix} = \dfrac{1}{5}t \begin{bmatrix} 3 \\ 5 \end{bmatrix}$, i.e., $B_2 = \left\{ \begin{bmatrix} 3 \\ 5 \end{bmatrix} \right\}$.

19. $0 = |\lambda I - A| = \begin{vmatrix} \lambda - 5 & -3 & 7 \\ 1 & \lambda - 1 & -1 \\ -3 & -3 & \lambda + 5 \end{vmatrix}$

$$= (\lambda - 5)[(\lambda - 1)(\lambda + 5) - (-3)(-1)] + 3[(1)(\lambda + 5) - (-3)(-1)] + 7[(1)(-3) - (-3)(\lambda - 1)]$$

$$= (\lambda - 5)(\lambda^2 + 4\lambda - 8) + 3(\lambda + 2) + 7(3\lambda - 6)$$

$$= \lambda^3 - \lambda^2 - 4\lambda + 4 = (\lambda^3 - \lambda^2) + (-4\lambda + 4)$$

$$= \lambda^2(\lambda - 1) + -4(\lambda - 1) = (\lambda^2 - 4)(\lambda - 1) = (\lambda - 1)(\lambda - 2)(\lambda + 2)$$

Thus, the eigenvalues of A are 1, 2 and -2,
so the eigenvalues of A^{10} are $(1)^{10} = 1$, $(2)^{10} = 1024$ and $(-2)^{10} = 1024$.

$$\lambda = 1 \longrightarrow \begin{bmatrix} -4 & -3 & 7 & 0 \\ 1 & 0 & -1 & 0 \\ -3 & -3 & 6 & 0 \end{bmatrix} \longrightarrow \begin{bmatrix} 1 & 0 & -1 & 0 \\ -4 & -3 & 7 & 0 \\ -3 & -3 & 6 & 0 \end{bmatrix} \longrightarrow \begin{bmatrix} 1 & 0 & -1 & 0 \\ 0 & -3 & 3 & 0 \\ 0 & -3 & 3 & 0 \end{bmatrix} \longrightarrow$$

$$\begin{bmatrix} 1 & 0 & -1 & 0 \\ 0 & 1 & -1 & 0 \\ 0 & 0 & 0 & 0 \end{bmatrix}$$

Let $x_3 = r$;

then $x_2 - x_3 = 0$, i.e., $x_2 = x_3 = r$

and $x_1 - x_3 = 0$, i.e., $x_1 = x_3 = r$

so $\begin{bmatrix} x_1 \\ x_2 \\ x_3 \end{bmatrix} = \begin{bmatrix} r \\ r \\ r \end{bmatrix} = r \begin{bmatrix} 1 \\ 1 \\ 1 \end{bmatrix}$, i.e., $B_1 = \left\{ \begin{bmatrix} 1 \\ 1 \\ 1 \end{bmatrix} \right\}$ (for $\lambda = 1$).

$$\lambda = 2 \longrightarrow \begin{bmatrix} -3 & -3 & 7 & 0 \\ 1 & 1 & -1 & 0 \\ -3 & -3 & 7 & 0 \end{bmatrix} \longrightarrow \begin{bmatrix} 1 & 1 & -1 & 0 \\ -3 & -3 & 7 & 0 \\ -3 & -3 & 7 & 0 \end{bmatrix} \longrightarrow \begin{bmatrix} 1 & 1 & -1 & 0 \\ 0 & 0 & 4 & 0 \\ 0 & 0 & 4 & 0 \end{bmatrix} \longrightarrow$$

$$\begin{bmatrix} 1 & 1 & 0 & 0 \\ 0 & 0 & 1 & 0 \\ 0 & 0 & 0 & 0 \end{bmatrix}$$

Let $x_2 = s$;

then $x_1 + x_2 = 0$, i.e., $x_1 = -x_2 = -s$

and $x_3 = 0$

so $\begin{bmatrix} x_1 \\ x_2 \\ x_3 \end{bmatrix} = \begin{bmatrix} -s \\ s \\ 0 \end{bmatrix} = s \begin{bmatrix} -1 \\ 1 \\ 0 \end{bmatrix}$.

$$\lambda = -2 \longrightarrow \begin{bmatrix} -7 & -3 & 7 & 0 \\ 1 & -3 & -1 & 0 \\ -3 & -3 & 3 & 0 \end{bmatrix} \longrightarrow \begin{bmatrix} 1 & -3 & -1 & 0 \\ -7 & -3 & 7 & 0 \\ -3 & -3 & 3 & 0 \end{bmatrix} \longrightarrow \begin{bmatrix} 1 & -3 & -1 & 0 \\ 0 & -24 & 0 & 0 \\ 0 & -12 & 0 & 0 \end{bmatrix} \longrightarrow$$

$$\begin{bmatrix} 1 & 0 & -1 & 0 \\ 0 & 1 & 0 & 0 \\ 0 & 0 & 0 & 0 \end{bmatrix}$$

Let $x_3 = t$;

then $x_1 - x_3 = 0$, i.e., $x_1 = x_3 = t$

and $x_2 = 0$

so $\begin{bmatrix} x_1 \\ x_2 \\ x_3 \end{bmatrix} = \begin{bmatrix} t \\ 0 \\ t \end{bmatrix} = t \begin{bmatrix} 1 \\ 0 \\ 1 \end{bmatrix}$, i.e., $B_2 = \left\{ \begin{bmatrix} -1 \\ 1 \\ 1 \end{bmatrix}, \begin{bmatrix} 1 \\ 0 \\ 1 \end{bmatrix} \right\}$ (for $\lambda = 1024$).

20. $0 = |\lambda I - A| = \begin{vmatrix} \lambda & 2 & -1 & -2 \\ 0 & \lambda+2 & 0 & -5 \\ 0 & 2 & \lambda+1 & -2 \\ 0 & 0 & 0 & \lambda-3 \end{vmatrix} = \lambda \begin{vmatrix} \lambda+2 & 0 & -5 \\ 2 & \lambda+1 & -2 \\ 0 & 0 & \lambda-3 \end{vmatrix}$

$$= \lambda(\lambda-3)(\lambda+2)(\lambda+1)$$

Thus, the eigenvalues of A are 0, -1, -2 and 3,
so the eigenvalues of A^5 are $(0)^5 = 0, (-1)^5 = -1, (-2)^5 = -32$ and $(3)^5 = 243$.

$$\lambda = 0 \longrightarrow \begin{bmatrix} 0 & 2 & -1 & -2 & 0 \\ 0 & 2 & 0 & -5 & 0 \\ 0 & 2 & 1 & -2 & 0 \\ 0 & 0 & 0 & -3 & 0 \end{bmatrix} \longrightarrow \begin{bmatrix} 0 & 1 & -1/2 & -1 & 0 \\ 0 & 0 & 1 & -3 & 0 \\ 0 & 0 & 2 & 0 & 0 \\ 0 & 0 & 0 & -3 & 0 \end{bmatrix} \longrightarrow$$

$$\begin{bmatrix} 0 & 1 & -1/2 & -1 & 0 \\ 0 & 0 & 1 & -3 & 0 \\ 0 & 0 & 0 & 6 & 0 \\ 0 & 0 & 0 & -3 & 0 \end{bmatrix} \longrightarrow \begin{bmatrix} 0 & 1 & 0 & 0 & 0 \\ 0 & 0 & 1 & 0 & 0 \\ 0 & 0 & 0 & 1 & 0 \\ 0 & 0 & 0 & 0 & 0 \end{bmatrix}$$

Let $x_1 = q$;

then $x_2 = 0$, $x_3 = 0$ and $x_4 = 0$

so $\begin{bmatrix} x_1 \\ x_2 \\ x_3 \\ x_4 \end{bmatrix} = \begin{bmatrix} q \\ 0 \\ 0 \\ 0 \end{bmatrix} = q \begin{bmatrix} 1 \\ 0 \\ 0 \\ 0 \end{bmatrix}$, i.e., $B_1 = \left\{ \begin{bmatrix} 1 \\ 0 \\ 0 \\ 0 \end{bmatrix} \right\}$ (for $\lambda = 0$).

$$\lambda = -1 \longrightarrow \begin{bmatrix} -1 & 2 & -1 & -2 & 0 \\ 0 & 1 & 0 & -5 & 0 \\ 0 & 2 & 0 & -2 & 0 \\ 0 & 0 & 0 & -4 & 0 \end{bmatrix} \longrightarrow \begin{bmatrix} 1 & -2 & 1 & 2 & 0 \\ 0 & 1 & 0 & -5 & 0 \\ 0 & 2 & 0 & -2 & 0 \\ 0 & 0 & 0 & -4 & 0 \end{bmatrix} \longrightarrow$$

$$\begin{bmatrix} 1 & -2 & 1 & 2 & 0 \\ 0 & 1 & 0 & -5 & 0 \\ 0 & 0 & 0 & 8 & 0 \\ 0 & 0 & 0 & -4 & 0 \end{bmatrix} \longrightarrow \begin{bmatrix} 1 & 0 & 1 & 0 & 0 \\ 0 & 1 & 0 & 0 & 0 \\ 0 & 0 & 0 & 1 & 0 \\ 0 & 0 & 0 & 0 & 0 \end{bmatrix}$$

Let $x_3 = r$;

then $x_1 + x_3 = 0$, i.e., $x_1 = -x_3 = -r$

and $x_2 = 0$ and $x_4 = 0$

so $\begin{bmatrix} x_1 \\ x_2 \\ x_3 \\ x_4 \end{bmatrix} = \begin{bmatrix} -r \\ 0 \\ r \\ 0 \end{bmatrix} = r \begin{bmatrix} -1 \\ 0 \\ 1 \\ 0 \end{bmatrix}$, i.e., $B_2 = \left\{ \begin{bmatrix} -1 \\ 0 \\ 1 \\ 0 \end{bmatrix} \right\}$ (for $\lambda = -1$).

$$\lambda = -2 \longrightarrow \begin{bmatrix} -2 & 2 & -1 & -2 & 0 \\ 0 & 0 & 0 & -5 & 0 \\ 0 & 2 & -1 & -2 & 0 \\ 0 & 0 & 0 & -5 & 0 \end{bmatrix} \longrightarrow \begin{bmatrix} 1 & -1 & 1/2 & 1 & 0 \\ 0 & 0 & 0 & -5 & 0 \\ 0 & 1 & -1/2 & -1 & 0 \\ 0 & 0 & 0 & -5 & 0 \end{bmatrix} \longrightarrow$$

$$\begin{bmatrix} 1 & -1 & 1/2 & 1 & 0 \\ 0 & 1 & -1/2 & -1 & 0 \\ 0 & 0 & 0 & -5 & 0 \\ 0 & 0 & 0 & -5 & 0 \end{bmatrix} \longrightarrow \begin{bmatrix} 1 & 0 & 0 & 0 & 0 \\ 0 & 1 & -1/2 & 0 & 0 \\ 0 & 0 & 0 & 1 & 0 \\ 0 & 0 & 0 & 0 & 0 \end{bmatrix}$$

Let $x_3 = s$;

then $x_2 - \dfrac{1}{2} x_3 = 0$ i.e., $x_2 = \dfrac{1}{2} x_3 = \dfrac{1}{2} s$

and $x_1 = 0$ and $x_4 = 0$

so $\begin{bmatrix} x_1 \\ x_2 \\ x_3 \\ x_4 \end{bmatrix} = \begin{bmatrix} 0 \\ (1/2)s \\ s \\ 0 \end{bmatrix} = s \begin{bmatrix} 0 \\ 1/2 \\ 1 \\ 0 \end{bmatrix} = \dfrac{1}{2} s \begin{bmatrix} 0 \\ 1 \\ 2 \\ 0 \end{bmatrix}$, i.e., $B_3 = \left\{ \begin{bmatrix} 0 \\ 1 \\ 2 \\ 0 \end{bmatrix} \right\}$ (for $\lambda = -32$).

$$\lambda = 3 \longrightarrow \begin{bmatrix} 3 & 2 & -1 & -2 & 0 \\ 0 & 5 & 0 & -5 & 0 \\ 0 & 2 & 4 & -2 & 0 \\ 0 & 0 & 0 & 0 & 0 \end{bmatrix} \longrightarrow \begin{bmatrix} 1 & 2/3 & -1/3 & -2/3 & 0 \\ 0 & 1 & 0 & -1 & 0 \\ 0 & 0 & 4 & 0 & 0 \\ 0 & 0 & 0 & 0 & 0 \end{bmatrix} \longrightarrow \begin{bmatrix} 1 & 0 & 0 & 0 & 0 \\ 0 & 1 & 0 & -1 & 0 \\ 0 & 0 & 1 & 0 & 0 \\ 0 & 0 & 0 & 0 & 0 \end{bmatrix}$$

Let $x_4 = t$;

then $x_2 - x_4 = 0$ i.e., $x_2 = x_4 = t$

and $x_1 = 0$ and $x_3 = 0$

so $\begin{bmatrix} x_1 \\ x_2 \\ x_3 \\ x_4 \end{bmatrix} = \begin{bmatrix} 0 \\ t \\ 0 \\ t \end{bmatrix} = t \begin{bmatrix} 0 \\ 1 \\ 0 \\ 1 \end{bmatrix}$, i.e., $B_4 = \left\{ \begin{bmatrix} 0 \\ 1 \\ 0 \\ 1 \end{bmatrix} \right\}$ (for $\lambda = 243$).

SECTION 7.2 *DIAGONALIZATION*

21. For $\lambda = -1$, dimension = 1.

 For $\lambda = -2$, dimension = 1 or 2.

22. For $\lambda = -2$, dimension = 1 or 2.

 For $\lambda = 2$, dimension = 1 or 2.

23. For $\lambda = 0$, dimension = 1 or 2.

 For $\lambda = -3$, dimension = 1 or 2.

 For $\lambda = 7$, dimension = 1.

24. For $\lambda = 1$, dimension = 1.

For $\lambda = 3$, dimension = 1 or 2.

For $\lambda = 5$, dimension = 1 or 2 or 3.

25. $0 = |\lambda I - A| = \begin{vmatrix} \lambda + 9 & 6 & 22 \\ -1 & \lambda - 2 & -2 \\ -4 & -2 & \lambda - 10 \end{vmatrix}$

$= (\lambda + 9)[(\lambda - 2)(\lambda - 10) - (-2)(-2)] - 6[(-1)(\lambda - 10) - (-4)(-2)]$
$\quad + 22[(-1)(-2) - (-4)(\lambda - 2)]$

$= (\lambda + 9)(\lambda^2 - 12\lambda + 16) - 6(-\lambda + 2) + 22(4\lambda - 6)$

$= (\lambda^3 - 3\lambda^2 - 92\lambda + 144) + (6\lambda - 12) + (88\lambda - 132)$

$= \lambda^3 - 3\lambda^2 + 2\lambda$

$= \lambda(\lambda^2 - 3\lambda + 2)$

$= \lambda(\lambda - 1)(\lambda - 2)$ so $\lambda = 0, 1, 2$

Since all the eigenvalues are distinct, A is diagonalizable.

26. $0 = |\lambda I - A| = \begin{vmatrix} \lambda - 1 & -2 & 1 \\ 0 & \lambda - 1 & 0 \\ 0 & 2 & \lambda - 3 \end{vmatrix} = (\lambda - 1)(\lambda - 1)(\lambda - 3)$ so $\lambda = 1, 1, 3$.

$\lambda_1 = 1 \longrightarrow \begin{bmatrix} 0 & -2 & 1 & 0 \\ 0 & 0 & 0 & 0 \\ 0 & 2 & -2 & 0 \end{bmatrix} \longrightarrow \begin{bmatrix} 0 & 1 & -1/2 & 0 \\ 0 & 0 & -1 & 0 \\ 0 & 0 & 0 & 0 \end{bmatrix}$ so   rank $= 1 < 2$

Since the geometric multiplicity is less than the algebraic multiplicity, A is not diagonalizable.

27. $0 = |\lambda I - A| = \begin{vmatrix} \lambda + 1 & -1 & 0 & -1 \\ 0 & \lambda - 3 & 3 & 0 \\ -1 & -2 & \lambda + 3 & 1 \\ 0 & 3 & -3 & \lambda \end{vmatrix}$

$= (\lambda + 1) \begin{vmatrix} \lambda - 3 & 3 & 0 \\ -2 & \lambda + 3 & 1 \\ 3 & -3 & \lambda \end{vmatrix} - 1 \begin{vmatrix} -1 & 0 & -1 \\ \lambda - 3 & 3 & 0 \\ 3 & -3 & \lambda \end{vmatrix}$

$= (\lambda + 1)[(\lambda - 3)(\lambda^2 + 3\lambda + 3) - 3(-2\lambda - 3)] - 1[(-1)(3\lambda) + (-1)(-3\lambda)]$

$= (\lambda + 1)(\lambda^3) - 1(0)$

$= (\lambda + 1)(\lambda^3)$ so $\lambda = 0, 0, 0, -1$

$\lambda_1 = 0 \longrightarrow \begin{bmatrix} 1 & -1 & 0 & -1 & 0 \\ 0 & -3 & 3 & 0 & 0 \\ -1 & -2 & 3 & 1 & 0 \\ 0 & 3 & -3 & 0 & 0 \end{bmatrix} \longrightarrow \begin{bmatrix} 1 & -1 & 0 & -1 & 0 \\ 0 & -3 & 3 & 0 & 0 \\ 0 & -3 & 3 & 0 & 0 \\ 0 & 3 & -3 & 0 & 0 \end{bmatrix} \longrightarrow \begin{bmatrix} 1 & -1 & 0 & -1 & 0 \\ 0 & 1 & -1 & 0 & 0 \\ 0 & 0 & 0 & 0 & 0 \\ 0 & 0 & 0 & 0 & 0 \end{bmatrix}$

so   rank $= 2 < 3$.

Since the geometric multiplicity is less than the algebraic multiplicity, A is not diagonalizable.

28. $0 = |\lambda I - A| = \begin{vmatrix} \lambda - 3 & 2 & 0 & 0 \\ -4 & \lambda + 3 & 0 & 0 \\ 0 & 0 & \lambda + 2 & -3 \\ 0 & 0 & -1 & \lambda \end{vmatrix}$

$= [(\lambda - 3)(\lambda + 3) - (-4)(2)][(\lambda + 2)(\lambda) - (-1)(-3)]$

$= (\lambda^2 - 1)(\lambda^2 + 2\lambda - 3)$

$= (\lambda + 1)(\lambda - 1)(\lambda - 1)(\lambda + 3)$ so $\lambda = 1, 1, -1, -3$

$\lambda_1 = 1 \longrightarrow \begin{bmatrix} -2 & 2 & 0 & 0 & 0 \\ -4 & 4 & 0 & 0 & 0 \\ 0 & 0 & 3 & -3 & 0 \\ 0 & 0 & -1 & 1 & 0 \end{bmatrix} \longrightarrow \begin{bmatrix} 1 & -1 & 0 & 0 & 0 \\ 0 & 0 & 0 & 0 & 0 \\ 0 & 0 & 3 & -3 & 0 \\ 0 & 0 & -1 & 1 & 0 \end{bmatrix} \longrightarrow \begin{bmatrix} 1 & -1 & 0 & 0 & 0 \\ 0 & 0 & 1 & -1 & 0 \\ 0 & 0 & 0 & 0 & 0 \\ 0 & 0 & 0 & 0 & 0 \end{bmatrix}$

so   rank $= 2$.

Since the geometric multiplicity is equal to the algebraic multiplicity for every eigenvalue, A is diagonalizable.

29. $0 = |\lambda I - A| = \begin{vmatrix} \lambda - 3 & 0 \\ -1 & \lambda - 9 \end{vmatrix} = (\lambda - 3)(\lambda - 9)$ so $\lambda = 3, 9$

$\lambda_1 = 3 \longrightarrow \begin{bmatrix} 0 & 0 & 0 \\ -1 & -6 & 0 \end{bmatrix} \longrightarrow \begin{bmatrix} 1 & 6 & 0 \\ 0 & 0 & 0 \end{bmatrix}$

Let $x_2 = s$;

then $x_1 + 6x_2 = 0$,   i.e., $x_1 = -6x_2 = -6s$

so $\begin{bmatrix} x_1 \\ x_2 \end{bmatrix} = \begin{bmatrix} -6s \\ s \end{bmatrix} = s \begin{bmatrix} -6 \\ 1 \end{bmatrix}$,   i.e., $B_1 = \left\{ \begin{bmatrix} -6 \\ 1 \end{bmatrix} \right\}$.

$\lambda_2 = 9 \longrightarrow \begin{bmatrix} 6 & 0 & 0 \\ -1 & 0 & 0 \end{bmatrix} \longrightarrow \begin{bmatrix} 1 & 0 & 0 \\ 0 & 0 & 0 \end{bmatrix}$

Let $x_2 = t$;

then $x_1 = 0$

so $\begin{bmatrix} x_1 \\ x_2 \end{bmatrix} = \begin{bmatrix} 0 \\ t \end{bmatrix} = t \begin{bmatrix} 0 \\ 1 \end{bmatrix}$,   i.e., $B_2 = \left\{ \begin{bmatrix} 0 \\ 1 \end{bmatrix} \right\}$.

$P = \begin{bmatrix} -6 & 0 \\ 1 & 1 \end{bmatrix}$, $P^{-1} = \frac{1}{-6} \begin{bmatrix} 1 & 0 \\ -1 & -6 \end{bmatrix} = \frac{1}{6} \begin{bmatrix} -1 & 0 \\ 1 & 6 \end{bmatrix}$

$P^{-1}AP = \frac{1}{6} \begin{bmatrix} -1 & 0 \\ 1 & 6 \end{bmatrix} \begin{bmatrix} 3 & 0 \\ 1 & 9 \end{bmatrix} \begin{bmatrix} -6 & 0 \\ 1 & 1 \end{bmatrix} = \frac{1}{6} \begin{bmatrix} -1 & 0 \\ 1 & 6 \end{bmatrix} \begin{bmatrix} -18 & 0 \\ 3 & 9 \end{bmatrix} = \frac{1}{6} \begin{bmatrix} 18 & 0 \\ 0 & 54 \end{bmatrix} = \begin{bmatrix} 3 & 0 \\ 0 & 9 \end{bmatrix}$.

30. $\quad 0 = |\lambda I - A| = \begin{vmatrix} \lambda - 4 & 12 \\ 6 & \lambda - 3 \end{vmatrix} = (\lambda - 4)(\lambda - 3) - (6)(12)$

$$= (\lambda^2 - 7\lambda + 12) - 72 = \lambda^2 - 7\lambda - 60$$

$$= (\lambda - 12)(\lambda + 5) \quad \text{so} \quad \lambda = 12, -5$$

$$\lambda_1 = 12 \longrightarrow \begin{bmatrix} 8 & 12 & 0 \\ 6 & 9 & 0 \end{bmatrix} \longrightarrow \begin{bmatrix} 1 & \frac{3}{2} & 0 \\ 0 & 0 & 0 \end{bmatrix}$$

Let $x_2 = s$;

then $x_1 + \dfrac{3}{2}x_2 = 0$, i.e., $x_1 = \dfrac{-3}{2}x_2 = \dfrac{-3}{2}s$

so $\begin{bmatrix} x_1 \\ x_2 \end{bmatrix} = \begin{bmatrix} \frac{-3}{2}s \\ s \end{bmatrix} = s\begin{bmatrix} \frac{-3}{2} \\ 1 \end{bmatrix} = \dfrac{1}{2}s\begin{bmatrix} -3 \\ 2 \end{bmatrix}$, i.e., $B_1 = \left\{ \begin{bmatrix} -3 \\ 2 \end{bmatrix} \right\}$.

$$\lambda_2 = -5 \longrightarrow \begin{bmatrix} -9 & 12 & 0 \\ 6 & -8 & 0 \end{bmatrix} \longrightarrow \begin{bmatrix} 1 & \frac{-4}{3} & 0 \\ 0 & 0 & 0 \end{bmatrix}$$

Let $x_2 = t$;

then $x_1 - \dfrac{4}{3}x_2 = 0$, i.e., $x_1 = \dfrac{4}{3}x_2 = \dfrac{4}{3}t$

so $\begin{bmatrix} x_1 \\ x_2 \end{bmatrix} = \begin{bmatrix} \frac{4}{3}t \\ t \end{bmatrix} = t\begin{bmatrix} \frac{4}{3} \\ 1 \end{bmatrix} = \dfrac{1}{3}t\begin{bmatrix} 4 \\ 3 \end{bmatrix}$, i.e., $B_2 = \left\{ \begin{bmatrix} 4 \\ 3 \end{bmatrix} \right\}$.

$$P = \begin{bmatrix} -3 & 4 \\ 2 & 3 \end{bmatrix} \quad , \quad P^{-1} = \dfrac{1}{-17}\begin{bmatrix} 3 & -4 \\ -2 & -3 \end{bmatrix} = \dfrac{1}{17}\begin{bmatrix} -3 & 4 \\ 2 & 3 \end{bmatrix}$$

$$P^{-1}AP = \dfrac{1}{17}\begin{bmatrix} -3 & 4 \\ 2 & 3 \end{bmatrix}\begin{bmatrix} 4 & -12 \\ -6 & 3 \end{bmatrix}\begin{bmatrix} -3 & 4 \\ 2 & 3 \end{bmatrix} = \dfrac{1}{17}\begin{bmatrix} -3 & 4 \\ 2 & 3 \end{bmatrix}\begin{bmatrix} -36 & -20 \\ 24 & -15 \end{bmatrix} = \dfrac{1}{17}\begin{bmatrix} 204 & 0 \\ 0 & -85 \end{bmatrix} =$$

$$\begin{bmatrix} 12 & 0 \\ 0 & -5 \end{bmatrix}.$$

31. $\quad 0 = |\lambda I - A| = \begin{vmatrix} \lambda & 0 & 0 \\ 0 & \lambda - 3 & -2 \\ 0 & 1 & \lambda \end{vmatrix} = \lambda[(\lambda - 3)\lambda - (1)(-2)]$

$$= \lambda(\lambda^2 - 3\lambda + 2)$$

$$= \lambda(\lambda - 1)(\lambda - 2) \quad \text{so} \quad \lambda = 0, 1, 2$$

$$\lambda_1 = 0 \longrightarrow \begin{bmatrix} 0 & 0 & 0 & 0 \\ 0 & -3 & -2 & 0 \\ 0 & 1 & 0 & 0 \end{bmatrix} \longrightarrow \begin{bmatrix} 0 & 1 & 0 & 0 \\ 0 & 0 & -2 & 0 \\ 0 & 0 & 0 & 0 \end{bmatrix} \longrightarrow \begin{bmatrix} 0 & 1 & 0 & 0 \\ 0 & 0 & 1 & 0 \\ 0 & 0 & 0 & 0 \end{bmatrix}$$

Let $x_1 = r$;

then $x_2 = 0$ and $x_3 = 0$

so $\begin{bmatrix} x_1 \\ x_2 \\ x_3 \end{bmatrix} = \begin{bmatrix} r \\ 0 \\ 0 \end{bmatrix} = r \begin{bmatrix} 1 \\ 0 \\ 0 \end{bmatrix}$, i.e., $B_1 = \left\{ \begin{bmatrix} 1 \\ 0 \\ 0 \end{bmatrix} \right\}$.

$\lambda_2 = 1 \longrightarrow \begin{bmatrix} 1 & 0 & 0 & 0 \\ 0 & -2 & -2 & 0 \\ 0 & 1 & 1 & 0 \end{bmatrix} \longrightarrow \begin{bmatrix} 1 & 0 & 0 & 0 \\ 0 & 1 & 1 & 0 \\ 0 & 0 & 0 & 0 \end{bmatrix}$

Let $x_3 = s$;

then $x_2 + x_3 = 0$, i.e., $x_2 = -x_3 = -s$

and $x_1 = 0$

so $\begin{bmatrix} x_1 \\ x_2 \\ x_3 \end{bmatrix} = \begin{bmatrix} 0 \\ -s \\ s \end{bmatrix} = s \begin{bmatrix} 0 \\ -1 \\ 1 \end{bmatrix}$, i.e., $B_2 = \left\{ \begin{bmatrix} 0 \\ -1 \\ 1 \end{bmatrix} \right\}$.

$\lambda_3 = 2 \longrightarrow \begin{bmatrix} 2 & 0 & 0 & 0 \\ 0 & -1 & -2 & 0 \\ 0 & 1 & 2 & 0 \end{bmatrix} \longrightarrow \begin{bmatrix} 1 & 0 & 0 & 0 \\ 0 & 1 & 2 & 0 \\ 0 & 0 & 0 & 0 \end{bmatrix}$

Let $x_3 = t$;

then $x_2 + 2x_3 = 0$, i.e., $x_2 = -2x_3 = -2t$

and $x_1 = 0$

so $\begin{bmatrix} x_1 \\ x_2 \\ x_3 \end{bmatrix} = \begin{bmatrix} 0 \\ -2t \\ t \end{bmatrix} = t \begin{bmatrix} 0 \\ -2 \\ 1 \end{bmatrix}$, i.e., $B_3 = \left\{ \begin{bmatrix} 0 \\ -2 \\ 1 \end{bmatrix} \right\}$.

$P = \begin{bmatrix} 1 & 0 & 0 \\ 0 & -1 & -2 \\ 0 & 1 & 1 \end{bmatrix}$, $P^{-1} = \frac{1}{1} \begin{bmatrix} 1 & 0 & 0 \\ 0 & 1 & -1 \\ 0 & 2 & -1 \end{bmatrix}^T = \begin{bmatrix} 1 & 0 & 0 \\ 0 & 1 & 2 \\ 0 & -1 & -1 \end{bmatrix}$

$P^{-1}AP = \begin{bmatrix} 1 & 0 & 0 \\ 0 & 1 & 2 \\ 0 & -1 & -1 \end{bmatrix} \begin{bmatrix} 0 & 0 & 0 \\ 0 & 3 & 2 \\ 0 & -1 & 0 \end{bmatrix} \begin{bmatrix} 1 & 0 & 0 \\ 0 & -1 & -2 \\ 0 & 1 & 1 \end{bmatrix} = \begin{bmatrix} 1 & 0 & 0 \\ 0 & 1 & 2 \\ 0 & -1 & -1 \end{bmatrix} \begin{bmatrix} 0 & 0 & 0 \\ 0 & -1 & -4 \\ 0 & 1 & 2 \end{bmatrix} =$

$\begin{bmatrix} 0 & 0 & 0 \\ 0 & 1 & 0 \\ 0 & 0 & 2 \end{bmatrix}$.

32. $0 = |\lambda I - A| = \begin{vmatrix} \lambda + 7 & 9 & -3 \\ -2 & \lambda - 4 & 2 \\ 3 & 3 & \lambda + 1 \end{vmatrix}$

$= (\lambda + 7)[(\lambda - 4)(\lambda + 1) - (3)(2)] - 9[-2(\lambda + 1) - (3)(2)] - 3[(-2)(3) - (3)(\lambda - 4)]$

$= (\lambda + 7)(\lambda^2 - 3\lambda - 10) - 9(-2\lambda - 8) - 3(-3\lambda + 6)$

$= (\lambda^3 + 4\lambda^2 - 31\lambda - 70) + (18\lambda + 72) + (9\lambda - 18)$

$= \lambda^3 + 4\lambda^2 - 4\lambda - 16$

$= (\lambda^3 + 4\lambda^2) + (-4\lambda - 16) = \lambda^2(\lambda + 4) - 4(\lambda + 4)$

$= (\lambda^2 - 4)(\lambda + 4) = (\lambda - 2)(\lambda + 2)(\lambda + 4)$

so $\lambda = 2, -2, -4$

$\lambda_1 = 2 \longrightarrow \begin{bmatrix} 9 & 9 & -3 & 0 \\ -2 & -2 & 2 & 0 \\ 3 & 3 & 3 & 0 \end{bmatrix} \longrightarrow \begin{bmatrix} 1 & 1 & -1 & 0 \\ 0 & 0 & 6 & 0 \\ 0 & 0 & 6 & 0 \end{bmatrix} \longrightarrow \begin{bmatrix} 1 & 1 & 0 & 0 \\ 0 & 0 & 1 & 0 \\ 0 & 0 & 0 & 0 \end{bmatrix}$

Let $x_2 = r$;

then $x_1 + x_2 = 0$, i.e., $x_1 = -x_2 = -r$

and $x_3 = 0$

so $\begin{bmatrix} x_1 \\ x_2 \\ x_3 \end{bmatrix} = \begin{bmatrix} r \\ -r \\ 0 \end{bmatrix} = r \begin{bmatrix} 1 \\ -1 \\ 0 \end{bmatrix}$, i.e., $B_1 = \left\{ \begin{bmatrix} 1 \\ -1 \\ 0 \end{bmatrix} \right\}$.

$\lambda_2 = -2 \longrightarrow \begin{bmatrix} 5 & 9 & -3 & 0 \\ -2 & -6 & 2 & 0 \\ 3 & 3 & -1 & 0 \end{bmatrix} \longrightarrow \begin{bmatrix} 1 & 3 & -1 & 0 \\ 0 & -6 & 2 & 0 \\ 0 & -6 & 2 & 0 \end{bmatrix} \longrightarrow \begin{bmatrix} 1 & 0 & 0 & 0 \\ 0 & 1 & -1/3 & 0 \\ 0 & 0 & 0 & 0 \end{bmatrix}$

Let $x_3 = s$;

then $x_2 - \frac{1}{3}x_3 = 0$, i.e., $x_2 = \frac{1}{3}x_3 = \frac{1}{3}s$

and $x_1 = 0$

so $\begin{bmatrix} x_1 \\ x_2 \\ x_3 \end{bmatrix} = \begin{bmatrix} 0 \\ \frac{1}{3}s \\ s \end{bmatrix} = s \begin{bmatrix} 0 \\ \frac{1}{3} \\ 1 \end{bmatrix} = \frac{1}{3}s \begin{bmatrix} 0 \\ 1 \\ 3 \end{bmatrix}$, i.e., $B_2 = \left\{ \begin{bmatrix} 0 \\ 1 \\ 3 \end{bmatrix} \right\}$.

$\lambda_3 = -4 \longrightarrow \begin{bmatrix} 3 & 9 & -3 & 0 \\ -2 & -8 & 2 & 0 \\ 3 & 3 & -3 & 0 \end{bmatrix} \longrightarrow \begin{bmatrix} 1 & 3 & -1 & 0 \\ 0 & -2 & 0 & 0 \\ 0 & -6 & 0 & 0 \end{bmatrix} \longrightarrow \begin{bmatrix} 1 & 0 & -1 & 0 \\ 0 & 1 & 0 & 0 \\ 0 & 0 & 0 & 0 \end{bmatrix}$

Let $x_3 = t$;

then $x_1 - x_3 = 0$, i.e., $x_1 = x_3 = t$

and $x_2 = 0$

so $\begin{bmatrix} x_1 \\ x_2 \\ x_3 \end{bmatrix} = \begin{bmatrix} t \\ 0 \\ t \end{bmatrix} = t \begin{bmatrix} 1 \\ 0 \\ 1 \end{bmatrix}$, i.e., $B_3 = \left\{ \begin{bmatrix} 1 \\ 0 \\ 1 \end{bmatrix} \right\}$.

$$P = \begin{bmatrix} 1 & 0 & 1 \\ -1 & 1 & 0 \\ 0 & 3 & 1 \end{bmatrix} , \quad P^{-1} = \frac{1}{-2} \begin{bmatrix} 1 & 1 & -3 \\ 3 & 1 & -3 \\ -1 & -1 & 1 \end{bmatrix}^T = \frac{1}{2} \begin{bmatrix} -1 & -3 & 1 \\ -1 & -1 & 1 \\ 3 & 3 & -1 \end{bmatrix}$$

$$P^{-1}AP = \frac{1}{2} \begin{bmatrix} -1 & -3 & 1 \\ -1 & -1 & 1 \\ 3 & 3 & -1 \end{bmatrix} \begin{bmatrix} -7 & -9 & 3 \\ 2 & 4 & -2 \\ -3 & -3 & -1 \end{bmatrix} \begin{bmatrix} 1 & 0 & 1 \\ -1 & 1 & 0 \\ 0 & 3 & 1 \end{bmatrix}$$

$$= \frac{1}{2} \begin{bmatrix} -1 & -3 & 1 \\ -1 & -1 & 1 \\ 3 & 3 & -1 \end{bmatrix} \begin{bmatrix} 2 & 0 & -4 \\ -2 & -2 & 0 \\ 0 & -6 & -4 \end{bmatrix} = \frac{1}{2} \begin{bmatrix} 4 & 0 & 0 \\ 0 & -4 & 0 \\ 0 & 0 & -8 \end{bmatrix} = \begin{bmatrix} 2 & 0 & 0 \\ 0 & -2 & 0 \\ 0 & 0 & -4 \end{bmatrix}.$$

33. $0 = |\lambda I - A| = \begin{vmatrix} \lambda - 2 & 0 & 0 \\ -1/2 & \lambda - 3 & -1 \\ 0 & 0 & \lambda - 2 \end{vmatrix} = (\lambda - 2)(\lambda - 3)(\lambda - 2)$ so $\lambda = 2, 2, 3$

$$\lambda_1 = 2 \longrightarrow \begin{bmatrix} 0 & 0 & 0 & 0 \\ -1/2 & -1 & -1 & 0 \\ 0 & 0 & 0 & 0 \end{bmatrix} \longrightarrow \begin{bmatrix} 1 & 2 & 2 & 0 \\ 0 & 0 & 0 & 0 \\ 0 & 0 & 0 & 0 \end{bmatrix}$$

Let $x_3 = r$ and $x_2 = s$;

then $x_1 + 2x_2 + 2x_3 = 0$, i.e., $x_1 = -2x_2 - 2x_3 = -2s - 2r$

so $\begin{bmatrix} x_1 \\ x_2 \\ x_3 \end{bmatrix} = \begin{bmatrix} -2s - 2r \\ s \\ r \end{bmatrix} = \begin{bmatrix} -2s \\ s \\ 0 \end{bmatrix} + \begin{bmatrix} -2r \\ 0 \\ r \end{bmatrix} = s \begin{bmatrix} -2 \\ 1 \\ 0 \end{bmatrix} + r \begin{bmatrix} -2 \\ 0 \\ 1 \end{bmatrix}$,

i.e., $B_1 = \left\{ \begin{bmatrix} -2 \\ 1 \\ 0 \end{bmatrix} , \begin{bmatrix} -2 \\ 0 \\ 1 \end{bmatrix} \right\}$.

$$\lambda_3 = 3 \longrightarrow \begin{bmatrix} 1 & 0 & 0 & 0 \\ -1/2 & 0 & -1 & 0 \\ 0 & 0 & 1 & 0 \end{bmatrix} \longrightarrow \begin{bmatrix} 1 & 0 & 0 & 0 \\ 0 & 0 & -1 & 0 \\ 0 & 0 & 1 & 0 \end{bmatrix} \longrightarrow \begin{bmatrix} 1 & 0 & 0 & 0 \\ 0 & 0 & 1 & 0 \\ 0 & 0 & 0 & 0 \end{bmatrix}$$

Let $x_2 = t$;

then $x_1 = 0$ and $x_3 = 0$

so $\begin{bmatrix} x_1 \\ x_2 \\ x_3 \end{bmatrix} = \begin{bmatrix} 0 \\ t \\ 0 \end{bmatrix} = t \begin{bmatrix} 0 \\ 1 \\ 0 \end{bmatrix}$, i.e., $B_2 = \left\{ \begin{bmatrix} 0 \\ 1 \\ 0 \end{bmatrix} \right\}$.

$$P = \begin{bmatrix} -2 & -2 & 0 \\ 1 & 0 & 1 \\ 0 & 1 & 0 \end{bmatrix} \quad , \quad P^{-1} = \tfrac{1}{2} \begin{bmatrix} -1 & 0 & 1 \\ 0 & 0 & 2 \\ -2 & 2 & 2 \end{bmatrix}^T = \tfrac{1}{2} \begin{bmatrix} -1 & 0 & -2 \\ 0 & 0 & 2 \\ 1 & 2 & 2 \end{bmatrix}$$

$$P^{-1}AP = \frac{1}{2} \begin{bmatrix} -1 & 0 & -2 \\ 0 & 0 & 2 \\ 1 & 2 & 2 \end{bmatrix} \begin{bmatrix} 2 & 0 & 0 \\ 1/2 & 3 & 1 \\ 0 & 0 & 2 \end{bmatrix} \begin{bmatrix} -2 & -2 & 0 \\ 1 & 0 & 1 \\ 0 & 1 & 0 \end{bmatrix}$$

$$= \frac{1}{2} \begin{bmatrix} -1 & 0 & -2 \\ 0 & 0 & 2 \\ 1 & 2 & 2 \end{bmatrix} \begin{bmatrix} -4 & -4 & 0 \\ 2 & 0 & 3 \\ 0 & 2 & 0 \end{bmatrix} = \frac{1}{2} \begin{bmatrix} 4 & 0 & 0 \\ 0 & 4 & 0 \\ 0 & 0 & 6 \end{bmatrix} = \begin{bmatrix} 2 & 0 & 0 \\ 0 & 2 & 0 \\ 0 & 0 & 3 \end{bmatrix}.$$

34. $\quad 0 = |\lambda I - A| = \begin{vmatrix} \lambda & 1 & -1 & 1 \\ 0 & \lambda-1 & 0 & 0 \\ -2 & 2 & \lambda-3 & 1 \\ 0 & 0 & 0 & \lambda-2 \end{vmatrix} = (\lambda-2) \begin{vmatrix} \lambda & 1 & -1 \\ 0 & \lambda-1 & 0 \\ 2 & 2 & \lambda-3 \end{vmatrix}$

$\quad = (\lambda-2)(\lambda-1)[(\lambda)(\lambda-3) - (2)(-1)] = (\lambda-2)(\lambda-1)(\lambda^2 - 3\lambda + 2)$

$\quad = (\lambda-2)(\lambda-1)(\lambda-1)(\lambda-2) = (\lambda-1)^2(\lambda-2)^2 \quad \text{so} \quad \lambda = 1, 1, 2, 2.$

$$\lambda_1 = 1 \longrightarrow \begin{bmatrix} 1 & 1 & -1 & 1 & 0 \\ 0 & 0 & 0 & 0 & 0 \\ 2 & 2 & -2 & 1 & 0 \\ 0 & 0 & 0 & -1 & 0 \end{bmatrix} \longrightarrow \begin{bmatrix} 1 & 1 & -1 & 1 & 0 \\ 0 & 0 & 0 & -1 & 0 \\ 0 & 0 & 0 & 0 & 0 \\ 0 & 0 & 0 & 0 & 0 \end{bmatrix} \longrightarrow \begin{bmatrix} 1 & 1 & -1 & 0 & 0 \\ 0 & 0 & 0 & 1 & 0 \\ 0 & 0 & 0 & 0 & 0 \\ 0 & 0 & 0 & 0 & 0 \end{bmatrix}$$

Let $\quad x_3 = r \quad$ and $\quad x_2 = q;$

then $\quad x_1 + x_2 - x_3 = 0 \quad$ i.e., $\quad x_1 = -x_2 + x_3 = -q + r$

and $\quad x_4 = 0$

so $\quad \begin{bmatrix} x_1 \\ x_2 \\ x_3 \\ x_4 \end{bmatrix} = \begin{bmatrix} -q+r \\ q \\ r \\ 0 \end{bmatrix} = \begin{bmatrix} -q \\ q \\ 0 \\ 0 \end{bmatrix} + \begin{bmatrix} r \\ 0 \\ r \\ 0 \end{bmatrix} = q \begin{bmatrix} -1 \\ 1 \\ 0 \\ 0 \end{bmatrix} + r \begin{bmatrix} 1 \\ 0 \\ 1 \\ 0 \end{bmatrix},$

i.e., $\quad B_1 = \left\{ \begin{bmatrix} -1 \\ 1 \\ 0 \\ 0 \end{bmatrix}, \begin{bmatrix} 1 \\ 0 \\ 1 \\ 0 \end{bmatrix} \right\}.$

$$\lambda_2 = 2 \longrightarrow \begin{bmatrix} 2 & 1 & -1 & 1 & 0 \\ 0 & 1 & 0 & 0 & 0 \\ 2 & 2 & -1 & 1 & 0 \\ 0 & 0 & 0 & 0 & 0 \end{bmatrix} \longrightarrow \begin{bmatrix} 1 & 1/2 & -1/2 & 1/2 & 0 \\ 0 & 1 & 0 & 0 & 0 \\ 0 & 1 & 0 & 0 & 0 \\ 0 & 0 & 0 & 0 & 0 \end{bmatrix} \longrightarrow \begin{bmatrix} 1 & 0 & -1/2 & 1/2 & 0 \\ 0 & 1 & 0 & 0 & 0 \\ 0 & 0 & 0 & 0 & 0 \\ 0 & 0 & 0 & 0 & 0 \end{bmatrix}$$

Let $x_4 = t$ and $x_3 = 3$;

then $x_1 - \dfrac{1}{2}x_3 + \dfrac{1}{2}x_4 = 0$, i.e., $x_1 = \dfrac{1}{2}x_3 - \dfrac{1}{2}x_4 = \dfrac{1}{2}s - \dfrac{1}{2}t$

and $x_2 = 0$

so $\begin{bmatrix} x_1 \\ x_2 \\ x_3 \\ x_4 \end{bmatrix} = \begin{bmatrix} (1/2)s - (1/2)t \\ 0 \\ s \\ t \end{bmatrix} = \begin{bmatrix} (1/2)s \\ 0 \\ s \\ 0 \end{bmatrix} + \begin{bmatrix} (-1/2)t \\ 0 \\ 0 \\ t \end{bmatrix} = s\begin{bmatrix} (1/2) \\ 0 \\ 1 \\ 0 \end{bmatrix} + t\begin{bmatrix} (-1/2) \\ 0 \\ 0 \\ 1 \end{bmatrix}$

$= \dfrac{1}{2}s\begin{bmatrix} 1 \\ 0 \\ 2 \\ 0 \end{bmatrix} + \dfrac{1}{2}t\begin{bmatrix} -1 \\ 0 \\ 0 \\ 2 \end{bmatrix}$, i.e., $B_2 = \left\{ \begin{bmatrix} 1 \\ 0 \\ 2 \\ 0 \end{bmatrix}, \begin{bmatrix} -1 \\ 0 \\ 0 \\ 2 \end{bmatrix} \right\}$.

$P = \begin{bmatrix} -1 & 1 & 1 & -1 \\ 1 & 0 & 0 & 0 \\ 0 & 1 & 2 & 0 \\ 0 & 0 & 0 & 2 \end{bmatrix}$, $P^{-1} = \dfrac{1}{-2}\begin{bmatrix} 0 & -4 & 2 & 0 \\ -2 & -4 & 2 & 0 \\ 0 & 2 & -2 & 0 \\ 0 & -2 & 1 & -1 \end{bmatrix}^T = \dfrac{1}{2}\begin{bmatrix} 0 & 2 & 0 & 0 \\ 4 & 4 & -2 & 2 \\ -2 & -2 & 2 & -1 \\ 0 & 0 & 0 & 1 \end{bmatrix}$

$P^{-1}AP = \dfrac{1}{2}\begin{bmatrix} 0 & 2 & 0 & 0 \\ 4 & 4 & -2 & 2 \\ -2 & -2 & 2 & -1 \\ 0 & 0 & 0 & 1 \end{bmatrix}\begin{bmatrix} 0 & -1 & 1 & -1 \\ 0 & 1 & 0 & 0 \\ -2 & -2 & 3 & -1 \\ 0 & 0 & 0 & 2 \end{bmatrix}\begin{bmatrix} -1 & 1 & 1 & -1 \\ 1 & 0 & 0 & 0 \\ 0 & 1 & 2 & 0 \\ 0 & 0 & 0 & 2 \end{bmatrix}$

$= \dfrac{1}{2}\begin{bmatrix} 0 & 2 & 0 & 0 \\ 4 & 4 & -2 & 2 \\ -2 & -2 & 2 & -1 \\ 0 & 0 & 0 & 1 \end{bmatrix}\begin{bmatrix} -1 & 1 & 2 & -2 \\ 1 & 0 & 0 & 0 \\ 0 & 1 & 4 & 0 \\ 0 & 0 & 0 & 4 \end{bmatrix} = \dfrac{1}{2}\begin{bmatrix} 2 & 0 & 0 & 0 \\ 0 & 2 & 0 & 0 \\ 0 & 0 & 4 & 0 \\ 0 & 0 & 0 & 4 \end{bmatrix} = \begin{bmatrix} 1 & 0 & 0 & 0 \\ 0 & 1 & 0 & 0 \\ 0 & 0 & 2 & 0 \\ 0 & 0 & 0 & 2 \end{bmatrix}$.

35. $0 = |\lambda I - A| = \begin{vmatrix} \lambda - 4 & 3 \\ -5 & \lambda + 4 \end{vmatrix} = (\lambda - 4)(\lambda + 4) - (-5)(3)$

$= \lambda^2 - 16 + 15 = \lambda^2 - 1 = (\lambda - 1)(\lambda + 1)$

Thus, the eigenvalues of A are 1 and -1,
so the eigenvalues of A^{15} are $(1)^{15} = 1$ and $(-1)^{15} = -1$.

$\lambda = 1 \longrightarrow \begin{bmatrix} -3 & 3 & 0 \\ -5 & 5 & 0 \end{bmatrix} \longrightarrow \begin{bmatrix} 1 & -1 & 0 \\ 0 & 0 & 0 \end{bmatrix}$

Let $x_2 = s$;

then $x_1 - x_2 = 0$, i.e., $x_1 = x_2 = s$

so $\begin{bmatrix} x_1 \\ x_2 \end{bmatrix} = \begin{bmatrix} s \\ s \end{bmatrix} = s\begin{bmatrix} 1 \\ 1 \end{bmatrix}$, i.e., $B_1 = \left\{ \begin{bmatrix} 1 \\ 1 \end{bmatrix} \right\}$.

$\lambda = -1 \longrightarrow \begin{bmatrix} -5 & 3 & 0 \\ -5 & 3 & 0 \end{bmatrix} \longrightarrow \begin{bmatrix} 1 & -3/5 & 0 \\ 0 & 0 & 0 \end{bmatrix}$

Let $x_2 = t$;

then $x_1 - \dfrac{3}{5}x_2 = 0$, i.e., $x_1 = \dfrac{3}{5}x_2 = \dfrac{3}{5}t$

so $\begin{bmatrix} x_1 \\ x_2 \end{bmatrix} = \begin{bmatrix} (3/5)t \\ t \end{bmatrix} = t\begin{bmatrix} 3/5 \\ 1 \end{bmatrix} = \dfrac{1}{5}t\begin{bmatrix} 3 \\ 5 \end{bmatrix}$, i.e., $B_2 = \left\{ \begin{bmatrix} 3 \\ 5 \end{bmatrix} \right\}$.

$P = \begin{bmatrix} 1 & 3 \\ 1 & 5 \end{bmatrix}$, $P^{-1} = \dfrac{1}{2}\begin{bmatrix} 5 & -3 \\ -1 & 1 \end{bmatrix}$

$A^{15} = \begin{bmatrix} 1 & 3 \\ 1 & 5 \end{bmatrix}\begin{bmatrix} 1 & 0 \\ 0 & -1 \end{bmatrix}\dfrac{1}{2}\begin{bmatrix} 5 & -3 \\ -1 & 1 \end{bmatrix} = \dfrac{1}{2}\begin{bmatrix} 1 & 3 \\ 1 & 5 \end{bmatrix}\begin{bmatrix} 5 & -3 \\ 1 & -1 \end{bmatrix} = \dfrac{1}{2}\begin{bmatrix} 8 & -6 \\ 10 & -8 \end{bmatrix} = \begin{bmatrix} 4 & -3 \\ 5 & -4 \end{bmatrix}.$

36. $0 = |\lambda I - A| = \begin{vmatrix} \lambda - 5 & -3 & 7 \\ 1 & \lambda - 1 & -1 \\ -3 & -3 & \lambda + 5 \end{vmatrix}$

$= (\lambda - 5)[(\lambda - 1)(\lambda + 5) - (-3)(-1)] + 3[(1)(\lambda + 5) - (-3)(-1)] + 7[(1)(-3) - (-3)(\lambda - 1)]$

$= (\lambda - 5)(\lambda^2 + 4\lambda - 8) + 3(\lambda + 2) + 7(3\lambda - 6)$

$= \lambda^3 - \lambda^2 - 4\lambda + 4 = (\lambda^3 - \lambda^2) + (-4\lambda + 4)$

$= \lambda^2(\lambda - 1) + -4(\lambda - 1) = (\lambda^2 - 4)(\lambda - 1) = (\lambda - 1)(\lambda - 2)(\lambda + 2)$

Thus, the eigenvalues of A are 1, 2 and -2,
so the eigenvalues of A^{10} are $(1)^{10} = 1, (2)^{10} = 1024$ and $(-2)^{10} = 1024$.

$\lambda = 1 \longrightarrow \begin{bmatrix} -4 & -3 & 7 & 0 \\ 1 & 0 & -1 & 0 \\ -3 & -3 & 6 & 0 \end{bmatrix} \longrightarrow \begin{bmatrix} 1 & 0 & -1 & 0 \\ -4 & -3 & 7 & 0 \\ -3 & -3 & 6 & 0 \end{bmatrix} \longrightarrow \begin{bmatrix} 1 & 0 & -1 & 0 \\ 0 & -3 & 3 & 0 \\ 0 & -3 & 3 & 0 \end{bmatrix} \longrightarrow$

$\begin{bmatrix} 1 & 0 & -1 & 0 \\ 0 & 1 & -1 & 0 \\ 0 & 0 & 0 & 0 \end{bmatrix}$

Let $x_3 = r$;

then $x_2 - x_3 = 0$, i.e., $x_2 = x_3 = r$

and $x_1 - x_3 = 0$, i.e., $x_1 = x_3 = r$

so $\begin{bmatrix} x_1 \\ x_2 \\ x_3 \end{bmatrix} = \begin{bmatrix} r \\ r \\ r \end{bmatrix} = r\begin{bmatrix} 1 \\ 1 \\ 1 \end{bmatrix}$, i.e., $B_1 = \left\{ \begin{bmatrix} 1 \\ 1 \\ 1 \end{bmatrix} \right\}$ (for $\lambda = 1$).

$\lambda = 2 \longrightarrow \begin{bmatrix} -3 & -3 & 7 & 0 \\ 1 & 1 & -1 & 0 \\ -3 & -3 & 7 & 0 \end{bmatrix} \longrightarrow \begin{bmatrix} 1 & 1 & -1 & 0 \\ -3 & -3 & 7 & 0 \\ -3 & -3 & 7 & 0 \end{bmatrix} \longrightarrow \begin{bmatrix} 1 & 1 & -1 & 0 \\ 0 & 0 & 4 & 0 \\ 0 & 0 & 4 & 0 \end{bmatrix} \longrightarrow$

$$\begin{bmatrix} 1 & 1 & 0 & 0 \\ 0 & 0 & 1 & 0 \\ 0 & 0 & 0 & 0 \end{bmatrix}$$

Let $x_2 = s$;

then $x_1 + x_2 = 0$, i.e., $x_1 = -x_2 = -s$

and $x_3 = 0$

so $\begin{bmatrix} x_1 \\ x_2 \\ x_3 \end{bmatrix} = \begin{bmatrix} -s \\ s \\ 0 \end{bmatrix} = s\begin{bmatrix} -1 \\ 1 \\ 0 \end{bmatrix}$.

$$\lambda = -2 \longrightarrow \begin{bmatrix} -7 & -3 & 7 & 0 \\ 1 & -3 & -1 & 0 \\ -3 & -3 & 3 & 0 \end{bmatrix} \longrightarrow \begin{bmatrix} 1 & -3 & -1 & 0 \\ -7 & -3 & 7 & 0 \\ -3 & -3 & 3 & 0 \end{bmatrix} \longrightarrow \begin{bmatrix} 1 & -3 & -1 & 0 \\ 0 & -24 & 0 & 0 \\ 0 & -12 & 0 & 0 \end{bmatrix} \longrightarrow$$

$$\begin{bmatrix} 1 & 0 & -1 & 0 \\ 0 & 1 & 0 & 0 \\ 0 & 0 & 0 & 0 \end{bmatrix}$$

Let $x_3 = t$;

then $x_1 - x_3 = 0$, i.e., $x_1 = x_3 = t$

and $x_2 = 0$

so $\begin{bmatrix} x_1 \\ x_2 \\ x_3 \end{bmatrix} = \begin{bmatrix} t \\ 0 \\ t \end{bmatrix} = t\begin{bmatrix} 1 \\ 0 \\ 1 \end{bmatrix}$, i.e., $B_2 = \left\{ \begin{bmatrix} -1 \\ 1 \\ 1 \end{bmatrix}, \begin{bmatrix} 1 \\ 0 \\ 1 \end{bmatrix} \right\}$ (for $\lambda = 1024$).

$$P = \begin{bmatrix} 1 & -1 & 1 \\ 1 & 1 & 0 \\ 1 & 0 & 1 \end{bmatrix} , \quad P^{-1} = \frac{1}{1}\begin{bmatrix} 1 & -1 & -1 \\ 1 & 0 & -1 \\ -1 & 1 & 2 \end{bmatrix}^T = \begin{bmatrix} 1 & 1 & -1 \\ -1 & 0 & 1 \\ -1 & -1 & 2 \end{bmatrix}$$

$$A^{10} = \begin{bmatrix} 1 & -1 & 1 \\ 1 & 1 & 0 \\ 1 & 0 & 1 \end{bmatrix}\begin{bmatrix} 1 & 0 & 0 \\ 0 & 1024 & 0 \\ 0 & 0 & 1024 \end{bmatrix}\begin{bmatrix} 1 & 1 & -1 \\ -1 & 0 & 1 \\ -1 & -1 & 2 \end{bmatrix}$$

$$= \begin{bmatrix} 1 & -1 & 1 \\ 1 & 1 & 0 \\ 1 & 0 & 1 \end{bmatrix}\begin{bmatrix} 1 & 1 & -1 \\ -1024 & 0 & 1024 \\ -1024 & -1024 & 2048 \end{bmatrix} = \begin{bmatrix} 1 & -1023 & 1023 \\ -1023 & 1 & 1023 \\ -1023 & -1023 & 2047 \end{bmatrix}.$$

37. $0 = |\lambda I - A| = \begin{vmatrix} \lambda & 2 & -1 & -2 \\ 0 & \lambda+2 & 0 & -5 \\ 0 & 2 & \lambda+1 & -2 \\ 0 & 0 & 0 & \lambda-3 \end{vmatrix} = \lambda\begin{vmatrix} \lambda+2 & 0 & -5 \\ 2 & \lambda+1 & -2 \\ 0 & 0 & \lambda-3 \end{vmatrix}$

$= \lambda(\lambda-3)(\lambda+2)(\lambda+1)$

Thus, the eigenvalues of A are 0, -1, -2 and 3,

so the eigenvalues of A^5 are $(0)^5 = 0, (-1)^5 = -1, (-2)^5 = -32$ and $(3)^5 = 243$.

$$\lambda = 0 \longrightarrow \begin{bmatrix} 0 & 2 & -1 & -2 & 0 \\ 0 & 2 & 0 & -5 & 0 \\ 0 & 2 & 1 & -2 & 0 \\ 0 & 0 & 0 & -3 & 0 \end{bmatrix} \longrightarrow \begin{bmatrix} 0 & 1 & -1/2 & -1 & 0 \\ 0 & 0 & 1 & -3 & 0 \\ 0 & 0 & 2 & 0 & 0 \\ 0 & 0 & 0 & -3 & 0 \end{bmatrix} \longrightarrow$$

$$\begin{bmatrix} 0 & 1 & -1/2 & -1 & 0 \\ 0 & 0 & 1 & -3 & 0 \\ 0 & 0 & 0 & 6 & 0 \\ 0 & 0 & 0 & -3 & 0 \end{bmatrix} \longrightarrow \begin{bmatrix} 0 & 1 & 0 & 0 & 0 \\ 0 & 0 & 1 & 0 & 0 \\ 0 & 0 & 0 & 1 & 0 \\ 0 & 0 & 0 & 0 & 0 \end{bmatrix}$$

Let $x_1 = q$;

then $x_2 = 0$, $x_3 = 0$ and $x_4 = 0$

so $\begin{bmatrix} x_1 \\ x_2 \\ x_3 \\ x_4 \end{bmatrix} = \begin{bmatrix} q \\ 0 \\ 0 \\ 0 \end{bmatrix} = q \begin{bmatrix} 1 \\ 0 \\ 0 \\ 0 \end{bmatrix}$, i.e., $B_1 = \left\{ \begin{bmatrix} 1 \\ 0 \\ 0 \\ 0 \end{bmatrix} \right\}$ (for $\lambda = 0$).

$$\lambda = -1 \longrightarrow \begin{bmatrix} -1 & 2 & -1 & -2 & 0 \\ 0 & 1 & 0 & -5 & 0 \\ 0 & 2 & 0 & -2 & 0 \\ 0 & 0 & 0 & -4 & 0 \end{bmatrix} \longrightarrow \begin{bmatrix} 1 & -2 & 1 & 2 & 0 \\ 0 & 1 & 0 & -5 & 0 \\ 0 & 2 & 0 & -2 & 0 \\ 0 & 0 & 0 & -4 & 0 \end{bmatrix} \longrightarrow$$

$$\begin{bmatrix} 1 & -2 & 1 & 2 & 0 \\ 0 & 1 & 0 & -5 & 0 \\ 0 & 0 & 0 & 8 & 0 \\ 0 & 0 & 0 & -4 & 0 \end{bmatrix} \longrightarrow \begin{bmatrix} 1 & 0 & 1 & 0 & 0 \\ 0 & 1 & 0 & 0 & 0 \\ 0 & 0 & 0 & 1 & 0 \\ 0 & 0 & 0 & 0 & 0 \end{bmatrix}$$

Let $x_3 = r$;

then $x_1 + x_3 = 0$, i.e., $x_1 = -x_3 = -r$

and $x_2 = 0$ and $x_4 = 0$

so $\begin{bmatrix} x_1 \\ x_2 \\ x_3 \\ x_4 \end{bmatrix} = \begin{bmatrix} -r \\ 0 \\ r \\ 0 \end{bmatrix} = r \begin{bmatrix} -1 \\ 0 \\ 1 \\ 0 \end{bmatrix}$, i.e., $B_2 = \left\{ \begin{bmatrix} -1 \\ 0 \\ 1 \\ 0 \end{bmatrix} \right\}$ (for $\lambda = -1$).

$$\lambda = -2 \longrightarrow \begin{bmatrix} -2 & 2 & -1 & -2 & 0 \\ 0 & 0 & 0 & -5 & 0 \\ 0 & 2 & -1 & -2 & 0 \\ 0 & 0 & 0 & -5 & 0 \end{bmatrix} \longrightarrow \begin{bmatrix} 1 & -1 & 1/2 & 1 & 0 \\ 0 & 0 & 0 & -5 & 0 \\ 0 & 1 & -1/2 & -1 & 0 \\ 0 & 0 & 0 & -5 & 0 \end{bmatrix} \longrightarrow$$

$$\begin{bmatrix} 1 & -1 & 1/2 & 1 & 0 \\ 0 & 1 & -1/2 & -1 & 0 \\ 0 & 0 & 0 & -5 & 0 \\ 0 & 0 & 0 & -5 & 0 \end{bmatrix} \longrightarrow \begin{bmatrix} 1 & 0 & 0 & 0 & 0 \\ 0 & 1 & -1/2 & 0 & 0 \\ 0 & 0 & 0 & 1 & 0 \\ 0 & 0 & 0 & 0 & 0 \end{bmatrix}$$

Let $x_3 = s$;

then $x_2 - \frac{1}{2}x_3 = 0$ i.e., $x_2 = \frac{1}{2}x_3 = \frac{1}{2}s$

and $x_1 = 0$ and $x_4 = 0$

so $\begin{bmatrix} x_1 \\ x_2 \\ x_3 \\ x_4 \end{bmatrix} = \begin{bmatrix} 0 \\ (1/2)s \\ s \\ 0 \end{bmatrix} = s\begin{bmatrix} 0 \\ 1/2 \\ 1 \\ 0 \end{bmatrix} = \frac{1}{2}s\begin{bmatrix} 0 \\ 1 \\ 2 \\ 0 \end{bmatrix}$, i.e., $B_3 = \left\{ \begin{bmatrix} 0 \\ 1 \\ 2 \\ 0 \end{bmatrix} \right\}$ (for $\lambda = -32$).

$\lambda = 3 \longrightarrow \begin{bmatrix} 3 & 2 & -1 & -2 & 0 \\ 0 & 5 & 0 & -5 & 0 \\ 0 & 2 & 4 & -2 & 0 \\ 0 & 0 & 0 & 0 & 0 \end{bmatrix} \longrightarrow \begin{bmatrix} 1 & 2/3 & -1/3 & -2/3 & 0 \\ 0 & 1 & 0 & -1 & 0 \\ 0 & 0 & 4 & 0 & 0 \\ 0 & 0 & 0 & 0 & 0 \end{bmatrix} \longrightarrow \begin{bmatrix} 1 & 0 & 0 & 0 & 0 \\ 0 & 1 & 0 & -1 & 0 \\ 0 & 0 & 1 & 0 & 0 \\ 0 & 0 & 0 & 0 & 0 \end{bmatrix}$

Let $x_4 = t$;

then $x_2 - x_4 = 0$ i.e., $x_2 = x_4 = t$

and $x_1 = 0$ and $x_3 = 0$

so $\begin{bmatrix} x_1 \\ x_2 \\ x_3 \\ x_4 \end{bmatrix} = \begin{bmatrix} 0 \\ t \\ 0 \\ t \end{bmatrix} = t\begin{bmatrix} 0 \\ 1 \\ 0 \\ 1 \end{bmatrix}$, i.e., $B_4 = \left\{ \begin{bmatrix} 0 \\ 1 \\ 0 \\ 1 \end{bmatrix} \right\}$ (for $\lambda = 243$).

$P = \begin{bmatrix} 1 & -1 & 0 & 0 \\ 0 & 0 & 1 & 1 \\ 0 & 1 & 2 & 0 \\ 0 & 0 & 0 & 1 \end{bmatrix}$, $P^{-1} = \frac{1}{-1}\begin{bmatrix} -1 & 0 & 0 & 0 \\ 2 & 2 & -1 & 0 \\ -1 & -1 & 0 & 0 \\ -2 & -2 & 1 & -1 \end{bmatrix}^T = \begin{bmatrix} 1 & -2 & 1 & 2 \\ 0 & -2 & 1 & 2 \\ 0 & 1 & 0 & -1 \\ 0 & 0 & 0 & 1 \end{bmatrix}$

$A^5 = \begin{bmatrix} 1 & -1 & 0 & 0 \\ 0 & 0 & 1 & 1 \\ 0 & 1 & 2 & 0 \\ 0 & 0 & 0 & 1 \end{bmatrix}\begin{bmatrix} 0 & 0 & 0 & 0 \\ 0 & -1 & 0 & 0 \\ 0 & 0 & -32 & 0 \\ 0 & 0 & 0 & 243 \end{bmatrix}\begin{bmatrix} 1 & -2 & 1 & 2 \\ 0 & -2 & 1 & 2 \\ 0 & 1 & 0 & -1 \\ 0 & 0 & 0 & 1 \end{bmatrix}$

$= \begin{bmatrix} 1 & -1 & 0 & 0 \\ 0 & 0 & 1 & 1 \\ 0 & 1 & 2 & 0 \\ 0 & 0 & 0 & 1 \end{bmatrix}\begin{bmatrix} 0 & 0 & 0 & 0 \\ 0 & 2 & -1 & -2 \\ 0 & -32 & 0 & 32 \\ 0 & 0 & 0 & 243 \end{bmatrix} = \begin{bmatrix} 0 & -2 & 1 & 2 \\ 0 & -32 & 0 & 275 \\ 0 & -62 & -1 & 62 \\ 0 & 0 & 0 & 243 \end{bmatrix}$.

38. $0 = |\lambda I - A| = \begin{vmatrix} \lambda - 4 & 5 \\ 3 & \lambda - 2 \end{vmatrix} = (\lambda - 4)(\lambda - 2) - (3)(5)$

$= (\lambda^2 - 6\lambda + 8) - 15 = \lambda^2 - 6\lambda - 7$

$= (\lambda - 7)(\lambda + 1)$ so $\lambda = 7, -1$

$\lambda_1 = 7 \longrightarrow \begin{bmatrix} 3 & 5 & 0 \\ 3 & 5 & 0 \end{bmatrix} \longrightarrow \begin{bmatrix} 1 & \frac{5}{3} & 0 \\ 0 & 0 & 0 \end{bmatrix}$

164

Let $x_2 = s$;

then $x_1 + \dfrac{5}{3}x_2 = 0$, i.e., $x_1 = \dfrac{-5}{3}x_2 = \dfrac{-5}{3}s$

so $\begin{bmatrix} x_1 \\ x_2 \end{bmatrix} = \begin{bmatrix} \frac{-5}{3}s \\ s \end{bmatrix} = s\begin{bmatrix} \frac{-5}{3} \\ 1 \end{bmatrix} = \dfrac{1}{3}s\begin{bmatrix} -5 \\ 3 \end{bmatrix}$, i.e., $B_1 = \left\{ \begin{bmatrix} -5 \\ 3 \end{bmatrix} \right\}$.

$\lambda_2 = -1 \longrightarrow \begin{bmatrix} -5 & 5 & 0 \\ 3 & -3 & 0 \end{bmatrix} \longrightarrow \begin{bmatrix} 1 & -1 & 0 \\ 0 & 0 & 0 \end{bmatrix}$

Let $x_2 = t$;

then $x_1 - x_2 = 0$, i.e., $x_1 = x_2 = t$

so $\begin{bmatrix} x_1 \\ x_2 \end{bmatrix} = \begin{bmatrix} t \\ t \end{bmatrix} = t\begin{bmatrix} 1 \\ 1 \end{bmatrix}$, i.e., $B_2 = \left\{ \begin{bmatrix} 1 \\ 1 \end{bmatrix} \right\}$.

$P = \begin{bmatrix} -5 & 1 \\ 3 & 1 \end{bmatrix}$, $P^{-1} = \dfrac{1}{-8}\begin{bmatrix} 1 & -1 \\ -3 & -5 \end{bmatrix} = \dfrac{1}{8}\begin{bmatrix} -1 & 1 \\ 3 & 5 \end{bmatrix}$

$A^n = \begin{bmatrix} -5 & 1 \\ 3 & 1 \end{bmatrix}\begin{bmatrix} 7^n & 0 \\ 0 & (-1)^n \end{bmatrix}\dfrac{1}{8}\begin{bmatrix} -1 & 1 \\ 3 & 5 \end{bmatrix} = \dfrac{1}{8}\begin{bmatrix} -5 & 1 \\ 3 & 1 \end{bmatrix}\begin{bmatrix} -7^n & 7^n \\ 3(-1)^n & 5(-1)^n \end{bmatrix}$

$= \dfrac{1}{8}\begin{bmatrix} 5(7)^n + 3(-1)^n & -5(7)^n + 5(-1)^n \\ -3(7)^n + 3(-1)^n & 3(7)^n + 5(-1)^n \end{bmatrix}$.

SECTION 7.3   *ORTHOGONAL DIAGONALIZATION*

39. $0 = |\lambda I - A| = \begin{vmatrix} \lambda - 4 & -3 \\ -3 & \lambda + 4 \end{vmatrix} = \lambda^2 - 16 - 9 = \lambda^2 - 25 = (\lambda - 5)(\lambda + 5)$

For $\lambda_1 = 5$, dimension $= 1$; and for $\lambda_2 = -5$, dimension $= 1$.

40. $0 = |\lambda I - A| = \begin{vmatrix} \lambda + 1 & 0 & -2 \\ 0 & \lambda - 1 & -2 \\ -2 & -2 & \lambda \end{vmatrix} = (\lambda + 1)(\lambda^2 - \lambda - 4) - 2(2\lambda - 2)$

$= (\lambda^3 - 5\lambda - 4) + (-4\lambda + 4) = \lambda^3 - 9\lambda = \lambda(\lambda^2 - 9) = \lambda(\lambda - 3)(\lambda + 3)$

For $\lambda_1 = 0$, dimension $= 1$; for $\lambda_2 = 3$, dimension $= 1$; and for $\lambda_3 = -3$, dimension $= 1$.

41. $0 = |\lambda I - A| = \begin{vmatrix} \lambda - 5 & 2 & -4 \\ 2 & \lambda - 8 & -2 \\ -4 & -2 & \lambda - 5 \end{vmatrix}$

$= (\lambda - 5)(\lambda^2 - 13\lambda + 36) - 2(2\lambda - 18) - 4(4\lambda - 36)$

$= (\lambda - 5)(\lambda - 4)(\lambda - 9) - 4(\lambda - 9) - 16(\lambda - 9)$

$= (\lambda - 9)[(\lambda - 5)(\lambda - 4) - 4 - 16] = (\lambda - 9)(\lambda^2 - 9\lambda) = \lambda(\lambda - 9)^2$.

For $\lambda_1 = 0$, dimension $= 1$; and for $\lambda_2 = 9$, dimension $= 2$.

42. $0 = |\lambda I - A| = \begin{vmatrix} \lambda - 2 & 0 & 0 & 0 \\ 0 & \lambda - 2 & 0 & 0 \\ 0 & 0 & \lambda - 2 & -2 \\ 0 & 0 & -2 & \lambda - 3 \end{vmatrix} = (\lambda - 2)(\lambda - 2)[(\lambda - 2)(\lambda - 3) - (-2)(-2)]$

$$= (\lambda - 2)^2(\lambda^2 - 5\lambda + 2)$$

For $\lambda_1 = 2$, dimension = 2.

For $\lambda_2 = \dfrac{5 + \sqrt{25 - 4(2)}}{2} = \dfrac{5 + \sqrt{17}}{2}$, dimension = 1.

For $\lambda_3 = \dfrac{5 - \sqrt{17}}{2}$, dimension = 1.

43. $0 = |\lambda I - A| = \begin{vmatrix} \lambda - 3 & -4 \\ -4 & \lambda + 3 \end{vmatrix} = (\lambda^2 - 9) - 16 = \lambda^2 - 25 = (\lambda - 5)(\lambda + 5)$ so $\lambda = 5, -5$.

$\lambda_1 = 5 \longrightarrow \begin{bmatrix} 2 & -4 & 0 \\ -4 & 8 & 0 \end{bmatrix} \longrightarrow \begin{bmatrix} 1 & -2 & 0 \\ 0 & 0 & 0 \end{bmatrix}$

Let $x_2 = s$;

then $x_1 - 2x_2 = 0$, i.e., $x_1 = 2x_2 = 2s$

so $\begin{bmatrix} x_1 \\ x_2 \end{bmatrix} = \begin{bmatrix} 2s \\ s \end{bmatrix} = s\begin{bmatrix} 2 \\ 1 \end{bmatrix}$, i.e., $B_1 = \left\{ \begin{bmatrix} 2 \\ 1 \end{bmatrix} \right\}$.

$\begin{bmatrix} 2 \\ 1 \end{bmatrix} \Big/ \left\| \begin{bmatrix} 2 \\ 1 \end{bmatrix} \right\| = \begin{bmatrix} 2 \\ 1 \end{bmatrix} \Big/ \sqrt{5} = \begin{bmatrix} 2/\sqrt{5} \\ 1/\sqrt{5} \end{bmatrix}$.

$\lambda_2 = -5 \longrightarrow \begin{bmatrix} -8 & -4 & 0 \\ -4 & -2 & 0 \end{bmatrix} \longrightarrow \begin{bmatrix} 1 & 1/2 & 0 \\ 0 & 0 & 0 \end{bmatrix}$

Let $x_2 = t$;

then $x_1 + (1/2)x_2 = 0$, i.e., $x_1 = \dfrac{-1}{2}x_2 = \dfrac{-1}{2}t$

so $\begin{bmatrix} x_1 \\ x_2 \end{bmatrix} = \begin{bmatrix} \frac{-1}{2}t \\ t \end{bmatrix} = t\begin{bmatrix} \frac{-1}{2} \\ 1 \end{bmatrix} = \frac{1}{2}t\begin{bmatrix} -1 \\ 2 \end{bmatrix}$, i.e., $B_2 = \left\{ \begin{bmatrix} -1 \\ 2 \end{bmatrix} \right\}$.

$\begin{bmatrix} -1 \\ 2 \end{bmatrix} \Big/ \left\| \begin{bmatrix} -1 \\ 2 \end{bmatrix} \right\| = \begin{bmatrix} -1 \\ 2 \end{bmatrix} \Big/ \sqrt{5} = \begin{bmatrix} -1/\sqrt{5} \\ 2/\sqrt{5} \end{bmatrix}$.

$P = \begin{bmatrix} 2/\sqrt{5} & -1/\sqrt{5} \\ 1/\sqrt{5} & 2/\sqrt{5} \end{bmatrix} = \frac{1}{\sqrt{5}}\begin{bmatrix} 2 & -1 \\ 1 & 2 \end{bmatrix}$, $P^{-1} = P^T = \frac{1}{\sqrt{5}}\begin{bmatrix} 2 & 1 \\ -1 & 2 \end{bmatrix}$

$P^{-1}AP = \frac{1}{\sqrt{5}}\begin{bmatrix} 2 & 1 \\ -1 & 2 \end{bmatrix}\begin{bmatrix} 3 & 4 \\ 4 & -3 \end{bmatrix}\frac{1}{\sqrt{5}}\begin{bmatrix} 2 & -1 \\ 1 & 2 \end{bmatrix} = \frac{1}{5}\begin{bmatrix} 2 & 1 \\ -1 & 2 \end{bmatrix}\begin{bmatrix} 10 & 5 \\ 5 & -10 \end{bmatrix}$

$$= \frac{1}{5}\begin{bmatrix} 25 & 0 \\ 0 & -25 \end{bmatrix} = \begin{bmatrix} 5 & 0 \\ 0 & -5 \end{bmatrix}.$$

44. $0 = |\lambda I - A| = \begin{vmatrix} \lambda - 5 & -2 \\ -2 & \lambda - 2 \end{vmatrix} = (\lambda^2 - 7\lambda + 10) - 4 = \lambda^2 - 7\lambda + 6 = (\lambda - 1)(\lambda - 6)$

so $\quad \lambda = 1, 6.$

$$\lambda_1 = 1 \longrightarrow \begin{bmatrix} -4 & -2 & 0 \\ -2 & -1 & 0 \end{bmatrix} \longrightarrow \begin{bmatrix} 1 & 1/2 & 0 \\ 0 & 0 & 0 \end{bmatrix}$$

Let $\quad x_2 = s;$

then $\quad x_1 + \dfrac{1}{2} x_2 = 0 \quad$, i.e., $\quad x_1 = \dfrac{-1}{2} x_2 = \dfrac{-1}{2} s$

so $\quad \begin{bmatrix} x_1 \\ x_2 \end{bmatrix} = \begin{bmatrix} \frac{-1}{2} s \\ s \end{bmatrix} = s \begin{bmatrix} \frac{-1}{2} \\ 1 \end{bmatrix} = \dfrac{1}{2} s \begin{bmatrix} -1 \\ 2 \end{bmatrix} \quad$, i.e., $\quad B_1 = \left\{ \begin{bmatrix} -1 \\ 2 \end{bmatrix} \right\}.$

$$\begin{bmatrix} -1 \\ 2 \end{bmatrix} \Big/ \left\| \begin{bmatrix} -1 \\ 2 \end{bmatrix} \right\| = \begin{bmatrix} -1 \\ 2 \end{bmatrix} \Big/ \sqrt{5} = \begin{bmatrix} -1/\sqrt{5} \\ 2/\sqrt{5} \end{bmatrix}.$$

$$\lambda_2 = 6 \longrightarrow \begin{bmatrix} 1 & -2 & 0 \\ -2 & 4 & 0 \end{bmatrix} \longrightarrow \begin{bmatrix} 1 & -2 & 0 \\ 0 & 0 & 0 \end{bmatrix}$$

Let $\quad x_2 = t;$

then $\quad x_1 - 2x_2 = 0 \quad$, i.e., $\quad x_1 = 2x_2 = 2t$

so $\quad \begin{bmatrix} x_1 \\ x_2 \end{bmatrix} = \begin{bmatrix} 2t \\ t \end{bmatrix} = t \begin{bmatrix} 2 \\ 1 \end{bmatrix} \quad$, i.e., $\quad B_2 = \left\{ \begin{bmatrix} 2 \\ 1 \end{bmatrix} \right\}.$

$$\begin{bmatrix} 2 \\ 1 \end{bmatrix} \Big/ \left\| \begin{bmatrix} 2 \\ 1 \end{bmatrix} \right\| = \begin{bmatrix} 2 \\ 1 \end{bmatrix} \Big/ \sqrt{5} = \begin{bmatrix} 2/\sqrt{5} \\ 1/\sqrt{5} \end{bmatrix}.$$

$$P = \begin{bmatrix} -1/\sqrt{5} & 2/\sqrt{5} \\ 2/\sqrt{5} & 1/\sqrt{5} \end{bmatrix} = \dfrac{1}{\sqrt{5}} \begin{bmatrix} -1 & 2 \\ 2 & 1 \end{bmatrix} \quad, \quad P^{-1} = P^T = \dfrac{1}{\sqrt{5}} \begin{bmatrix} -1 & 2 \\ 2 & 1 \end{bmatrix}$$

$$P^{-1}AP = \dfrac{1}{\sqrt{5}} \begin{bmatrix} -1 & 2 \\ 2 & 1 \end{bmatrix} \begin{bmatrix} 5 & 2 \\ 2 & 2 \end{bmatrix} \dfrac{1}{\sqrt{5}} \begin{bmatrix} -1 & 2 \\ 2 & 1 \end{bmatrix} = \dfrac{1}{5} \begin{bmatrix} -1 & 2 \\ 2 & 1 \end{bmatrix} \begin{bmatrix} -1 & 12 \\ 2 & 6 \end{bmatrix}$$

$$= \dfrac{1}{5} \begin{bmatrix} 5 & 0 \\ 0 & 30 \end{bmatrix} = \begin{bmatrix} 1 & 0 \\ 0 & 6 \end{bmatrix}$$

45. $0 = |\lambda I - A| = \begin{vmatrix} \lambda - 13 & 5 \\ 5 & \lambda - 13 \end{vmatrix} = (\lambda^2 - 26\lambda + 169) - 25 = \lambda^2 - 26\lambda + 144$

$= (\lambda - 8)(\lambda - 18) \quad$ so $\quad \lambda = 8, 18$

$$\lambda_1 = 8 \longrightarrow \begin{bmatrix} -5 & 5 & 0 \\ 5 & -5 & 0 \end{bmatrix} \longrightarrow \begin{bmatrix} 1 & -1 & 0 \\ 0 & 0 & 0 \end{bmatrix}$$

Let $x_2 = s$;

then $x_1 - x_2 = 0$, i.e., $x_1 = x_2 = s$

so $\begin{bmatrix} x_1 \\ x_2 \end{bmatrix} = \begin{bmatrix} s \\ s \end{bmatrix} = s \begin{bmatrix} 1 \\ 1 \end{bmatrix}$, i.e., $B_1 = \left\{ \begin{bmatrix} 1 \\ 1 \end{bmatrix} \right\}$.

$$\begin{bmatrix} 1 \\ 1 \end{bmatrix} \bigg/ \left\| \begin{bmatrix} 1 \\ 1 \end{bmatrix} \right\| = \begin{bmatrix} 1 \\ 1 \end{bmatrix} \bigg/ \sqrt{2} = \begin{bmatrix} 1/\sqrt{2} \\ 1/\sqrt{2} \end{bmatrix}.$$

$$\lambda_2 = 18 \longrightarrow \begin{bmatrix} 5 & 5 & 0 \\ 5 & 5 & 0 \end{bmatrix} \longrightarrow \begin{bmatrix} 1 & 1 & 0 \\ 0 & 0 & 0 \end{bmatrix}$$

Let $x_2 = t$;

then $x_1 + x_2 = 0$, i.e., $x_1 = -x_2 = -t$

so $\begin{bmatrix} x_1 \\ x_2 \end{bmatrix} = \begin{bmatrix} -t \\ t \end{bmatrix} = t \begin{bmatrix} -1 \\ 1 \end{bmatrix}$, i.e., $B_2 = \left\{ \begin{bmatrix} -1 \\ 1 \end{bmatrix} \right\}$.

$$\begin{bmatrix} -1 \\ 1 \end{bmatrix} \bigg/ \left\| \begin{bmatrix} -1 \\ 1 \end{bmatrix} \right\| = \begin{bmatrix} -1 \\ 1 \end{bmatrix} \bigg/ \sqrt{2} = \begin{bmatrix} -1/\sqrt{2} \\ 1/\sqrt{2} \end{bmatrix}.$$

$$P = \begin{bmatrix} 1/\sqrt{2} & -1/\sqrt{2} \\ 1/\sqrt{2} & 1/\sqrt{2} \end{bmatrix} = \frac{1}{\sqrt{2}} \begin{bmatrix} 1 & -1 \\ 1 & 1 \end{bmatrix} , \quad P^{-1} = P^T = \frac{1}{\sqrt{2}} \begin{bmatrix} 1 & 1 \\ -1 & 1 \end{bmatrix}$$

$$P^{-1}AP = \frac{1}{\sqrt{2}} \begin{bmatrix} 1 & 1 \\ -1 & 1 \end{bmatrix} \begin{bmatrix} 13 & -5 \\ -5 & 13 \end{bmatrix} \frac{1}{\sqrt{2}} \begin{bmatrix} 1 & -1 \\ 1 & 1 \end{bmatrix} = \frac{1}{2} \begin{bmatrix} 1 & 1 \\ -1 & 1 \end{bmatrix} \begin{bmatrix} 8 & -18 \\ 8 & 18 \end{bmatrix}$$

$$= \frac{1}{2} \begin{bmatrix} 16 & 0 \\ 0 & 36 \end{bmatrix} = \begin{bmatrix} 8 & 0 \\ 0 & 18 \end{bmatrix}$$

46. $0 = |\lambda I - A| = \begin{vmatrix} \lambda+1 & -2 & 0 \\ -2 & \lambda & -2 \\ 0 & -2 & \lambda-1 \end{vmatrix} = (\lambda+1)(\lambda^2 - \lambda - 4) + 2(-2\lambda + 2)$

$\quad = (\lambda^3 - 5\lambda - 4) + (-4\lambda + 4) = \lambda^3 - 9\lambda = \lambda(\lambda^2 - 9)$

$\quad = \lambda(\lambda - 3)(\lambda + 3)$ so $\lambda = 0, 3, -3$

$$\lambda_1 = 0 \longrightarrow \begin{bmatrix} 1 & -2 & 0 & 0 \\ -2 & 0 & -2 & 0 \\ 0 & -2 & -1 & 0 \end{bmatrix} \longrightarrow \begin{bmatrix} 1 & -2 & 0 & 0 \\ 0 & -4 & -2 & 0 \\ 0 & -2 & -1 & 0 \end{bmatrix} \longrightarrow \begin{bmatrix} 1 & 0 & 1 & 0 \\ 0 & 1 & 1/2 & 0 \\ 0 & 0 & 0 & 0 \end{bmatrix}$$

Let $x_3 = r$;

then $x_2 + \frac{1}{2}x_3 = 0$, i.e., $x_2 = \frac{-1}{2}x_3 = \frac{-1}{2}r$

and $x_1 + x_3 = 0$, i.e., $x_1 = -x_3 = -r$

so $\begin{bmatrix} x_1 \\ x_2 \\ x_3 \end{bmatrix} = \begin{bmatrix} -r \\ (-1/2)r \\ r \end{bmatrix} = r \begin{bmatrix} -1 \\ -1/2 \\ 1 \end{bmatrix} = \frac{1}{2}r \begin{bmatrix} -2 \\ -1 \\ 2 \end{bmatrix}$, i.e., $B_1 = \left\{ \begin{bmatrix} -2 \\ -1 \\ 2 \end{bmatrix} \right\}$.

$$(-2,-1,2)/\|(-2,-1,2)\| = (-2,-1,2)/\sqrt{9} = (-2/3,-1/3,2/3).$$

$$\lambda_2 = 3 \longrightarrow \begin{bmatrix} 4 & -2 & 0 & 0 \\ -2 & 3 & -2 & 0 \\ 0 & -2 & 2 & 0 \end{bmatrix} \longrightarrow \begin{bmatrix} 1 & -1/2 & 0 & 0 \\ 0 & 2 & -2 & 0 \\ 0 & -2 & 2 & 0 \end{bmatrix} \longrightarrow \begin{bmatrix} 1 & 0 & -1/2 & 0 \\ 0 & 1 & -1 & 0 \\ 0 & 0 & 0 & 0 \end{bmatrix}$$

Let $x_3 = s$;

then $x_2 - x_3 = 0$, i.e., $x_2 = x_3 = s$

and $x_1 - \dfrac{1}{2}x_3 = 0$, i.e., $x_1 = \dfrac{1}{2}x_3 = \dfrac{1}{2}s$

so $\begin{bmatrix} x_1 \\ x_2 \\ x_3 \end{bmatrix} = \begin{bmatrix} (1/2)s \\ s \\ s \end{bmatrix} = s\begin{bmatrix} 1/2 \\ 1 \\ 1 \end{bmatrix} = \dfrac{1}{2}s\begin{bmatrix} 1 \\ 2 \\ 2 \end{bmatrix}$, i.e., $B_2 = \left\{ \begin{bmatrix} 1 \\ 2 \\ 2 \end{bmatrix} \right\}.$

$$(1,2,2)/\|(1,2,2)\| = (1,2,2)/\sqrt{9} = (1/3,2/3,2/3).$$

$$\lambda_3 = -3 \longrightarrow \begin{bmatrix} -2 & -2 & 0 & 0 \\ -2 & -3 & -2 & 0 \\ 0 & -2 & -4 & 0 \end{bmatrix} \longrightarrow \begin{bmatrix} 1 & 1 & 0 & 0 \\ 0 & -1 & -2 & 0 \\ 0 & -2 & -4 & 0 \end{bmatrix} \longrightarrow \begin{bmatrix} 1 & 0 & -2 & 0 \\ 0 & 1 & 2 & 0 \\ 0 & 0 & 0 & 0 \end{bmatrix}$$

Let $x_3 = t$;

then $x_2 + 2x_3 = 0$, i.e., $x_2 = -2x_3 = -2t$

and $x_1 - 2x_3 = 0$, i.e., $x_1 = 2x_3 = 2t$

so $\begin{bmatrix} x_1 \\ x_2 \\ x_3 \end{bmatrix} = \begin{bmatrix} 2t \\ -2t \\ t \end{bmatrix} = t\begin{bmatrix} 2 \\ -2 \\ 1 \end{bmatrix}$, i.e., $B_3 = \left\{ \begin{bmatrix} 2 \\ -2 \\ 1 \end{bmatrix} \right\}.$

$$(2,-2,1)/\|(2,-2,1)\| = (2,-2,1)/\sqrt{9} = (2/3,-2/3,1/3).$$

$$P = \begin{bmatrix} -2/3 & 1/3 & 2/3 \\ -1/3 & 2/3 & -2/3 \\ 2/3 & 2/3 & 1/3 \end{bmatrix} = \tfrac{1}{3}\begin{bmatrix} -2 & 1 & 2 \\ -1 & 2 & -2 \\ 2 & 2 & 1 \end{bmatrix} \quad , \quad P^{-1} = P^T = \tfrac{1}{3}\begin{bmatrix} -2 & -1 & 2 \\ 1 & 2 & 2 \\ 2 & -2 & 1 \end{bmatrix}$$

$$P^{-1}AP = \frac{1}{3}\begin{bmatrix} -2 & -1 & 2 \\ 1 & 2 & 2 \\ 2 & -2 & 1 \end{bmatrix}\begin{bmatrix} -1 & 2 & 0 \\ 2 & 0 & 2 \\ 0 & 2 & 1 \end{bmatrix}\frac{1}{3}\begin{bmatrix} -2 & 1 & 2 \\ -1 & 2 & -2 \\ 2 & 2 & 1 \end{bmatrix}$$

$$= \frac{1}{9}\begin{bmatrix} -2 & -1 & 2 \\ 1 & 2 & 2 \\ 2 & -2 & 1 \end{bmatrix}\begin{bmatrix} 0 & 3 & -6 \\ 0 & 6 & 6 \\ 0 & 6 & -3 \end{bmatrix} = \frac{1}{9}\begin{bmatrix} 0 & 0 & 0 \\ 0 & 27 & 0 \\ 0 & 0 & -27 \end{bmatrix} = \begin{bmatrix} 0 & 0 & 0 \\ 0 & 3 & 0 \\ 0 & 0 & -3 \end{bmatrix}$$

47. $0 = |\lambda I - A| = \begin{vmatrix} \lambda - 1 & -1 & -1 \\ -1 & \lambda - 1 & -1 \\ -1 & -1 & \lambda - 1 \end{vmatrix}$

$$= (\lambda - 1)(\lambda^2 - 2\lambda + 1 - 1) + 1(-\lambda + 1 - 1) - 1(1 + \lambda - 1)$$

$$= (\lambda - 1)(\lambda^2 - 2\lambda) + 1(-\lambda) - 1(\lambda)$$

$$= (\lambda^3 - 3\lambda^2 + 2\lambda) - \lambda - \lambda = \lambda^3 - 3\lambda^2 = \lambda^2(\lambda - 3) \quad \text{so} \quad \lambda = 0, 0, 3$$

$$\lambda_1 = 0 \longrightarrow \begin{bmatrix} -1 & -1 & -1 & 0 \\ -1 & -1 & -1 & 0 \\ -1 & -1 & -1 & 0 \end{bmatrix} \longrightarrow \begin{bmatrix} 1 & 1 & 1 & 0 \\ 0 & 0 & 0 & 0 \\ 0 & 0 & 0 & 0 \end{bmatrix}$$

Let $x_3 = s$ and $x_2 = r$;

then $x_1 + x_2 + x_3 = 0$, i.e., $x_1 = -x_2 - x_3 = -r - s$

so $\begin{bmatrix} x_1 \\ x_2 \\ x_3 \end{bmatrix} = \begin{bmatrix} -r - s \\ r \\ s \end{bmatrix} = \begin{bmatrix} -r \\ r \\ 0 \end{bmatrix} + \begin{bmatrix} -s \\ 0 \\ s \end{bmatrix} = r \begin{bmatrix} -1 \\ 1 \\ 0 \end{bmatrix} + s \begin{bmatrix} -1 \\ 0 \\ 1 \end{bmatrix}$,

i.e., $B_1 = \left\{ \begin{bmatrix} -1 \\ 1 \\ 0 \end{bmatrix}, \begin{bmatrix} -1 \\ 0 \\ 1 \end{bmatrix} \right\}$

$$(-1, 0, 1) - \frac{(-1, 0, 1) \cdot (-1, 1, 0)}{(-1, 1, 0) \cdot (-1, 1, 0)}(-1, 1, 0) = (-1, 0, 1) - \frac{1}{2}(-1, 1, 0) =$$

$$\left(\frac{-1}{2}, \frac{-1}{2}, 1 \right) = \frac{-1}{2}(1, 1, -2)$$

$$(-1, 1, 0)/\|(-1, 1, 0)\| = (-1, 1, 0)/\sqrt{2} = \left(\frac{-1}{\sqrt{2}}, \frac{1}{\sqrt{2}}, 0 \right)$$

$$(1, 1, -2)/\|(1, 1, -2)\| = (1, 1, -2)/\sqrt{6} = \left(\frac{1}{\sqrt{6}}, \frac{1}{\sqrt{6}}, \frac{-2}{\sqrt{6}} \right)$$

$$\lambda_2 = 3 \longrightarrow \begin{bmatrix} 2 & -1 & -1 & 0 \\ -1 & 2 & -1 & 0 \\ -1 & -1 & 2 & 0 \end{bmatrix} \longrightarrow \begin{bmatrix} 1 & -1/2 & -1/2 & 0 \\ 0 & 3/2 & -3/2 & 0 \\ 0 & -3/2 & 3/2 & 0 \end{bmatrix} \longrightarrow \begin{bmatrix} 1 & 0 & -1 & 0 \\ 0 & 1 & -1 & 0 \\ 0 & 0 & 0 & 0 \end{bmatrix}$$

Let $x_3 = t$;

then $x_2 - x_3 = 0$, i.e., $x_2 = x_3 = t$

and $x_1 - x_3 = 0$, i.e., $x_1 = x_3 = t$

so $\begin{bmatrix} x_1 \\ x_2 \\ x_3 \end{bmatrix} = \begin{bmatrix} t \\ t \\ t \end{bmatrix} = t \begin{bmatrix} 1 \\ 1 \\ 1 \end{bmatrix}$, i.e., $B_2 = \left\{ \begin{bmatrix} 1 \\ 1 \\ 1 \end{bmatrix} \right\}$.

$$(1, 1, 1)/\|(1, 1, 1)\| = (1, 1, 1)/\sqrt{3} = \left(\frac{1}{\sqrt{3}}, \frac{1}{\sqrt{3}}, \frac{1}{\sqrt{3}} \right).$$

$$P = \begin{bmatrix} \frac{-1}{\sqrt{2}} & \frac{1}{\sqrt{6}} & \frac{1}{\sqrt{3}} \\ \frac{1}{\sqrt{2}} & \frac{1}{\sqrt{6}} & \frac{1}{\sqrt{3}} \\ 0 & \frac{-2}{\sqrt{6}} & \frac{1}{\sqrt{3}} \end{bmatrix} \quad , \quad P^{-1} = P^T = \begin{bmatrix} \frac{-1}{\sqrt{2}} & \frac{1}{\sqrt{2}} & 0 \\ \frac{1}{\sqrt{6}} & \frac{1}{\sqrt{6}} & \frac{-2}{\sqrt{6}} \\ \frac{1}{\sqrt{3}} & \frac{1}{\sqrt{3}} & \frac{1}{\sqrt{3}} \end{bmatrix}$$

$$P^{-1}AP = \begin{bmatrix} \frac{-1}{\sqrt{2}} & \frac{1}{\sqrt{2}} & 0 \\ \frac{1}{\sqrt{6}} & \frac{1}{\sqrt{6}} & \frac{-2}{\sqrt{6}} \\ \frac{1}{\sqrt{3}} & \frac{1}{\sqrt{3}} & \frac{1}{\sqrt{3}} \end{bmatrix} \begin{bmatrix} 1 & 1 & 1 \\ 1 & 1 & 1 \\ 1 & 1 & 1 \end{bmatrix} \begin{bmatrix} \frac{-1}{\sqrt{2}} & \frac{1}{\sqrt{6}} & \frac{1}{\sqrt{3}} \\ \frac{1}{\sqrt{2}} & \frac{1}{\sqrt{6}} & \frac{1}{\sqrt{3}} \\ 0 & \frac{-2}{\sqrt{6}} & \frac{1}{\sqrt{3}} \end{bmatrix}$$

$$= \begin{bmatrix} \frac{-1}{\sqrt{2}} & \frac{1}{\sqrt{2}} & 0 \\ \frac{1}{\sqrt{6}} & \frac{1}{\sqrt{6}} & \frac{-2}{\sqrt{6}} \\ \frac{1}{\sqrt{3}} & \frac{1}{\sqrt{3}} & \frac{1}{\sqrt{3}} \end{bmatrix} \begin{bmatrix} 0 & 0 & \frac{3}{\sqrt{3}} \\ 0 & 0 & \frac{3}{\sqrt{3}} \\ 0 & 0 & \frac{3}{\sqrt{3}} \end{bmatrix}$$

$$= \begin{bmatrix} 0 & 0 & 0 \\ 0 & 0 & 0 \\ 0 & 0 & 3 \end{bmatrix}$$

48. $0 = |\lambda I - A| = \begin{vmatrix} \lambda & -2 & -2 \\ -2 & \lambda & -2 \\ -2 & -2 & \lambda \end{vmatrix} = \lambda(\lambda^2 - 4) + 2(-2\lambda - 4) - 2(4 + 2\lambda)$

$\qquad = \lambda(\lambda - 2)(\lambda + 2) + -4(\lambda + 2) + -4(\lambda + 2)$

$\qquad = (\lambda + 2)[\lambda(\lambda - 2) + -4 + -4] = (\lambda + 2)(\lambda^2 - 2\lambda - 8)$

$\qquad = (\lambda + 2)(\lambda + 2)(\lambda - 4) \quad \text{so} \quad \lambda = -2, -2, 4$

$$\lambda_1 = -2 \longrightarrow \begin{bmatrix} -2 & -2 & -2 & 0 \\ -2 & -2 & -2 & 0 \\ -2 & -2 & -2 & 0 \end{bmatrix} \longrightarrow \begin{bmatrix} 1 & 1 & 1 & 0 \\ 0 & 0 & 0 & 0 \\ 0 & 0 & 0 & 0 \end{bmatrix}$$

Let $x_3 = s$ and $x_2 = r$;

then $x_1 + x_2 + x_3 = 0$, i.e., $x_1 = -x_2 - x_3 = -r - s$

so $\begin{bmatrix} x_1 \\ x_2 \\ x_3 \end{bmatrix} = \begin{bmatrix} -r-s \\ r \\ s \end{bmatrix} = \begin{bmatrix} -r \\ r \\ 0 \end{bmatrix} + \begin{bmatrix} -s \\ 0 \\ s \end{bmatrix} = r \begin{bmatrix} -1 \\ 1 \\ 0 \end{bmatrix} + s \begin{bmatrix} -1 \\ 0 \\ 1 \end{bmatrix}$,

i.e., $B_1 = \left\{ \begin{bmatrix} -1 \\ 1 \\ 0 \end{bmatrix}, \begin{bmatrix} -1 \\ 0 \\ 1 \end{bmatrix} \right\}$

$$(-1,0,1) - \frac{(-1,0,1)\cdot(-1,1,0)}{(-1,1,0)\cdot(-1,1,0)}(-1,1,0) = (-1,0,1) - \frac{1}{2}(-1,1,0) =$$

$$\left(\frac{-1}{2}, \frac{-1}{2}, 1\right) = \frac{-1}{2}(1,1,-2)$$

$$(-1,1,0)/\|(-1,1,0)\| = (-1,1,0)/\sqrt{2} = \left(\frac{-1}{\sqrt{2}}, \frac{1}{\sqrt{2}}, 0\right)$$

$$(1,1,-2)/\|(1,1,-2)\| = (1,1,-2)/\sqrt{6} = \left(\frac{1}{\sqrt{6}}, \frac{1}{\sqrt{6}}, \frac{-2}{\sqrt{6}}\right)$$

$$\lambda_2 = 4 \longrightarrow \begin{bmatrix} 4 & -2 & -2 & 0 \\ -2 & 4 & -2 & 0 \\ -2 & -2 & 4 & 0 \end{bmatrix} \longrightarrow \begin{bmatrix} 1 & -1/2 & -1/2 & 0 \\ 0 & 3 & -3 & 0 \\ 0 & -3 & 3 & 0 \end{bmatrix} \longrightarrow \begin{bmatrix} 1 & 0 & -1 & 0 \\ 0 & 1 & -1 & 0 \\ 0 & 0 & 0 & 0 \end{bmatrix}$$

Let $x_3 = t$;

then $x_2 - x_3 = 0$, i.e., $x_2 = x_3 = t$

and $x_1 - x_3 = 0$, i.e., $x_1 = x_3 = t$

so $\begin{bmatrix} x_1 \\ x_2 \\ x_3 \end{bmatrix} = \begin{bmatrix} t \\ t \\ t \end{bmatrix} = t\begin{bmatrix} 1 \\ 1 \\ 1 \end{bmatrix}$, i.e., $B_2 = \left\{ \begin{bmatrix} 1 \\ 1 \\ 1 \end{bmatrix} \right\}$.

$$(1,1,1)/\|(1,1,1)\| = (1,1,1)/\sqrt{3} = \left(\frac{1}{\sqrt{3}}, \frac{1}{\sqrt{3}}, \frac{1}{\sqrt{3}}\right).$$

$$P = \begin{bmatrix} \frac{-1}{\sqrt{2}} & \frac{1}{\sqrt{6}} & \frac{1}{\sqrt{3}} \\ \frac{1}{\sqrt{2}} & \frac{1}{\sqrt{6}} & \frac{1}{\sqrt{3}} \\ 0 & \frac{-2}{\sqrt{6}} & \frac{1}{\sqrt{3}} \end{bmatrix} \quad , \quad P^{-1} = P^T = \begin{bmatrix} \frac{-1}{\sqrt{2}} & \frac{1}{\sqrt{2}} & 0 \\ \frac{1}{\sqrt{6}} & \frac{1}{\sqrt{6}} & \frac{-2}{\sqrt{6}} \\ \frac{1}{\sqrt{3}} & \frac{1}{\sqrt{3}} & \frac{1}{\sqrt{3}} \end{bmatrix}$$

$$P^{-1}AP = \begin{bmatrix} \frac{-1}{\sqrt{2}} & \frac{1}{\sqrt{2}} & 0 \\ \frac{1}{\sqrt{6}} & \frac{1}{\sqrt{6}} & \frac{-2}{\sqrt{6}} \\ \frac{1}{\sqrt{3}} & \frac{1}{\sqrt{3}} & \frac{1}{\sqrt{3}} \end{bmatrix} \begin{bmatrix} 0 & 2 & 2 \\ 2 & 0 & 2 \\ 2 & 2 & 0 \end{bmatrix} \begin{bmatrix} \frac{-1}{\sqrt{2}} & \frac{1}{\sqrt{6}} & \frac{1}{\sqrt{3}} \\ \frac{1}{\sqrt{2}} & \frac{1}{\sqrt{6}} & \frac{1}{\sqrt{3}} \\ 0 & \frac{-2}{\sqrt{6}} & \frac{1}{\sqrt{3}} \end{bmatrix}$$

$$= \begin{bmatrix} \frac{-1}{\sqrt{2}} & \frac{1}{\sqrt{2}} & 0 \\ \frac{1}{\sqrt{6}} & \frac{1}{\sqrt{6}} & \frac{-2}{\sqrt{6}} \\ \frac{1}{\sqrt{3}} & \frac{1}{\sqrt{3}} & \frac{1}{\sqrt{3}} \end{bmatrix} \begin{bmatrix} \frac{2}{\sqrt{2}} & \frac{-2}{\sqrt{6}} & \frac{4}{\sqrt{3}} \\ \frac{-2}{\sqrt{2}} & \frac{-2}{\sqrt{6}} & \frac{4}{\sqrt{3}} \\ 0 & \frac{4}{\sqrt{6}} & \frac{4}{\sqrt{3}} \end{bmatrix} = \begin{bmatrix} -2 & 0 & 0 \\ 0 & -2 & 0 \\ 0 & 0 & 4 \end{bmatrix}$$

49. $0 = |\lambda I - A| = \begin{vmatrix} \lambda - 1 & -1 & 0 & 0 \\ -1 & \lambda - 1 & 0 & 0 \\ 0 & 0 & \lambda - 1 & -2 \\ 0 & 0 & -2 & \lambda - 1 \end{vmatrix}$

$\quad = [(\lambda - 1)(\lambda - 1) - (-1)(-1)][(\lambda - 1)(\lambda - 1) - (-2)(-2)]$

$\quad = (\lambda^2 - 2\lambda)(\lambda^2 - 2\lambda - 3) = \lambda(\lambda - 2)(\lambda - 3)(\lambda + 1)$ so $\lambda = 0, 2, 3, -1$

172

$$\lambda_1 = 0 \longrightarrow \begin{bmatrix} -1 & -1 & 0 & 0 & 0 \\ -1 & -1 & 0 & 0 & 0 \\ 0 & 0 & -1 & -2 & 0 \\ 0 & 0 & -2 & -1 & 0 \end{bmatrix} \longrightarrow \begin{bmatrix} 1 & 1 & 0 & 0 & 0 \\ 0 & 0 & 0 & 0 & 0 \\ 0 & 0 & 1 & 2 & 0 \\ 0 & 0 & 0 & 3 & 0 \end{bmatrix} \longrightarrow \begin{bmatrix} 1 & 1 & 0 & 0 & 0 \\ 0 & 0 & 1 & 0 & 0 \\ 0 & 0 & 0 & 1 & 0 \\ 0 & 0 & 0 & 0 & 0 \end{bmatrix}$$

Let $x_2 = q$;

then $x_1 + x_2 = 0$, i.e., $x_1 = -x_2 = -q$

and $x_3 = 0$ and $x_4 = 0$

so $\begin{bmatrix} x_1 \\ x_2 \\ x_3 \\ x_4 \end{bmatrix} = \begin{bmatrix} -q \\ q \\ 0 \\ 0 \end{bmatrix} = q \begin{bmatrix} -1 \\ 1 \\ 0 \\ 0 \end{bmatrix}$ i.e., $B_1 = \left\{ \begin{bmatrix} -1 \\ 1 \\ 0 \\ 0 \end{bmatrix} \right\}$

$$(-1,1,0,0)/\|(-1,1,0,0)\| = (-1,1,0,0)/\sqrt{2} = \left(\tfrac{-1}{\sqrt{2}}, \tfrac{1}{\sqrt{2}}, 0, 0 \right).$$

$$\lambda_2 = 2 \longrightarrow \begin{bmatrix} 1 & -1 & 0 & 0 & 0 \\ -1 & 1 & 0 & 0 & 0 \\ 0 & 0 & 1 & -2 & 0 \\ 0 & 0 & -2 & 1 & 0 \end{bmatrix} \longrightarrow \begin{bmatrix} 1 & -1 & 0 & 0 & 0 \\ 0 & 0 & 0 & 0 & 0 \\ 0 & 0 & 1 & -2 & 0 \\ 0 & 0 & 0 & -3 & 0 \end{bmatrix} \longrightarrow \begin{bmatrix} 1 & -1 & 0 & 0 & 0 \\ 0 & 0 & 1 & 0 & 0 \\ 0 & 0 & 0 & 1 & 0 \\ 0 & 0 & 0 & 0 & 0 \end{bmatrix}$$

Let $x_2 = r$;

then $x_1 - x_2 = 0$, i.e., $x_1 = x_2 = r$

and $x_3 = 0$ and $x_4 = 0$

so $\begin{bmatrix} x_1 \\ x_2 \\ x_3 \\ x_4 \end{bmatrix} = \begin{bmatrix} r \\ r \\ 0 \\ 0 \end{bmatrix} = r \begin{bmatrix} 1 \\ 1 \\ 0 \\ 0 \end{bmatrix}$ i.e., $B_2 = \left\{ \begin{bmatrix} 1 \\ 1 \\ 0 \\ 0 \end{bmatrix} \right\}$

$$(1,1,0,0)/\|(1,1,0,0)\| = (1,1,0,0)/\sqrt{2} = \left(\tfrac{1}{\sqrt{2}}, \tfrac{1}{\sqrt{2}}, 0, 0 \right).$$

$$\lambda_3 = 3 \longrightarrow \begin{bmatrix} 2 & -1 & 0 & 0 & 0 \\ -1 & 2 & 0 & 0 & 0 \\ 0 & 0 & 2 & -2 & 0 \\ 0 & 0 & -2 & 2 & 0 \end{bmatrix} \longrightarrow \begin{bmatrix} 1 & -2 & 0 & 0 & 0 \\ 2 & -1 & 0 & 0 & 0 \\ 0 & 0 & 2 & -2 & 0 \\ 0 & 0 & -2 & 2 & 0 \end{bmatrix} \longrightarrow$$

$$\begin{bmatrix} 1 & -2 & 0 & 0 & 0 \\ 0 & 3 & 0 & 0 & 0 \\ 0 & 0 & 2 & -2 & 0 \\ 0 & 0 & -2 & 2 & 0 \end{bmatrix} \longrightarrow \begin{bmatrix} 1 & 0 & 0 & 0 & 0 \\ 0 & 1 & 0 & 0 & 0 \\ 0 & 0 & 1 & -1 & 0 \\ 0 & 0 & 0 & 0 & 0 \end{bmatrix}$$

Let $x_4 = s$;

then $x_3 - x_4 = 0$, i.e., $x_3 = x_4 = s$

and $x_1 = 0$ and $x_2 = 0$

so $\begin{bmatrix} x_1 \\ x_2 \\ x_3 \\ x_4 \end{bmatrix} = \begin{bmatrix} 0 \\ 0 \\ s \\ s \end{bmatrix} = s \begin{bmatrix} 0 \\ 0 \\ 1 \\ 1 \end{bmatrix}$ i.e., $B_3 = \left\{ \begin{bmatrix} 0 \\ 0 \\ 1 \\ 1 \end{bmatrix} \right\}$

$$(0,0,1,1)/\|(0,0,1,1)\| = (0,0,1,1)/\sqrt{2} = \left(0,0,\tfrac{1}{\sqrt{2}},\tfrac{1}{\sqrt{2}}\right).$$

$$\lambda_4 = -1 \longrightarrow \begin{bmatrix} -2 & -1 & 0 & 0 & 0 \\ -1 & -2 & 0 & 0 & 0 \\ 0 & 0 & -2 & -2 & 0 \\ 0 & 0 & -2 & -2 & 0 \end{bmatrix} \longrightarrow \begin{bmatrix} -1 & -2 & 0 & 0 & 0 \\ -2 & -1 & 0 & 0 & 0 \\ 0 & 0 & -2 & -2 & 0 \\ 0 & 0 & -2 & -2 & 0 \end{bmatrix} \longrightarrow$$

$$\begin{bmatrix} 1 & 2 & 0 & 0 & 0 \\ 0 & 3 & 0 & 0 & 0 \\ 0 & 0 & -2 & -2 & 0 \\ 0 & 0 & -2 & -2 & 0 \end{bmatrix} \longrightarrow \begin{bmatrix} 1 & 0 & 0 & 0 & 0 \\ 0 & 1 & 0 & 0 & 0 \\ 0 & 0 & 1 & 1 & 0 \\ 0 & 0 & 0 & 0 & 0 \end{bmatrix}$$

Let $x_4 = t$;

then $x_3 + x_4 = 0$, i.e., $x_3 = -x_4 = -t$

and $x_1 = 0$ and $x_2 = 0$

so $\begin{bmatrix} x_1 \\ x_2 \\ x_3 \\ x_4 \end{bmatrix} = \begin{bmatrix} 0 \\ 0 \\ -t \\ t \end{bmatrix} = t \begin{bmatrix} 0 \\ 0 \\ -1 \\ 1 \end{bmatrix}$ i.e., $B_4 = \left\{ \begin{bmatrix} 0 \\ 0 \\ -1 \\ 1 \end{bmatrix} \right\}$

$$(0,0,-1,1)/\|(0,0,-1,1)\| = (0,0,-1,1)/\sqrt{2} = \left(0,0,\tfrac{-1}{\sqrt{2}},\tfrac{1}{\sqrt{2}}\right).$$

$$P = \begin{bmatrix} \frac{-1}{\sqrt{2}} & \frac{1}{\sqrt{2}} & 0 & 0 \\ \frac{1}{\sqrt{2}} & \frac{1}{\sqrt{2}} & 0 & 0 \\ 0 & 0 & \frac{1}{\sqrt{2}} & \frac{-1}{\sqrt{2}} \\ 0 & 0 & \frac{1}{\sqrt{2}} & \frac{1}{\sqrt{2}} \end{bmatrix} \quad , \quad P^{-1} = P^T = \begin{bmatrix} \frac{-1}{\sqrt{2}} & \frac{1}{\sqrt{2}} & 0 & 0 \\ \frac{1}{\sqrt{2}} & \frac{1}{\sqrt{2}} & 0 & 0 \\ 0 & 0 & \frac{1}{\sqrt{2}} & \frac{1}{\sqrt{2}} \\ 0 & 0 & \frac{-1}{\sqrt{2}} & \frac{1}{\sqrt{2}} \end{bmatrix}$$

$$P^{-1}AP = \begin{bmatrix} \frac{-1}{\sqrt{2}} & \frac{1}{\sqrt{2}} & 0 & 0 \\ \frac{1}{\sqrt{2}} & \frac{1}{\sqrt{2}} & 0 & 0 \\ 0 & 0 & \frac{1}{\sqrt{2}} & \frac{1}{\sqrt{2}} \\ 0 & 0 & \frac{-1}{\sqrt{2}} & \frac{1}{\sqrt{2}} \end{bmatrix} \begin{bmatrix} 1 & 1 & 0 & 0 \\ 1 & 1 & 0 & 0 \\ 0 & 0 & 1 & 2 \\ 0 & 0 & 2 & 1 \end{bmatrix} \begin{bmatrix} \frac{-1}{\sqrt{2}} & \frac{1}{\sqrt{2}} & 0 & 0 \\ \frac{1}{\sqrt{2}} & \frac{1}{\sqrt{2}} & 0 & 0 \\ 0 & 0 & \frac{1}{\sqrt{2}} & \frac{-1}{\sqrt{2}} \\ 0 & 0 & \frac{1}{\sqrt{2}} & \frac{1}{\sqrt{2}} \end{bmatrix}$$

$$= \begin{bmatrix} \frac{-1}{\sqrt{2}} & \frac{1}{\sqrt{2}} & 0 & 0 \\ \frac{1}{\sqrt{2}} & \frac{1}{\sqrt{2}} & 0 & 0 \\ 0 & 0 & \frac{1}{\sqrt{2}} & \frac{1}{\sqrt{2}} \\ 0 & 0 & \frac{-1}{\sqrt{2}} & \frac{1}{\sqrt{2}} \end{bmatrix} \begin{bmatrix} 0 & \frac{2}{\sqrt{2}} & 0 & 0 \\ 0 & \frac{2}{\sqrt{2}} & 0 & 0 \\ 0 & 0 & \frac{3}{\sqrt{2}} & \frac{1}{\sqrt{2}} \\ 0 & 0 & \frac{3}{\sqrt{2}} & \frac{-1}{\sqrt{2}} \end{bmatrix} = \begin{bmatrix} 0 & 0 & 0 & 0 \\ 0 & 2 & 0 & 0 \\ 0 & 0 & 3 & 0 \\ 0 & 0 & 0 & -1 \end{bmatrix}$$

50.
$$0 = |\lambda I - A| = \begin{vmatrix} \lambda - 2 & -1 & 0 & 0 \\ -1 & \lambda - 2 & 0 & 0 \\ 0 & 0 & \lambda - 2 & -3 \\ 0 & 0 & -3 & \lambda - 2 \end{vmatrix}$$

$$= [(\lambda - 2)(\lambda - 2) - (-1)(-1)][(\lambda - 2)(\lambda - 2) - (-3)(-3)]$$

$$= (\lambda^2 - 4\lambda + 3)(\lambda^2 - 4\lambda - 5) = (\lambda - 1)(\lambda - 3)(\lambda - 5)(\lambda + 1) \quad \text{so} \quad \lambda = 1, 3, 5, -1$$

$$\lambda_1 = 1 \longrightarrow \begin{bmatrix} -1 & -1 & 0 & 0 & 0 \\ -1 & -1 & 0 & 0 & 0 \\ 0 & 0 & -1 & -3 & 0 \\ 0 & 0 & -3 & -1 & 0 \end{bmatrix} \longrightarrow \begin{bmatrix} 1 & 1 & 0 & 0 & 0 \\ 0 & 0 & 0 & 0 & 0 \\ 0 & 0 & 1 & 3 & 0 \\ 0 & 0 & 0 & 8 & 0 \end{bmatrix} \longrightarrow \begin{bmatrix} 1 & 1 & 0 & 0 & 0 \\ 0 & 0 & 1 & 0 & 0 \\ 0 & 0 & 0 & 1 & 0 \\ 0 & 0 & 0 & 0 & 0 \end{bmatrix}$$

Let $x_2 = q$;

then $x_1 + x_2 = 0$, i.e., $x_1 = -x_2 = -q$

and $x_3 = 0$ and $x_4 = 0$

so $\begin{bmatrix} x_1 \\ x_2 \\ x_3 \\ x_4 \end{bmatrix} = \begin{bmatrix} -q \\ q \\ 0 \\ 0 \end{bmatrix} = q \begin{bmatrix} -1 \\ 1 \\ 0 \\ 0 \end{bmatrix}$ i.e., $B_1 = \left\{ \begin{bmatrix} -1 \\ 1 \\ 0 \\ 0 \end{bmatrix} \right\}$

$$(-1, 1, 0, 0)/\|(-1, 1, 0, 0)\| = (-1, 1, 0, 0)/\sqrt{2} = \left(\frac{-1}{\sqrt{2}}, \frac{1}{\sqrt{2}}, 0, 0 \right).$$

$$\lambda_2 = 3 \longrightarrow \begin{bmatrix} 1 & -1 & 0 & 0 & 0 \\ 1 & -1 & 0 & 0 & 0 \\ 0 & 0 & 1 & -3 & 0 \\ 0 & 0 & -3 & 1 & 0 \end{bmatrix} \longrightarrow \begin{bmatrix} 1 & -1 & 0 & 0 & 0 \\ 0 & 0 & 0 & 0 & 0 \\ 0 & 0 & 1 & -3 & 0 \\ 0 & 0 & 0 & -8 & 0 \end{bmatrix} \longrightarrow \begin{bmatrix} 1 & -1 & 0 & 0 & 0 \\ 0 & 0 & 1 & 0 & 0 \\ 0 & 0 & 0 & 1 & 0 \\ 0 & 0 & 0 & 0 & 0 \end{bmatrix}$$

175

Let $x_2 = r$;

then $x_1 - x_2 = 0$, i.e., $x_1 = x_2 = r$

and $x_3 = 0$ and $x_4 = 0$

so $\begin{bmatrix} x_1 \\ x_2 \\ x_3 \\ x_4 \end{bmatrix} = \begin{bmatrix} r \\ r \\ 0 \\ 0 \end{bmatrix} = r \begin{bmatrix} 1 \\ 1 \\ 0 \\ 0 \end{bmatrix}$ i.e., $B_2 = \left\{ \begin{bmatrix} 1 \\ 1 \\ 0 \\ 0 \end{bmatrix} \right\}$

$$(1,1,0,0)/\|(1,1,0,0)\| = (1,1,0,0)/\sqrt{2} = \left(\tfrac{1}{\sqrt{2}}, \tfrac{1}{\sqrt{2}}, 0, 0 \right).$$

$$\lambda_3 = 5 \longrightarrow \begin{bmatrix} 3 & -1 & 0 & 0 & 0 \\ -1 & 3 & 0 & 0 & 0 \\ 0 & 0 & 3 & -3 & 0 \\ 0 & 0 & -3 & 3 & 0 \end{bmatrix} \longrightarrow \begin{bmatrix} -1 & 3 & 0 & 0 & 0 \\ 3 & -1 & 0 & 0 & 0 \\ 0 & 0 & 3 & -3 & 0 \\ 0 & 0 & -3 & 3 & 0 \end{bmatrix} \longrightarrow$$

$$\begin{bmatrix} 1 & -3 & 0 & 0 & 0 \\ 0 & 8 & 0 & 0 & 0 \\ 0 & 0 & 3 & -3 & 0 \\ 0 & 0 & -3 & 3 & 0 \end{bmatrix} \longrightarrow \begin{bmatrix} 1 & 0 & 0 & 0 & 0 \\ 0 & 1 & 0 & 0 & 0 \\ 0 & 0 & 1 & -1 & 0 \\ 0 & 0 & 0 & 0 & 0 \end{bmatrix}$$

Let $x_4 = s$;

then $x_3 - x_4 = 0$, i.e., $x_3 = x_4 = s$

and $x_1 = 0$ and $x_2 = 0$

so $\begin{bmatrix} x_1 \\ x_2 \\ x_3 \\ x_4 \end{bmatrix} = \begin{bmatrix} 0 \\ 0 \\ s \\ s \end{bmatrix} = s \begin{bmatrix} 0 \\ 0 \\ 1 \\ 1 \end{bmatrix}$ i.e., $B_3 = \left\{ \begin{bmatrix} 0 \\ 0 \\ 1 \\ 1 \end{bmatrix} \right\}$

$$(0,0,1,1)/\|(0,0,1,1)\| = (0,0,1,1)/\sqrt{2} = \left(0, 0, \tfrac{1}{\sqrt{2}}, \tfrac{1}{\sqrt{2}} \right).$$

$$\lambda_4 = -1 \longrightarrow \begin{bmatrix} -3 & -1 & 0 & 0 & 0 \\ -1 & -3 & 0 & 0 & 0 \\ 0 & 0 & -3 & -3 & 0 \\ 0 & 0 & -3 & -3 & 0 \end{bmatrix} \longrightarrow \begin{bmatrix} -1 & -3 & 0 & 0 & 0 \\ -3 & -1 & 0 & 0 & 0 \\ 0 & 0 & -3 & -3 & 0 \\ 0 & 0 & -3 & -3 & 0 \end{bmatrix} \longrightarrow$$

$$\begin{bmatrix} 1 & 3 & 0 & 0 & 0 \\ 0 & 8 & 0 & 0 & 0 \\ 0 & 0 & -3 & -3 & 0 \\ 0 & 0 & -3 & -3 & 0 \end{bmatrix} \longrightarrow \begin{bmatrix} 1 & 0 & 0 & 0 & 0 \\ 0 & 1 & 0 & 0 & 0 \\ 0 & 0 & 1 & 1 & 0 \\ 0 & 0 & 0 & 0 & 0 \end{bmatrix}$$

Let $x_4 = t$;

then $x_3 + x_4 = 0$, i.e., $x_3 = -x_4 = -t$

and $x_1 = 0$ and $x_2 = 0$

so $\begin{bmatrix} x_1 \\ x_2 \\ x_3 \\ x_4 \end{bmatrix} = \begin{bmatrix} 0 \\ 0 \\ -t \\ t \end{bmatrix} = t \begin{bmatrix} 0 \\ 0 \\ -1 \\ 1 \end{bmatrix}$ i.e., $B_4 = \left\{ \begin{bmatrix} 0 \\ 0 \\ -1 \\ 1 \end{bmatrix} \right\}$

$$(0,0,-1,1)/\|(0,0,-1,1)\| = (0,0,-1,1)/\sqrt{2} = \left(0,0,\tfrac{-1}{\sqrt{2}},\tfrac{1}{\sqrt{2}}\right).$$

$$P = \begin{bmatrix} \frac{-1}{\sqrt{2}} & \frac{1}{\sqrt{2}} & 0 & 0 \\ \frac{1}{\sqrt{2}} & \frac{1}{\sqrt{2}} & 0 & 0 \\ 0 & 0 & \frac{1}{\sqrt{2}} & \frac{-1}{\sqrt{2}} \\ 0 & 0 & \frac{1}{\sqrt{2}} & \frac{1}{\sqrt{2}} \end{bmatrix} \quad , \quad P^{-1} = P^T = \begin{bmatrix} \frac{-1}{\sqrt{2}} & \frac{1}{\sqrt{2}} & 0 & 0 \\ \frac{1}{\sqrt{2}} & \frac{1}{\sqrt{2}} & 0 & 0 \\ 0 & 0 & \frac{1}{\sqrt{2}} & \frac{1}{\sqrt{2}} \\ 0 & 0 & \frac{-1}{\sqrt{2}} & \frac{1}{\sqrt{2}} \end{bmatrix}$$

$$P^{-1}AP = \begin{bmatrix} \frac{-1}{\sqrt{2}} & \frac{1}{\sqrt{2}} & 0 & 0 \\ \frac{1}{\sqrt{2}} & \frac{1}{\sqrt{2}} & 0 & 0 \\ 0 & 0 & \frac{1}{\sqrt{2}} & \frac{1}{\sqrt{2}} \\ 0 & 0 & \frac{-1}{\sqrt{2}} & \frac{1}{\sqrt{2}} \end{bmatrix} \begin{bmatrix} 2 & 1 & 0 & 0 \\ 1 & 2 & 0 & 0 \\ 0 & 0 & 2 & 3 \\ 0 & 0 & 3 & 2 \end{bmatrix} \begin{bmatrix} \frac{-1}{\sqrt{2}} & \frac{1}{\sqrt{2}} & 0 & 0 \\ \frac{1}{\sqrt{2}} & \frac{1}{\sqrt{2}} & 0 & 0 \\ 0 & 0 & \frac{1}{\sqrt{2}} & \frac{-1}{\sqrt{2}} \\ 0 & 0 & \frac{1}{\sqrt{2}} & \frac{1}{\sqrt{2}} \end{bmatrix}$$

$$= \begin{bmatrix} \frac{-1}{\sqrt{2}} & \frac{1}{\sqrt{2}} & 0 & 0 \\ \frac{1}{\sqrt{2}} & \frac{1}{\sqrt{2}} & 0 & 0 \\ 0 & 0 & \frac{1}{\sqrt{2}} & \frac{1}{\sqrt{2}} \\ 0 & 0 & \frac{-1}{\sqrt{2}} & \frac{1}{\sqrt{2}} \end{bmatrix} \begin{bmatrix} \frac{-1}{\sqrt{2}} & \frac{3}{\sqrt{2}} & 0 & 0 \\ \frac{1}{\sqrt{2}} & \frac{3}{\sqrt{2}} & 0 & 0 \\ 0 & 0 & \frac{5}{\sqrt{2}} & \frac{1}{\sqrt{2}} \\ 0 & 0 & \frac{5}{\sqrt{2}} & \frac{-1}{\sqrt{2}} \end{bmatrix} = \begin{bmatrix} 1 & 0 & 0 & 0 \\ 0 & 3 & 0 & 0 \\ 0 & 0 & 5 & 0 \\ 0 & 0 & 0 & -1 \end{bmatrix}$$

51. $0 = |\lambda I - A| = \begin{vmatrix} \lambda - 1 & -2 & 0 & 0 \\ -2 & \lambda - 1 & 0 & 0 \\ 0 & 0 & \lambda - 2 & -1 \\ 0 & 0 & -1 & \lambda - 2 \end{vmatrix}$

$= [(\lambda - 1)(\lambda - 1) - (-2)(-2)][(\lambda - 2)(\lambda - 2) - (-1)(-1)]$

$= (\lambda^2 - 2\lambda - 3)(\lambda^2 - 4\lambda + 3) = (\lambda + 1)(\lambda - 3)(\lambda - 1)(\lambda - 3)$ so $\lambda = -1, 1, 3, 3$

$\lambda_1 = -1 \longrightarrow \begin{bmatrix} -2 & -2 & 0 & 0 & 0 \\ -2 & -2 & 0 & 0 & 0 \\ 0 & 0 & -3 & -1 & 0 \\ 0 & 0 & -1 & -3 & 0 \end{bmatrix} \longrightarrow \begin{bmatrix} 1 & 1 & 0 & 0 & 0 \\ 0 & 0 & 0 & 0 & 0 \\ 0 & 0 & -1 & -3 & 0 \\ 0 & 0 & -3 & -1 & 0 \end{bmatrix} \longrightarrow \begin{bmatrix} 1 & 1 & 0 & 0 & 0 \\ 0 & 0 & 1 & 3 & 0 \\ 0 & 0 & 0 & 8 & 0 \\ 0 & 0 & 0 & 0 & 0 \end{bmatrix} \longrightarrow$

$\begin{bmatrix} 1 & 1 & 0 & 0 & 0 \\ 0 & 0 & 1 & 0 & 0 \\ 0 & 0 & 0 & 1 & 0 \\ 0 & 0 & 0 & 0 & 0 \end{bmatrix}$

Let $x_2 = q$;

then $x_1 + x_2 = 0$, i.e., $x_1 = -x_2 = -q$

and $x_3 = 0$ and $x_4 = 0$

so $\begin{bmatrix} x_1 \\ x_2 \\ x_3 \\ x_4 \end{bmatrix} = \begin{bmatrix} -q \\ q \\ 0 \\ 0 \end{bmatrix} = q \begin{bmatrix} -1 \\ 1 \\ 0 \\ 0 \end{bmatrix}$ i.e., $B_1 = \left\{ \begin{bmatrix} -1 \\ 1 \\ 0 \\ 0 \end{bmatrix} \right\}$

$$(-1,1,0,0)/\|(-1,1,0,0)\| = (-1,1,0,0)/\sqrt{2} = \left(\tfrac{-1}{\sqrt{2}}, \tfrac{1}{\sqrt{2}}, 0, 0 \right).$$

$$\lambda_2 = 1 \longrightarrow \begin{bmatrix} 0 & -2 & 0 & 0 & 0 \\ -2 & 0 & 0 & 0 & 0 \\ 0 & 0 & -1 & -1 & 0 \\ 0 & 0 & -1 & -1 & 0 \end{bmatrix} \longrightarrow \begin{bmatrix} -2 & 0 & 0 & 0 & 0 \\ 0 & -2 & 0 & 0 & 0 \\ 0 & 0 & -1 & -1 & 0 \\ 0 & 0 & -1 & -1 & 0 \end{bmatrix} \longrightarrow \begin{bmatrix} 1 & 0 & 0 & 0 & 0 \\ 0 & 1 & 0 & 0 & 0 \\ 0 & 0 & 1 & 1 & 0 \\ 0 & 0 & 0 & 0 & 0 \end{bmatrix}$$

Let $x_4 = r$;

then $x_3 + x_4 = 0$, i.e., $x_3 = -x_4 = -r$

and $x_1 = 0$ and $x_2 = 0$

so $\begin{bmatrix} x_1 \\ x_2 \\ x_3 \\ x_4 \end{bmatrix} = \begin{bmatrix} 0 \\ 0 \\ -r \\ r \end{bmatrix} = r \begin{bmatrix} 0 \\ 0 \\ -1 \\ 1 \end{bmatrix}$ i.e., $B_2 = \left\{ \begin{bmatrix} 0 \\ 0 \\ -1 \\ 1 \end{bmatrix} \right\}$

$$(0,0,-1,1)/\|(0,0,-1,1)\| = (0,0,-1,1)/\sqrt{2} = \left(0,0, \tfrac{-1}{\sqrt{2}}, \tfrac{1}{\sqrt{2}} \right).$$

$$\lambda_3 = 3 \longrightarrow \begin{bmatrix} 2 & -2 & 0 & 0 & 0 \\ -2 & 2 & 0 & 0 & 0 \\ 0 & 0 & 1 & -1 & 0 \\ 0 & 0 & -1 & 1 & 0 \end{bmatrix} \longrightarrow \begin{bmatrix} 1 & -1 & 0 & 0 & 0 \\ 0 & 0 & 0 & 0 & 0 \\ 0 & 0 & 1 & -1 & 0 \\ 0 & 0 & 0 & 0 & 0 \end{bmatrix} \longrightarrow \begin{bmatrix} 1 & -1 & 0 & 0 & 0 \\ 0 & 0 & 1 & -1 & 0 \\ 0 & 0 & 0 & 0 & 0 \\ 0 & 0 & 0 & 0 & 0 \end{bmatrix}$$

Let $x_4 = t$ and $x_2 = s$;

then $x_3 - x_4 = 0$, i.e., $x_3 = x_4 = t$

and $x_1 - x_2 = 0$ i.e., $x_1 = x_2 = s$

so $\begin{bmatrix} x_1 \\ x_2 \\ x_3 \\ x_4 \end{bmatrix} = \begin{bmatrix} s \\ s \\ t \\ t \end{bmatrix} = \begin{bmatrix} s \\ s \\ 0 \\ 0 \end{bmatrix} + \begin{bmatrix} 0 \\ 0 \\ t \\ t \end{bmatrix} = s \begin{bmatrix} 1 \\ 1 \\ 0 \\ 0 \end{bmatrix} + t \begin{bmatrix} 0 \\ 0 \\ 1 \\ 1 \end{bmatrix}$ i.e., $B_3 = \left\{ \begin{bmatrix} 1 \\ 1 \\ 0 \\ 0 \end{bmatrix}, \begin{bmatrix} 0 \\ 0 \\ 1 \\ 1 \end{bmatrix} \right\}$

$$(0,0,1,1) - \tfrac{(0,0,1,1)\cdot(1,1,0,0)}{(1,1,0,0)\cdot(1,1,0,0)}(1,1,0,0) = (0,0,1,1) - 0(1,1,0,0) - (0,0,1,1)$$

$$(1,1,0,0)/\|(1,1,0,0)\| = (1,1,0,0)/\sqrt{2} = \left(\tfrac{1}{\sqrt{2}}, \tfrac{1}{\sqrt{2}}, 0, 0 \right).$$

$$(0,0,1,1)/\|(0,0,1,1)\| = (0,0,1,1)/\sqrt{2} = \left(0,0, \tfrac{1}{\sqrt{2}}, \tfrac{1}{\sqrt{2}} \right).$$

$$P = \begin{bmatrix} \frac{-1}{\sqrt{2}} & \frac{1}{\sqrt{2}} & 0 & 0 \\ \frac{1}{\sqrt{2}} & \frac{1}{\sqrt{2}} & 0 & 0 \\ 0 & 0 & \frac{-1}{\sqrt{2}} & \frac{1}{\sqrt{2}} \\ 0 & 0 & \frac{1}{\sqrt{2}} & \frac{1}{\sqrt{2}} \end{bmatrix} \quad , \quad P^{-1} = P^T = \begin{bmatrix} \frac{-1}{\sqrt{2}} & \frac{1}{\sqrt{2}} & 0 & 0 \\ \frac{1}{\sqrt{2}} & \frac{1}{\sqrt{2}} & 0 & 0 \\ 0 & 0 & \frac{-1}{\sqrt{2}} & \frac{1}{\sqrt{2}} \\ 0 & 0 & \frac{1}{\sqrt{2}} & \frac{1}{\sqrt{2}} \end{bmatrix}$$

$$P^{-1}AP = \begin{bmatrix} \frac{-1}{\sqrt{2}} & \frac{1}{\sqrt{2}} & 0 & 0 \\ \frac{1}{\sqrt{2}} & \frac{1}{\sqrt{2}} & 0 & 0 \\ 0 & 0 & \frac{-1}{\sqrt{2}} & \frac{1}{\sqrt{2}} \\ 0 & 0 & \frac{1}{\sqrt{2}} & \frac{1}{\sqrt{2}} \end{bmatrix} \begin{bmatrix} 1 & 2 & 0 & 0 \\ 2 & 1 & 0 & 0 \\ 0 & 0 & 2 & 1 \\ 0 & 0 & 1 & 2 \end{bmatrix} \begin{bmatrix} \frac{-1}{\sqrt{2}} & \frac{1}{\sqrt{2}} & 0 & 0 \\ \frac{1}{\sqrt{2}} & \frac{1}{\sqrt{2}} & 0 & 0 \\ 0 & 0 & \frac{-1}{\sqrt{2}} & \frac{1}{\sqrt{2}} \\ 0 & 0 & \frac{1}{\sqrt{2}} & \frac{1}{\sqrt{2}} \end{bmatrix}$$

$$= \begin{bmatrix} \frac{-1}{\sqrt{2}} & \frac{1}{\sqrt{2}} & 0 & 0 \\ \frac{1}{\sqrt{2}} & \frac{1}{\sqrt{2}} & 0 & 0 \\ 0 & 0 & \frac{-1}{\sqrt{2}} & \frac{1}{\sqrt{2}} \\ 0 & 0 & \frac{1}{\sqrt{2}} & \frac{1}{\sqrt{2}} \end{bmatrix} \begin{bmatrix} \frac{1}{\sqrt{2}} & \frac{3}{\sqrt{2}} & 0 & 0 \\ \frac{-1}{\sqrt{2}} & \frac{3}{\sqrt{2}} & 0 & 0 \\ 0 & 0 & \frac{-1}{\sqrt{2}} & \frac{3}{\sqrt{2}} \\ 0 & 0 & \frac{1}{\sqrt{2}} & \frac{3}{\sqrt{2}} \end{bmatrix} = \begin{bmatrix} -1 & 0 & 0 & 0 \\ 0 & 3 & 0 & 0 \\ 0 & 0 & 1 & 0 \\ 0 & 0 & 0 & 3 \end{bmatrix}.$$

In questions 1–6, show whether the given function is a linear transformation.

1. $T : R^2 \to R^3$, where $T(x, y) = \left(\frac{1}{2}x + \frac{1}{2}y, x + y, x - y \right)$.

2. $T : R^3 \to R$, where $T(\mathbf{x}) = \mathbf{w} \cdot \mathbf{x}$ and $\mathbf{w}$ is a fixed vector in R^3.

3. $T : M_{22} \to R$, where $T\left(\begin{bmatrix} a & b \\ c & d \end{bmatrix} \right) = a - d$.

4. $T : M_{22} \to M_{22}$, where $T\left(\begin{bmatrix} a & b \\ c & d \end{bmatrix} \right) = \begin{bmatrix} a - d & b \\ c & ad \end{bmatrix}$.

5. $T : P_2 \to P_2$, where $T(a_0 + a_1 x + a_2 x^2) = a_0 + a_1(x - 1) + a_2(x - 1)^2$.

6. $T : V \to V$, where V is the vector space of everywhere differentiable functions and $T(f) = \frac{d}{dx}(xf)$.

7. Consider the basis $S = \{\mathbf{v}_1, \mathbf{v}_2\}$ for R^2, where $\mathbf{v}_1 = (1, 1)$ and $\mathbf{v}_2 = (-1, 1)$. Let $T : R^2 \to R^2$ be the linear operator such that $T(\mathbf{v}_1) = (3, 5)$ and $T(\mathbf{v}_2) = (-2, 3)$.
   (a) Find a formula for $T(x_1, x_2)$.
   (b) Use your formula to compute $T(4, -2)$.

8. Consider the basis $S = \{\mathbf{v}_1, \mathbf{v}_2\}$ for R^2, where $\mathbf{v}_1 = (1, 2)$ and $\mathbf{v}_2 = (4, 7)$. Let $T : R^2 \to R^3$ be the linear transformation such that $T(\mathbf{v}_1) = (1, 3, 3)$ and $T(\mathbf{v}_2) = (0, 1, 1)$.
   (a) Find a formula for $T(x_1, x_2)$.
   (b) Use your formula to compute $T(2, 3)$.

9. Consider the basis $S = \{\mathbf{v}_1, \mathbf{v}_2, \mathbf{v}_3\}$ for R^3, where $\mathbf{v}_1 = (2, -1, 0)$, $\mathbf{v}_2 = (2, 0, 2)$, and $\mathbf{v}_3 = (4, 1, 7)$. Let $T : R^3 \to R^2$ be the linear transformation such that $T(\mathbf{v}_1) = (1, 1)$, $T(\mathbf{v}_2) = (4, 1)$ and $T(\mathbf{v}_3) = (0, 5)$.
   (a) Find a formula for $T(x_1, x_2, x_3)$.
   (b) Use your formula to compute $T(2, 1, 5)$.

10. Consider the basis $S = \{\mathbf{v}_1, \mathbf{v}_2, \mathbf{v}_3\}$ for R^3, where $\mathbf{v}_1 = (1, 0, -5)$, $\mathbf{v}_2 = (-1, 1, 4)$, and $\mathbf{v}_3 = (0, 1, 0)$. Let $T : R^3 \to R^3$ be the linear transformation such that $T(\mathbf{v}_1) = (1, 2, 1)$, $T(\mathbf{v}_2) = (2, 0, -3)$ and $T(\mathbf{v}_3) = (1, 1, 1)$.
   (a) Find a formula for $T(x_1, x_2, x_3)$.
   (b) Use your formula to compute $T(3, 6, -13)$.

11. In each part, determine the domain and codomain of $T_2 \circ T_1$, and a formula for $T_2 \circ T_1$.
   (a) $T_1(x, y) = (2x + y, x - y)$, $T_2(x, y) = (x + 3y, 2x - 5y)$.
   (b) $T_1(x, y) = (x - 3y, y)$, $T_2(x, y) = (x, y, x + y)$.
   (c) $T_1(a_0 + a_1 x + a_2 x^2) = a_0 x + a_1 x^2 + a_2 x^3$, $T_2(a_0 + a_1 x + a_2 x^2 + a_3 x^3) = a_1 + 2a_2 x + 3a_3 x^2$.

12. In each part, determine the domain and codomain of $T_3 \circ T_2 \circ T_1$, and a formula for $T_3 \circ T_2 \circ T_1$.

   (a) $T_1(x,y) = (x+y, x-y)$, $T_2(x,y) = (3x-y, x+2y)$, $T_3(x,y) = (y, x+y)$.

   (b) $T_1(x_1, x_2, x_3, x_4, x_5) = (x_1 - x_3 - x_5, x_2 - x_4, x_1 + 3x_3 + x_5, x_2 + x_3 + x_4)$,
   $T_2(x_1, x_2, x_3, x_4) = (x_1 + x_3, x_2 + x_4, x_1 - x_2 - x_3 + x_4)$,
   $T_3(x_1, x_2, x_3) = (x_1 - x_2 + x_3, 2x_1 + x_2 - 3x_3)$.

   (c) $T_1(a_0 + a_1 x + a_2 x^2) = a_0 + a_1(x-1) + a_2(x-1)^2$,
   $T_2(a_0 + a_1 x + a_2 x^2) = a_0 + 2a_1 x + 3a_2 x^2$,
   $T_3(a_0 + a_1 x + a_2 x^2) = a_0 + a_1(x+1) + a_2(x+1)^2$.

In questions 13–19, for the given linear transformation determine the following:

   (a)   a basis for the range

   (b)   a basis for the kernel

   (c)   the rank and nullity

13. $T: R^2 \to R^2$ defined by $T(x,y) = (x - 2y, 2x + 3y)$.

14. $T: R^3 \to R^4$ defined by $T(x,y,z) = (x + 2y + z, -x - 2y - 5z, 2x + 4y, x + 2y + 2z)$.

15. $T: R^3 \to R^3$ defined by multiplication by $A = \begin{bmatrix} 1 & -1 & -2 \\ 3 & -1 & 0 \\ 1 & 1 & 4 \end{bmatrix}$.

16. $T: R^4 \to R^3$ defined by multiplication by $A = \begin{bmatrix} 3 & -3 & -3 & 3 \\ 2 & 1 & 1 & 2 \\ 2 & 0 & 0 & 5 \end{bmatrix}$.

17. $T: P_2 \to P_2$ defined by $T(a_0 + a_1 x + a_2 x^2) = a_0 + a_1(x+1) + a_2(x+1)^2$.

18. $D: P_2 \to P_1$ defined by $D(\mathbf{p}) = \frac{d}{dx}\mathbf{p}$.

19. $J: P_1 \to R$ defined by $J(\mathbf{p}) = \int_{-1}^{1} \mathbf{p}\,dx$.

20. In each part, use the given information to find the nullity of T.

   (a) $T: R^3 \to R^8$ has rank 2.   (b) $T: R^5 \to R^2$ has range the x-axis.

   (c) $T: P_3 \to P_3$ has rank 3.   (d) $T: M_{23} \to M_{33}$ has rank 6.

In questions 21–28, determine whether the linear transformation T has an inverse and, if it does, find a formula for T^{-1}.

21. $T: R^2 \to R^2$, where $T(x,y) = (x + 2y, 3x - y)$.

22. $T: R^2 \to R^3$, where $T(x,y) = (6x - 9y, -2x + 3y, 4x - 6y)$.

182

23. $T : R^2 \rightarrow R^2$, where T is multiplication by $A = \begin{bmatrix} \pi + 3 & \pi^2 - 9 \\ 1 & \pi - 3 \end{bmatrix}$.

24. $T : R^3 \rightarrow R^3$, where T is multiplication by $A = \begin{bmatrix} 3 & 6 & 9 \\ 3 & 8 & 10 \\ -2 & -7 & -5 \end{bmatrix}$.

25. $T : M_{22} \rightarrow M_{22}$, where $T\left(\begin{bmatrix} a & b \\ c & d \end{bmatrix}\right) = \begin{bmatrix} d & c \\ b & a \end{bmatrix}$.

26. $T : R^2 \rightarrow R^1$, where T projects each point orthogonally onto the x–axis.

27. $T : P_2 \rightarrow P_3$, where $T(p(x)) = xp(x)$.

28. $T : P_3 \rightarrow P_3$, where $T(p(x)) = p(x - 3)$.

29. In each part use the given information to determine whether the linear transformation T is one–to–one.

    (a) $T : R^m \rightarrow R^n$; rank $(T) = m$
    (b) $T : R^m \rightarrow R^{m+n}$; rank $(T) = m - 1$
    (c) $T : P_m \rightarrow P_n$; $m > n$
    (d) $T : M_{22} \rightarrow P_3$ and $R(T) = P_3$.

30. Let $T : R^2 \rightarrow R^2$ be a linear operator, and suppose $[T]_B = \begin{bmatrix} 1 & 2 \\ -1 & 3 \end{bmatrix}$ is the matrix for T with respect to the basis $B = \{v_1, v_2\}$, where $v_1 = (1, 1)$ and $v_2 = (1, -1)$.

    (a)   Find $[T(v_1)]_B$ and $[T(v_2)]_B$.
    (b)   Find $T(v_1)$ and $T(v_2)$.
    (c)   Find a formula for T.
    (d)   Use the formula from (c) to compute $T(2, 4)$.

31. Let $T : R^2 \rightarrow R^3$ be a linear transformation, and suppose $[T]_{B', B} = \begin{bmatrix} 2 & 1 \\ 1 & 3 \\ 3 & 0 \end{bmatrix}$ is the matrix for T with respect to the bases $B = \{v_1, v_2\}$ and $B' = \{w_1, w_2, w_3\}$, where $v_1 = (1, 2)$, $v_2 = (1, 3)$, $w_1 = (1, -1, 1)$, $w_2 = (1, 0, 1)$, $w_3 = (0, 1, -1)$.

    (a)   Find $[T(v_1)]_{B'}$ and $[T(v_2)]_{B'}$.
    (b)   Find $T(v_1)$ and (v_2).
    (c)   Find a formula for T.
    (d)   Use the formula from (c) to compute $T(3, 7)$.

32. Let $T : R^2 \rightarrow R^2$ be the linear operator defined by $T(x, y) = (2x - y, 2x + y)$.

    (a)   Find the matrix $[T]_B$, where $B = \{v_1, v_2\}$ and $v_1 = (1, 1)$, $v_2 = (1, 2)$.
    (b)   Use the matrix from (a) to compute $T(5, -3)$.

33. Let $T : R^3 \rightarrow R^2$ be the linear transformation defined by $T(x, y, z) = (x - y + 2z, 3x + 2y - z)$.

   (a) Find the matrix $[T]_{B',B}$, where $B = \{u_1, u_2, u_3\}$, $B' = \{v_1, v_2\}$, and $u_1 = (1, 0, 1)$, $u_2 = (0, 1, -1)$, $u_3 = (1, -1, 1)$, $v_1 = (1, 2)$, $v_2 = (1, 3)$.

   (b) Use the matrix from (a) to compute $T(3, 1, -1)$.

34. Let $T : R^3 \rightarrow R^3$ be the linear operator defined by $T(x_1, x_2, x_3) = (x_2 + x_3, x_1 + x_3, x_1 + x_2)$.

   (a) Find the matrix $[T]_B$, where $B = \{v_1, v_2, v_3\}$, and $v_1 = (1, 1, 3)$, $v_2 = (1, 2, 0)$, $v_3 = (-1, 0, 1)$.

   (b) Use the matrix from (a) to compute $T(1, 1, 1)$.

35. Let $T : P_1 \rightarrow P_2$ be the linear transformation defined by $T(p(x)) = xp(x + 1)$.

   (a) Find the matrix $[T]_{B',B}$, where $B = \{u_1, u_2\}$, $B' = \{v_1, v_2, v_3\}$, and $u_1 = 1$, $u_2 = x$, $v_1 = 1$, $v_2 = x$, $v_3 = x^2$.

   (b) Use the matrix from (a) to compute $T(3x - 5)$.

36. Let $T : P_2 \rightarrow P_1$ be the linear transformation defined by $T(p) = \frac{dp}{dx}$.

   (a) Find the matrix $[T]_{B',B}$, where $B = \{u_1, u_2, u_3\}$, $B' = \{v_1, v_2\}$, and $u_1 = 1$, $u_2 = x$, $u_3 = x^2$, $v_1 = 1$, $v_2 = x$.

   (b) Use the matrix from (a) to differentiate $4 - 3x + 2x^2$.

37. Let $T : P_2 \rightarrow P_2$ be the linear operator defined by $T(p(x)) = p(3x - 2)$.

   (a) Find the matrix $[T]_B$, where $B = \{v_1, v_2, v_3\}$ and $v_1 = 1$, $v_2 = x$, $v_3 = x^2$.

   (b) Use the matrix from (a) to compute $T(4 - 3x + 2x^2)$.

38. Consider $V = \text{span } \{e^x, e^{2x}, e^{3x}\}$, a subspace of the vector space of real functions. Let $T : V \rightarrow V$ be the linear operator defined by

$$T(f) = \frac{d^2 f}{dx^2} + 3\frac{df}{dx} + 2f.$$

   (a) Find the matrix $[T]_B$, where $B = \{v_1, v_2, v_3\}$ and $v_1 = e^x$, $v_2 = e^{2x}$, $v_3 = e^{3x}$.

   (b) Use the matrix from (a) to solve the differential equation $T(f) = e^x + 2e^{2x} + e^{3x}$, where f is an element of V.

In questions 39–45, find $[T]_B$, and then find $[T]_{B'}$ using the equation $[T]_{B'} = P^{-1}[T]_B P$.

39. $T : R^2 \rightarrow R^2$ is defined by $T\left(\begin{bmatrix} x_1 \\ x_2 \end{bmatrix}\right) = \begin{bmatrix} 2x_1 + x_2 \\ x_1 - x_2 \end{bmatrix}$; $B = \{u_1, u_2\}$ and $B' = \{v_1, v_2\}$ where

$u_1 = \begin{bmatrix} 1 \\ 3 \end{bmatrix}$, $u_2 = \begin{bmatrix} 2 \\ 5 \end{bmatrix}$, $v_1 = \begin{bmatrix} 2 \\ 3 \end{bmatrix}$, $v_2 = \begin{bmatrix} 1 \\ 2 \end{bmatrix}$.

40. $T : R^2 \rightarrow R^2$ is the orthogonal projection onto the line $y = x$; $B = \{u_1, u_2\}$ and $B' = \{v_1, v_2\}$ where

$u_1 = \begin{bmatrix} 1 \\ 1 \end{bmatrix}$, $u_2 = \begin{bmatrix} 1 \\ -1 \end{bmatrix}$, $v_1 = \begin{bmatrix} 1 \\ 0 \end{bmatrix}$, $v_2 = \begin{bmatrix} 0 \\ 1 \end{bmatrix}$.

41. $T: R^3 \rightarrow R^3$ is defined by $T\left(\begin{bmatrix} x_1 \\ x_2 \\ x_3 \end{bmatrix}\right) = \begin{bmatrix} x_2 \\ x_1 - x_3 \\ x_2 + x_3 - x_1 \end{bmatrix}$; $B = \{\mathbf{u}_1, \mathbf{u}_2, \mathbf{u}_3\}$ and $B' = \{\mathbf{v}_1, \mathbf{v}_2, \mathbf{v}_3\}$

where $\mathbf{u}_1 = \begin{bmatrix} 1 \\ 0 \\ 1 \end{bmatrix}$, $\mathbf{u}_2 = \begin{bmatrix} 1 \\ 1 \\ 0 \end{bmatrix}$, $\mathbf{u}_3 = \begin{bmatrix} 0 \\ -1 \\ 0 \end{bmatrix}$, $\mathbf{v}_1 = \begin{bmatrix} 1 \\ 0 \\ 1 \end{bmatrix}$, $\mathbf{v}_2 = \begin{bmatrix} 0 \\ 1 \\ -1 \end{bmatrix}$, $\mathbf{v}_3 = \begin{bmatrix} 2 \\ 1 \\ 0 \end{bmatrix}$.

42. $T: R^3 \rightarrow R^3$ is the orthogonal projection onto the yz–plane; $B = \{\mathbf{u}_1, \mathbf{u}_2, \mathbf{u}_3\}$ and $B' = \{\mathbf{v}_1, \mathbf{v}_2, \mathbf{v}_3\}$

where $\mathbf{u}_1 = \begin{bmatrix} 1 \\ 0 \\ 0 \end{bmatrix}$, $\mathbf{u}_2 = \begin{bmatrix} 0 \\ 1 \\ 0 \end{bmatrix}$, $\mathbf{u}_3 = \begin{bmatrix} 0 \\ 0 \\ 1 \end{bmatrix}$, $\mathbf{v}_1 = \begin{bmatrix} 1 \\ 0 \\ 0 \end{bmatrix}$, $\mathbf{v}_2 = \begin{bmatrix} 1 \\ 1 \\ 0 \end{bmatrix}$, $\mathbf{v}_3 = \begin{bmatrix} 1 \\ 1 \\ 1 \end{bmatrix}$.

43. $T: P_2 \rightarrow P_2$ is defined by $T(p(x)) = p(x - 2)$; $B = \{\mathbf{u}_1, \mathbf{u}_2, \mathbf{u}_3\}$ and $B' = \{\mathbf{v}_1, \mathbf{v}_2, \mathbf{v}_3\}$ where $\mathbf{u}_1 = 1$, $\mathbf{u}_2 = x$, $\mathbf{u}_3 = x^2$, $\mathbf{v}_1 = 1 + x$, $\mathbf{v}_2 = 1 - x^2$, $\mathbf{v}_3 = x - x^2$.

44. $T: P_2 \rightarrow P_2$ is defined by $T(p) = x\frac{dp}{dx}$; $B = \{\mathbf{u}_1, \mathbf{u}_2, \mathbf{u}_3\}$ and $B' = \{\mathbf{v}_1, \mathbf{v}_2, \mathbf{v}_3\}$ where $\mathbf{u}_1 = 1$, $\mathbf{u}_2 = x$, $\mathbf{u}_3 = x^2$, $\mathbf{v}_1 = x$, $\mathbf{v}_2 = x^2 + 1$, $\mathbf{v}_3 = x^2 - 1$.

45. $T: P_2 \rightarrow P_2$ is defined by $T(p) = \frac{d^2p}{dx^2} - p + \frac{1}{x}\frac{d}{dx}(x^2p)$; $B = \{\mathbf{u}_1, \mathbf{u}_2, \mathbf{u}_3\}$ and $B' = \{\mathbf{v}_1, \mathbf{v}_2, \mathbf{v}_3\}$ where $\mathbf{u}_1 = 1$, $\mathbf{u}_2 = x$, $\mathbf{u}_3 = x^2$, $\mathbf{v}_1 = 1 + x + x^2$, $\mathbf{v}_2 = 2 + 3x + 2x^2$, $\mathbf{v}_3 = 2 + 2x + 3x^2$.

In questions 46–49,

    (a)   Determine the eigenvalues of T.

    (b)   Determine a basis B' such that $[T]_{B'}$ is diagonal.

    (c)   Determine $[T]_{B'}$.

46. $T: R^2 \rightarrow R^2$ is defined by $T\left(\begin{bmatrix} x_1 \\ x_2 \end{bmatrix}\right) = \begin{bmatrix} 3x_1 + 4x_2 \\ 4x_1 - 3x_2 \end{bmatrix}$.

47. $T: R^2 \rightarrow R^2$ is defined by $T\left(\begin{bmatrix} x_1 \\ x_2 \end{bmatrix}\right) = \begin{bmatrix} 5x_1 - 3x_2 \\ x_1 + x_2 \end{bmatrix}$.

48. $T: R^3 \rightarrow R^3$ is defined by $T\left(\begin{bmatrix} x_1 \\ x_2 \\ x_3 \end{bmatrix}\right) = \begin{bmatrix} -x_1 + 4x_2 - 2x_3 \\ -3x_1 + 4x_2 \\ -3x_1 + x_2 + 3x_3 \end{bmatrix}$.

49. $T: R^3 \rightarrow R^3$ is defined by $T\left(\begin{bmatrix} x_1 \\ x_2 \\ x_3 \end{bmatrix}\right) = \begin{bmatrix} -7x_1 - 9x_2 + 3x_3 \\ 2x_1 + 4x_2 - 2x_3 \\ -3x_1 - 3x_2 - x_3 \end{bmatrix}$.

50. Consider the linear operator $T: R^2 \rightarrow R^2$ defined by $T\left(\begin{bmatrix} x_1 \\ x_2 \end{bmatrix}\right) = \begin{bmatrix} x_1 + 2x_2 \\ 2x_1 + x_2 \end{bmatrix}$.

    (a)   Determine the eigenvalues of T.

    (b)   Determine a basis B' such that $[T]_{B'}$ is diagonal.

    (c)   Use $[T]_{B'}$ to compute $T^5\left(\begin{bmatrix} 2 \\ -1 \end{bmatrix}\right)$.

51. Consider the linear operator $T : R^3 \rightarrow R^3$ defined by $T\left(\begin{bmatrix} x_1 \\ x_2 \\ x_3 \end{bmatrix}\right) = \begin{bmatrix} -9x_1 - 6x_2 - 22x_3 \\ x_1 + 2x_2 + 2x_3 \\ 4x_1 + 2x_2 + 10x_3 \end{bmatrix}.$

    (a)   Determine the eigenvalues of T.

    (b)   Determine a basis B' such that $[T]_{B'}$ is diagonal.

    (c)   Use $[T]_{B'}$ to compute $T^5\left(\begin{bmatrix} -2 \\ 1 \\ 2 \end{bmatrix}\right).$

In questions 52–54,

    (a)   Apply the linear operator $T(\mathbf{x}) = A\mathbf{x}$ to $\mathbf{x} = \begin{bmatrix} 3 \\ 4 \\ 5 \end{bmatrix}.$

    (b)   Show that if $a^2 + b^2 = c^2$ and $T\left(\begin{bmatrix} a \\ b \\ c \end{bmatrix}\right) = \begin{bmatrix} \alpha \\ \beta \\ \gamma \end{bmatrix}$ then $\alpha^2 + \beta^2 = \gamma^2.$

    (c)   Show that T is invertible.

    (d)   Determine $T^{-1}\left(\begin{bmatrix} 5 \\ 12 \\ 13 \end{bmatrix}\right).$

    (e)   Determine the eigenvalues of T.

    (f)   Determine a basis for each eigenspace of T. Is T diagonalizable?

52. $A = \begin{bmatrix} 1 & -2 & 2 \\ 2 & -1 & 2 \\ 2 & -2 & 3 \end{bmatrix}$ 53. $\begin{bmatrix} -1 & 2 & 2 \\ -2 & 1 & 2 \\ -2 & 2 & 3 \end{bmatrix}$ 54. $\begin{bmatrix} 1 & 2 & 2 \\ 2 & 1 & 2 \\ 2 & 2 & 3 \end{bmatrix}.$

WRITING QUESTIONS

55. In studying linear algebra, why are functions between vector spaces not very important unless they are linear transformations?

56. Justify the following: "Knowing how a linear operator acts on a basis for its domain is a basis for understanding how it acts on the rest of its domain."

57. Explain why matrices are valuable tools for studying linear transformations between **any pair** of finite–dimensional vector spaces.

58. What is the significance of a linear transformation being invertible?

59. Why is it sometimes harder to compute $[T]_{B'}$ directly than to compute it by using the formula $[T]_{B'} = P^{-1}[T]_B P?$

60. Why is it useful to diagonalize a linear operator?

SECTION 8.1 *GENERAL LINEAR TRANSFORMATIONS*

1. $T(\mathbf{u} + \mathbf{v}) = T((x_1, y_1) + (x_2, y_2))$

$\qquad = T(x_1 + x_2, y_1 + y_2)$

$\qquad = \left(\frac{1}{2}(x_1 + x_2) + \frac{1}{2}(y_1 + y_2), (x_1 + x_2) + (y_1 + y_2), (x_1 + x_2) - (y_1 + y_2)\right)$

$\qquad = \left(\frac{1}{2}x_1 + \frac{1}{2}x_2 + \frac{1}{2}y_1 + \frac{1}{2}y_2, x_1 + x_2 + y_1 + y_2, x_1 + x_2 - y_1 - y_2\right)$

$T(\mathbf{u}) + T(\mathbf{v}) = T(x_1, y_1) + T(x_2, y_2)$

$\qquad = \left(\frac{1}{2}x_1 + \frac{1}{2}y_1, x_1 + y_1, x_1 - y_1\right) + \left(\frac{1}{2}x_2 + \frac{1}{2}y_2, x_2 + y_2, x_2 - y_2\right)$

$\qquad = \left(\frac{1}{2}x_1 + \frac{1}{2}y_1 + \frac{1}{2}x_2 + \frac{1}{2}y_2, x_1 + y_1 + x_2 + y_2, x_1 - y_1 + x_2 - y_2\right)$

$\qquad = \left(\frac{1}{2}x_1 + \frac{1}{2}x_2 + \frac{1}{2}y_1 + \frac{1}{2}y_2, x_1 + x_2 + y_1 + y_2, x_1 + x_2 - y_1 - y_2\right)$

$\qquad = T(\mathbf{u} + \mathbf{v})$

$T(k\mathbf{u}) = T(k(x, y))$

$\qquad = T(kx, ky)$

$\qquad = \left(\frac{1}{2}kx + \frac{1}{2}ky, kx + ky, kx - ky\right)$

$kT(\mathbf{u}) = kT(x, y)$

$\qquad = k\left(\frac{1}{2}x + \frac{1}{2}y, x + y, x - y\right)$

$\qquad = \left(\frac{1}{2}kx + \frac{1}{2}ky, kx + ky, kx - ky\right)$

$\qquad = T(k\mathbf{u})$

This is a linear transformation.

2. $T(\mathbf{u} + \mathbf{v}) = \mathbf{w} \cdot (\mathbf{u} + \mathbf{v})$

$\qquad\qquad = \mathbf{w} \cdot \mathbf{u} + \mathbf{w} \cdot \mathbf{v}$

$T(\mathbf{u}) + T(\mathbf{v}) = \mathbf{w} \cdot \mathbf{u} + \mathbf{w} \cdot \mathbf{v}$

$\qquad\qquad = T(\mathbf{u} + \mathbf{v})$

$T(k\mathbf{u}) = \mathbf{w} \cdot k\mathbf{u}$

$\qquad = k(\mathbf{w} \cdot \mathbf{u})$

$kT(\mathbf{u}) = k(\mathbf{w} \cdot \mathbf{u})$

$\qquad = T(k\mathbf{u})$

This is a linear transformation.

3. $T(\mathbf{u} + \mathbf{v}) = T\left(\begin{bmatrix} a & b \\ c & d \end{bmatrix} + \begin{bmatrix} e & f \\ g & h \end{bmatrix}\right)$

$= \left(\begin{bmatrix} a+e & b+f \\ c+g & d+h \end{bmatrix}\right)$

$= (a+e) - (d+h)$

$= a + e - d - h$

$T(\mathbf{u}) + T(\mathbf{v}) = T\left(\begin{bmatrix} a & b \\ c & d \end{bmatrix}\right) + T\left(\begin{bmatrix} e & f \\ g & h \end{bmatrix}\right)$

$= (a-d) + (e-h)$

$= a + e - d - h$

$= T(\mathbf{u} + \mathbf{v})$

$T(k\mathbf{u}) = T\left(k\begin{bmatrix} a & b \\ c & d \end{bmatrix}\right)$

$= T\left(\begin{bmatrix} ka & kb \\ kc & kd \end{bmatrix}\right)$

$= ka - kd$

$kT(\mathbf{u}) = kT\left(\begin{bmatrix} a & b \\ c & d \end{bmatrix}\right)$

$= k(a-d)$

$= ka - kd$

$= T(k\mathbf{u})$

This is a linear transformation.

4. $T(\mathbf{u} + \mathbf{v}) = T\left(\begin{bmatrix} a & b \\ c & d \end{bmatrix} + \begin{bmatrix} e & f \\ g & h \end{bmatrix}\right)$

$= \left(\begin{bmatrix} a+e & b+f \\ c+g & d+h \end{bmatrix}\right)$

$= \begin{bmatrix} (a+e)-(d+h) & b+f \\ c+g & (a+e)(d+h) \end{bmatrix}$

$= \begin{bmatrix} a+e-d-h & b+f \\ c+g & ad+ed+ah+eh \end{bmatrix}$

$T(\mathbf{u}) + T(\mathbf{v}) = T\left(\begin{bmatrix} a & b \\ c & d \end{bmatrix}\right) + T\left(\begin{bmatrix} e & f \\ g & h \end{bmatrix}\right)$

$= \begin{bmatrix} a-d & b \\ c & ad \end{bmatrix} + \begin{bmatrix} e-h & f \\ g & eh \end{bmatrix}$

$= \begin{bmatrix} a-d+e-h & b+f \\ c+g & ad+eh \end{bmatrix}$

$= \begin{bmatrix} a+e-d-h & b+f \\ c+g & ad+eh \end{bmatrix}$

$\neq T(\mathbf{u} + \mathbf{v})$

$$T(k\mathbf{u}) = T\left(k\begin{bmatrix} a & b \\ c & d \end{bmatrix}\right)$$

$$= T\left(\begin{bmatrix} ka & kb \\ kc & kd \end{bmatrix}\right)$$

$$= \begin{bmatrix} ka - kd & kb \\ kc & (ka)(kd) \end{bmatrix}$$

$$= \begin{bmatrix} ka - kd & kb \\ kc & k^2ad \end{bmatrix}$$

$$kT(\mathbf{u}) = kT\left(\begin{bmatrix} a & b \\ c & d \end{bmatrix}\right)$$

$$= k\begin{bmatrix} a - d & b \\ c & ad \end{bmatrix}$$

$$= \begin{bmatrix} ka - kd & kb \\ kc & kad \end{bmatrix}$$

$$\neq T(k\mathbf{u})$$

On both counts, this is not a linear transformation.

5. $T(\mathbf{u} + \mathbf{v}) = T\left((a_0 + a_1x + a_2x^2) + (b_0 + b_1x + b_2x^2)\right)$

$$= T\left((a_0 + b_0) + (a_1 + b_1)x + (a_2 + b_2)x^2\right)$$

$$= (a_0 + b_0) + (a_1 + b_1)(x - 1) + (a_2 + b_2)(x - 1)^2$$

$$T(\mathbf{u}) + T(\mathbf{v}) = T(a_0 + a_1x + a_2x^2) + T(b_0 + b_1x + b_2x^2)$$

$$= (a_0 + a_1(x - 1) + a_2(x - 1)^2) + (b_0 + b_1(x - 1) + b_2(x - 1)^2)$$

$$= (a_0 + b_0) + (a_1 + b_1)(x - 1) + (a_2 + b_2)(x - 1)^2$$

$$= T(\mathbf{u} + \mathbf{v})$$

$$T(k\mathbf{u}) = T\left(k(a_0 + a_1x + a_2x^2)\right)$$

$$= T(ka_0 + ka_1x + ka_2x^2)$$

$$= ka_0 + ka_1(x - 1) + ka_2(x - 1)^2$$

$$kT(\mathbf{u}) = kT(a_0 + a_1x + a_2x^2)$$

$$= k(a_0 + a_1(x - 1) + a_2(x - 1)^2)$$

$$= ka_0 + ka_1(x - 1) + ka_2(x - 1)^2$$

$$= T(k\mathbf{u})$$

This is a linear transformation.

6. $T(\mathbf{u} + \mathbf{v}) = T(f + g)$

$$= \frac{d}{dx}(x(f + g))$$

$$= x\frac{d}{dx}(f + g) + (f + g)\frac{d}{dx}x$$

$$= x(f' + g') + (f + g)$$

$$T(\mathbf{u}) + T(\mathbf{v}) = T(f) + T(g)$$

$$= \frac{d}{dx}(xf) + \frac{d}{dx}(xg)$$

$$= \left(x\frac{d}{dx}f + f\frac{d}{dx}x\right) + \left(x\frac{d}{dx}g + g\frac{d}{dx}x\right)$$

$$= (xf' + f) + (xg' + g)$$

$$= (xf' + xg') + (f + g)$$

$$= x(f' + g') + (f + g)$$

$$= T(\mathbf{u} + \mathbf{v})$$

$$T(k\mathbf{u}) = T(kf)$$

$$= \frac{d}{dx}(xkf)$$

$$= k\frac{d}{dx}(xf)$$

$$kT(\mathbf{u}) = kT(f)$$

$$= k\frac{d}{dx}(xf)$$

$$= T(k\mathbf{u})$$

This is a linear transformation.

7. (a) $\quad (x_1, x_2) = c_1\mathbf{v}_1 + c_2\mathbf{v}_2$

$$= c_1(1,1) + c_2(-1,1)$$

$$\begin{bmatrix} 1 & -1 & x_1 \\ 1 & 1 & x_2 \end{bmatrix} \longrightarrow \begin{bmatrix} 1 & -1 & x_1 \\ 0 & 2 & x_2 - x_1 \end{bmatrix} \longrightarrow \begin{bmatrix} 1 & 0 & \frac{1}{2}x_1 + \frac{1}{2}x_2 \\ 0 & 1 & \frac{1}{2}x_2 - \frac{1}{2}x_1 \end{bmatrix}$$

Thus, $\quad (x_1, x_2) = \left(\frac{1}{2}x_1 + \frac{1}{2}x_2\right)\mathbf{v}_1 + \left(\frac{1}{2}x_2 - \frac{1}{2}x_1\right)\mathbf{v}_2$

$$T(x_1, x_2) = \left(\frac{1}{2}x_1 + \frac{1}{2}x_2\right)T(\mathbf{v}_1) + \left(\frac{1}{2}x_2 - \frac{1}{2}x_1\right)T(\mathbf{v}_2)$$

$$= \left(\frac{1}{2}x_1 + \frac{1}{2}x_2\right)(3,5) + \left(\frac{1}{2}x_2 - \frac{1}{2}x_1\right)(-2,3)$$

$$= \left(\frac{3}{2}x_1 + \frac{3}{2}x_2, \frac{5}{2}x_1 + \frac{5}{2}x_2\right) + \left(-\frac{2}{2}x_2 + \frac{2}{2}x_1, \frac{3}{2}x_2 - \frac{3}{2}x_1\right)$$

$$= \left(\frac{5}{2}x_1 + \frac{1}{2}x_2, x_1 + 4x_2\right)$$

(b) $\quad T(4, -2) = (10 + -1, 4 + -8) = (9, -4)$.

8. (a) $\quad (x_1, x_2) = c_1\mathbf{v}_1 + c_2\mathbf{v}_2$

$$= c_1(1,2) + c_2(4,7)$$

$$\begin{bmatrix} 1 & 4 & x_1 \\ 2 & 7 & x_2 \end{bmatrix} \longrightarrow \begin{bmatrix} 1 & 4 & x_1 \\ 0 & -1 & x_2 - 2x_1 \end{bmatrix} \longrightarrow \begin{bmatrix} 1 & 0 & -7x_1 + 4x_2 \\ 0 & 1 & 2x_1 - x_2 \end{bmatrix}$$

Thus, $(x_1, x_2) = (-7x_1 + 4x_2)\mathbf{v}_1 + (2x_1 - x_2)\mathbf{v}_2$

$\qquad T(x_1, x_2) = (-7x_1 + 4x_2)T(\mathbf{v}_1) + (2x_1 - x_2)T(\mathbf{v}_2)$

$\qquad\qquad = (-7x_1 + 4x_2)(1, 3, 3) + (2x_1 - x_2)(0, 1, 1)$

$\qquad\qquad = (-7x_1 + 4x_2, -21x_1 + 12x_2, -21x_1 + 12x_2) + (0, 2x_1 - x_2, 2x_1 - x_2)$

$\qquad\qquad = (-7x_1 + 4x_2, -19x_1 + 11x_2, -19x_1 + 11x_2)$

(b) $T(2, 3) = (-14 + 12, -38 + 33, -38 + 33) = (-2, -5, -5).$

9. (a) $(x_1, x_2, x_3) = c_1\mathbf{v}_1 + c_2\mathbf{v}_2 + c_3\mathbf{v}_3$

$\qquad\qquad = c_1(2, -1, 0) + c_2(2, 0, 2) + c_3(4, 1, 7)$

$$\begin{bmatrix} c_1 \\ c_2 \\ c_3 \end{bmatrix} = \begin{bmatrix} 2 & 2 & 4 \\ -1 & 0 & 1 \\ 0 & 2 & 7 \end{bmatrix}^{-1} \begin{bmatrix} x_1 \\ x_2 \\ x_3 \end{bmatrix} = \frac{1}{2}\begin{bmatrix} -2 & 7 & -2 \\ -6 & 14 & -4 \\ 2 & -6 & 2 \end{bmatrix}^T \begin{bmatrix} x_1 \\ x_2 \\ x_3 \end{bmatrix}$$

$$= \frac{1}{2}\begin{bmatrix} -2 & -6 & 2 \\ 7 & 14 & -6 \\ -2 & -4 & 2 \end{bmatrix} \begin{bmatrix} x_1 \\ x_2 \\ x_3 \end{bmatrix} = \begin{bmatrix} -x_1 - 3x_2 + x_3 \\ \frac{7}{2}x_1 + 7x_2 - 3x_3 \\ -x_1 - 2x_2 + x_3 \end{bmatrix}$$

Thus, $(x_1, x_2, x_3) = (-x_1 - 3x_2 + x_3)\mathbf{v}_1 + \left(\frac{7}{2}x_1 + 7x_2 - 3x_3\right)\mathbf{v}_2 + (-x_1 - 2x_2 + x_3)\mathbf{v}_3$

$\qquad T(x_1, x_2, x_3) = (-x_1 - 3x_2 + x_3)T(\mathbf{v}_1) + \left(\frac{7}{2}x_1 + 7x_2 - 3x_3\right)T(\mathbf{v}_2)$

$\qquad\qquad\qquad\qquad + (-x_1 - 2x_2 + x_3)T(\mathbf{v}_3)$

$\qquad\qquad = (-x_1 - 3x_2 + x_3)(1, 1) + \left(\frac{7}{2}x_1 + 7x_2 - 3x_3\right)(4, 1) + (-x_1 - 2x_2 + x_3)(0, 5)$

$\qquad\qquad = (-x_1 - 3x_2 + x_3, -x_1 - 3x_2 + x_3) + \left(14x_1 + 28x_2 - 12x_3, \frac{7}{2}x_1 + 7x_2 - 3x_3\right)$

$\qquad\qquad\qquad\qquad + (0, -5x_1 - 10x_2 + 5x_3)$

$\qquad\qquad = \left(13x_1 + 25x_2 - 11x_3, \frac{-5}{2}x_1 - 6x_2 + 3x_3\right)$

(b) $T(2, 1, 5) = (26 + 25 - 55, -5 - 6 + 15) = (-4, 4).$

10. (a) $(x_1, x_2, x_3) = c_1\mathbf{v}_1 + c_2\mathbf{v}_2 + c_3\mathbf{v}_3$

$\qquad\qquad = c_1(1, 0, -5) + c_2(-1, 1, 4) + c_3(0, 1, 0)$

$$\begin{bmatrix} c_1 \\ c_2 \\ c_3 \end{bmatrix} = \begin{bmatrix} 1 & -1 & 0 \\ 0 & 1 & 1 \\ -5 & 4 & 0 \end{bmatrix}^{-1} \begin{bmatrix} x_1 \\ x_2 \\ x_3 \end{bmatrix} = \frac{1}{1}\begin{bmatrix} -4 & -5 & 5 \\ 0 & 0 & 1 \\ -1 & -1 & 1 \end{bmatrix}^T \begin{bmatrix} x_1 \\ x_2 \\ x_3 \end{bmatrix}$$

$$= \begin{bmatrix} -4 & 0 & -1 \\ -5 & 0 & -1 \\ 5 & 1 & 1 \end{bmatrix} \begin{bmatrix} x_1 \\ x_2 \\ x_3 \end{bmatrix} = \begin{bmatrix} -4x_1 - x_3 \\ -5x_1 - x_3 \\ 5x_1 + x_2 + x_3 \end{bmatrix}$$

Thus, $(x_1, x_2, x_3) = (-4x_1 - x_3)\mathbf{v}_1 + (-5x_1 - x_3)\mathbf{v}_2 + (5x_1 + x_2 + x_3)\mathbf{v}_3$

$$T(x_1, x_2, x_3) = (-4x_1 - x_3)T(\mathbf{v}_1) + (-5x_1 - x_3)T(\mathbf{v}_2) + (5x_1 + x_2 + x_3)T(\mathbf{v}_3)$$
$$= (-4x_1 - x_3)(1, 2, 1) + (-5x_1 - x_3)(2, 0, -3) + (5x_1 + x_2 + x_3)(1, 1, 1)$$
$$= (-4x_1 - x_3, -8x_1 - 2x_3, -4x_1 - x_3) + (-10x_1 - 2x_3, 0, 15x_1 + 3x_3)$$
$$\qquad\qquad + (5x_1 + x_2 + x_3, 5x_1 + x_2 + x_3, 5x_1 + x_2 + x_3)$$
$$= (-9x_1 + x_2 - 2x_3, -3x_1 + x_2 - x_3, 16x_1 + x_2 + 3x_3)$$

(b) $T(3, 6, -13) = (-27 + 6 + 26, -9 + 6 + 13, 48 + 6 - 39) = (5, 10, 15)$.

11. (a) $\operatorname{dom}(T_2 \circ T_1) = \operatorname{dom}(T_1) = R^2$

$\operatorname{codom}(T_2 \circ T_1) = \operatorname{codom}(T_2) = R^2$

$T_2 \circ T_1(x, y) = T_2(2x + y, x - y)$
$$= ((2x + y) + 3(x - y), 2(2x + y) - 5(x - y))$$
$$= (5x - 2y, -x + 7y)$$

(b) $\operatorname{dom}(T_2 \circ T_1) = \operatorname{dom}(T_1) = R^2$

$\operatorname{codom}(T_2 \circ T_1) = \operatorname{codom}(T_2) = R^3$

$T_2 \circ T_1(x, y) = T_2(x - 3y, y)$
$$= (x - 3y, y, (x - 3y) + y)$$
$$= (x - 3y, y, x - 2y)$$

(c) $\operatorname{dom}(T_2 \circ T_1) = \operatorname{dom}(T_1) = P_2$

$\operatorname{codom}(T_2 \circ T_1) = \operatorname{codom}(T_2) = P_2$

Note $T_1(\mathbf{p}) = x\mathbf{p}$ and $T_2(\mathbf{p}) = \mathbf{p}'$

so $T_2 \circ T_1(\mathbf{p}) = T_2(x\mathbf{p})$
$$= (x\mathbf{p})'$$
$$= x\mathbf{p}' + \mathbf{p}',$$

i.e., $T_2 \circ T_1(a_0 + a_1 x + a_2 x^2) = x(a_1 + 2a_2 x) + (a_0 + a_1 x + a_2 x^2)$
$$= a_0 + 2a_1 x + 3a_2 x^2$$

12. (a) $\operatorname{dom}(T_3 \circ T_2 \circ T_1) = \operatorname{dom}(T_1) = R^2$

$\operatorname{codom}(T_3 \circ T_2 \circ T_1) = \operatorname{codom}(T_3) = R^2$

$T_3 \circ T_2 \circ T_1(x, y) = T_3 \circ T_2(x + y, x - y)$
$$= T_3\big(3(x + y) - (x - y), (x + y) + 2(x - y)\big)$$
$$= T_3(2x + 4y, 3x - y)$$
$$= \big(3x - y, (2x + 4y) + (3x - y)\big)$$
$$= (3x - y, 5x + 3y)$$

(b) $\operatorname{dom}(T_3 \circ T_2 \circ T_1) = \operatorname{dom}(T_1) = R^5$

$\operatorname{codom}(T_3 \circ T_2 \circ T_1) = \operatorname{codom}(T_3) = R^2$

$$T_3 \circ T_2 \circ T_1(x_1, x_2, x_3, x_4, x_5) = T_3 \circ T_2(x_1 - x_3 - x_5, x_2 - x_4, x_1 + 3x_3 + x_5, x_2 + x_3 + x_4)$$
$$= T_3\big((x_1 - x_3 - x_5) + (x_1 + 3x_3 + x_5), (x_2 - x_4) + (x_2 + x_3 + x_4),$$
$$(x_1 - x_3 - x_5) - (x_2 - x_4) - (x_1 + 3x_3 + x_5) + (x_2 + x_3 + x_4)\big)$$
$$= T_3(2x_1 + 2x_3, 2x_2 + x_3, -3x_3 + 2x_4 - 2x_5)$$
$$= \big((2x_1 + 2x_3) - (2x_2 + x_3) + (-3x_3 + 2x_4 - 2x_5),$$
$$2(2x_1 + 2x_3) + (2x_2 + x_3) - 3(-3x_3 + 2x_4 - 2x_5)\big)$$
$$= (2x_1 - 2x_2 - 2x_3 + 2x_4 - 2x_5, 4x_1 + 2x_2 + 14x_3 - 6x_4 + 6x_5)$$

(c) $\operatorname{dom}(T_3 \circ T_2 \circ T_1) = \operatorname{dom}(T_1) = P_2$

$\operatorname{codom}(T_3 \circ T_2 \circ T_1) = \operatorname{codom}(T_3) = P_2$

$$T_3 \circ T_2 \circ T_1(a_0 + a_1 x + a_2 x^2) = T_3 \circ T_2(a_0 + a_1(x-1) + a_2(x-1)^2)$$
$$= T_3 \circ T_2(a_0 + a_1 x - a_1 + a_2 x^2 - 2a_2 x + a_2)$$
$$= T_3 \circ T_2\big((a_0 - a_1 + a_2) + (a_1 - 2a_1)x + a_2 x^2\big)$$
$$= T_3\big((a_0 - a_1 + a_2) + 2(a_1 - 2a_2)x + 3a_2 x^2\big)$$
$$= (a_0 - a_1 + a_2) + 2(a_1 - 2a_2)(x+1) + 3a_2(x+1)^2$$
$$= a_0 - a_1 + a_2 + 2(a_1 - 2a_2)x + 2(a_1 - 2a_2)+$$
$$3a_2 x^2 + 6a_2 x + 3a_2$$
$$= (a_0 + a_1) + 2(a_1 + a_2)x + 3a_2 x^2$$

SECTION 8.2   KERNEL AND RANGE

13. (a) $(x - 2y, 2x + 3y) = (b_1, b_2)$

$$\begin{bmatrix} 1 & -2 & b_1 \\ 2 & 3 & b_2 \end{bmatrix} \longrightarrow \begin{bmatrix} 1 & -2 & b_1 \\ 0 & 7 & -2b_1 + b_2 \end{bmatrix} \longrightarrow \begin{bmatrix} 1 & -2 & b_1 \\ 0 & 1 & \frac{-2}{7}b_1 + \frac{1}{7}b_2 \end{bmatrix}$$

Since the system is consistent for all b_i, then $R(T) = R^2$, and a basis is $B = \{(1,0),(0,1)\}$.

(b) $(x - 2y, 2x + 3y) = (0,0)$

$$\begin{bmatrix} 1 & -2 & 0 \\ 2 & 3 & 0 \end{bmatrix} \longrightarrow \begin{bmatrix} 1 & -2 & 0 \\ 0 & 7 & 0 \end{bmatrix} \longrightarrow \begin{bmatrix} 1 & 0 & 0 \\ 0 & 1 & 0 \end{bmatrix}$$

Since the only solution is $x = 0, y = 0$, then $\ker(T) = \{(0,0)\}$, which has no basis.

(c) rank $(T) = 2$,   nullity $(T) = 0$.

14. (a) $(x + 2y + z, -x - 2y - 5z, 2x + 4y, x + 2y + 2z) = (b_1, b_2, b_3, b_4)$

$$\begin{bmatrix} 1 & 2 & 1 & b_1 \\ -1 & -2 & -5 & b_2 \\ 2 & 4 & 0 & b_3 \\ 1 & 2 & 2 & b_4 \end{bmatrix} \longrightarrow \begin{bmatrix} 1 & 2 & 1 & b_1 \\ 0 & 0 & -4 & b_1 + b_2 \\ 0 & 0 & -2 & -2b_1 + b_3 \\ 0 & 0 & 1 & -b_1 + b_4 \end{bmatrix} \longrightarrow \begin{bmatrix} 1 & 2 & 1 & b_1 \\ 0 & 0 & 1 & \frac{-1}{4}b_1 - \frac{1}{4}b_2 \\ 0 & 0 & 0 & \frac{-5}{2}b_1 - \frac{1}{2}b_2 + b_3 \\ 0 & 0 & 0 & \frac{-3}{4}b_1 + \frac{1}{4}b_2 + b_4 \end{bmatrix}$$

For consistency, $\dfrac{-5}{2}b_1 - \dfrac{1}{2}b_2 + b_3 = 0,$ i.e., $b_3 = \dfrac{5}{2}b_1 + \dfrac{1}{2}b_2$

and $\dfrac{-3}{4}b_1 + \dfrac{1}{4}b_2 + b_4 = 0,$ i.e., $b_4 = \dfrac{3}{4}b_1 - \dfrac{1}{4}b_2$

Let $b_1 = s$ and $b_2 = t$;

then $(b_1, b_2, b_3, b_4) = \left(s, t, \dfrac{5}{2}s + \dfrac{1}{2}t, \dfrac{3}{4}s - \dfrac{1}{4}t\right)$

$$= \left(s, 0, \dfrac{5}{2}s, \dfrac{3}{4}s\right) + \left(0, t, \dfrac{1}{2}t, \dfrac{-1}{4}t\right)$$

$$= s\left(1, 0, \dfrac{5}{2}, \dfrac{3}{4}\right) + t\left(0, 1, \dfrac{1}{2}, \dfrac{-1}{4}\right)$$

$$= \dfrac{1}{4}s(4, 0, 10, 3) + \dfrac{1}{4}t(0, 4, 2, -1)$$

so a basis for $R(T)$ is $B = \{(4, 0, 10, 3), (0, 4, 2, -1)\}$.

(b) $(x + 2y + z, -x - 2y - 5z, 2x + 4y, x + 2y + 2z) = (0, 0, 0, 0)$

$$\begin{bmatrix} 1 & 2 & 1 & 0 \\ -1 & -2 & -5 & 0 \\ 2 & 4 & 0 & 0 \\ 1 & 2 & 2 & 0 \end{bmatrix} \longrightarrow \begin{bmatrix} 1 & 2 & 1 & 0 \\ 0 & 0 & -4 & 0 \\ 0 & 0 & -2 & 0 \\ 0 & 0 & 1 & 0 \end{bmatrix} \longrightarrow \begin{bmatrix} 1 & 2 & 0 & 0 \\ 0 & 0 & 1 & 0 \\ 0 & 0 & 0 & 0 \\ 0 & 0 & 0 & 0 \end{bmatrix}$$

Let $y = t$;

then $x + 2y = 0$ i.e., $x = -2y = -2t$

and $z = 0$

so $(x, y, z) = (-2t, t, 0) = t(-2, 1, 0)$

so a basis for $\ker(T)$ is $B = \{(-2, 1, 0)\}$.

(c) rank $(T) = 2$, nullity $(T) = 1$.

15.
$$\begin{bmatrix} 1 & -1 & -2 \\ 3 & -1 & 0 \\ 1 & 1 & 4 \end{bmatrix} \longrightarrow \begin{bmatrix} 1 & -1 & -2 \\ 0 & 2 & 6 \\ 0 & 2 & 6 \end{bmatrix} \longrightarrow \begin{bmatrix} 1 & 0 & 1 \\ 0 & 1 & 3 \\ 0 & 0 & 0 \end{bmatrix}$$

(a) Since leading 1's remain in columns 1 and 2,

a basis for $R(T)$ is $B = \left\{ \begin{bmatrix} 1 \\ 3 \\ 1 \end{bmatrix}, \begin{bmatrix} -1 \\ -1 \\ 1 \end{bmatrix} \right\}$.

(b) Let $x_3 = t$;

then $x_1 + x_3 = 0,$ i.e., $x_1 = -x_3 = -t$

and $x_2 + 3x_3 = 0,$ i.e., $x_2 = -3x_3 = -3t$

so $\begin{bmatrix} x_1 \\ x_2 \\ x_3 \end{bmatrix} = \begin{bmatrix} -t \\ -3t \\ t \end{bmatrix} = t \begin{bmatrix} -1 \\ -3 \\ 1 \end{bmatrix}$

so a basis for $\ker(T)$ is $B = \left\{ \begin{bmatrix} -1 \\ -3 \\ 1 \end{bmatrix} \right\}$.

(c) rank $(T) = 2$, nullity $(T) = 1$.

16. $\begin{bmatrix} 3 & -3 & -3 & 3 \\ 2 & 1 & 1 & 2 \\ 2 & 0 & 0 & 5 \end{bmatrix} \longrightarrow \begin{bmatrix} 1 & -1 & -1 & 1 \\ 0 & 3 & 3 & 0 \\ 0 & 2 & 2 & 3 \end{bmatrix} \longrightarrow \begin{bmatrix} 1 & -1 & -1 & 0 \\ 0 & 1 & 1 & 0 \\ 0 & 0 & 0 & 3 \end{bmatrix} \longrightarrow \begin{bmatrix} 1 & 0 & 0 & 0 \\ 0 & 1 & 1 & 0 \\ 0 & 0 & 0 & 1 \end{bmatrix}$

(a) Since leading 1's remain in columns 1,2 and 4,

a basis for $R(T)$ is $B = \left\{ \begin{bmatrix} 3 \\ 2 \\ 2 \end{bmatrix}, \begin{bmatrix} -3 \\ 1 \\ 0 \end{bmatrix}, \begin{bmatrix} 3 \\ 2 \\ 5 \end{bmatrix} \right\}$.

(b) Let $x_3 = t$;

then $x_1 = 0$

and $x_2 + x_3 = 0$, i.e., $x_2 = -x_3 = -t$

and $x_4 = 0$

so $\begin{bmatrix} x_1 \\ x_2 \\ x_3 \\ x_4 \end{bmatrix} = \begin{bmatrix} 0 \\ -t \\ t \\ 0 \end{bmatrix} = t \begin{bmatrix} 0 \\ -1 \\ 1 \\ 0 \end{bmatrix}$

so a basis for $\ker(T)$ is $B = \left\{ \begin{bmatrix} 0 \\ -1 \\ 1 \\ 0 \end{bmatrix} \right\}$.

(c) rank $(T) = 3$, nullity $(T) = 1$.

17. (a) $a_0 + a_1(x + 1) + a_2(x + 1)^2 = b_0 + b_1 x + b_2 x^2$

$a_0 + a_1 x + a_1 + a_2 x^2 + 2a_2 x + a_2 = b_0 + b_1 x + b_2 x^2$

$(a_0 + a_1 + a_2) + (a_1 + 2a_2)x + a_2 x^2 = b_0 + b_1 x + b_2 x^2$

$\begin{bmatrix} 1 & 1 & 1 \\ 0 & 1 & 2 \\ 0 & 0 & 1 \end{bmatrix} \begin{bmatrix} a_0 \\ a_1 \\ a_2 \end{bmatrix} = \begin{bmatrix} b_0 \\ b_1 \\ b_2 \end{bmatrix}$

Since the system is consistent for all b_i,

then $R(T) = P_2$, and a basis is $B = \{1, x, x^2\}$.

(b) $a_0 + a_1(x + 1) + a_2(x + 1)^2 = 0$

Since the only solution is $a_0 = 0, a_1 = 0, a_2 = 0$,

then $\ker(T) = \{0\}$, which has no basis.

(c) rank $(T) = 3$, nullity $(T) = 0$.

18. (a) $\dfrac{d}{dx}(a_0 + a_1x + a_2x^2) = b_0 + b_1x$

$$a_1 + 2a_2x = b_0 + b_1x$$

Thus $\quad a_1 = b_0 \quad a_2 = \dfrac{1}{2}b_1,$

so the system is consistent for all $\quad b_i,$

i.e., $\quad R(D) = P_1,\quad$ and a basis is $\quad B = \{1, x\}.$

(b) $\dfrac{d}{dx}(a_0 + a_1x + a_2x^2) = 0$

$$a_1 + 2a_2x = 0$$

Since $\quad a_1 = 0 \quad$ and $\quad a_2 = 0 \quad$ but a_0 is unrestricted,

then $\quad \ker(D) = \{a_0 : a_0 \text{ is real }\}$

and a basis is $\quad B = \{1\}.$

(c) $\quad$ rank $(D) = 2,\quad$ nullity $(D) = 1.$

19. (a) $\displaystyle\int_{-1}^{1}(a_0 + a_1x)dx = b$

$$\left[a_0x + \dfrac{1}{2}a_1x^2\right]_{-1}^{1} = b$$

$$\left(a_0 + \dfrac{1}{2}a_1\right) - \left(-a_0 + \dfrac{1}{2}a_1\right) = b$$

$$2a_0 = b$$

Thus $\quad a_0 = \dfrac{1}{2}b,$

so the system is consistent for all $b,$

i.e., $\quad R(J) = R,\quad$ and a basis is $\quad B = \{1\}.$

(b) $\displaystyle\int_{-1}^{1}(a_0 + a_1x)dx = 0$

$$\left[a_0x + \dfrac{1}{2}a_1x^2\right]_{-1}^{1} = 0$$

$$\left(a_0 + \dfrac{1}{2}a_1\right) - \left(-a_0 + \dfrac{1}{2}a_1\right) = 0$$

$$2a_0 = 0$$

Since $\quad a_0 = 0 \quad$ but a_1 is unrestricted,

then $\quad \ker(J) = \{a_1x : a_1 \text{ is real }\}$

and a basis is $\quad B = \{x\}.$

(c) $\quad$ rank $(J) = 1,\quad$ nullity $(J) = 1.$

20. (a) rank (T) + nullity $(T) = \dim \operatorname{dom} (T)$
  2   + nullity $(T) =$ 3
        nullity $(T) =$ 1.

  (b) rank (T) + nullity $(T) = \dim \operatorname{dom} (T)$
   1   + nullity $(T) =$ 5
        nullity $(T) =$ 4.

  (c) rank (T) + nullity $(T) = \dim \operatorname{dom} (T)$
   3   + nullity $(T) =$ 4
        nullity $(T) =$ 1.

  (d) rank (T) + nullity $(T) = \dim \operatorname{dom} (T)$
   6   + nullity $(T) =$ 6
        nullity $(T) =$ 0.

SECTION 8.3   *INVERSE LINEAR TRANSFORMATIONS*

21. $[T] = \begin{bmatrix} 1 & 2 \\ 3 & -1 \end{bmatrix}$ is invertible; $[T]^{-1} = \dfrac{1}{-7} \begin{bmatrix} -1 & -2 \\ -3 & 1 \end{bmatrix} = \dfrac{1}{7} \begin{bmatrix} 1 & 2 \\ 3 & -1 \end{bmatrix}$

   so $T^{-1}(x,y) = \left(\dfrac{1}{7}x + \dfrac{2}{7}y, \dfrac{3}{7}x - \dfrac{1}{7}y \right).$

22. $[T] = \begin{bmatrix} 6 & -9 \\ -2 & 3 \\ 4 & -6 \end{bmatrix}$; $\begin{bmatrix} 6 & -9 & 0 \\ -2 & 3 & 0 \\ 4 & -6 & 0 \end{bmatrix} \longrightarrow \begin{bmatrix} 1 & -3/2 & 0 \\ 0 & 0 & 0 \\ 0 & 0 & 0 \end{bmatrix}$ so $\ker(T) \neq \{\mathbf{0}\}$,

   thus T is not invertible.

23. $\det A = (\pi + 3)(\pi - 3) - (1)(\pi^2 - 9) = (\pi^2 - 9) - (\pi^2 - 9) = 0$

   so A is not invertible, thus T is not invertible.

24. $\det A = 3(30) - 3(33) - 2(-12) = 15 \neq 0$ so A is invertible; so T^{-1} is multiplication by

   $$A^{-1} = \frac{1}{15} \begin{bmatrix} 30 & -5 & -5 \\ -33 & 3 & 9 \\ -12 & -3 & 6 \end{bmatrix}^{T} = \frac{1}{15} \begin{bmatrix} 30 & -33 & -12 \\ -5 & 3 & -3 \\ -5 & 9 & 6 \end{bmatrix}$$

25. $[T] = \begin{bmatrix} 0 & 0 & 0 & 1 \\ 0 & 0 & 1 & 0 \\ 0 & 1 & 0 & 0 \\ 1 & 0 & 0 & 0 \end{bmatrix}$ is invertible; $[T]^{-1} = \dfrac{1}{1} \begin{bmatrix} 0 & 0 & 0 & 1 \\ 0 & 0 & 1 & 0 \\ 0 & 1 & 0 & 0 \\ 1 & 0 & 0 & 0 \end{bmatrix}^{T} = \begin{bmatrix} 0 & 0 & 0 & 1 \\ 0 & 0 & 1 & 0 \\ 0 & 1 & 0 & 0 \\ 1 & 0 & 0 & 0 \end{bmatrix} = [T]$

   so $T^{-1} = T$

26. $\ker(T) = \{(x,0); x \text{ is real }\} \neq \{0\}$, so T is not invertible.

27. $\ker(T) = \{p \text{ in } P_2 : xp = 0\} = \{p \text{ in } P_2 : p = 0\} = \{0\}$,

    so T is invertible. Namely, $T^{-1} : R(T) \to P_2$ where $T^{-1}(p(x)) = \dfrac{p(x)}{x}$,

    since $T\left(T^{-1}(\mathbf{p})\right) = T\left(\dfrac{\mathbf{P}}{x}\right) = x\left(\dfrac{\mathbf{P}}{x}\right) = \mathbf{p}$ and $T\left(T^{-1}(\mathbf{p})\right) = T^{-1}(x\mathbf{p}) = \dfrac{x\mathbf{p}}{x} = \mathbf{p}$.

28. $\ker(T) = \{p \text{ in } P_3 : p(x-3) = 0\} = \{p \text{ in } P_3 : p(x) = 0\} = \{0\}$,

    so T is invertible. Namely, $T^{-1} : P_3 \to P_3$ where $T^{-1}(p(x)) = p(x+3)$,

    since $T\left(T^{-1}(p(x))\right) = T(p(x+3)) = p(x+3-3) = p(x)$

    and $T^{-1}\left(T(p(x))\right) = T^{-1}(p(x-3)) = p(x-3+3) = p(x)$.

29. (a) rank $(T) = m$

    dim dom $(T) = \dim(R^m) = m$

    nullity $(T) = $ dim dom $(T) - $ rank $(T) = m - m = 0$,   so T is one–to–one.

    (b) rank $(T) = m - 1$

    dim dom $(T) = \dim(R^m) = m$

    nullity $(T) = $ dim dom $(T) - $ rank $(T) = m - (m-1) = 1$,   so T is not one–to–one.

    (c) rank $(T) \leq \dim(P_n) = n + 1$

    dim dom $(T) = \dim(P_m) = m + 1$

    nullity $(T) = $ dim dom $(T) - $ rank $(T) \geq (m+1) - (n+1) = m - n > 0$,

    $$\text{so } T \text{ is not one–to–one.}$$

    (d) rank $(T) = \dim R(T) = \dim(P_3) = 4$

    dim dom $(T) = \dim(M_{22}) = 4$

    nullity $(T) = $ dim dom $(T) - $ rank $(T) = 4 - 4 = 0$,   so T is one–to–one.

SECTION 8.4   *MATRICES OF GENERAL LINEAR TRANSFORMATIONS*

30. (a) $[T(\mathbf{v}_1)]_B = \begin{bmatrix} 1 \\ -1 \end{bmatrix}$, $[T(\mathbf{v}_2)]_B = \begin{bmatrix} 2 \\ 3 \end{bmatrix}$.

    (b) $T(\mathbf{v}_1) = 1\mathbf{v}_1 + -1\mathbf{v}_2 = 1(1,1) + -1(1,-1) = (0,2)$

    $T(\mathbf{v}_2) = 2\mathbf{v}_1 + 3\mathbf{v}_2 = 2(1,1) + 3(1,-1) = (5,-1)$.

    (c) $T\left(\begin{bmatrix} x \\ y \end{bmatrix}\right) = \begin{bmatrix} 0 & 5 \\ 2 & -1 \end{bmatrix} \begin{bmatrix} x \\ y \end{bmatrix}_B = \begin{bmatrix} 0 & 5 \\ 2 & -1 \end{bmatrix} \begin{bmatrix} 1 & 1 \\ 1 & -1 \end{bmatrix}^{-1} \begin{bmatrix} x \\ y \end{bmatrix}$

    $$= \begin{bmatrix} 0 & 5 \\ 2 & -1 \end{bmatrix} \frac{1}{2} \begin{bmatrix} 1 & 1 \\ 1 & -1 \end{bmatrix} \begin{bmatrix} x \\ y \end{bmatrix} = \frac{1}{2} \begin{bmatrix} 5 & -5 \\ 1 & 3 \end{bmatrix} \begin{bmatrix} x \\ y \end{bmatrix} = \frac{1}{2} \begin{bmatrix} 5x - 5y \\ x + 3y \end{bmatrix},$$

    $$\text{i.e.,}\quad T(x,y) = \left(\frac{5}{2}x - \frac{5}{2}y, \frac{1}{2}x + \frac{3}{2}y\right).$$

    (d) $T(2,4) = (5 - 10, 1 + 6) = (-5, 7)$.

31. (a) $[T(\mathbf{v}_1)]_{B'} = \begin{bmatrix} 2 \\ 1 \\ 3 \end{bmatrix}$, $[T(\mathbf{v}_2)]_{B'} = \begin{bmatrix} 1 \\ 3 \\ 0 \end{bmatrix}$.

(b) $T(\mathbf{v}_1) = 2\mathbf{w}_1 + 1\mathbf{w}_2 + 3\mathbf{w}_3 = 2(1,-1,1) + 1(1,0,1) + 3(0,1,-1) = (3,1,0)$
$T(\mathbf{v}_2) = 1\mathbf{w}_1 + 3\mathbf{w}_2 + 0\mathbf{w}_3 = 1(1,-1,1) + 3(1,0,1) + 0(0,1,-1) = (4,-1,4)$.

(c) $T\left(\begin{bmatrix} x \\ y \end{bmatrix}\right) = \begin{bmatrix} 3 & 4 \\ 1 & -1 \\ 0 & 4 \end{bmatrix} \begin{bmatrix} x \\ y \end{bmatrix}_B = \begin{bmatrix} 3 & 4 \\ 1 & -1 \\ 0 & 4 \end{bmatrix} \begin{bmatrix} 1 & 1 \\ 2 & 3 \end{bmatrix}^{-1} \begin{bmatrix} x \\ y \end{bmatrix}$

$= \begin{bmatrix} 3 & 4 \\ 1 & -1 \\ 0 & 4 \end{bmatrix} \begin{bmatrix} 3 & -1 \\ -2 & 1 \end{bmatrix} \begin{bmatrix} x \\ y \end{bmatrix} = \begin{bmatrix} 1 & 1 \\ 5 & -2 \\ -8 & 4 \end{bmatrix} \begin{bmatrix} x \\ y \end{bmatrix} = \begin{bmatrix} x+y \\ 5x-2y \\ -8x+4y \end{bmatrix}$,

i.e., $T(x,y) = (x+y, 5x-2y, -8x+4y)$.

(d) $T(3,7) = (3+7, 15-14, -24+28) = (10,1,4)$.

32. (a) $T(\mathbf{v}_1) = T(1,1) = (1,3)$; $T(\mathbf{v}_2) = T(1,2) = (0,4)$

$[T(\mathbf{v}_1)]_B = \begin{bmatrix} 1 & 1 \\ 1 & 2 \end{bmatrix}^{-1} \begin{bmatrix} 1 \\ 3 \end{bmatrix} = \begin{bmatrix} 2 & -1 \\ -1 & 1 \end{bmatrix} \begin{bmatrix} 1 \\ 3 \end{bmatrix} = \begin{bmatrix} -1 \\ 2 \end{bmatrix}$

$[T(\mathbf{v}_2)]_B = \begin{bmatrix} 1 & 1 \\ 1 & 2 \end{bmatrix}^{-1} \begin{bmatrix} 0 \\ 4 \end{bmatrix} = \begin{bmatrix} 2 & -1 \\ -1 & 1 \end{bmatrix} \begin{bmatrix} 0 \\ 4 \end{bmatrix} = \begin{bmatrix} -4 \\ 4 \end{bmatrix}$.

so $[T]_B = \begin{bmatrix} -1 & -4 \\ 2 & 4 \end{bmatrix}$.

(b) $[(5,-3)]_B = \begin{bmatrix} 2 & -1 \\ -1 & 1 \end{bmatrix} \begin{bmatrix} 5 \\ -3 \end{bmatrix} = \begin{bmatrix} 13 \\ -8 \end{bmatrix}$,

so $[T(5,-3)]_B = \begin{bmatrix} -1 & -4 \\ 2 & 4 \end{bmatrix} \begin{bmatrix} 13 \\ -8 \end{bmatrix} = \begin{bmatrix} 19 \\ -6 \end{bmatrix}$,

so $T(5,-3) = 19\mathbf{v}_1 + -6\mathbf{v}_2 = 19(1,1) + -6(1,2) = (13,7)$.

33. (a) $T(\mathbf{u}_1) = T(1,0,1) = (3,2)$
$T(\mathbf{u}_2) = T(0,1,-1) = (-3,3)$
$T(\mathbf{u}_3) = T(1,-1,1) = (4,0)$.

$[T(\mathbf{u}_1)]_{B'} = \begin{bmatrix} 1 & 1 \\ 2 & 3 \end{bmatrix}^{-1} \begin{bmatrix} 3 \\ 2 \end{bmatrix} = \begin{bmatrix} 3 & -1 \\ -2 & 1 \end{bmatrix} \begin{bmatrix} 3 \\ 2 \end{bmatrix} = \begin{bmatrix} 7 \\ -4 \end{bmatrix}$

$[T(\mathbf{u}_2)]_{B'} = \begin{bmatrix} 1 & 1 \\ 2 & 3 \end{bmatrix}^{-1} \begin{bmatrix} -3 \\ 3 \end{bmatrix} = \begin{bmatrix} 3 & -1 \\ -2 & 1 \end{bmatrix} \begin{bmatrix} -3 \\ 3 \end{bmatrix} = \begin{bmatrix} -12 \\ 9 \end{bmatrix}$

$$[T(\mathbf{u}_3)]_{B'} = \begin{bmatrix} 1 & 1 \\ 2 & 3 \end{bmatrix}^{-1} \begin{bmatrix} 4 \\ 0 \end{bmatrix} = \begin{bmatrix} 3 & -1 \\ -2 & 1 \end{bmatrix} \begin{bmatrix} 4 \\ 0 \end{bmatrix} = \begin{bmatrix} 12 \\ -8 \end{bmatrix}.$$

so $[T]_{B',B} = \begin{bmatrix} 7 & -12 & 12 \\ -4 & 9 & -8 \end{bmatrix}.$

(b) $[(3,1,-1)]_B = \begin{bmatrix} 1 & 0 & 1 \\ 0 & 1 & -1 \\ 1 & -1 & 1 \end{bmatrix}^{-1} \begin{bmatrix} 3 \\ 1 \\ -1 \end{bmatrix} = \dfrac{1}{-1} \begin{bmatrix} 0 & -1 & -1 \\ -1 & 0 & 1 \\ -1 & 1 & 1 \end{bmatrix}^T \begin{bmatrix} 3 \\ 1 \\ -1 \end{bmatrix}$

$$= \begin{bmatrix} 0 & 1 & 1 \\ 1 & 0 & -1 \\ 1 & -1 & -1 \end{bmatrix} \begin{bmatrix} 3 \\ 1 \\ -1 \end{bmatrix} = \begin{bmatrix} 0 \\ 4 \\ 3 \end{bmatrix},$$

so $[T(3,1,-1)]_{B'} = \begin{bmatrix} 7 & -12 & 12 \\ -4 & 9 & -8 \end{bmatrix} \begin{bmatrix} 0 \\ 4 \\ 3 \end{bmatrix} = \begin{bmatrix} -12 \\ 12 \end{bmatrix},$

so $T(3,1,-1) = -12\mathbf{v}_1 + 12\mathbf{v}_2 = -12(1,2) + 12(1,3) = (0,12).$

34. (a) $T(\mathbf{v}_1) = (4,4,2)$

$T(\mathbf{v}_2) = (2,1,3)$

$T(\mathbf{v}_3) = (1,0,-1).$

$$\begin{bmatrix} 1 & 1 & -1 \\ 1 & 2 & 0 \\ 3 & 0 & 1 \end{bmatrix}^{-1} = \frac{1}{7} \begin{bmatrix} 2 & -1 & -6 \\ -1 & 4 & 3 \\ 2 & -1 & 1 \end{bmatrix}^T = \frac{1}{7} \begin{bmatrix} 2 & -1 & 2 \\ -1 & 4 & -1 \\ -6 & 3 & 1 \end{bmatrix},$$

so $[T]_B = \dfrac{1}{7} \begin{bmatrix} 2 & -1 & 2 \\ -1 & 4 & -1 \\ -6 & 3 & 1 \end{bmatrix} \begin{bmatrix} 4 & 2 & 1 \\ 4 & 1 & 0 \\ 2 & 3 & -1 \end{bmatrix} = \dfrac{1}{7} \begin{bmatrix} 8 & 9 & 0 \\ 10 & -1 & 0 \\ -10 & -6 & -7 \end{bmatrix}.$

(b) $[(1,1,1)]_B = \dfrac{1}{7} \begin{bmatrix} 2 & -1 & 2 \\ -1 & 4 & -1 \\ -6 & 3 & 1 \end{bmatrix} \begin{bmatrix} 1 \\ 1 \\ 1 \end{bmatrix} = \dfrac{1}{7} \begin{bmatrix} 3 \\ 2 \\ -2 \end{bmatrix},$

so $[T(1,1,1)]_B = \dfrac{1}{7} \begin{bmatrix} 8 & 9 & 0 \\ 10 & -1 & 0 \\ -10 & -6 & -7 \end{bmatrix} \dfrac{1}{7} \begin{bmatrix} 3 \\ 2 \\ -2 \end{bmatrix} = \dfrac{1}{49} \begin{bmatrix} 42 \\ 28 \\ -28 \end{bmatrix} = \dfrac{2}{7} \begin{bmatrix} 3 \\ 2 \\ -2 \end{bmatrix},$

so $T(1,1,1) = \dfrac{2}{7}[3\mathbf{v}_1 + 2\mathbf{v}_2 - 2\mathbf{v}_3]$

$$= \dfrac{2}{7}[3(1,1,3) + 2(1,2,0) - 2(-1,0,1)]$$

$$= \dfrac{2}{7}[(7,7,7)] = (2,2,2)$$

35. (a) $T(\mathbf{u}_1) = T(1) = x(1) = x$

$T(\mathbf{u}_2) = T(x) = x(x+1) = x + x^2$

$[T(\mathbf{u}_1)]_{B'} = [x]_{B'} = [0 \cdot 1 + 1 \cdot x + 0 \cdot x^2]_{B'} = \begin{bmatrix} 0 \\ 1 \\ 0 \end{bmatrix}$

$[T(\mathbf{u}_2)]_{B'} = [x + x^2]_{B'} = [0 \cdot 1 + 1 \cdot x + 1 \cdot x^2]_{B'} = \begin{bmatrix} 0 \\ 1 \\ 1 \end{bmatrix}$,

so $[T]_{B',B} = \begin{bmatrix} 0 & 0 \\ 1 & 1 \\ 0 & 1 \end{bmatrix}$

(b) $[3x - 5]_B = [-5 \cdot 1 + 3 \cdot x]_B = \begin{bmatrix} -5 \\ 3 \end{bmatrix}$,

$[T(3x - 5)]_{B'} = \begin{bmatrix} 0 & 0 \\ 1 & 1 \\ 0 & 1 \end{bmatrix} \begin{bmatrix} -5 \\ 3 \end{bmatrix} = \begin{bmatrix} 0 \\ -2 \\ 3 \end{bmatrix}$,

so $T(3x - 5) = 0\mathbf{v}_1 - 2\mathbf{v}_2 + 3\mathbf{v}_3 = 0 \cdot 1 + -2 \cdot x + 3 \cdot x^2 = -2x + 3x^2$.

36. (a) $T(\mathbf{u}_1) = T(1) = \dfrac{d}{dx} 1 = 0$

$T(\mathbf{u}_2) = T(x) = \dfrac{d}{dx} x = 1$

$T(\mathbf{u}_3) = T(x^2) = \dfrac{d}{dx} x^2 = 2x$

$[T(\mathbf{u}_1)]_{B'} = [0]_{B'} = [0 \cdot 1 + 0 \cdot x]_{B'} = \begin{bmatrix} 0 \\ 0 \end{bmatrix}$,

$[T(\mathbf{u}_2)]_{B'} = [1]_{B'} = [1 \cdot 1 + 0 \cdot x]_{B'} = \begin{bmatrix} 1 \\ 0 \end{bmatrix}$,

$[T(\mathbf{u}_3)]_{B'} = [2x]_{B'} = [0 \cdot 1 + 2 \cdot x]_{B'} = \begin{bmatrix} 0 \\ 2 \end{bmatrix}$,

so $[T]_{B',B} = \begin{bmatrix} 0 & 1 & 0 \\ 0 & 0 & 2 \end{bmatrix}$.

(b) $[4 - 3x + 2x^2]_B = [4 \cdot 1 - 3 \cdot x + 2 \cdot x^2]_B = \begin{bmatrix} 4 \\ -3 \\ 2 \end{bmatrix}$,

$[T(4 - 3x + 2x^2)]_{B'} = \begin{bmatrix} 0 & 1 & 0 \\ 0 & 0 & 2 \end{bmatrix} \begin{bmatrix} 4 \\ -3 \\ 2 \end{bmatrix} = \begin{bmatrix} -3 \\ 4 \end{bmatrix}$,

so $\dfrac{d}{dx}(4 - 3x + 2x^2) = T(4 - 3x + 2x^2) = -3\mathbf{v}_1 + 4\mathbf{v}_2 = -3 \cdot 1 + 4 \cdot x = -3 + 4x$

37. (a) $T(\mathbf{v}_1) = T(1) = 1$

$T(\mathbf{v}_2) = T(x) = 3x - 2$

$T(\mathbf{v}_3) = T(x^2) = (3x - 2)^2 = 9x^2 - 12x + 4$

$$[T(\mathbf{v}_1)]_B = [1]_B = [1\cdot 1 + 0\cdot x + x\cdot x^2] = \begin{bmatrix} 1 \\ 0 \\ 0 \end{bmatrix},$$

$$[T(\mathbf{v}_2)]_B = [3x - 2]_B = [-2\cdot 1 + 3\cdot x + 0\cdot x^2] = \begin{bmatrix} -2 \\ 3 \\ 0 \end{bmatrix},$$

$$[T(\mathbf{v}_3)]_B = [9x^2 - 12x + 4]_B = [4\cdot 1 + -12\cdot x + 9\cdot x^2] = \begin{bmatrix} 4 \\ -12 \\ 9 \end{bmatrix},$$

so $[T]_B = \begin{bmatrix} 1 & -2 & 4 \\ 0 & 3 & -12 \\ 0 & 0 & 9 \end{bmatrix}.$

   (b) $[4 - 3x + 2x^2]_B = [4\cdot 1 - 3\cdot x + 2\cdot x^2]_B = \begin{bmatrix} 4 \\ -3 \\ 2 \end{bmatrix},$

$$[T(4 - 3x + 2x^2)]_B = \begin{bmatrix} 0 & -2 & 4 \\ 0 & 3 & -12 \\ 0 & 0 & 9 \end{bmatrix} \begin{bmatrix} 4 \\ -3 \\ 2 \end{bmatrix} = \begin{bmatrix} 18 \\ -33 \\ 18 \end{bmatrix},$$

so $T(4 - 3x + 2x^2) = 18\mathbf{v}_1 - 33\mathbf{v}_2 + 18\mathbf{v}_3 = 18 - 33x + 18x^2.$

38. (a) $T(\mathbf{v}_1) = T(e^x) = \dfrac{d^2 e^x}{dx^2} + 3\dfrac{de^x}{dx} + 2e^x = e^x + 3e^x + 2e^x = 6e^x$

$T(\mathbf{v}_2) = T(e^{2x}) = \dfrac{d^2 e^{2x}}{dx^2} + 3\dfrac{de^{2x}}{dx} + 2e^{2x} = 4e^{2x} + 6e^{2x} + 2e^{2x} = 12e^{2x}$

$T(\mathbf{v}_3) = T(e^{3x}) = \dfrac{d^2 e^{3x}}{dx^2} + 3\dfrac{de^{3x}}{dx} + 2e^{3x} = 9e^{3x} + 9e^{3x} + 2e^{3x} = 20e^{3x}$

$$[T(\mathbf{v}_1)]_B = \begin{bmatrix} 6 \\ 0 \\ 0 \end{bmatrix}$$

$$[T(\mathbf{v}_2)]_B = \begin{bmatrix} 0 \\ 12 \\ 0 \end{bmatrix}$$

$$[T(\mathbf{v}_3)]_B = \begin{bmatrix} 0 \\ 0 \\ 20 \end{bmatrix},$$

so $[T]_B = \begin{bmatrix} 6 & 0 & 0 \\ 0 & 12 & 0 \\ 0 & 0 & 20 \end{bmatrix}.$

(b) $\begin{bmatrix} 6 & 0 & 0 & 1 \\ 0 & 12 & 0 & 2 \\ 0 & 0 & 20 & 1 \end{bmatrix} \longrightarrow \begin{bmatrix} 1 & 0 & 0 & 1/6 \\ 0 & 1 & 0 & 1/6 \\ 0 & 0 & 1 & 1/20 \end{bmatrix}$

so the only solution f in V is $\dfrac{1}{6}e^x + \dfrac{1}{6}e^{2x} + \dfrac{1}{20}e^{3x}$

39. $T(\mathbf{u}_1) = \begin{bmatrix} 5 \\ -2 \end{bmatrix}, \quad T(\mathbf{u}_2) = \begin{bmatrix} 9 \\ -3 \end{bmatrix},$

so $[T]_B = \begin{bmatrix} 1 & 2 \\ 3 & 5 \end{bmatrix}^{-1} \begin{bmatrix} 5 & 9 \\ -2 & -3 \end{bmatrix} = \dfrac{1}{-1}\begin{bmatrix} 5 & -2 \\ -3 & 1 \end{bmatrix}\begin{bmatrix} 5 & 9 \\ -2 & -3 \end{bmatrix}$

$= \begin{bmatrix} -5 & 2 \\ 3 & -1 \end{bmatrix}\begin{bmatrix} 5 & 9 \\ -2 & -3 \end{bmatrix} = \begin{bmatrix} -29 & -51 \\ 17 & 30 \end{bmatrix}.$

$P_{B,B'} = \begin{bmatrix} 1 & 2 \\ 3 & 5 \end{bmatrix}^{-1} \begin{bmatrix} 2 & 1 \\ 3 & 2 \end{bmatrix} = \begin{bmatrix} -5 & 2 \\ 3 & -1 \end{bmatrix}\begin{bmatrix} 2 & 1 \\ 3 & 2 \end{bmatrix} = \begin{bmatrix} -4 & -1 \\ 3 & 1 \end{bmatrix},$

$P_{B,B'}^{-1} = \begin{bmatrix} -4 & -1 \\ 3 & 1 \end{bmatrix}^{-1} = \dfrac{1}{-1}\begin{bmatrix} 1 & 1 \\ -3 & -4 \end{bmatrix} = \begin{bmatrix} -1 & -1 \\ 3 & 4 \end{bmatrix},$

so $[T]_{B'} = P^{-1}[T]_B P = \begin{bmatrix} -1 & -1 \\ 3 & 4 \end{bmatrix}\begin{bmatrix} -29 & -51 \\ 17 & 30 \end{bmatrix}\begin{bmatrix} -4 & -1 \\ 3 & 1 \end{bmatrix}$

$= \begin{bmatrix} -1 & -1 \\ 3 & 4 \end{bmatrix}\begin{bmatrix} -37 & -22 \\ 22 & 13 \end{bmatrix} = \begin{bmatrix} 15 & 9 \\ -23 & -14 \end{bmatrix}.$

40. $T(\mathbf{u}_1) = \begin{bmatrix} 1 \\ 1 \end{bmatrix}$ and $T(\mathbf{u}_2) = \begin{bmatrix} 0 \\ 0 \end{bmatrix}$ by inspection,

so $[T]_B = \begin{bmatrix} \begin{bmatrix} 1 \\ 1 \end{bmatrix}_B : \begin{bmatrix} 0 \\ 0 \end{bmatrix}_B \end{bmatrix} = \begin{bmatrix} 1 & 0 \\ 0 & 0 \end{bmatrix}.$

$P_{B,B'} = \begin{bmatrix} 1 & 1 \\ 1 & -1 \end{bmatrix}^{-1}\begin{bmatrix} 1 & 0 \\ 0 & 1 \end{bmatrix} = \dfrac{1}{-2}\begin{bmatrix} -1 & -1 \\ -1 & 1 \end{bmatrix} = \dfrac{1}{2}\begin{bmatrix} 1 & 1 \\ 1 & -1 \end{bmatrix},$

$P_{B,B'}^{-1} = \left(\dfrac{1}{2}\begin{bmatrix} 1 & 1 \\ 1 & -1 \end{bmatrix}\right)^{-1} = 2\begin{bmatrix} 1 & 1 \\ 1 & -1 \end{bmatrix}^{-1} = 2\cdot\dfrac{1}{2}\begin{bmatrix} 1 & 1 \\ 1 & -1 \end{bmatrix} = \begin{bmatrix} 1 & 1 \\ 1 & -1 \end{bmatrix},$

so $[T]_{B'} = P^{-1}[T]_B P = \begin{bmatrix} 1 & 1 \\ 1 & -1 \end{bmatrix}\begin{bmatrix} 1 & 0 \\ 0 & 0 \end{bmatrix}\dfrac{1}{2}\begin{bmatrix} 1 & 1 \\ 1 & -1 \end{bmatrix}$

$= \begin{bmatrix} 1 & 1 \\ 1 & -1 \end{bmatrix}\begin{bmatrix} 1 & 1 \\ 0 & 0 \end{bmatrix} = \dfrac{1}{2}\begin{bmatrix} 1 & 1 \\ 1 & 1 \end{bmatrix} = \begin{bmatrix} 1/2 & 1/2 \\ 1/2 & 1/2 \end{bmatrix}.$

41. $T(\mathbf{u}_1) = \begin{bmatrix} 0 \\ 0 \\ 0 \end{bmatrix}$, $\quad T(\mathbf{u}_2) = \begin{bmatrix} 1 \\ 1 \\ 0 \end{bmatrix}$, $\quad T(\mathbf{u}_3) = \begin{bmatrix} -1 \\ 0 \\ -1 \end{bmatrix}$,

so $\quad [T]_B = \begin{bmatrix} 1 & 1 & 0 \\ 0 & 1 & -1 \\ 1 & 0 & 0 \end{bmatrix}^{-1} \begin{bmatrix} 0 & 1 & -1 \\ 0 & 1 & 0 \\ 0 & 0 & -1 \end{bmatrix} = \dfrac{1}{-1}\begin{bmatrix} 0 & -1 & -1 \\ 0 & 0 & 1 \\ -1 & 1 & 1 \end{bmatrix}^{T} \begin{bmatrix} 0 & 1 & -1 \\ 0 & 1 & 0 \\ 0 & 0 & -1 \end{bmatrix}$

$\quad = \begin{bmatrix} 0 & 0 & 1 \\ 1 & 0 & -1 \\ 1 & -1 & -1 \end{bmatrix} \begin{bmatrix} 0 & 1 & -1 \\ 0 & 1 & 0 \\ 0 & 0 & -1 \end{bmatrix} = \begin{bmatrix} 0 & 0 & -1 \\ 0 & 1 & 0 \\ 0 & 0 & 0 \end{bmatrix}.$

$P_{B,B'} = \begin{bmatrix} 1 & 1 & 0 \\ 0 & 1 & -1 \\ 1 & 0 & 0 \end{bmatrix}^{-1} \begin{bmatrix} 1 & 0 & 2 \\ 0 & 1 & 1 \\ 1 & -1 & 0 \end{bmatrix} = \begin{bmatrix} 0 & 0 & 1 \\ 1 & 0 & -1 \\ 1 & -1 & -1 \end{bmatrix} \begin{bmatrix} 1 & 0 & 2 \\ 0 & 1 & 1 \\ 1 & -1 & 0 \end{bmatrix} = \begin{bmatrix} 1 & -1 & 0 \\ 0 & 1 & 2 \\ 0 & 0 & 1 \end{bmatrix},$

$P_{B,B'}^{-1} = \begin{bmatrix} 1 & -1 & 0 \\ 0 & 1 & 2 \\ 0 & 0 & 1 \end{bmatrix}^{-1} = \dfrac{1}{1}\begin{bmatrix} 1 & 0 & 0 \\ 1 & 1 & 0 \\ -2 & -2 & 1 \end{bmatrix}^{T} = \begin{bmatrix} 1 & 1 & -2 \\ 0 & 1 & -2 \\ 0 & 0 & 1 \end{bmatrix},$

so $\quad [T]_{B'} = P^{-1}[T]_B P = \begin{bmatrix} 1 & 1 & -2 \\ 0 & 1 & -2 \\ 0 & 0 & 1 \end{bmatrix} \begin{bmatrix} 0 & 0 & -1 \\ 0 & 1 & 0 \\ 0 & 0 & 0 \end{bmatrix} \begin{bmatrix} 1 & -1 & 0 \\ 0 & 1 & 2 \\ 0 & 0 & 1 \end{bmatrix}$

$\quad = \begin{bmatrix} 1 & 1 & -2 \\ 0 & 1 & -2 \\ 0 & 0 & 1 \end{bmatrix} \begin{bmatrix} 0 & 0 & -1 \\ 0 & 1 & 2 \\ 0 & 0 & 0 \end{bmatrix} = \begin{bmatrix} 0 & 1 & 1 \\ 0 & 1 & 2 \\ 0 & 0 & 0 \end{bmatrix}.$

42. $T(\mathbf{u}_1) = \begin{bmatrix} 0 \\ 0 \\ 0 \end{bmatrix}$, $\quad T(\mathbf{u}_2) = \begin{bmatrix} 0 \\ 1 \\ 0 \end{bmatrix}$, $\quad T(\mathbf{u}_3) = \begin{bmatrix} 0 \\ 0 \\ 1 \end{bmatrix}$, $\quad$ by inspection,

so $\quad [T]_B = \begin{bmatrix} \begin{bmatrix} 0 \\ 0 \\ 0 \end{bmatrix}_B & \vdots & \begin{bmatrix} 0 \\ 1 \\ 0 \end{bmatrix}_B & \vdots & \begin{bmatrix} 0 \\ 0 \\ 1 \end{bmatrix}_B \end{bmatrix} = \begin{bmatrix} 0 & 0 & 0 \\ 0 & 1 & 0 \\ 0 & 0 & 1 \end{bmatrix}.$

$P_{B,B'} = \begin{bmatrix} 1 & 0 & 0 \\ 0 & 1 & 0 \\ 0 & 0 & 1 \end{bmatrix}^{-1} \begin{bmatrix} 1 & 1 & 1 \\ 0 & 1 & 1 \\ 0 & 0 & 1 \end{bmatrix} = \begin{bmatrix} 1 & 1 & 1 \\ 0 & 1 & 1 \\ 0 & 0 & 1 \end{bmatrix},$

$P_{B,B'}^{-1} = \begin{bmatrix} 1 & 1 & 1 \\ 0 & 1 & 1 \\ 0 & 0 & 1 \end{bmatrix}^{-1} = \dfrac{1}{1}\begin{bmatrix} 1 & 0 & 0 \\ -1 & 1 & 0 \\ 0 & -1 & 1 \end{bmatrix}^{T} = \begin{bmatrix} 1 & -1 & 0 \\ 0 & 1 & -1 \\ 0 & 0 & 1 \end{bmatrix},$

so $\quad [T]_{B'} = P^{-1}[T]_B P = \begin{bmatrix} 1 & -1 & 0 \\ 0 & 1 & -1 \\ 0 & 0 & 1 \end{bmatrix} \begin{bmatrix} 0 & 0 & 0 \\ 0 & 1 & 0 \\ 0 & 0 & 1 \end{bmatrix} \begin{bmatrix} 1 & 1 & 1 \\ 0 & 1 & 1 \\ 0 & 0 & 1 \end{bmatrix}$

$\quad = \begin{bmatrix} 1 & -1 & 0 \\ 0 & 1 & -1 \\ 0 & 0 & 1 \end{bmatrix} \begin{bmatrix} 0 & 0 & 0 \\ 0 & 1 & 1 \\ 0 & 0 & 1 \end{bmatrix} = \begin{bmatrix} 0 & -1 & -1 \\ 0 & 1 & 0 \\ 0 & 0 & 1 \end{bmatrix}.$

43. $T(\mathbf{u}_1) = 1, \quad T(\mathbf{u}_2) = x - 2, \quad T(\mathbf{u}_3) = (x-2)^2 = x^2 - 4x + 4,$

so $[T]_B = \begin{bmatrix} 1 & -2 & 4 \\ 0 & 1 & -4 \\ 0 & 0 & 1 \end{bmatrix}.$

$P_{B,B'} = \left[[1+x]_B \vdots [1-x^2]_B \vdots [x-x^2]_B \right] = \begin{bmatrix} 1 & 1 & 0 \\ 1 & 0 & 1 \\ 0 & -1 & -1 \end{bmatrix},$

$P_{B,B'}^{-1} = \begin{bmatrix} 1 & 1 & 0 \\ 1 & 0 & 1 \\ 0 & -1 & -1 \end{bmatrix}^{-1} = \frac{1}{2} \begin{bmatrix} 1 & 1 & -1 \\ 1 & -1 & 1 \\ 1 & -1 & -1 \end{bmatrix}^T = \frac{1}{2} \begin{bmatrix} 1 & 1 & 1 \\ 1 & -1 & -1 \\ -1 & 1 & -1 \end{bmatrix},$

so $[T]_{B'} = P^{-1}[T]_B P = \frac{1}{2} \begin{bmatrix} 1 & 1 & 1 \\ 1 & -1 & -1 \\ -1 & 1 & -1 \end{bmatrix} \begin{bmatrix} 1 & -2 & 4 \\ 0 & 1 & -4 \\ 0 & 0 & 1 \end{bmatrix} \begin{bmatrix} 1 & 1 & 0 \\ 1 & 0 & 1 \\ 0 & -1 & -1 \end{bmatrix}$

$= \frac{1}{2} \begin{bmatrix} 1 & 1 & 1 \\ 1 & -1 & -1 \\ -1 & 1 & -1 \end{bmatrix} \begin{bmatrix} -1 & -3 & -6 \\ 1 & 4 & 5 \\ 0 & -1 & -1 \end{bmatrix} = \frac{1}{2} \begin{bmatrix} 0 & 0 & -2 \\ -2 & -6 & -10 \\ 2 & 8 & 12 \end{bmatrix} = \begin{bmatrix} 0 & 0 & -1 \\ -1 & -3 & -5 \\ 1 & 4 & 6 \end{bmatrix}.$

44. $T(\mathbf{u}_1) = x \dfrac{d}{dx}(1) = x \cdot 0 = 0 = 0 \cdot 1 + 0 \cdot x + 0 \cdot x^2$

$T(\mathbf{u}_2) = x \dfrac{d}{dx}(x) = x \cdot 1 = x = 0 \cdot 1 + 1 \cdot x + 1 \cdot x^2$

$T(\mathbf{u}_3) = x \dfrac{d}{dx}(x^2) = x \cdot 2x = 2x^2 = 0 \cdot 1 + 0 \cdot x + 2 \cdot x^2,$

so $[T]_B = \begin{bmatrix} 0 & 0 & 0 \\ 0 & 1 & 0 \\ 0 & 0 & 2 \end{bmatrix}.$

$P_{B,B'} = \left[[x]_B \vdots [x^2+1]_B \vdots [x^2-1]_B \right] = \begin{bmatrix} 0 & 1 & -1 \\ 1 & 0 & 0 \\ 0 & 1 & 1 \end{bmatrix},$

$P_{B,B'}^{-1} = \begin{bmatrix} 0 & 1 & -1 \\ 1 & 0 & 0 \\ 0 & 1 & 1 \end{bmatrix}^{-1} = \frac{1}{-2} \begin{bmatrix} 0 & -1 & 1 \\ -2 & 0 & 0 \\ 0 & -1 & -1 \end{bmatrix}^T = \frac{1}{2} \begin{bmatrix} 0 & 2 & 0 \\ 1 & 0 & 1 \\ -1 & 0 & 1 \end{bmatrix},$

so $[T]_{B'} = P^{-1}[T]_B P = \frac{1}{2} \begin{bmatrix} 0 & 2 & 0 \\ 1 & 0 & 1 \\ -1 & 0 & 1 \end{bmatrix} \begin{bmatrix} 0 & 0 & 0 \\ 0 & 1 & 0 \\ 0 & 0 & 2 \end{bmatrix} \begin{bmatrix} 0 & 1 & -1 \\ 1 & 0 & 0 \\ 0 & 1 & 1 \end{bmatrix}$

$= \frac{1}{2} \begin{bmatrix} 0 & 2 & 0 \\ 1 & 0 & 1 \\ -1 & 0 & 1 \end{bmatrix} \begin{bmatrix} 0 & 0 & 0 \\ 1 & 0 & 0 \\ 0 & 2 & 2 \end{bmatrix} = \frac{1}{2} \begin{bmatrix} 2 & 0 & 0 \\ 0 & 2 & 2 \\ 0 & 2 & 2 \end{bmatrix} = \begin{bmatrix} 1 & 0 & 0 \\ 0 & 1 & 1 \\ 0 & 1 & 1 \end{bmatrix}.$

45. $$T(\mathbf{u}_1) = \frac{d^2}{dx^2}(1) - 1 + \frac{1}{x}\frac{d}{dx}(x^2 \cdot 1) = 0 - 1 + \frac{1}{x}(2x) = 1$$

$$T(\mathbf{u}_2) = \frac{d^2}{dx^2}(x) - x + \frac{1}{x}\frac{d}{dx}(x^2 \cdot x) = 0 - x + \frac{1}{x}(x^2) = 2x$$

$$T(\mathbf{u}_3) = \frac{d^2}{dx^2}(x^2) - x^2 + \frac{1}{x}\frac{d}{dx}(x^2 \cdot x^2) = 2 - x^2 + \frac{1}{x}(4x^3) = 2 + 3x^2$$

so $$[T]_B = \begin{bmatrix} 1 & 0 & 2 \\ 0 & 2 & 0 \\ 0 & 0 & 3 \end{bmatrix}.$$

$$P_{B,B'} = \left[[1+x+x^2]_B \vdots [2+3x+2x^2]_B \vdots [2+2x+3x^2]_B \right] = \begin{bmatrix} 1 & 2 & 2 \\ 1 & 3 & 2 \\ 1 & 2 & 3 \end{bmatrix},$$

$$P_{B,B'}^{-1} = \begin{bmatrix} 1 & 2 & 2 \\ 1 & 3 & 2 \\ 1 & 2 & 3 \end{bmatrix}^{-1} = \frac{1}{1}\begin{bmatrix} 5 & -1 & -1 \\ -2 & 1 & 0 \\ -2 & 0 & 1 \end{bmatrix}^T = \begin{bmatrix} 5 & -2 & -2 \\ -1 & 1 & 0 \\ -1 & 0 & 1 \end{bmatrix},$$

so $$[T]_{B'} = P^{-1}[T]_B P = \begin{bmatrix} 5 & -2 & -2 \\ -1 & 1 & 0 \\ -1 & 0 & 1 \end{bmatrix}\begin{bmatrix} 1 & 0 & 2 \\ 0 & 2 & 0 \\ 0 & 0 & 3 \end{bmatrix}\begin{bmatrix} 1 & 2 & 2 \\ 1 & 3 & 2 \\ 1 & 2 & 3 \end{bmatrix}$$

$$= \begin{bmatrix} 5 & -2 & -2 \\ -1 & 1 & 0 \\ -1 & 0 & 1 \end{bmatrix}\begin{bmatrix} 3 & 6 & 8 \\ 2 & 6 & 4 \\ 3 & 6 & 9 \end{bmatrix} = \begin{bmatrix} 5 & 6 & 14 \\ -1 & 0 & -4 \\ 0 & 0 & 1 \end{bmatrix}.$$

46. (a) Let B be the standard basis for R^2; then $[T]_B = \begin{bmatrix} 3 & 4 \\ 4 & -3 \end{bmatrix}$.

$$0 = \begin{vmatrix} \lambda - 3 & -4 \\ -4 & \lambda + 3 \end{vmatrix} = (\lambda - 3)(\lambda + 3) - (-4)(-4) = \lambda^2 - 9 - 16 = \lambda^2 - 25 = (\lambda - 5)(\lambda + 5),$$

so $\lambda = 5, -5$.

(b) $\lambda_1 = 5 \longrightarrow \begin{bmatrix} 2 & -4 & 0 \\ -4 & 8 & 0 \end{bmatrix} \longrightarrow \begin{bmatrix} 1 & -2 & 0 \\ 0 & 0 & 0 \end{bmatrix}$

Let $x_2 = s$;

then $x_1 - 2x_2 = 0$,   i.e., $x_1 = 2x_2 = 2s$

so $\begin{bmatrix} x_1 \\ x_2 \end{bmatrix} = \begin{bmatrix} 2s \\ s \end{bmatrix} = s\begin{bmatrix} 2 \\ 1 \end{bmatrix}$

$\lambda_2 = -5 \longrightarrow \begin{bmatrix} -8 & -4 & 0 \\ -4 & -2 & 0 \end{bmatrix} \longrightarrow \begin{bmatrix} 1 & 1/2 & 0 \\ 0 & 0 & 0 \end{bmatrix}$

Let $x_2 = t$;

then $x_1 + \frac{1}{2}x_2 = 0$,   i.e., $x_1 = \frac{-1}{2}x_2 = \frac{-1}{2}t$

so $\begin{bmatrix} x_1 \\ x_2 \end{bmatrix} = \begin{bmatrix} -1/2t \\ t \end{bmatrix} = t\begin{bmatrix} -1/2 \\ 1 \end{bmatrix} = \frac{1}{2}t\begin{bmatrix} -1 \\ 2 \end{bmatrix}$

$$B' = \left\{ \begin{bmatrix} 2 \\ 1 \end{bmatrix}, \begin{bmatrix} -1 \\ 2 \end{bmatrix} \right\}.$$

(c) $\quad [T]_{B'} = \begin{bmatrix} 2 & -1 \\ 1 & 2 \end{bmatrix}^{-1} \begin{bmatrix} 3 & 4 \\ 4 & -3 \end{bmatrix} \begin{bmatrix} 2 & -1 \\ 1 & 2 \end{bmatrix} = \begin{bmatrix} 2 & -1 \\ 1 & 2 \end{bmatrix}^{-1} \begin{bmatrix} 10 & 5 \\ 5 & -10 \end{bmatrix}$

$\qquad = \dfrac{1}{5} \begin{bmatrix} 2 & 1 \\ -1 & 2 \end{bmatrix} \begin{bmatrix} 10 & 5 \\ 5 & -10 \end{bmatrix} = \dfrac{1}{5} \begin{bmatrix} 25 & 0 \\ 0 & -25 \end{bmatrix} = \begin{bmatrix} 5 & 0 \\ 0 & -5 \end{bmatrix}.$

47. (a) Let B be the standard basis for R^2; then $[T]_B = \begin{bmatrix} 5 & -3 \\ 1 & 1 \end{bmatrix}.$

$$0 = \begin{vmatrix} \lambda - 5 & 3 \\ -1 & \lambda - 1 \end{vmatrix} = (\lambda - 5)(\lambda - 1) - (-1)(3) = \lambda^2 - 6\lambda + 8 = (\lambda - 2)(\lambda - 4),$$

so $\quad \lambda = 2, 4.$

(b) $\lambda_1 = 2 \longrightarrow \begin{bmatrix} -3 & 3 & 0 \\ -1 & 1 & 0 \end{bmatrix} \longrightarrow \begin{bmatrix} 1 & -1 & 0 \\ 0 & 0 & 0 \end{bmatrix}$

Let $\quad x_2 = s;$

then $\quad x_1 - x_2 = 0$, i.e., $\quad x_1 = x_2 = s$

so $\quad \begin{bmatrix} x_1 \\ x_2 \end{bmatrix} = \begin{bmatrix} s \\ s \end{bmatrix} = s \begin{bmatrix} 1 \\ 1 \end{bmatrix}$

$\lambda_2 = 4 \longrightarrow \begin{bmatrix} -1 & 3 & 0 \\ -1 & 3 & 0 \end{bmatrix} \longrightarrow \begin{bmatrix} 1 & -3 & 0 \\ 0 & 0 & 0 \end{bmatrix}$

Let $\quad x_2 = t;$

then $\quad x_1 - 3x_2 = 0$, i.e., $\quad x_1 = 3x_2 = 3t$

so $\quad \begin{bmatrix} x_1 \\ x_2 \end{bmatrix} = \begin{bmatrix} 3t \\ t \end{bmatrix} = t \begin{bmatrix} 3 \\ 1 \end{bmatrix}$

$$B' = \left\{ \begin{bmatrix} 1 \\ 1 \end{bmatrix}, \begin{bmatrix} 3 \\ 1 \end{bmatrix} \right\}.$$

(c) $\quad [T]_{B'} = \begin{bmatrix} 1 & 3 \\ 1 & 1 \end{bmatrix}^{-1} \begin{bmatrix} 5 & -3 \\ 1 & 1 \end{bmatrix} \begin{bmatrix} 1 & 3 \\ 1 & 1 \end{bmatrix} = \begin{bmatrix} 1 & 3 \\ 1 & 1 \end{bmatrix}^{-1} \begin{bmatrix} 2 & 12 \\ 2 & 4 \end{bmatrix}$

$\qquad = \dfrac{1}{-2} \begin{bmatrix} 1 & -3 \\ -1 & 1 \end{bmatrix} \begin{bmatrix} 2 & 12 \\ 2 & 4 \end{bmatrix} = \dfrac{-1}{2} \begin{bmatrix} -4 & 0 \\ 0 & -8 \end{bmatrix} = \begin{bmatrix} 2 & 0 \\ 0 & 4 \end{bmatrix}.$

48. (a) Let B be the standard basis for R^3; then $[T]_B = \begin{bmatrix} -1 & 4 & -2 \\ -3 & 4 & 0 \\ -3 & 1 & 3 \end{bmatrix}.$

$$0 = \begin{vmatrix} \lambda + 1 & -4 & 2 \\ 3 & \lambda - 4 & 0 \\ 3 & -1 & \lambda - 3 \end{vmatrix}$$

$\qquad = 2(-3 - 3\lambda + 12) + (\lambda - 3)(\lambda^2 - 3\lambda - 4 + 12)$

$\qquad = 2(-3\lambda + 9) + (\lambda - 3)(\lambda^2 - 3\lambda + 8)$

$\qquad = (\lambda - 3)[-6 + (\lambda^2 - 3\lambda + 8)]$

$$= (\lambda - 3)(\lambda^2 - 3\lambda + 2) = (\lambda - 3)(\lambda - 2)(\lambda - 1),$$

so $\quad \lambda = 1, 2, 3.$

(b) $\lambda_1 = 1 \longrightarrow \begin{bmatrix} 2 & -4 & 2 & 0 \\ 3 & -3 & 0 & 0 \\ 3 & -1 & -2 & 0 \end{bmatrix} \longrightarrow \begin{bmatrix} 1 & -2 & 1 & 0 \\ 0 & 3 & -3 & 0 \\ 0 & 5 & -5 & 0 \end{bmatrix} \longrightarrow \begin{bmatrix} 1 & 0 & -1 & 0 \\ 0 & 1 & -1 & 0 \\ 0 & 0 & 0 & 0 \end{bmatrix}$

Let $\quad x_3 = r;$

then $\quad x_1 - x_3 = 0 \quad$, i.e., $\quad x_1 = x_3 = r$

and $\quad x_2 - x_3 = 0 \quad$, i.e., $\quad x_2 = x_3 = r$

so $\quad \begin{bmatrix} x_1 \\ x_2 \\ x_3 \end{bmatrix} = \begin{bmatrix} r \\ r \\ r \end{bmatrix} = r \begin{bmatrix} 1 \\ 1 \\ 1 \end{bmatrix}$

$\lambda_2 = 2 \longrightarrow \begin{bmatrix} 3 & -4 & 2 & 0 \\ 3 & -2 & 0 & 0 \\ 3 & -1 & -1 & 0 \end{bmatrix} \longrightarrow \begin{bmatrix} 1 & -4/3 & 2/3 & 0 \\ 0 & 2 & -2 & 0 \\ 0 & 3 & -3 & 0 \end{bmatrix} \longrightarrow \begin{bmatrix} 1 & 0 & -2/3 & 0 \\ 0 & 1 & -1 & 0 \\ 0 & 0 & 0 & 0 \end{bmatrix}$

Let $\quad x_3 = s;$

then $\quad x_1 - \dfrac{2}{3}x_3 = 0 \quad$, i.e., $\quad x_1 = \dfrac{2}{3}x_3 = \dfrac{2}{3}s$

and $\quad x_2 - x_3 = 0 \quad$, i.e., $\quad x_2 = x_3 = s$

so $\quad \begin{bmatrix} x_1 \\ x_2 \\ x_3 \end{bmatrix} = \begin{bmatrix} 2/3s \\ s \\ s \end{bmatrix} = t \begin{bmatrix} 2/3 \\ 1 \\ 1 \end{bmatrix} = \dfrac{1}{3}s \begin{bmatrix} 2 \\ 3 \\ 3 \end{bmatrix}$

$\lambda_3 = 3 \longrightarrow \begin{bmatrix} 4 & -4 & 2 & 0 \\ 3 & -1 & 0 & 0 \\ 3 & -1 & 0 & 0 \end{bmatrix} \longrightarrow \begin{bmatrix} 1 & -1 & 1/2 & 0 \\ 0 & 2 & -3/2 & 0 \\ 0 & 2 & -3/2 & 0 \end{bmatrix} \longrightarrow \begin{bmatrix} 1 & 0 & -1/4 & 0 \\ 0 & 1 & -3/4 & 0 \\ 0 & 0 & 0 & 0 \end{bmatrix}$

Let $\quad x_3 = t;$

then $\quad x_1 - \dfrac{1}{4}x_3 = 0 \quad$, i.e., $\quad x_1 = \dfrac{1}{4}x_3 = \dfrac{1}{4}t$

and $\quad x_2 - \dfrac{3}{4}x_3 = 0 \quad$, i.e., $\quad x_2 = \dfrac{3}{4}x_3 = \dfrac{3}{4}t$

so $\quad \begin{bmatrix} x_1 \\ x_2 \\ x_3 \end{bmatrix} = \begin{bmatrix} 1/4t \\ 3/4t \\ t \end{bmatrix} = t \begin{bmatrix} 1/4 \\ 3/4 \\ 1 \end{bmatrix} = \dfrac{1}{4}t \begin{bmatrix} 1 \\ 3 \\ 4 \end{bmatrix}$

$B' = \left\{ \begin{bmatrix} 1 \\ 1 \\ 1 \end{bmatrix}, \begin{bmatrix} 2 \\ 3 \\ 3 \end{bmatrix}, \begin{bmatrix} 1 \\ 3 \\ 4 \end{bmatrix} \right\}.$

(c) $\quad [T]_{B'} = \begin{bmatrix} 1 & 2 & 1 \\ 1 & 3 & 3 \\ 1 & 3 & 4 \end{bmatrix}^{-1} \begin{bmatrix} -1 & 4 & -2 \\ -3 & 4 & 0 \\ -3 & 1 & 3 \end{bmatrix} \begin{bmatrix} 1 & 2 & 1 \\ 1 & 3 & 3 \\ 1 & 3 & 4 \end{bmatrix} = \begin{bmatrix} 1 & 2 & 1 \\ 1 & 3 & 3 \\ 1 & 3 & 4 \end{bmatrix}^{-1} \begin{bmatrix} 1 & 4 & 3 \\ 1 & 6 & 9 \\ 1 & 6 & 12 \end{bmatrix}$

$$= \frac{1}{1} \begin{bmatrix} 3 & -1 & 0 \\ -5 & 3 & -1 \\ 3 & -2 & 1 \end{bmatrix}^T \begin{bmatrix} 1 & 4 & 3 \\ 1 & 6 & 9 \\ 1 & 6 & 12 \end{bmatrix} = \begin{bmatrix} 3 & -5 & 3 \\ -1 & 3 & -2 \\ 0 & -1 & 1 \end{bmatrix} \begin{bmatrix} 1 & 4 & 3 \\ 1 & 6 & 9 \\ 1 & 6 & 12 \end{bmatrix}$$

$$= \begin{bmatrix} 1 & 0 & 0 \\ 0 & 2 & 0 \\ 0 & 0 & 3 \end{bmatrix}$$

49. (a) Let B be the standard basis for R^3; then $[T]_B = \begin{bmatrix} -7 & -9 & 3 \\ 2 & 4 & -2 \\ -3 & -3 & -1 \end{bmatrix}$.

$$0 = \begin{vmatrix} \lambda + 7 & 9 & -3 \\ -2 & \lambda - 4 & 2 \\ 3 & 3 & \lambda + 1 \end{vmatrix}$$

$$= (\lambda + 7)[(\lambda - 4)(\lambda + 1) - (3)(2)] - 9[-2(\lambda + 1) - (3)(2)] - 3[(-2)(3) - (3)(\lambda - 4)]$$

$$= (\lambda + 7)(\lambda^3 - 3\lambda - 10) - 9(-2\lambda - 8) - 3(-3\lambda + 6)$$

$$= (\lambda^3 + 4\lambda^2 - 31\lambda - 70) + (18\lambda + 72) + (9\lambda - 18)$$

$$= \lambda^3 + 4\lambda^2 - 4\lambda - 16$$

$$= (\lambda^3 + 4\lambda^2) + (-4\lambda - 16)$$

$$= \lambda^2(\lambda + 4) + -4(\lambda + 4)$$

$$= (\lambda^2 - 4)(\lambda + 4) = (\lambda - 2)(\lambda + 2)(\lambda + 4), \quad \text{so} \quad \lambda = 2, -2, -4.$$

(b) $\lambda_1 = 2 \longrightarrow \begin{bmatrix} 9 & 9 & -3 & 0 \\ -2 & -2 & 2 & 0 \\ 3 & 3 & 3 & 0 \end{bmatrix} \longrightarrow \begin{bmatrix} 1 & 1 & -1 & 0 \\ 0 & 0 & 6 & 0 \\ 0 & 0 & 6 & 0 \end{bmatrix} \longrightarrow \begin{bmatrix} 1 & 1 & 0 & 0 \\ 0 & 0 & 1 & 0 \\ 0 & 0 & 0 & 0 \end{bmatrix}$

Let $x_2 = r$;

then $x_1 + x_2 = 0$, i.e., $x_1 = -x_2 = -r$

and $x_3 = 0$

so $\begin{bmatrix} x_1 \\ x_2 \\ x_3 \end{bmatrix} = \begin{bmatrix} -r \\ r \\ 0 \end{bmatrix} = r \begin{bmatrix} -1 \\ 1 \\ 0 \end{bmatrix}$

$\lambda_2 = -2 \longrightarrow \begin{bmatrix} 5 & 9 & -3 & 0 \\ -2 & -6 & 2 & 0 \\ 3 & 3 & -1 & 0 \end{bmatrix} \longrightarrow \begin{bmatrix} 1 & 3 & -1 & 0 \\ 0 & -6 & 2 & 0 \\ 0 & -6 & 2 & 0 \end{bmatrix} \longrightarrow \begin{bmatrix} 1 & 0 & 0 & 0 \\ 0 & 1 & -1/3 & 0 \\ 0 & 0 & 0 & 0 \end{bmatrix}$

Let $x_3 = s$;

then $x_2 - \frac{1}{3}x_3 = 0$, i.e., $x_2 = \frac{1}{3}x_3 = \frac{1}{3}s$

and $x_1 = 0$

209

$$\text{so} \quad \begin{bmatrix} x_1 \\ x_2 \\ x_3 \end{bmatrix} = \begin{bmatrix} 0 \\ 1/3s \\ s \end{bmatrix} = s \begin{bmatrix} 0 \\ 1/3 \\ 1 \end{bmatrix} = \frac{1}{3}s \begin{bmatrix} 0 \\ 1 \\ 3 \end{bmatrix}$$

$$\lambda_3 = -4 \longrightarrow \begin{bmatrix} 3 & 9 & -3 & 0 \\ -2 & -8 & 2 & 0 \\ 3 & 3 & -3 & 0 \end{bmatrix} \longrightarrow \begin{bmatrix} 1 & 3 & -1 & 0 \\ 0 & -2 & 0 & 0 \\ 0 & -6 & 0 & 0 \end{bmatrix} \longrightarrow \begin{bmatrix} 1 & 0 & -1 & 0 \\ 0 & 1 & 0 & 0 \\ 0 & 0 & 0 & 0 \end{bmatrix}$$

Let $x_3 = t$;

then $x_1 - x_3 = 0$, i.e., $x_1 = x_3 = t$

and $x_2 = 0$

$$\text{so} \quad \begin{bmatrix} x_1 \\ x_2 \\ x_3 \end{bmatrix} = \begin{bmatrix} t \\ 0 \\ t \end{bmatrix} = t \begin{bmatrix} 1 \\ 0 \\ 1 \end{bmatrix}$$

$$B' = \left\{ \begin{bmatrix} -1 \\ 1 \\ 0 \end{bmatrix}, \begin{bmatrix} 0 \\ 1 \\ 3 \end{bmatrix}, \begin{bmatrix} 1 \\ 0 \\ 1 \end{bmatrix} \right\}.$$

(c) $[T]_{B'} = \begin{bmatrix} -1 & 0 & 1 \\ 1 & 1 & 0 \\ 0 & 3 & 1 \end{bmatrix}^{-1} \begin{bmatrix} -7 & -9 & 3 \\ 2 & 4 & -2 \\ -3 & -3 & -1 \end{bmatrix} \begin{bmatrix} -1 & 0 & 1 \\ 1 & 1 & 0 \\ 0 & 3 & 1 \end{bmatrix} = \begin{bmatrix} -1 & 0 & 1 \\ 1 & 1 & 0 \\ 0 & 3 & 1 \end{bmatrix}^{-1} \begin{bmatrix} -2 & 0 & -4 \\ 2 & -2 & 0 \\ 0 & -6 & -4 \end{bmatrix}$

$$= \frac{1}{2} \begin{bmatrix} 1 & -1 & 3 \\ 3 & -1 & 3 \\ -1 & 1 & -1 \end{bmatrix}^T \begin{bmatrix} -2 & 0 & -4 \\ 2 & -2 & 0 \\ 0 & -6 & -4 \end{bmatrix} = \begin{bmatrix} 1 & 3 & -1 \\ -1 & -1 & 1 \\ 3 & 3 & -1 \end{bmatrix} \begin{bmatrix} -1 & 0 & -2 \\ 1 & -1 & 0 \\ 0 & -3 & -2 \end{bmatrix}$$

$$= \begin{bmatrix} 2 & 0 & 0 \\ 0 & -2 & 0 \\ 0 & 0 & -4 \end{bmatrix}.$$

50. (a) $A = [T] = \begin{bmatrix} 1 & 2 \\ 2 & 1 \end{bmatrix}$

$$0 = \begin{vmatrix} \lambda - 1 & -2 \\ -2 & \lambda - 1 \end{vmatrix} = (\lambda - 1)(\lambda - 1) - (-2)(-2) = (\lambda^2 - 2\lambda + 1) - 4$$

$$= \lambda^2 - 2\lambda - 3 = (\lambda - 3)(\lambda + 1), \quad \text{so} \quad \lambda = 3, -1.$$

(b) $\lambda_1 = 3 \longrightarrow \begin{bmatrix} 2 & -2 & 0 \\ -2 & 2 & 0 \end{bmatrix} \longrightarrow \begin{bmatrix} 1 & -1 & 0 \\ 0 & 0 & 0 \end{bmatrix}$

Let $x_2 = s$;

then $x_1 - x_2 = 0$, i.e., $x_1 = x_2 = s$

$$\text{so} \quad \begin{bmatrix} x_1 \\ x_2 \end{bmatrix} = \begin{bmatrix} s \\ s \end{bmatrix} = s \begin{bmatrix} 1 \\ 1 \end{bmatrix}$$

(b) $\lambda_2 = -1 \longrightarrow \begin{bmatrix} -2 & -2 & 0 \\ -2 & -2 & 0 \end{bmatrix} \longrightarrow \begin{bmatrix} 1 & 1 & 0 \\ 0 & 0 & 0 \end{bmatrix}$

Let $x_2 = t$;

then $x_1 + x_2 = 0$, i.e., $x_1 = -x_2 = -t$

so $\begin{bmatrix} x_1 \\ x_2 \end{bmatrix} = \begin{bmatrix} -t \\ t \end{bmatrix} = t\begin{bmatrix} -1 \\ 1 \end{bmatrix}$

$B' = \left\{ \begin{bmatrix} 1 \\ 1 \end{bmatrix}, \begin{bmatrix} -1 \\ 1 \end{bmatrix}, \right\}.$

(c) $P = \begin{bmatrix} 1 & -1 \\ 1 & 1 \end{bmatrix}$, $P^{-1} = \begin{bmatrix} 1 & -1 \\ 1 & 1 \end{bmatrix}^{-1} = \frac{1}{2}\begin{bmatrix} 1 & 1 \\ -1 & 1 \end{bmatrix}$

$[T]_{B'} = P^{-1}AP = \begin{bmatrix} 3 & 0 \\ 0 & -1 \end{bmatrix}$

$A^5 = P[T]_{B'}^5 P^{-1} = \begin{bmatrix} 1 & -1 \\ 1 & 1 \end{bmatrix}\begin{bmatrix} 3 & 0 \\ 0 & -1 \end{bmatrix}^5 \frac{1}{2}\begin{bmatrix} 1 & 1 \\ -1 & 1 \end{bmatrix}$

$= \begin{bmatrix} 1 & -1 \\ 1 & 1 \end{bmatrix}\begin{bmatrix} 243 & 0 \\ 0 & -1 \end{bmatrix}\frac{1}{2}\begin{bmatrix} 1 & 1 \\ -1 & 1 \end{bmatrix} = \frac{1}{2}\begin{bmatrix} 1 & -1 \\ 1 & 1 \end{bmatrix}\begin{bmatrix} 243 & 243 \\ 1 & -1 \end{bmatrix}$

$= \frac{1}{2}\begin{bmatrix} 242 & 244 \\ 244 & 242 \end{bmatrix} = \begin{bmatrix} 121 & 122 \\ 122 & 121 \end{bmatrix}$

$T^5\left(\begin{bmatrix} 2 \\ -1 \end{bmatrix}\right) = A^5\begin{bmatrix} 2 \\ -1 \end{bmatrix} = \begin{bmatrix} 121 & 122 \\ 122 & 121 \end{bmatrix}\begin{bmatrix} 2 \\ -1 \end{bmatrix} = \begin{bmatrix} 120 \\ 123 \end{bmatrix}.$

51. (a) $A = [T] = \begin{bmatrix} -9 & -6 & -22 \\ 1 & 2 & 2 \\ 4 & 2 & 10 \end{bmatrix}.$

$0 = \begin{vmatrix} \lambda+9 & 6 & 22 \\ -1 & \lambda-2 & -2 \\ -4 & -2 & \lambda-10 \end{vmatrix}$

$= (\lambda+9)[(\lambda-2)(\lambda-10) - (-2)(-2)] - 6[(-1)(\lambda-10) - (-4)(-2)] +$
$\qquad\qquad 22[(-1)(-2) - (-4)(\lambda-2)]$

$= (\lambda+9)(\lambda^2 - 12\lambda + 16) - 6(-\lambda+2) + 22(4\lambda-6)$

$= (\lambda^3 - 3\lambda^2 - 92\lambda + 144) + (6\lambda-12) + (88\lambda-132)$

$= \lambda^3 - 3\lambda^2 + 2\lambda = \lambda(\lambda^2 - 3\lambda + 2) = \lambda(\lambda-1)(\lambda-2)$ so $\lambda = 0, 1, 2.$

(b) $\lambda_1 = 0 \longrightarrow \begin{bmatrix} 9 & 6 & 22 & 0 \\ -1 & -2 & -2 & 0 \\ -4 & -2 & -10 & 0 \end{bmatrix} \longrightarrow \begin{bmatrix} 1 & 2 & 2 & 0 \\ 0 & -12 & 4 & 0 \\ 0 & 6 & -2 & 0 \end{bmatrix} \longrightarrow \begin{bmatrix} 1 & 0 & 8/3 & 0 \\ 0 & 1 & -1/3 & 0 \\ 0 & 0 & 0 & 0 \end{bmatrix}$

Let $x_3 = r$;

then $x_2 - \frac{1}{3}x_3 = 0$, i.e., $x_2 = \frac{1}{3}x_3 = \frac{1}{3}r$

and $\quad x_1 + \dfrac{8}{3}x_3 = 0 \quad$, i.e., $\quad x_1 = \dfrac{-8}{3}x_3 = \dfrac{-8}{3}r$

so $\quad \begin{bmatrix} x_1 \\ x_2 \\ x_3 \end{bmatrix} = \begin{bmatrix} -8/3r \\ 1/3r \\ r \end{bmatrix} = r\begin{bmatrix} -8/3 \\ 1/3 \\ 1 \end{bmatrix} = \dfrac{1}{3}r\begin{bmatrix} -8 \\ 1 \\ 3 \end{bmatrix}$

$\lambda_2 = 1 \longrightarrow \begin{bmatrix} 10 & 6 & 22 & 0 \\ -1 & -1 & -2 & 0 \\ -4 & -2 & -9 & 0 \end{bmatrix} \longrightarrow \begin{bmatrix} 1 & 1 & 2 & 0 \\ 0 & -4 & 2 & 0 \\ 0 & 2 & -1 & 0 \end{bmatrix} \longrightarrow \begin{bmatrix} 1 & 0 & 5/2 & 0 \\ 0 & 1 & -1/2 & 0 \\ 0 & 0 & 0 & 0 \end{bmatrix}$

Let $\quad x_3 = s$;

then $\quad x_2 - \dfrac{1}{2}x_3 = 0 \quad$, i.e., $\quad x_2 = \dfrac{1}{2}x_3 = \dfrac{1}{2}s$

and $\quad x_1 + \dfrac{5}{2}x_3 = 0 \quad$, i.e., $\quad x_1 = \dfrac{-5}{2}x_3 = \dfrac{-5}{2}s$

so $\quad \begin{bmatrix} x_1 \\ x_2 \\ x_3 \end{bmatrix} = \begin{bmatrix} -5/2s \\ 1/2s \\ s \end{bmatrix} = s\begin{bmatrix} -5/2 \\ 1/2 \\ 1 \end{bmatrix} = \dfrac{1}{2}s\begin{bmatrix} -5 \\ 1 \\ 2 \end{bmatrix}$

$\lambda_3 = 2 \longrightarrow \begin{bmatrix} 11 & 6 & 22 & 0 \\ -1 & 0 & -2 & 0 \\ -4 & -2 & -8 & 0 \end{bmatrix} \longrightarrow \begin{bmatrix} 1 & 0 & 2 & 0 \\ 0 & 6 & 0 & 0 \\ 0 & -2 & 0 & 0 \end{bmatrix} \longrightarrow \begin{bmatrix} 1 & 0 & 2 & 0 \\ 0 & 1 & 0 & 0 \\ 0 & 0 & 0 & 0 \end{bmatrix}$

Let $\quad x_3 = t$;

then $\quad x_1 + 2x_3 = 0 \quad$, i.e., $\quad x_1 = -2x_3 = -2t$

and $\quad x_2 = 0$

so $\quad \begin{bmatrix} x_1 \\ x_2 \\ x_3 \end{bmatrix} = \begin{bmatrix} -2t \\ 0 \\ t \end{bmatrix} = t\begin{bmatrix} -2 \\ 0 \\ 1 \end{bmatrix}$

$B' = \left\{ \begin{bmatrix} -8 \\ 1 \\ 3 \end{bmatrix}, \begin{bmatrix} -5 \\ 1 \\ 2 \end{bmatrix}, \begin{bmatrix} -2 \\ 0 \\ 1 \end{bmatrix} \right\}$

(c) $\quad P = \begin{bmatrix} -8 & -5 & -2 \\ 1 & 1 & 0 \\ 3 & 2 & 1 \end{bmatrix}$, $\quad P^{-1} = \dfrac{1}{-1}\begin{bmatrix} 1 & -1 & -1 \\ 1 & -2 & 1 \\ 2 & -2 & -3 \end{bmatrix}^T = \begin{bmatrix} -1 & -1 & -2 \\ 1 & 2 & 2 \\ 1 & -1 & 3 \end{bmatrix}$

$[T]_{B'} = P^{-1}AP = \begin{bmatrix} 0 & 0 & 0 \\ 0 & 1 & 0 \\ 0 & 0 & 2 \end{bmatrix}$

$A^5 = P[T]_{B'}^5 P^{-1} = \begin{bmatrix} -8 & -5 & -2 \\ 1 & 1 & 0 \\ 3 & 2 & 1 \end{bmatrix}\begin{bmatrix} 0 & 0 & 0 \\ 0 & 1 & 0 \\ 0 & 0 & 32 \end{bmatrix}\begin{bmatrix} -1 & -1 & -2 \\ 1 & 2 & 2 \\ 1 & -1 & 3 \end{bmatrix}$

$$= \begin{bmatrix} -8 & -5 & -2 \\ 1 & 1 & 0 \\ 3 & 2 & 1 \end{bmatrix} \begin{bmatrix} 0 & 0 & 0 \\ 1 & 2 & 2 \\ 32 & -32 & 96 \end{bmatrix} = \begin{bmatrix} -69 & 54 & -202 \\ 1 & 2 & 2 \\ 34 & -28 & 100 \end{bmatrix}$$

$$T^5\left(\begin{bmatrix} -2 \\ 1 \\ 2 \end{bmatrix}\right) = A^5 \begin{bmatrix} -2 \\ 1 \\ 2 \end{bmatrix} = \begin{bmatrix} -69 & 54 & -202 \\ 1 & 2 & 2 \\ 34 & -28 & 100 \end{bmatrix} \begin{bmatrix} -2 \\ 1 \\ 2 \end{bmatrix} = \begin{bmatrix} -212 \\ 4 \\ 104 \end{bmatrix}$$

52. (a) $\begin{bmatrix} 1 & -2 & 2 \\ 2 & -1 & 2 \\ 2 & -2 & 3 \end{bmatrix} \begin{bmatrix} 3 \\ 4 \\ 5 \end{bmatrix} = \begin{bmatrix} 5 \\ 12 \\ 13 \end{bmatrix}$

(b) $\begin{bmatrix} \alpha \\ \beta \\ \gamma \end{bmatrix} = \begin{bmatrix} 1 & -2 & 2 \\ 2 & -1 & 2 \\ 2 & -2 & 3 \end{bmatrix} \begin{bmatrix} a \\ b \\ c \end{bmatrix} = \begin{bmatrix} a - 2b + 2c \\ 2a - b + 2c \\ 2a - 2b + 3c \end{bmatrix}$

Given $a^2 + b^2 - c^2 = 0$, we must show $\alpha^2 + \beta^2 - \gamma^2 = 0$; but

$\alpha^2 + \beta^2 - \gamma^2 = (a - 2b + 2c)^2 + (2a - b + 2c)^2 - (2a - 2b + 3c)^2$

$\quad = (a^2 + 4b^2 + 4c^2 - 4ab + 4ac - 8bc)$

$\quad\quad + (4a^2 + b^2 + 4c^2 - 4ab + 8ac - 4bc)$

$\quad\quad\quad - (4a^2 + 4b^2 + 9c^2 - 8ab + 12ac - 12bc)$

$\quad = a^2 + b^2 - c^2$

$\quad = 0.$

(c) det $A = (1)(1) + 2(2) + 2(-2) = 1 \neq 0$.

(d) $T^{-1}\left(\begin{bmatrix} 5 \\ 12 \\ 13 \end{bmatrix}\right) = A^{-1} \begin{bmatrix} 5 \\ 12 \\ 13 \end{bmatrix} = \begin{bmatrix} 3 \\ 4 \\ 5 \end{bmatrix}$ from part (a).

(e) $0 = \begin{vmatrix} \lambda - 1 & 2 & -2 \\ -2 & \lambda + 1 & -2 \\ -2 & 2 & \lambda - 3 \end{vmatrix}$

$\quad = (\lambda - 1)(\lambda^2 - 2\lambda + 1) - 2(-2\lambda + 2) - 2(2\lambda - 2)$

$\quad = (\lambda - 1)(\lambda^2 - 2\lambda + 1) = (\lambda - 1)^3$ so $\lambda = 1, 1, 1$

(f) $\lambda = 1 \longrightarrow \begin{bmatrix} 0 & 2 & -2 & 0 \\ -2 & 2 & -2 & 0 \\ -2 & 2 & -2 & 0 \end{bmatrix} \longrightarrow \begin{bmatrix} 1 & -1 & 1 & 0 \\ 0 & 2 & -2 & 0 \\ 0 & 0 & 0 & 0 \end{bmatrix} \longrightarrow \begin{bmatrix} 1 & 0 & 0 & 0 \\ 0 & 1 & -1 & 0 \\ 0 & 0 & 0 & 0 \end{bmatrix}$

Let $x_3 = t$;

then $x_2 - x_3 = 0$, i.e., $x_2 = x_3 = t$

and $x_1 = 0$

so $\begin{bmatrix} x_1 \\ x_2 \\ x_3 \end{bmatrix} = \begin{bmatrix} 0 \\ t \\ t \end{bmatrix} = t \begin{bmatrix} 0 \\ 1 \\ 1 \end{bmatrix}$

(f)   Since $B = \left\{ \begin{bmatrix} 0 \\ 1 \\ 1 \end{bmatrix} \right\}$ has only 1 element (not 3), T is not diagonalizable.

53. (a) $\begin{bmatrix} -1 & 2 & 2 \\ -2 & 1 & 2 \\ -2 & 2 & 3 \end{bmatrix} \begin{bmatrix} 3 \\ 4 \\ 5 \end{bmatrix} = \begin{bmatrix} 15 \\ 8 \\ 17 \end{bmatrix}$

(b) $\begin{bmatrix} \alpha \\ \beta \\ \gamma \end{bmatrix} = \begin{bmatrix} -1 & 2 & 2 \\ -2 & 1 & 2 \\ -2 & 2 & 3 \end{bmatrix} \begin{bmatrix} a \\ b \\ c \end{bmatrix} = \begin{bmatrix} -a + 2b + 2c \\ -2a + b + 2c \\ -2a + 2b + 3c \end{bmatrix}$

Given $a^2 + b^2 - c^2 = 0$,   we must show $\alpha^2 + \beta^2 - \gamma^2 = 0$;   but

$\alpha^2 + \beta^2 - \gamma^2 = (-a + 2b + 2c)^2 + (-2a + b + 2c)^2 - (-2a + 2b + 3c)^2$

$\qquad = (a^2 + 4b^2 + 4c^2 - 4ab - 4ac + 8bc)$

$\qquad\quad + (4a^2 + b^2 + 4c^2 - 4ab - 8ac + 4bc)$

$\qquad\qquad - (4a^2 + 4b^2 + 9c^2 - 8ab - 12ac + 12bc)$

$\qquad = a^2 + b^2 - c^2$

$\qquad = 0$

(c) $\det A = (-1)(-1) + (-2)(-2) + 2(-2) = 1 \neq 0$

(d) $T^{-1}\left(\begin{bmatrix} 5 \\ 12 \\ 13 \end{bmatrix} \right) = A^{-1} \begin{bmatrix} 5 \\ 12 \\ 13 \end{bmatrix} = \begin{bmatrix} -1 & 2 & 2 \\ -2 & 1 & 2 \\ -2 & 2 & 3 \end{bmatrix}^{-1} \begin{bmatrix} 5 \\ 12 \\ 13 \end{bmatrix}$

$\qquad = \dfrac{1}{1} \begin{bmatrix} -1 & 2 & -2 \\ -2 & 1 & -2 \\ 2 & -2 & 3 \end{bmatrix}^{T} \begin{bmatrix} 5 \\ 12 \\ 13 \end{bmatrix} = \begin{bmatrix} -1 & -2 & 2 \\ 2 & 1 & -2 \\ -2 & -2 & 3 \end{bmatrix} \begin{bmatrix} 5 \\ 12 \\ 13 \end{bmatrix} = \begin{bmatrix} -3 \\ -4 \\ 5 \end{bmatrix}$

(e) $0 = \begin{vmatrix} \lambda + 1 & -2 & -2 \\ 2 & \lambda - 1 & -2 \\ 2 & -2 & \lambda - 3 \end{vmatrix}$

$\qquad = (\lambda + 1)(\lambda^2 - 4\lambda - 1) + 2(2\lambda - 2) - 2(-2\lambda - 2)$

$\qquad = (\lambda + 1)(\lambda^2 - 4\lambda - 1) + 2(2\lambda - 2) + 4(\lambda + 1)$

$\qquad = (\lambda + 1)(\lambda^2 - 4\lambda + 3) + 2(2\lambda - 2)$

$\qquad = (\lambda + 1)(\lambda - 3)(\lambda - 1) + 4(\lambda - 1)$

$\qquad = [(\lambda + 1)(\lambda - 3) + 4](\lambda - 1)$

$\qquad = (\lambda^2 - 2\lambda + 1)(\lambda - 1) = (\lambda - 1)^3$ so $\lambda = 1, 1, 1$

(f) $\lambda = 1 \longrightarrow \begin{bmatrix} 2 & -2 & -2 & 0 \\ 2 & 0 & -2 & 0 \\ 2 & -2 & -2 & 0 \end{bmatrix} \longrightarrow \begin{bmatrix} 1 & -1 & -1 & 0 \\ 0 & 2 & 0 & 0 \\ 0 & 0 & 0 & 0 \end{bmatrix} \longrightarrow \begin{bmatrix} 1 & 0 & -1 & 0 \\ 0 & 1 & 0 & 0 \\ 0 & 0 & 0 & 0 \end{bmatrix}$

(e)   Let $x_3 = t$;

then $x_1 - x_3 = 0$, i.e., $x_1 = x_3 = t$

and $x_2 = 0$

so $\begin{bmatrix} x_1 \\ x_2 \\ x_3 \end{bmatrix} = \begin{bmatrix} t \\ 0 \\ t \end{bmatrix} = t \begin{bmatrix} 1 \\ 0 \\ 1 \end{bmatrix}$

Since $B = \left\{ \begin{bmatrix} 1 \\ 0 \\ 1 \end{bmatrix} \right\}$ has only 1 element (not 3), T is not diagonalizable.

54. (a) $\begin{bmatrix} 1 & 2 & 2 \\ 2 & 1 & 2 \\ 2 & 2 & 3 \end{bmatrix} \begin{bmatrix} 3 \\ 4 \\ 5 \end{bmatrix} = \begin{bmatrix} 21 \\ 20 \\ 29 \end{bmatrix}$

(b) $\begin{bmatrix} \alpha \\ \beta \\ \gamma \end{bmatrix} = \begin{bmatrix} 1 & 2 & 2 \\ 2 & 1 & 2 \\ 2 & 2 & 3 \end{bmatrix} \begin{bmatrix} a \\ b \\ c \end{bmatrix} = \begin{bmatrix} a + 2b + 2c \\ 2a + b + 2c \\ 2a + 2b + 3c \end{bmatrix}$

Given $a^2 + b^2 - c^2 = 0$, we must show $\alpha^2 + \beta^2 - \gamma^2 = 0$; but

$\alpha^2 + \beta^2 - \gamma^2 = (a + 2b + 2c)^2 + (2a + b + 2c)^2 - (2a + 2b + 3c)^2$

$= (a^2 + 4b^2 + 4c^2 + 4ab + 4ac + 8bc)$

$\quad + (4a^2 + b^2 + 4c^2 + 4ab + 8ac + 4bc)$

$\quad\quad - (4a^2 + 4b^2 + 9c^2 + 8ab + 12ac + 12bc)$

$= a^2 + b^2 - c^2$

$= 0$

(c) det $A = 1(-1) - 2(2) + 2(2) = -1$

(d) $T^{-1} \left(\begin{bmatrix} 5 \\ 12 \\ 13 \end{bmatrix} \right) = A^{-1} \begin{bmatrix} 5 \\ 12 \\ 13 \end{bmatrix} = \begin{bmatrix} 1 & 2 & 2 \\ 2 & 1 & 2 \\ 2 & 2 & 3 \end{bmatrix}^{-1} \begin{bmatrix} 5 \\ 12 \\ 13 \end{bmatrix}$

$= \frac{1}{-1} \begin{bmatrix} -1 & -2 & 2 \\ -2 & -1 & 2 \\ 2 & 2 & -3 \end{bmatrix}^T \begin{bmatrix} 5 \\ 12 \\ 13 \end{bmatrix} = \begin{bmatrix} 1 & 2 & -2 \\ 2 & 1 & -2 \\ -2 & -2 & 3 \end{bmatrix} \begin{bmatrix} 5 \\ 12 \\ 13 \end{bmatrix} = \begin{bmatrix} 3 \\ -4 \\ 5 \end{bmatrix}$

(e) $0 = \begin{vmatrix} \lambda - 1 & -2 & -2 \\ -2 & \lambda - 1 & -2 \\ -2 & -2 & \lambda - 3 \end{vmatrix}$

$= (\lambda - 1)(\lambda^2 - 4\lambda - 1) + 2(-2\lambda + 2) - 2(2\lambda + 2)$

$= (\lambda - 1)(\lambda^2 - 4\lambda - 1) + -4(\lambda - 1) - 2(2\lambda + 2)$

$= (\lambda - 1)[(\lambda^2 - 4\lambda - 1) - 4] - 2(2\lambda + 2)$

$= (\lambda - 1)(\lambda^2 - 4\lambda - 5) - 2(2\lambda + 2)$

$= (\lambda - 1)(\lambda - 5)(\lambda + 1) - 4(\lambda + 1)$

215

(e) $= [(\lambda-1)(\lambda-5)-4](\lambda+1)$

$= (\lambda^2 - 6\lambda + 1)(\lambda+1)$ so $\lambda = -1$ and $3 \pm 2\sqrt{2}$

(f) $\lambda = -1 \longrightarrow \begin{bmatrix} -2 & -2 & -2 & 0 \\ -2 & -2 & -2 & 0 \\ -2 & -2 & -4 & 0 \end{bmatrix} \longrightarrow \begin{bmatrix} 1 & 1 & 1 & 0 \\ 0 & 0 & -2 & 0 \\ 0 & 0 & 0 & 0 \end{bmatrix} \longrightarrow \begin{bmatrix} 1 & 1 & 0 & 0 \\ 0 & 0 & 1 & 0 \\ 0 & 0 & 0 & 0 \end{bmatrix}$

Let $x_2 = r$;

then $x_1 + x_2 = 0$,   i.e., $x_1 = -x_2 = -r$

and $x_3 = 0$

so $\begin{bmatrix} x_1 \\ x_2 \\ x_3 \end{bmatrix} = \begin{bmatrix} -r \\ r \\ 0 \end{bmatrix} = r \begin{bmatrix} -1 \\ 1 \\ 0 \end{bmatrix}$,   i.e., $B_1 = \left\{ \begin{bmatrix} -1 \\ 1 \\ 0 \end{bmatrix} \right\}$.

$\lambda_2 = 3 + 2\sqrt{2} \longrightarrow \begin{bmatrix} 2+2\sqrt{2} & -2 & -2 & 0 \\ -2 & 2+2\sqrt{2} & -2 & 0 \\ -2 & -2 & 2\sqrt{2} & 0 \end{bmatrix} \longrightarrow \begin{bmatrix} -2 & -2 & 2\sqrt{2} & 0 \\ -2 & 2+2\sqrt{2} & -2 & 0 \\ 2+2\sqrt{2} & -2 & -2 & 0 \end{bmatrix}$

$\longrightarrow \begin{bmatrix} 1 & 1 & -\sqrt{2} & 0 \\ 0 & 4+2\sqrt{2} & -2\sqrt{2}-2 & 0 \\ 0 & -4-2\sqrt{2} & 2\sqrt{2}+2 & 0 \end{bmatrix} \longrightarrow \begin{bmatrix} 1 & 0 & (-1/2)\sqrt{2} & 0 \\ 0 & 1 & (-1/2)\sqrt{2} & 0 \\ 0 & 0 & 0 & 0 \end{bmatrix}$

Let $x_3 = s$;

then $x_2 - \dfrac{1}{2}\sqrt{2}x_3 = 0$,   i.e., $x_2 = \dfrac{1}{2}\sqrt{2}x_3 = \dfrac{1}{2}\sqrt{2}s$

and $x_1 - \dfrac{1}{2}\sqrt{2}x_3 = 0$,   i.e., $x_1 = \dfrac{1}{2}\sqrt{2}x_3 = \dfrac{1}{2}\sqrt{2}s$

so $\begin{bmatrix} x_1 \\ x_2 \\ x_3 \end{bmatrix} = \begin{bmatrix} (1/2)\sqrt{2}s \\ (1/2)\sqrt{2}s \\ s \end{bmatrix} = s \begin{bmatrix} (1/2)\sqrt{2} \\ (1/2)\sqrt{2} \\ 1 \end{bmatrix} = \dfrac{1}{2}\sqrt{2}s \begin{bmatrix} 1 \\ 1 \\ \sqrt{2} \end{bmatrix}$,   i.e., $B_1 = \left\{ \begin{bmatrix} 1 \\ 1 \\ \sqrt{2} \end{bmatrix} \right\}$.

$\lambda_3 = 3 - 2\sqrt{2} \longrightarrow \begin{bmatrix} 2-2\sqrt{2} & -2 & -2 & 0 \\ -2 & 2-2\sqrt{2} & -2 & 0 \\ -2 & -2 & -2\sqrt{2} & 0 \end{bmatrix} \longrightarrow \begin{bmatrix} -2 & -2 & -2\sqrt{2} & 0 \\ -2 & 2-2\sqrt{2} & -2 & 0 \\ 2-2\sqrt{2} & -2 & -2 & 0 \end{bmatrix}$

$\longrightarrow \begin{bmatrix} 1 & 1 & \sqrt{2} & 0 \\ 0 & 4-2\sqrt{2} & 2\sqrt{2}-2 & 0 \\ 0 & -4+2\sqrt{2} & -2\sqrt{2}+2 & 0 \end{bmatrix} \longrightarrow \begin{bmatrix} 1 & 0 & (1/2)\sqrt{2} & 0 \\ 0 & 1 & (1/2)\sqrt{2} & 0 \\ 0 & 0 & 0 & 0 \end{bmatrix}$

Let $x_3 = t$;

then $x_2 + \dfrac{1}{2}\sqrt{2}x_3 = 0$,   i.e., $x_2 = \dfrac{-1}{2}\sqrt{2}x_3 = \dfrac{-1}{2}\sqrt{2}t$

and $x_1 + \dfrac{1}{2}\sqrt{2}x_3 = 0$,   i.e., $x_1 = \dfrac{-1}{2}\sqrt{2}x_3 = \dfrac{-1}{2}\sqrt{2}t$

so
$$\begin{bmatrix} x_1 \\ x_2 \\ x_3 \end{bmatrix} = \begin{bmatrix} (-1/2)\sqrt{2}t \\ (-1/2)\sqrt{2}t \\ t \end{bmatrix} = t \begin{bmatrix} (-1/2)\sqrt{2} \\ (-1/2)\sqrt{2} \\ 1 \end{bmatrix} = \frac{-1}{2}\sqrt{2}t \begin{bmatrix} 1 \\ 1 \\ -\sqrt{2} \end{bmatrix},$$

i.e.,
$$B_3 = \left\{ \begin{bmatrix} 1 \\ 1 \\ -\sqrt{2} \end{bmatrix} \right\}$$

Since T has 3 distinct eigenvalues, T is diagonalizable; in fact, since A is symmetric, T is orthogonally diagonalizable.

CHAPTER 9: ADDITIONAL TOPICS

1. (a) Solve the system

$$y_1' = y_1 + y_2$$

$$y_2' = y_1 + y_2$$

(b) Find the solution that satifies the initial conditions $y_1(0) = 3$, $y_2(0) = 5$.

2. (a) Solve the system

$$y_1' = -5y_1 + 3y_2$$

$$y_2' = -y_1 - y_2$$

(b) Find the solution that satisfies the initial conditions $y_1'(0) = 2$, $y_2'(0) = -2$.

3. (a) Solve the system

$$y_1' = y_1 + y_2 + y_3$$

$$y_2' = \qquad\quad - y_3$$

$$y_3' = \quad - y_2$$

(b) Find the solution that satisfies the initial conditions $y_1(0) = 5, y_2(0) = -4, y_3(0) = 0$.

4. (a) Solve the system

$$y_1' = 3y_1 + 3y_2 + 2y_3$$

$$y_2' = y_1 + y_2 - 2y_3$$

$$y_3' = -y_1 - 3y_2$$

(b) Find the solution that satisfies the inital conditions $y_1'(0) = 0$, $y_2'(0) = -16$, $y_3'(0) = 4$.

5. (a) Solve the differential equation $y'' + y' - 20y = 0$.

(b) Find the solution that satisfies the initial conditions $y(0) = 10$, $y'(0) = 13$.

6. (a) Solve the differential equation $y''' + 4y'' - y' - 4y = 0$.

(b) Find the solution that satisfies the initial conditions $y(0) = 7$, $y'(0) = 6$, $y''(0) = -8$.

7. (a) Find the standard matrix for the plane linear operator T which maps every point into its reflection about the line $y = x$.

(b) Use the matrix to compute $T(3, 2)$.

8. (a) Find the standard matrix for the plane linear operator T which expands by a factor of 3 in the y-direction.

   (b) Use the matrix to compute $T(-2, 1)$.

9. (a) Find the standard matrix for the plane linear operator T which rotates every point $60°$ around the origin.

   (b) Use the matrix to compute $T(2, -8)$.

10. (a) Find the standard matrix for the plane linear operator T which shears by a factor of 3 in the y-direction.

    (b) Use the matrix to compute $T(-2, -2)$.

11. (a) Find the standard matrix for the plane linear operator which compresses by a factor of $\frac{1}{2}$ in the x-direction, then shears by a factor of 3 in the x-direction.

    (b) Use the matrix to compute $T(1, 1)$.

12. (a) Find the standard matrix for the plane linear operator which rotates about the origin through $-45°$, then reflects about the line $y = -x$.

    (b) Use the matrix to compute $T(4, 2)$.

13. Find the least squares straight line fit to the three points $(-1, -1), (1, 2), (3, 5)$.

14. Find the least squares straight line fit to the four points $(0, 1), (1, 3), (2, 4), (3, 4)$.

15. Find the least squares quadratic polynomial fit to the four points $(-1, 1), (0, 0), (1, 1), (2, 2)$.

16. Find the least squares quadratic polynomial fit to the five points $(0, -\frac{5}{3}), (1, 2), (2, 2), (3, -\frac{10}{3}), (4, -4)$.

17. Find the least squares cubic polynomial fit to the four points $(-1, 0), (0, -2), (1, 1), (3, -4)$.

18. Find the least squares approximation of $f(x) = 2 - x$ over the interval $[0, 2\pi]$ by a trigonometric polynomial of order n.

19. Find the least squares approximation of $f(x) = e^x$ over the interval $[0, 2\pi]$ by a trigonometric polynomial of order n.

20. Find the least squares approximation of $f(x) = x^2$ over the interval $[0, 1]$ by a function of the form $a + be^x$.

21. Find the least squares approximation of $f(x) = e^{2x}$ over the interval $[0, 1]$ by a function of the form $ae^x + be^{-x}$.

22. In each part, determine whether the expression is a quadratic form and, if it is, express it in the matrix notation $\mathbf{x}^T A \mathbf{x}$, where A is a symmetric matrix.

(a) $2x^2 - 4xy + y^2$

(b) $x^2 - 5y^2 + 4x + y$

(c) $x_1^2 + 5x_1x_2$

(d) $(2x_1 + \sqrt{2}x_2)^2$

(e) $3x_1^2 + 5x_2^2 - 7x_3^2 - 5x_1x_2 - 6x_2x_3$

(f) $14x_1x_2 - x_3^2$

23. In each part, convert the quadratic form into an expression that does not use matrices.

(a) $\begin{bmatrix} x & y \end{bmatrix} \begin{bmatrix} 2 & 1 \\ 1 & -1 \end{bmatrix} \begin{bmatrix} x \\ y \end{bmatrix}$

(b) $\begin{bmatrix} x & y \end{bmatrix} \begin{bmatrix} 0 & 3/2 \\ 3/2 & 0 \end{bmatrix} \begin{bmatrix} x \\ y \end{bmatrix}$

(c) $\begin{bmatrix} x_1 & x_2 \end{bmatrix} \begin{bmatrix} \pi & \pi \\ \pi & -\pi \end{bmatrix} \begin{bmatrix} x_1 \\ x_2 \end{bmatrix}$

(d) $\begin{bmatrix} x_1 & x_2 & x_3 \end{bmatrix} \begin{bmatrix} 1 & -3 & 0 \\ -3 & 4 & -5 \\ 0 & -5 & 7 \end{bmatrix} \begin{bmatrix} x_1 \\ x_2 \\ x_3 \end{bmatrix}$

(e) $\begin{bmatrix} x_1 & x_2 & x_3 \end{bmatrix} \begin{bmatrix} 1 & -1/2 & 1 \\ -1/2 & 0 & 0 \\ 1 & 0 & 4 \end{bmatrix} \begin{bmatrix} x_1 \\ x_2 \\ x_3 \end{bmatrix}$

(f) $\begin{bmatrix} x_1 & x_2 & x_3 \end{bmatrix} \begin{bmatrix} 5 & 0 & 0 \\ 0 & 12 & 0 \\ 0 & 0 & -13 \end{bmatrix} \begin{bmatrix} x_1 \\ x_2 \\ x_3 \end{bmatrix}$

24. In each part, compute the maximum and minumum values of the quadratic form subject to the constraint $x_1^2 + x_2^2 = 1$, and determine the values of x_1 and x_2 at which the maximum and minimum occur.

(a) $2x_1^2 + 3x_2^2$

(b) $2x_1^2 + 3x_1x_2 + 2x_2^2$

(c) $x_1^2 + 2x_1x_2 + x_2^2$

(d) $2x_1^2 + 3x_1x_2 + x_2^2$

25. In each part, compute the maximum and minimum values of the quadratic form subject to the constraint $x_1^2 + x_2^2 + x_3^2 = 1$, and determine the values of x_1, x_2 and x_3 at which the maximum and minimum occur.

(a) $x_1^2 - 4x_1x_2 - 4x_2x_3 - x_3^2$

(b) $2x_1^2 + 2x_2^2 + 2x_3^2 - 2x_1x_3$

(c) $-2x_1^2 + 5x_2^2 + 7x_3^2 + 12x_1x_3$

26. Classify each matrix as positive definite, positive semidefinite, negative definite, negative semidefinite, or indefinite.

(a) $A = \begin{bmatrix} 3 & 0 & 0 \\ 0 & 0 & 0 \\ 0 & 0 & 17 \end{bmatrix}$

(b) $A = \begin{bmatrix} \pi + 4 & 0 & 0 \\ 0 & \pi - 4 & 0 \\ 0 & 0 & \pi^2 - 16 \end{bmatrix}$

(c) $A = \begin{bmatrix} 3 & -1 & 0 \\ -1 & 3 & 0 \\ 0 & 0 & 4 \end{bmatrix}$

(d) $A = \begin{bmatrix} -6 & 1 \\ 1 & -6 \end{bmatrix}$

(e) $A = \begin{bmatrix} 1 & 0 & -2 \\ 0 & 1 & 3 \\ -2 & 3 & 0 \end{bmatrix}$

(f) $A = \begin{bmatrix} -3 & 0 & 1 \\ 0 & 0 & 0 \\ 1 & 0 & -1 \end{bmatrix}$

27. In each part, use a change of variables to reduce the quadratic form to a sum of squares.

(a) $4x_1^2 + 4x_2^2 + 14x_1x_2$

(b) $3x_1^2 + 5x_2^2 - 2\sqrt{35}x_1x_2$

(c) $-2x_1x_2 - 2x_2x_3 + 2x_1x_3$

(d) $x_1^2 - x_3^2 - 4x_1x_2 - 4x_2x_3$

In questions 28-30, rotate the coordinate axes to remove the xy-term. Name the conic and give its equation in the rotated coordinate system.

28. $x^2 - 6xy + y^2 + 8 = 0$

29. $x^2 + 4xy + 4y^2 + 4x - 2y + 5 = 0$

30. $6x^2 - 4xy + 3y^2 = 14$

In questions 31-33, rotate and translate the coordinate axes to put the conic in standard position. Name the conic and give its equation in the final coordinate system.

31. $-3x^2 + 2xy - 3y^2 + 2x + 2y + 7 = 0$

32. $4x^2 - 24xy + 11y^2 + 40x - 70y = 105$

33. $59x^2 + 24xy + 66y^2 - 170x - 60y - 325 = 0$

34. In each part, express the quadratic equation in the matrix form $\mathbf{x}^T A \mathbf{x} + K \mathbf{x} + j = 0$.

(a) $2x^2 - 3y^2 + z^2 + 4xy - 3y - z = 1$ (b) $12x^2 + y^2 - z^2 - 2xy - 4yz + x + y + z - 6 = 0$

(c) $x^2 - y^2 - z^2 + 6xz - yz + 16y - 100z = 8$ (d) $6x^2 + 9z^2 + 3xy + 4xz + 5yz = 11x - 17z$

In questions 35-37, rotate the coordinate axes to remove the cross-product terms. Name the quadric and give its equation in the rotated coordinate system.

35. $x^2 - z^2 - 4xy - 4yz - 12x - 3y - 18z + 12 = 0$

36. $2xy + 2xz + 2yz + 12x = 14$

37. $2x^2 + 2y^2 + 2z^2 - 2xy - 2xz - 2yz + 3x + 3y + 3z = 0$

In questions 38-40, rotate and translate the coordinate axes to put the quadric in standard position. Name the quadric and give its equation in the final coordinate system.

38. $-8xy + 6yz + 12x + 20y + 16z = 0$

39. $3y^2 + 4xz + 4x + 4z + 22 = 0$

40. $14x^2 + 14y^2 + 17z^2 - 8xy - 4xz - 4yz + 36x + 36y + 18z + 9 = 0$

In questions 41-45, compute the number of operations of addition and multiplication required to carry out the indicated procedure if A is an $n \times n$ matrix, assuming that

(a) $n = 3$ (b) $n = 15$ (c) $n = 25$ (d) $n = 300$

41. How many additions $\left(\frac{1}{3}n^3 + \frac{1}{2}n^2 - \frac{5}{6}n\right)$ and how many multiplications $\left(\frac{1}{3}n^3 + n^2 - \frac{1}{3}n\right)$ are required to solve $A\mathbf{x} = \mathbf{b}$ by Gaussian or Gauss-Jordan elimination?

42. How many additions $(n^3 - 2n^2 + n)$ and how many multiplications (n^3) are required to determine A^{-1} by reducing $[A \vdots I]$ to $[I \vdots A^{-1}]$?

43. How many additions $(n^3 - n^2)$ and how many multiplications $(n^3 + n^2)$ are required to solve $A\mathbf{x} = \mathbf{b}$ using $\mathbf{x} = A^{-1}\mathbf{b}$?

44. How many additions $(\frac{1}{3}n^3 - \frac{1}{2}n^2 + \frac{1}{6}n)$ and how many multiplications $(\frac{1}{3}n^3 + \frac{2}{3}n - 1)$ are required to compute $\det(A)$ by row reduction?

45. How many additions $(\frac{1}{3}n^4 - \frac{1}{6}n^3 - \frac{1}{3}n^2 + \frac{1}{6}n)$ and how many multiplications $(\frac{1}{3}n^4 + \frac{1}{3}n^3 + \frac{2}{3}n^2 + \frac{2}{3}n - 1)$ are required to solve $A\mathbf{x} = \mathbf{b}$ by Cramer's Rule?

In questions 46-50, use an LU-decomposition to solve the system.

46. $\begin{bmatrix} 4 & 20 \\ 3 & 2 \end{bmatrix} \begin{bmatrix} x_1 \\ x_2 \end{bmatrix} = \begin{bmatrix} 4 \\ -10 \end{bmatrix}$

47. $\begin{bmatrix} -3 & 6 \\ -2 & 1 \end{bmatrix} \begin{bmatrix} x_1 \\ x_2 \end{bmatrix} = \begin{bmatrix} 3 \\ -4 \end{bmatrix}$

48. $\begin{bmatrix} 1 & 2 & -1 \\ 2 & 6 & -6 \\ 3 & 7 & -1 \end{bmatrix} \begin{bmatrix} x_1 \\ x_2 \\ x_3 \end{bmatrix} = \begin{bmatrix} 2 \\ -4 \\ 14 \end{bmatrix}$

49. $\begin{bmatrix} 1 & -3 & 2 \\ 2 & 0 & 1 \\ 3 & -7 & 7 \end{bmatrix} \begin{bmatrix} x_1 \\ x_2 \\ x_3 \end{bmatrix} = \begin{bmatrix} 8 \\ 1 \\ 25 \end{bmatrix}$

50. $\begin{bmatrix} 1 & 1 & 1 & -1 \\ 2 & 5 & 2 & -2 \\ 0 & 1 & 2 & -4 \\ -3 & 1 & 0 & 0 \end{bmatrix} \begin{bmatrix} x_1 \\ x_2 \\ x_3 \\ x_4 \end{bmatrix} = \begin{bmatrix} 4 \\ 5 \\ -3 \\ -13 \end{bmatrix}$

In questions 51-52, find a factorization $A = PLU$, where P is obtained from I by interchanging rows, L is lower triangular, and U is upper triangular.

51. $A = \begin{bmatrix} 0 & 3 & 3 \\ 1 & 0 & -1 \\ -1 & 2 & 0 \end{bmatrix}$

52. $A = \begin{bmatrix} 0 & 2 & 4 \\ 2 & 4 & 3 \\ 1 & 2 & 3 \end{bmatrix}$

WRITING QUESTIONS

53. Refute the following: "Linear algebra is useful only for studying linear objects, like lines and planes."

54. Compare and contrast a shear and an earthquake. (You may use words and drawings.)

55. The textbook explains how to find a least squares approximation to a set of data points. Explain what the term "least squares" refers to. Explain it so a high school student could understand. (You may use words and drawings.)

56. Consider a quadratic form in the variables x_1 and x_2. The textbook explains how to find the maximum and minimum values of the form, subject to the constraint $x_1^2 + x_2^2 = 1$. Explain what these maximum and minimum values represent graphically. (You may use words and drawings.)

57. In our procedure for placing a conic section or quadric surface into standard position, why must the determinant of the transition matrix be positive 1?

58. The number of additions and multiplications needed to carry out Gaussian elimination, Cramer's rule, and many other procedures, is a polynomial. Why is the degree of this polynomial an important practical matter?

59. How are *LU*-decompositions useful in solving systems of linear equations?

1. (a) $A = \begin{bmatrix} 1 & 1 \\ 1 & 1 \end{bmatrix}$

$$0 = \begin{vmatrix} \lambda - 1 & -1 \\ -1 & \lambda - 1 \end{vmatrix} = (\lambda - 1)^2 - (-1)^2 = (\lambda^2 - 2\lambda + 1) - 1 = \lambda^2 - 2\lambda$$

$$= \lambda(\lambda - 2), \quad \text{so} \quad \lambda = 0, 2$$

$$\lambda_1 = 0 \longrightarrow \begin{bmatrix} -1 & -1 & 0 \\ -1 & -1 & 0 \end{bmatrix} \longrightarrow \begin{bmatrix} 1 & 1 & 0 \\ 0 & 0 & 0 \end{bmatrix}$$

Let $x_2 = s$;

then $x_1 + x_2 = 0$, *i.e.* $x_1 = -x_2 = -s$

so $\begin{bmatrix} x_1 \\ x_2 \end{bmatrix} = \begin{bmatrix} -s \\ s \end{bmatrix} = s \begin{bmatrix} -1 \\ 1 \end{bmatrix}$.

$$\lambda_2 = 2 \longrightarrow \begin{bmatrix} 1 & -1 & 0 \\ -1 & 1 & 0 \end{bmatrix} \longrightarrow \begin{bmatrix} 1 & -1 & 0 \\ 0 & 0 & 0 \end{bmatrix}$$

Let $x_2 = t$;

then $x_1 - x_2 = 0$, *i.e.* $x_1 = x_2 = t$

so $\begin{bmatrix} x_1 \\ x_2 \end{bmatrix} = \begin{bmatrix} t \\ t \end{bmatrix} = t \begin{bmatrix} 1 \\ 1 \end{bmatrix}$.

$P = \begin{bmatrix} -1 & 1 \\ 1 & 1 \end{bmatrix}, \quad D = P^{-1}AP = \begin{bmatrix} 0 & 0 \\ 0 & 2 \end{bmatrix},$

$U = \begin{bmatrix} c_1 e^{0x} \\ c_2 e^{2x} \end{bmatrix} = \begin{bmatrix} c_1 \\ c_2 e^{2x} \end{bmatrix}, \quad Y = PU = \begin{bmatrix} -1 & 1 \\ 1 & 1 \end{bmatrix} \begin{bmatrix} c_1 \\ c_2 e^{2x} \end{bmatrix} = \begin{bmatrix} -c_1 + c_2 e^{2x} \\ c_1 + c_2 e^{2x} \end{bmatrix}$

so $y_1 = -c_1 + c_2 e^{2x}$, $y_2 = c_1 + c_2 e^{2x}$.

(b) $y_1(0) = -c_1 + c_2 = 3$

$y_2(0) = c_1 + c_2 = 5$

$$\begin{bmatrix} c_1 \\ c_2 \end{bmatrix} = \begin{bmatrix} -1 & 1 \\ 1 & 1 \end{bmatrix}^{-1} \begin{bmatrix} 3 \\ 5 \end{bmatrix} = -\tfrac{1}{2} \begin{bmatrix} 1 & -1 \\ -1 & -1 \end{bmatrix} \begin{bmatrix} 3 \\ 5 \end{bmatrix} = \begin{bmatrix} 1 \\ 4 \end{bmatrix};$$

$y_1 = -1 + 4e^{2x}$, $y_2 = 1 + 4e^{2x}$

2. (a) $A = \begin{bmatrix} -5 & 3 \\ -1 & -1 \end{bmatrix}$

225

$$0 = \begin{vmatrix} \lambda+5 & -3 \\ 1 & \lambda+1 \end{vmatrix} = (\lambda+5)(\lambda+1) - (1)(-3) = (\lambda^2 + 6\lambda + 5) + 3$$

$$= \lambda^2 + 6\lambda + 8 = (\lambda+2)(\lambda+4), \quad \text{so} \quad \lambda = -2, -4$$

$$\lambda_1 = -2 \longrightarrow \begin{bmatrix} 3 & -3 & 0 \\ 1 & -1 & 0 \end{bmatrix} \longrightarrow \begin{bmatrix} 1 & -1 & 0 \\ 0 & 0 & 0 \end{bmatrix}$$

Let $x_2 = s$;

then $x_1 - x_2 = 0$, $\quad i.e. \quad x_1 = x_2 = s$

so $\begin{bmatrix} x_1 \\ x_2 \end{bmatrix} = \begin{bmatrix} s \\ s \end{bmatrix} = s \begin{bmatrix} 1 \\ 1 \end{bmatrix}$.

$$\lambda_2 = -4 \longrightarrow \begin{bmatrix} 1 & -3 & 0 \\ 1 & -3 & 0 \end{bmatrix} \longrightarrow \begin{bmatrix} 1 & -3 & 0 \\ 0 & 0 & 0 \end{bmatrix}$$

Let $x_2 = t$;

then $x_1 - 3x_2 = 0$, $\quad i.e. \quad x_1 = 3x_2 = 3t$

so $\begin{bmatrix} x_1 \\ x_2 \end{bmatrix} = \begin{bmatrix} 3t \\ t \end{bmatrix} = t \begin{bmatrix} 3 \\ 1 \end{bmatrix}$.

$$P = \begin{bmatrix} 1 & 3 \\ 1 & 1 \end{bmatrix}, \quad D = P^{-1}AP = \begin{bmatrix} -2 & 0 \\ 0 & -4 \end{bmatrix},$$

$$U = \begin{bmatrix} c_1 e^{-2x} \\ c_2 e^{-4x} \end{bmatrix}, \quad Y = PU = \begin{bmatrix} 1 & 3 \\ 1 & 1 \end{bmatrix} \begin{bmatrix} c_1 e^{-2x} \\ c_2 e^{-4x} \end{bmatrix} = \begin{bmatrix} c_1 e^{-2x} + 3c_2 e^{-4x} \\ c_1 e^{-2x} + c_2 e^{-4x} \end{bmatrix}$$

so $y_1 = c_1 e^{-2x} + 3c_2 e^{-4x}$, $\quad y_2 = c_1 e^{-2x} + c_2 e^{-4x}$.

(b) $y_1' = -2c_1 e^{-2x} + -12c_2 e^{-4x}$, $\quad y_1'(0) = -2c_1 + -12c_2 = 2$

$y_2' = -2c_1 e^{-2x} + -4c_2 e^{-4x}$, $\quad y_2'(0) = -2c_1 + -4c_2 = -2$

$$\begin{bmatrix} c_1 \\ c_2 \end{bmatrix} = \begin{bmatrix} -2 & -12 \\ -2 & -4 \end{bmatrix}^{-1} \begin{bmatrix} 2 \\ -2 \end{bmatrix} = -\frac{1}{16} \begin{bmatrix} -4 & 12 \\ 2 & -2 \end{bmatrix} \begin{bmatrix} 2 \\ -2 \end{bmatrix} = \begin{bmatrix} 2 \\ -1/2 \end{bmatrix};$$

$y_1 = 2e^{-2x} - \frac{3}{2}e^{-4x}$, $y_2 = 2e^{-2x} - \frac{1}{2}e^{-4x}$.

3. (a) $\quad A = \begin{bmatrix} 1 & 1 & 1 \\ 0 & 0 & -1 \\ 0 & -1 & 0 \end{bmatrix}$

$$0 = \begin{vmatrix} \lambda-1 & -1 & -1 \\ 0 & \lambda & 1 \\ 0 & 1 & \lambda \end{vmatrix} = (\lambda-1)(\lambda^2-1) = (\lambda-1)(\lambda-1)(\lambda+1), \text{ so } \lambda = 1, -1.$$

$$\lambda_1 = 1 \longrightarrow \begin{bmatrix} 0 & -1 & -1 & 0 \\ 0 & 1 & 1 & 0 \\ 0 & 1 & 1 & 0 \end{bmatrix} \longrightarrow \begin{bmatrix} 0 & 1 & 1 & 0 \\ 0 & 0 & 0 & 0 \\ 0 & 0 & 0 & 0 \end{bmatrix}$$

Let $x_3 = s$ and $x_1 = r$;

then $x_2 + x_3 = 0$,   i.e. $x_2 = -x_3 = -s$

so $\begin{bmatrix} x_1 \\ x_2 \\ x_3 \end{bmatrix} = \begin{bmatrix} r \\ -s \\ s \end{bmatrix} = \begin{bmatrix} r \\ 0 \\ 0 \end{bmatrix} + \begin{bmatrix} 0 \\ -s \\ s \end{bmatrix} = r\begin{bmatrix} 1 \\ 0 \\ 0 \end{bmatrix} + s\begin{bmatrix} 0 \\ -1 \\ 1 \end{bmatrix}$

$$\lambda_2 = -1 \longrightarrow \begin{bmatrix} -2 & -1 & -1 & 0 \\ 0 & -1 & 1 & 0 \\ 0 & 1 & -1 & 0 \end{bmatrix} \longrightarrow \begin{bmatrix} 1 & 1/2 & 1/2 & 0 \\ 0 & 1 & -1 & 0 \\ 0 & 0 & 0 & 0 \end{bmatrix} \longrightarrow \begin{bmatrix} 1 & 0 & 1 & 0 \\ 0 & 1 & -1 & 0 \\ 0 & 0 & 0 & 0 \end{bmatrix}$$

Let $x_3 = t$;

then $x_2 - x_3 = 0$,   i.e. $x_2 = x_3 = t$

and $x_1 + x_3 = 0$,   i.e. $x_1 = -x_3 = -t$

so $\begin{bmatrix} x_1 \\ x_2 \\ x_3 \end{bmatrix} = \begin{bmatrix} -t \\ t \\ t \end{bmatrix} = t\begin{bmatrix} -1 \\ 1 \\ 1 \end{bmatrix}$

$$P = \begin{bmatrix} 1 & 0 & -1 \\ 0 & -1 & 1 \\ 0 & 1 & 1 \end{bmatrix}, \qquad D = P^{-1}AP = \begin{bmatrix} 1 & 0 & 0 \\ 0 & 1 & 0 \\ 0 & 0 & -1 \end{bmatrix}$$

$$U = \begin{bmatrix} c_1 e^{x} \\ c_2 e^{x} \\ c_3 e^{-x} \end{bmatrix}, \qquad Y = PU = \begin{bmatrix} 1 & 0 & -1 \\ 0 & -1 & 1 \\ 0 & 1 & 1 \end{bmatrix} \begin{bmatrix} c_1 e^{x} \\ c_2 e^{x} \\ c_3 e^{-x} \end{bmatrix} = \begin{bmatrix} c_1 e^{x} - c_3 e^{-x} \\ -c_2 e^{x} + c_3 e^{-x} \\ c_2 e^{x} + c_3 e^{-x} \end{bmatrix}$$

so $y_1 = c_1 e^{x} - c_3 e^{-x}$, $y_2 = -c_2 e^{x} + c_3 e^{-x}$, $y_3 = c_2 e^{x} + c_3 e^{-x}$.

(b) $y_1(0) = c_1 - c_3 = 5$

     $y_2(0) = -c_2 + c_3 = -4$

     $y_3(0) = c_2 + c_3 = 0$

$$\begin{bmatrix} c_1 \\ c_2 \\ c_3 \end{bmatrix} = \begin{bmatrix} 1 & 0 & -1 \\ 0 & -1 & 1 \\ 0 & 1 & 1 \end{bmatrix}^{-1} \begin{bmatrix} 5 \\ -4 \\ 0 \end{bmatrix} = -\frac{1}{2}\begin{bmatrix} -2 & 0 & 0 \\ -1 & 1 & -1 \\ -1 & -1 & -1 \end{bmatrix}^{T} \begin{bmatrix} 5 \\ -4 \\ 0 \end{bmatrix}$$

$$= \frac{1}{2}\begin{bmatrix} 2 & 1 & 1 \\ 0 & -1 & 1 \\ 0 & 1 & 1 \end{bmatrix} \begin{bmatrix} 5 \\ -4 \\ 0 \end{bmatrix} = \frac{1}{2}\begin{bmatrix} 6 \\ 4 \\ -4 \end{bmatrix} = \begin{bmatrix} 3 \\ 2 \\ -2 \end{bmatrix};$$

$y_1 = 3e^{x} + 2e^{-x}$, $y_2 = -2e^{x} + -2e^{-x}$, $y_3 = 2e^{x} + -2e^{-x}$.

4. (a)　$A = \begin{bmatrix} 3 & 3 & 2 \\ 1 & 1 & -2 \\ -1 & -3 & 0 \end{bmatrix}$

$$0 = \begin{vmatrix} \lambda - 3 & -3 & -2 \\ -1 & \lambda - 1 & 2 \\ 1 & 3 & \lambda \end{vmatrix} = (\lambda - 3)(\lambda^2 - \lambda - 6) + 1(-3\lambda + 6) + 1(-6 + 2\lambda - 2)$$

$$= (\lambda - 3)(\lambda^2 - \lambda - 6) + -\lambda - 2$$

$$= (\lambda - 3)(\lambda - 3)(\lambda + 2) + -1(\lambda + 2)$$

$$= [(\lambda - 3)(\lambda - 3) + -1](\lambda + 2)$$

$$= (\lambda^2 - 6\lambda + 8)(\lambda + 2)$$

$$= (\lambda - 2)(\lambda - 4)(\lambda + 2) \quad \text{so} \quad \lambda = 2, 4, -2$$

$$\lambda_1 = 2 \longrightarrow \begin{bmatrix} -1 & -3 & -2 & 0 \\ -1 & 1 & 2 & 0 \\ 1 & 3 & 2 & 0 \end{bmatrix} \longrightarrow \begin{bmatrix} 1 & 3 & 2 & 0 \\ 0 & 4 & 4 & 0 \\ 0 & 0 & 0 & 0 \end{bmatrix} \longrightarrow \begin{bmatrix} 1 & 0 & -1 & 0 \\ 0 & 1 & 1 & 0 \\ 0 & 0 & 0 & 0 \end{bmatrix}$$

Let $x_3 = r$;

then $x_2 + x_3 = 0$, i.e. $x_2 = -x_3 = -r$

and $x_1 - x_3 = 0$, i.e. $x_1 = x_3 = r$

so $\begin{bmatrix} x_1 \\ x_2 \\ x_3 \end{bmatrix} = \begin{bmatrix} r \\ -r \\ r \end{bmatrix} = r \begin{bmatrix} 1 \\ -1 \\ 1 \end{bmatrix}$

$$\lambda_2 = 4 \longrightarrow \begin{bmatrix} 1 & -3 & -2 & 0 \\ -1 & 3 & 2 & 0 \\ 1 & 3 & 4 & 0 \end{bmatrix} \longrightarrow \begin{bmatrix} 1 & -3 & -2 & 0 \\ 0 & 0 & 0 & 0 \\ 0 & 6 & 6 & 0 \end{bmatrix} \longrightarrow \begin{bmatrix} 1 & 0 & 1 & 0 \\ 0 & 1 & 1 & 0 \\ 0 & 0 & 0 & 0 \end{bmatrix}$$

Let $x_3 = s$;

then $x_2 + x_3 = 0$, i.e. $x_2 = -x_3 = -s$

and $x_1 + x_3 = 0$, i.e. $x_1 = -x_3 = -s$

so $\begin{bmatrix} x_1 \\ x_2 \\ x_3 \end{bmatrix} = \begin{bmatrix} -s \\ -s \\ s \end{bmatrix} = s \begin{bmatrix} -1 \\ -1 \\ 1 \end{bmatrix}$

$$\lambda_3 = -2 \longrightarrow \begin{bmatrix} -5 & -3 & -2 & 0 \\ -1 & -3 & 2 & 0 \\ 1 & 3 & -2 & 0 \end{bmatrix} \longrightarrow \begin{bmatrix} 1 & 3 & -2 & 0 \\ -1 & -3 & 2 & 0 \\ -5 & -3 & -2 & 0 \end{bmatrix} \longrightarrow \begin{bmatrix} 1 & 3 & -2 & 0 \\ 0 & 0 & 0 & 0 \\ 0 & 12 & -12 & 0 \end{bmatrix}$$

$$\longrightarrow \begin{bmatrix} 1 & 0 & 1 & 0 \\ 0 & 1 & -1 & 0 \\ 0 & 0 & 0 & 0 \end{bmatrix}$$

Let $x_3 = t$;

then $x_2 - x_3 = 0$, *i.e.* $x_2 = x_3 = t$

and $x_1 + x_3 = 0$, i.e. $x_1 = -x_3 = -t$

so $\begin{bmatrix} x_1 \\ x_2 \\ x_3 \end{bmatrix} = \begin{bmatrix} -t \\ t \\ t \end{bmatrix} = t \begin{bmatrix} -1 \\ 1 \\ 1 \end{bmatrix}$

$$P = \begin{bmatrix} 1 & -1 & -1 \\ -1 & -1 & 1 \\ 1 & 1 & 1 \end{bmatrix}, \qquad D = P^{-1}AP = \begin{bmatrix} 2 & 0 & 0 \\ 0 & 4 & 0 \\ 0 & 0 & -2 \end{bmatrix},$$

$$U = \begin{bmatrix} c_1 e^{2x} \\ c_2 e^{4x} \\ c_3 e^{-2x} \end{bmatrix}, \quad Y = PU = \begin{bmatrix} 1 & -1 & -1 \\ -1 & -1 & 1 \\ 1 & 1 & 1 \end{bmatrix} \begin{bmatrix} c_1 e^{2x} \\ c_2 e^{4x} \\ c_3 e^{-2x} \end{bmatrix} = \begin{bmatrix} c_1 e^{2x} - c_2 e^{4x} - c_3 e^{-2x} \\ -c_1 e^{2x} - c_2 e^{4x} + c_3 e^{-2x} \\ c_1 e^{2x} + c_2 e^{4x} + c_3 e^{-2x} \end{bmatrix}$$

so $y_1 = c_1 e^{2x} - c_2 e^{4x} - c_3 e^{-2x}$, $y_2 = -c_1 e^{2x} - c_2 e^{4x} + c_3 e^{-2x}$, $y_3 = c_1 e^{2x} + c_2 e^{4x} + c_3 e^{-2x}$.

4. (b) $\qquad y_1' = 2c_1 e^{2x} - 4c_2 e^{4x} + 2c_3 e^{-2x}$, $\quad y_1'(0) = 2c_1 - 4c_2 + 2c_3 = 0$

$\qquad\qquad\qquad y_2' = -2c_1 e^{2x} - 4c_2 e^{4x} - 2c_3 e^{-2x}$, $\quad y_2'(0) = -2c_1 - 4c_2 - 2c_3 = -16$

$\qquad\qquad\qquad y_3' = 2c_1 e^{2x} + 4c_2 e^{4x} - 2c_3 e^{-2x}$, $\quad y_3'(0) = 2c_1 + 4c_2 - 2c_3 = 4$

$$\begin{bmatrix} c_1 \\ c_2 \\ c_3 \end{bmatrix} = \begin{bmatrix} 2 & -4 & 2 \\ -2 & -4 & -2 \\ 2 & 4 & -2 \end{bmatrix}^{-1} \begin{bmatrix} 0 \\ -16 \\ 4 \end{bmatrix} = \frac{1}{64} \begin{bmatrix} 16 & -8 & 0 \\ 0 & -8 & -16 \\ 16 & 0 & -16 \end{bmatrix}^{T} \begin{bmatrix} 0 \\ -16 \\ 4 \end{bmatrix}$$

$$= \frac{1}{8} \begin{bmatrix} 2 & 0 & 2 \\ -1 & -1 & 0 \\ 0 & -2 & -2 \end{bmatrix} \begin{bmatrix} 0 \\ -16 \\ 4 \end{bmatrix} = \frac{1}{8} \begin{bmatrix} 8 \\ 16 \\ 24 \end{bmatrix} = \begin{bmatrix} 1 \\ 2 \\ 3 \end{bmatrix};$$

$y_1 = e^{2x} - 2e^{4x} - 3e^{-2x}$, $\qquad y_2 = -e^{2x} - 2e^{4x} + 3e^{-2x}$, $\qquad y_3 = e^{2x} + 2e^{4x} + 3e^{-2x}$.

5. (a) Let $\quad y_1 = y$ and $y_2 = y'$;

$\qquad$ then $y_1' = y' = y_2$

$\qquad$ and $y_2' = y'' = -y' + 20y = 20y_1 - y_2$

$\qquad$ so $\begin{bmatrix} y_1' \\ y_2' \end{bmatrix} = \begin{bmatrix} 0 & 1 \\ 20 & -1 \end{bmatrix} \begin{bmatrix} y_1 \\ y_2 \end{bmatrix}.$

$A = \begin{bmatrix} 0 & 1 \\ 20 & -1 \end{bmatrix}$

$0 = \begin{vmatrix} \lambda & -1 \\ -20 & \lambda+1 \end{vmatrix} = \lambda(\lambda+1) - (-20)(-1) = \lambda^2 + \lambda - 20 = (\lambda-4)(\lambda+5)$ so $\lambda = 4, -5$.

$\lambda_1 = 4 \longrightarrow \begin{bmatrix} 4 & -1 & 0 \\ -20 & 5 & 0 \end{bmatrix} \longrightarrow \begin{bmatrix} 1 & -1/4 & 0 \\ 0 & 0 & 0 \end{bmatrix}$

$\qquad\qquad$ Let $x_2 = s$;

229

then $x_1 - \frac{1}{4}x_2 = 0$,   *i.e.* $x_1 = \frac{1}{4}x_2 = \frac{1}{4}s$

so $\begin{bmatrix} x_1 \\ x_2 \end{bmatrix} = \begin{bmatrix} (1/4)s \\ s \end{bmatrix} = s\begin{bmatrix} 1/4 \\ 1 \end{bmatrix} = \frac{1}{4}s\begin{bmatrix} 1 \\ 4 \end{bmatrix}.$

$\lambda_2 = -5 \longrightarrow \begin{bmatrix} -5 & -1 & 0 \\ -20 & -4 & 0 \end{bmatrix} \longrightarrow \begin{bmatrix} 1 & 1/5 & 0 \\ 0 & 0 & 0 \end{bmatrix}$

Let $x_2 = t$;

then $x_1 + \frac{1}{5}x_2 = 0$,   *i.e.* $x_1 = -\frac{1}{5}x_2 = -\frac{1}{5}t$

so $\begin{bmatrix} x_1 \\ x_2 \end{bmatrix} = \begin{bmatrix} (-1/5)t \\ t \end{bmatrix} = t\begin{bmatrix} -1/5 \\ 1 \end{bmatrix} = \frac{1}{5}t\begin{bmatrix} -1 \\ 5 \end{bmatrix}.$

$P = \begin{bmatrix} 1 & -1 \\ 4 & 5 \end{bmatrix}, \qquad D = P^{-1}AP = \begin{bmatrix} 4 & 0 \\ 0 & -5 \end{bmatrix},$

$U = \begin{bmatrix} c_1e^{4x} \\ c_2e^{-5x} \end{bmatrix}, \quad Y = PU = \begin{bmatrix} 1 & -1 \\ 4 & 5 \end{bmatrix}\begin{bmatrix} c_1e^{4x} \\ c_2e^{-5x} \end{bmatrix} = \begin{bmatrix} c_1e^{4x} - c_2e^{-5x} \\ 4c_1e^{4x} + 5c_2e^{-5x} \end{bmatrix}$

so $y = y_1 = c_1e^{4x} - c_2e^{-5x}.$

(b) $y = c_1e^{4x} - c_2e^{-5x}$, $y(0) = c_1 - c_2 = 10$

$y' = 4c_1e^{4x} + 5c_2e^{-5x}$, $y'(0) = 4c_1 + 5c_2 = 13$

$\begin{bmatrix} c_1 \\ c_2 \end{bmatrix} = \begin{bmatrix} 1 & -1 \\ 4 & 5 \end{bmatrix}^{-1}\begin{bmatrix} 10 \\ 13 \end{bmatrix} = \frac{1}{9}\begin{bmatrix} 5 & 1 \\ -4 & 1 \end{bmatrix}\begin{bmatrix} 10 \\ 13 \end{bmatrix} = \frac{1}{9}\begin{bmatrix} 63 \\ -27 \end{bmatrix} = \begin{bmatrix} 7 \\ -3 \end{bmatrix};$

$y = 7e^{4x} + 3e^{-5x}.$

6. (a)   Let $y_1 = y, y_2 = y'$ and $y_3 = y''$;

then $y_1' = y' = y_2$

and $y_2' = y'' = y_3$

and $y_3' = y''' = -4y'' + y' + 4y = 4y_1 + y_2 - 4y_3$

so $\begin{bmatrix} y_1' \\ y_2' \\ y_3' \end{bmatrix} = \begin{bmatrix} 0 & 1 & 0 \\ 0 & 0 & 1 \\ 4 & 1 & -4 \end{bmatrix}\begin{bmatrix} y_1 \\ y_2 \\ y_3 \end{bmatrix}$

$A = \begin{bmatrix} 0 & 1 & 0 \\ 0 & 0 & 1 \\ 4 & 1 & -4 \end{bmatrix}$

$$0 = \begin{vmatrix} \lambda & -1 & 0 \\ 0 & \lambda & -1 \\ -4 & -1 & \lambda+4 \end{vmatrix} = \lambda[\lambda(\lambda+4) - (-1)(-1)] + 1[0(\lambda+4) - (-4)(-1)]$$

$$= \lambda(\lambda^2 + 4\lambda - 1) + -4$$

$$= \lambda^3 + 4\lambda^2 - \lambda - 4$$

$$= \lambda^2(\lambda+4) - 1(\lambda+4)$$

$$= (\lambda^2 - 1)(\lambda+4) = (\lambda-1)(\lambda+1)(\lambda+4) \quad \text{so} \quad \lambda = 1, -1, -4$$

$$\lambda_1 = 1 \longrightarrow \begin{bmatrix} 1 & -1 & 0 & 0 \\ 0 & 1 & -1 & 0 \\ -4 & -1 & 5 & 0 \end{bmatrix} \longrightarrow \begin{bmatrix} 1 & -1 & 0 & 0 \\ 0 & 1 & -1 & 0 \\ 0 & -5 & 5 & 0 \end{bmatrix} \longrightarrow \begin{bmatrix} 1 & 0 & -1 & 0 \\ 0 & 1 & -1 & 0 \\ 0 & 0 & 0 & 0 \end{bmatrix}$$

Let $x_3 = r$;

then $x_2 - x_3 = 0$, i.e. $x_2 = x_3 = r$

and $x_1 - x_3 = 0$, i.e. $x_1 = x_3 = r$

so $\begin{bmatrix} x_1 \\ x_2 \\ x_3 \end{bmatrix} = \begin{bmatrix} r \\ r \\ r \end{bmatrix} = r \begin{bmatrix} 1 \\ 1 \\ 1 \end{bmatrix}$

$$\lambda_2 = -1 \longrightarrow \begin{bmatrix} -1 & -1 & 0 & 0 \\ 0 & -1 & -1 & 0 \\ -4 & -1 & 3 & 0 \end{bmatrix} \longrightarrow \begin{bmatrix} 1 & 1 & 0 & 0 \\ 0 & -1 & -1 & 0 \\ 0 & 3 & 3 & 0 \end{bmatrix} \longrightarrow \begin{bmatrix} 1 & 0 & -1 & 0 \\ 0 & 1 & 1 & 0 \\ 0 & 0 & 0 & 0 \end{bmatrix}$$

Let $x_3 = s$;

then $x_2 + x_3 = 0$, i.e. $x_2 = -x_3 = -s$

and $x_1 - x_3 = 0$, i.e. $x_1 = x_3 = s$

so $\begin{bmatrix} x_1 \\ x_2 \\ x_3 \end{bmatrix} = \begin{bmatrix} s \\ -s \\ s \end{bmatrix} = s \begin{bmatrix} 1 \\ -1 \\ 1 \end{bmatrix}.$

$$\lambda_3 = -4 \longrightarrow \begin{bmatrix} -4 & -1 & 0 & 0 \\ 0 & -4 & -1 & 0 \\ -4 & -1 & 0 & 0 \end{bmatrix} \longrightarrow \begin{bmatrix} 1 & 1/4 & 0 & 0 \\ 0 & -4 & -1 & 0 \\ 0 & 0 & 0 & 0 \end{bmatrix} \longrightarrow \begin{bmatrix} 1 & 0 & -1/16 & 0 \\ 0 & 1 & 1/4 & 0 \\ 0 & 0 & 0 & 0 \end{bmatrix}$$

Let $x_3 = t$;

then $x_2 + \frac{1}{4}x_3 = 0$, i.e. $x_2 = -\frac{1}{4}x_3 = -\frac{1}{4}t$

and $x_1 - \frac{1}{16}x_3 = 0$, i.e. $x_1 = \frac{1}{16}x_3 = \frac{1}{16}t$

so $\begin{bmatrix} x_1 \\ x_2 \\ x_3 \end{bmatrix} = \begin{bmatrix} (1/16)t \\ (-1/4)t \\ t \end{bmatrix} = t \begin{bmatrix} 1/16 \\ -1/4 \\ 1 \end{bmatrix} = \frac{1}{16}t \begin{bmatrix} 1 \\ -4 \\ 16 \end{bmatrix}$

$$P = \begin{bmatrix} 1 & 1 & 1 \\ 1 & -1 & -4 \\ 1 & 1 & 16 \end{bmatrix}, \qquad D = P^{-1}AP = \begin{bmatrix} 1 & 0 & 0 \\ 0 & -1 & 0 \\ 0 & 0 & -4 \end{bmatrix},$$

$$U = \begin{bmatrix} c_1 e^x \\ c_2 e^{-x} \\ c_3 e^{-4x} \end{bmatrix}, \qquad Y = PU = \begin{bmatrix} 1 & 1 & 1 \\ 1 & -1 & -4 \\ 1 & 1 & 16 \end{bmatrix} \begin{bmatrix} c_1 e^x \\ c_2 e^{-x} \\ c_3 e^{-4x} \end{bmatrix} = \begin{bmatrix} c_1 e^x + c_2 e^{-x} + c_3 e^{-4x} \\ c_1 e^x - c_2 e^{-x} - 4c_3 e^{-4x} \\ c_1 e^x + c_2 e^{-x} + 16c_3 e^{-4x} \end{bmatrix}$$

$$y = y_1 = c_1 e^x + c_2 e^{-x} + c_3 e^{-4x}.$$

(b) $y = c_1 e^x + c_2 e^{-x} + c_3 e^{-4x}$, $y(0) = c_1 + c_2 + c_3 = 7$

$y' = c_1 e^x - c_2 e^{-x} - 4c_3 e^{-4x}$, $y'(0) = c_1 - c_2 - 4c_3 = -2$

$y'' = c_1 e^x + c_2 e^{-x} + 16c_3 e^{-4x}$, $y''(0) = c_1 + c_2 + 16c_3 = -8$

$$\begin{bmatrix} c_1 \\ c_2 \\ c_3 \end{bmatrix} = \begin{bmatrix} 1 & 1 & 1 \\ 1 & -1 & -4 \\ 1 & 1 & 16 \end{bmatrix}^{-1} \begin{bmatrix} 7 \\ 6 \\ -8 \end{bmatrix} = \frac{1}{-30} \begin{bmatrix} -12 & -20 & 2 \\ -15 & 15 & 0 \\ -3 & 5 & -2 \end{bmatrix}^T \begin{bmatrix} 7 \\ 6 \\ -8 \end{bmatrix}$$

$$= \frac{1}{30} \begin{bmatrix} 12 & 15 & 3 \\ 20 & -15 & -5 \\ -2 & 0 & 2 \end{bmatrix} \begin{bmatrix} 7 \\ 6 \\ -8 \end{bmatrix} = \frac{1}{30} \begin{bmatrix} 150 \\ 90 \\ -30 \end{bmatrix} = \begin{bmatrix} 5 \\ 3 \\ -1 \end{bmatrix};$$

$$y = 5e^x + 3e^{-x} - e^{-4x}.$$

SECTION 9.2 GEOMETRY OF LINEAR OPERATORS ON R^2

7. (a) $T(1,0) = (0,1)$, $T(0,1) = (1,0)$

so $[T] = \begin{bmatrix} 0 & 1 \\ 1 & 0 \end{bmatrix}$

(b) $\begin{bmatrix} 0 & 1 \\ 1 & 0 \end{bmatrix} \begin{bmatrix} 3 \\ 2 \end{bmatrix} = \begin{bmatrix} 2 \\ 3 \end{bmatrix}$ so $T(3,2) = (2,3)$.

8. (a) $T(1,0) = (1,0)$, $T(0,1) = (0,3)$ so $[T] = \begin{bmatrix} 1 & 0 \\ 0 & 3 \end{bmatrix}$.

(b) $\begin{bmatrix} 1 & 0 \\ 0 & 3 \end{bmatrix} \begin{bmatrix} -2 \\ 1 \end{bmatrix} = \begin{bmatrix} -2 \\ 3 \end{bmatrix}$ so $T(-2,1) = (-2,3)$.

9. (a) $T(1,0) = \left(\frac{1}{2}, \frac{\sqrt{3}}{2}\right)$, $T(0,1) = \left(-\frac{\sqrt{3}}{2}, \frac{1}{2}\right)$ so $[T] = \begin{bmatrix} 1/2 & -\sqrt{3}/2 \\ \sqrt{3}/2 & 1/2 \end{bmatrix}$.

(b) $\begin{bmatrix} 1/2 & -\sqrt{3}/2 \\ \sqrt{3}/2 & 1/2 \end{bmatrix} \begin{bmatrix} 2 \\ -8 \end{bmatrix} = \begin{bmatrix} 1 + 4\sqrt{3} \\ \sqrt{3} - 4 \end{bmatrix}$ so $T(2,-8) = (1 + 4\sqrt{3}, \sqrt{3} - 4)$.

10. (a) $T(1,0) = (1,3)$, $T(0,1) = (0,1)$ so $[T] = \begin{bmatrix} 1 & 0 \\ 3 & 1 \end{bmatrix}$.

(b) $\begin{bmatrix} 1 & 0 \\ 3 & 1 \end{bmatrix} \begin{bmatrix} -2 \\ -2 \end{bmatrix} = \begin{bmatrix} -2 \\ -8 \end{bmatrix}$ so $T(-2,-2) = (-2,-8)$.

11. (a) $T_1(1,0) = (1/2, 0)$, $T_1(0,1) = (0,1)$ so $[T_1] = \begin{bmatrix} 1/2 & 0 \\ 0 & 1 \end{bmatrix}$,

$T_2(1,0) = (1,0)$, $T_2(0,1) = (3,1)$ so $[T_2] = \begin{bmatrix} 1 & 3 \\ 0 & 1 \end{bmatrix}$,

thus $[T] = [T_2 \circ T_1] = [T_2][T_1] = \begin{bmatrix} 1 & 3 \\ 0 & 1 \end{bmatrix} \begin{bmatrix} 1/2 & 0 \\ 0 & 1 \end{bmatrix} = \begin{bmatrix} 1/2 & 3 \\ 0 & 1 \end{bmatrix}$,

(b) $\begin{bmatrix} 1/2 & 3 \\ 0 & 1 \end{bmatrix} \begin{bmatrix} 1 \\ 1 \end{bmatrix} = \begin{bmatrix} 7/2 \\ 1 \end{bmatrix}$ so $T(1,1) = (\frac{7}{2}, 1)$.

12. (a) $T_1(1,0) = \left(-\frac{\sqrt{2}}{2}, -\frac{\sqrt{2}}{2}\right)$, $T_1(0,1) = \left(\frac{\sqrt{2}}{2}, \frac{\sqrt{2}}{2}\right)$ so $[T_1] = \begin{bmatrix} -\sqrt{2}/2 & \sqrt{2}/2 \\ -\sqrt{2}/2 & \sqrt{2}/2 \end{bmatrix}$,

$T_2(1,0) = (0,-1)$, $T_2(0,1) = (-1,0)$ so $[T_2] - \begin{bmatrix} 0 & -1 \\ -1 & 0 \end{bmatrix}$,

thus $[T] = [T_2 \circ T_1] = [T_2][T_1] = \begin{bmatrix} 0 & -1 \\ -1 & 0 \end{bmatrix} \begin{bmatrix} -\sqrt{2}/2 & \sqrt{2}/2 \\ -\sqrt{2}/2 & \sqrt{2}/2 \end{bmatrix} = \begin{bmatrix} \sqrt{2}/2 & -\sqrt{2}/2 \\ \sqrt{2}/2 & -\sqrt{2}/2 \end{bmatrix}$.

(b) $\begin{bmatrix} \sqrt{2}/2 & -\sqrt{2}/2 \\ \sqrt{2}/2 & -\sqrt{2}/2 \end{bmatrix} \begin{bmatrix} 4 \\ 2 \end{bmatrix} = \begin{bmatrix} \sqrt{2} \\ \sqrt{2} \end{bmatrix}$ so $T(4,2) = (\sqrt{2}, \sqrt{2})$.

SECTION 9.3 *LEAST SQUARES FITTING TO DATA*

13. $\mathbf{x} = \begin{bmatrix} -1 \\ 1 \\ 3 \end{bmatrix}$, $\mathbf{y} = \begin{bmatrix} -1 \\ 2 \\ 5 \end{bmatrix}$.

$M = \begin{bmatrix} 1 & -1 \\ 1 & 1 \\ 1 & 3 \end{bmatrix}$, $M^T M = \begin{bmatrix} 1 & 1 & 1 \\ -1 & 1 & 3 \end{bmatrix} \begin{bmatrix} 1 & -1 \\ 1 & 1 \\ 1 & 3 \end{bmatrix} = \begin{bmatrix} 3 & 3 \\ 3 & 11 \end{bmatrix}$,

$(M^T M)^{-1} = \frac{1}{24} \begin{bmatrix} 11 & -3 \\ -3 & 3 \end{bmatrix}$,

$(M^T M)^{-1} M^T \mathbf{y} = \frac{1}{24} \begin{bmatrix} 11 & -3 \\ -3 & 3 \end{bmatrix} \begin{bmatrix} 1 & 1 & 1 \\ -1 & 1 & 3 \end{bmatrix} \begin{bmatrix} -1 \\ 2 \\ 5 \end{bmatrix} = \frac{1}{24} \begin{bmatrix} 11 & -3 \\ -3 & 3 \end{bmatrix} \begin{bmatrix} 6 \\ 18 \end{bmatrix} = \frac{1}{24} \begin{bmatrix} 12 \\ 36 \end{bmatrix} = \begin{bmatrix} 1/2 \\ 3/2 \end{bmatrix}$.

Thus, $y = \frac{1}{2} + \frac{3}{2}x$ (note that this line traverses all three points).

14. $\mathbf{x} = \begin{bmatrix} 0 \\ 1 \\ 2 \\ 3 \end{bmatrix}$, $\mathbf{y} = \begin{bmatrix} 1 \\ 3 \\ 4 \\ 4 \end{bmatrix}$.

$$M = \begin{bmatrix} 1 & 0 \\ 1 & 1 \\ 1 & 2 \\ 1 & 3 \end{bmatrix}, \quad M^TM = \begin{bmatrix} 1 & 1 & 1 & 1 \\ 0 & 1 & 2 & 3 \end{bmatrix} \begin{bmatrix} 1 & 0 \\ 1 & 1 \\ 1 & 2 \\ 1 & 3 \end{bmatrix} = \begin{bmatrix} 4 & 6 \\ 6 & 14 \end{bmatrix},$$

$$(M^TM)^{-1} = \frac{1}{20} \begin{bmatrix} 14 & -6 \\ -6 & 4 \end{bmatrix} = \frac{1}{10} \begin{bmatrix} 7 & -3 \\ -3 & 2 \end{bmatrix},$$

$$(M^TM)^{-1}M^T\mathbf{y} = \frac{1}{10} \begin{bmatrix} 7 & -3 \\ -3 & 2 \end{bmatrix} \begin{bmatrix} 1 & 1 & 1 & 1 \\ 0 & 1 & 2 & 3 \end{bmatrix} \begin{bmatrix} 1 \\ 3 \\ 4 \\ 4 \end{bmatrix} = \frac{1}{10} \begin{bmatrix} 7 & -3 \\ -3 & 2 \end{bmatrix} \begin{bmatrix} 12 \\ 23 \end{bmatrix} = \frac{1}{10} \begin{bmatrix} 15 \\ 10 \end{bmatrix} = \begin{bmatrix} 3/2 \\ 1 \end{bmatrix}.$$

Thus, $y = \frac{3}{2} + x$.

15. $\mathbf{x} = \begin{bmatrix} -1 \\ 0 \\ 1 \\ 2 \end{bmatrix}, \quad \mathbf{y} = \begin{bmatrix} 1 \\ 0 \\ 1 \\ 2 \end{bmatrix}$

$$M = \begin{bmatrix} 1 & -1 & 1 \\ 1 & 0 & 0 \\ 1 & 1 & 1 \\ 1 & 2 & 4 \end{bmatrix}, \quad M^TM = \begin{bmatrix} 1 & 1 & 1 & 1 \\ -1 & 0 & 1 & 2 \\ 1 & 0 & 1 & 4 \end{bmatrix} \begin{bmatrix} 1 & -1 & 1 \\ 1 & 0 & 0 \\ 1 & 1 & 1 \\ 1 & 2 & 4 \end{bmatrix} = \begin{bmatrix} 4 & 2 & 6 \\ 2 & 6 & 8 \\ 6 & 8 & 18 \end{bmatrix},$$

$$(M^TM)^{-1} = \frac{1}{80} \begin{bmatrix} 44 & 12 & -20 \\ 12 & 36 & -20 \\ -20 & -20 & 20 \end{bmatrix}^T = \frac{1}{20} \begin{bmatrix} 11 & 3 & -5 \\ 3 & 9 & -5 \\ -5 & -5 & 5 \end{bmatrix},$$

$$(M^TM)^{-1}M^T\mathbf{y} = \frac{1}{20} \begin{bmatrix} 11 & 3 & -5 \\ 3 & 9 & -5 \\ -5 & -5 & 5 \end{bmatrix} \begin{bmatrix} 1 & 1 & 1 & 1 \\ -1 & 0 & 1 & 2 \\ 1 & 0 & 1 & 4 \end{bmatrix} \begin{bmatrix} 1 \\ 0 \\ 1 \\ 2 \end{bmatrix}$$

$$= \frac{1}{20} \begin{bmatrix} 11 & 3 & -5 \\ 3 & 9 & -5 \\ -5 & -5 & 5 \end{bmatrix} \begin{bmatrix} 4 \\ 4 \\ 10 \end{bmatrix} = \frac{1}{20} \begin{bmatrix} 6 \\ -2 \\ 10 \end{bmatrix} = \begin{bmatrix} 3/10 \\ -1/10 \\ 1/2 \end{bmatrix}.$$

Thus, $y = \frac{3}{10} - \frac{1}{10}x + \frac{1}{2}x^2$.

16. $\mathbf{x} = \begin{bmatrix} 0 \\ 1 \\ 2 \\ 3 \\ 4 \end{bmatrix}, \mathbf{y} = \begin{bmatrix} -5/3 \\ 2 \\ 2 \\ -10/3 \\ -4 \end{bmatrix}$

$$M = \begin{bmatrix} 1 & 0 & 0 \\ 1 & 1 & 1 \\ 1 & 2 & 4 \\ 1 & 3 & 9 \\ 1 & 4 & 16 \end{bmatrix}, M^TM = \begin{bmatrix} 1 & 1 & 1 & 1 & 1 \\ 0 & 1 & 2 & 3 & 4 \\ 0 & 1 & 4 & 9 & 16 \end{bmatrix} \begin{bmatrix} 1 & 0 & 0 \\ 1 & 1 & 1 \\ 1 & 2 & 4 \\ 1 & 3 & 9 \\ 1 & 4 & 16 \end{bmatrix} = \begin{bmatrix} 5 & 10 & 30 \\ 10 & 30 & 100 \\ 30 & 100 & 354 \end{bmatrix},$$

$$(M^T M)^{-1} = \tfrac{1}{700} \begin{bmatrix} 620 & -540 & 100 \\ -540 & 870 & -200 \\ 100 & -200 & 50 \end{bmatrix}^T = \tfrac{1}{70} \begin{bmatrix} 62 & -54 & 10 \\ -54 & 87 & -20 \\ 10 & -20 & 5 \end{bmatrix},$$

$$(M^T M)^{-1} M^T \mathbf{y} = \tfrac{1}{70} \begin{bmatrix} 62 & -54 & 10 \\ -54 & 87 & -20 \\ 10 & -20 & 5 \end{bmatrix} \begin{bmatrix} 1 & 1 & 1 & 1 & 1 \\ 0 & 1 & 2 & 3 & 4 \\ 0 & 1 & 4 & 9 & 16 \end{bmatrix} \begin{bmatrix} -5/3 \\ 2 \\ 2 \\ -10/3 \\ -4 \end{bmatrix}$$

$$= \tfrac{1}{70} \begin{bmatrix} 62 & -54 & 10 \\ -54 & 87 & -20 \\ 10 & -20 & 5 \end{bmatrix} \begin{bmatrix} -5 \\ -20 \\ -84 \end{bmatrix} = \tfrac{1}{70} \begin{bmatrix} -70 \\ 210 \\ -70 \end{bmatrix} = \begin{bmatrix} -1 \\ 3 \\ -1 \end{bmatrix}.$$

Thus, $y = -1 + 3x - x^2$.

17. $\quad \mathbf{x} = \begin{bmatrix} -1 \\ 0 \\ 1 \\ 3 \end{bmatrix}, \mathbf{y} = \begin{bmatrix} 0 \\ -2 \\ 1 \\ -4 \end{bmatrix}$

$$M = \begin{bmatrix} 1 & -1 & 1 & -1 \\ 1 & 0 & 0 & 0 \\ 1 & 1 & 1 & 1 \\ 1 & 3 & 9 & 27 \end{bmatrix}, M^T M = \begin{bmatrix} 1 & 1 & 1 & 1 \\ -1 & 0 & 1 & 3 \\ 1 & 0 & 1 & 9 \\ -1 & 0 & 1 & 27 \end{bmatrix} \begin{bmatrix} 1 & -1 & 1 & -1 \\ 1 & 0 & 0 & 0 \\ 1 & 1 & 1 & 1 \\ 1 & 3 & 9 & 27 \end{bmatrix} = \begin{bmatrix} 4 & 3 & 11 & 27 \\ 3 & 11 & 27 & 83 \\ 11 & 27 & 83 & 243 \\ 27 & 83 & 243 & 731 \end{bmatrix}$$

$$(M^T M)^{-1} = \tfrac{1}{2304} \begin{bmatrix} 2304 & -768 & -2304 & 768 \\ -768 & 1880 & 1200 & -584 \\ -2304 & 1200 & 3456 & -1200 \\ 768 & -584 & -1200 & 440 \end{bmatrix}^T = \tfrac{1}{288} \begin{bmatrix} 288 & -96 & -288 & 96 \\ -96 & 235 & 150 & -73 \\ -288 & 150 & 432 & -150 \\ 96 & -73 & -150 & 55 \end{bmatrix},$$

$$(M^T M)^{-1} M^T \mathbf{y} = \tfrac{1}{288} \begin{bmatrix} 288 & -96 & -288 & 96 \\ -96 & 235 & 150 & -73 \\ -288 & 150 & 432 & -150 \\ 96 & -73 & -150 & 55 \end{bmatrix} \begin{bmatrix} 1 & 1 & 1 & 1 \\ -1 & 0 & 1 & 3 \\ 1 & 0 & 1 & 9 \\ -1 & 0 & 1 & 27 \end{bmatrix} \begin{bmatrix} 0 \\ -2 \\ 1 \\ -4 \end{bmatrix}$$

$$= \tfrac{1}{288} \begin{bmatrix} 288 & -96 & -288 & 96 \\ -96 & 235 & 150 & -73 \\ -288 & 150 & 432 & -150 \\ 96 & -73 & -150 & 55 \end{bmatrix} \begin{bmatrix} -5 \\ -11 \\ -35 \\ -107 \end{bmatrix}$$

$$= \tfrac{1}{288} \begin{bmatrix} -576 \\ 456 \\ 720 \\ -312 \end{bmatrix} = \begin{bmatrix} -2 \\ 19/12 \\ 5/2 \\ -13/12 \end{bmatrix}.$$

Thus, $y = -2 + \tfrac{19}{12}x + \tfrac{5}{2}x^2 - \tfrac{13}{12}x^3$ (note that this curve traverses all four points).

18. $a_0 = \frac{1}{\pi}\int_0^{2\pi}(2-x)dx = \frac{1}{\pi}\left[2x - \frac{1}{2}x^2\right]_0^{2\pi} = \frac{1}{\pi}\left[4\pi - 2\pi^2\right] = 4 - 2\pi$

For $k > 0$, $a_k = \frac{1}{\pi}\int_0^{2\pi}(2-x)\cos kx\,dx;$ let $u = 2 - x, du = -dx,$ $dv = \cos kx\,dx,$

$$v = \int\cos kx\,dx = \frac{1}{k}\sin kx$$

$$= \frac{1}{\pi}\left[\frac{2-x}{k}\sin kx + \frac{1}{k}\int\sin kx\,dx\right]_0^{2\pi}$$

$$= \frac{1}{\pi}\left[\frac{2-x}{k}\sin kx - \frac{1}{k^2}\cos kx\right]_0^{2\pi}$$

$$= \frac{1}{\pi}\left[(0 - \frac{1}{k^2}) - (0 - \frac{1}{k^2})\right] = 0$$

$b_k = \frac{1}{\pi}\int_0^{2\pi}(2-x)\sin kx\,dx;$ let $u = 2 - x,$ $du = -dx, dv = \sin kx\,dx,$

$$v = \int\sin kx\,dx = -\frac{1}{k}\cos kx$$

$$= \frac{1}{\pi}\left[\frac{x-2}{k}\cos kx - \frac{1}{k}\int\cos kx\,dx\right]_0^{2\pi}$$

$$= \frac{1}{\pi}\left[\frac{x-2}{k}\cos kx - \frac{1}{k^2}\sin kx\right]_0^{2\pi}$$

$$= \frac{1}{\pi}\left[\left(\frac{2\pi-2}{k} - 0\right) - \left(-\frac{2}{k} - 0\right)\right] = \frac{1}{\pi}\left[\frac{2\pi}{k}\right] = \frac{2}{k}$$

Thus, $f(x) = x - 2 \approx 4 - 2\pi + 2\sin x + \sin 2x + \frac{2}{3}\sin 3x + \cdots + \frac{2}{n}\sin nx.$

19. $a_0 = \frac{1}{\pi}\int_0^{2\pi}e^x dx = \frac{1}{\pi}\left[e^x\right]_0^{2\pi} = \frac{1}{\pi}(e^{2\pi} - 1)$

For $k > 0$, $a_k = \frac{1}{\pi}\int_0^{2\pi}e^x\cos kx\,dx;$ let $u = e^x,$ $du = e^x dx,$ $dv = \cos kx\,dx,$

$$v = \int\cos kx\,dx = \frac{1}{k}\sin kx$$

so $\int e^x\cos kx\,dx = \frac{e^x}{k}\sin kx - \frac{1}{k}\int e^x\sin kx\,dx;$ let $u = e^x, du = e^x dx, dv = \sin kx\,dx,$

$$v = \int\sin kx\,dx = \frac{-1}{k}\cos kx$$

$$= \frac{e^x}{k} \sin kx - \frac{1}{k}\left[-\frac{e^x}{k}\cos kx + \frac{1}{k}\int e^x \cos kx dx\right]$$

$$= \frac{e^x}{k} \sin kx + \frac{e^x}{k^2}\cos kx - \frac{1}{k^2}\int e^x \cos kx dx$$

so $\quad \left(1 + \frac{1}{k^2}\right)\int e^x \cos kx dx = \frac{e^x}{k}\sin kx + \frac{e^x}{k^2}\cos kx$

$$\frac{k^2+1}{k^2}\int e^x \cos kx dx = \frac{e^x}{k}\sin kx + \frac{e^x}{k^2}\cos kx$$

$$\int e^x \cos kx dx = \frac{k^2}{k^2+1}\left(\frac{e^x}{k}\sin kx + \frac{e^x}{k^2}\cos kx\right)$$

$$= \frac{1}{k^2+1}\left(ke^x \sin kx + e^x \cos kx\right)$$

so $\quad a_k = \frac{1}{\pi}\frac{1}{k^2+1}\left[ke^x \sin kx + e^x \cos kx\right]_0^{2\pi}$

$$= \frac{1}{\pi}\frac{1}{k^2+1}\left[(0 + e^{2\pi}) - (0+1)\right] = \frac{e^{2\pi}-1}{\pi(k^2+1)}$$

$$b_k = \frac{1}{\pi}\int_0^{2\pi} e^x \sin kx dx; \quad \text{let} \quad u = e^x, \; du = e^x dx, \; dv = \sin kx dx,$$

$$v = \int \sin kx dx = \frac{-1}{k}\cos kx$$

so $\quad \int e^x \sin kx dx = -\frac{e^x}{k}\cos kx + \frac{1}{k}\int e^x \cos kx dx;$

$\quad$ let $\quad u = e^x, \quad du = e^x dx, \quad dv = \cos kx dx, \quad v = \int \cos kx dx = \frac{1}{k}\sin kx$

$$= -\frac{e^x}{k}\cos kx + \frac{1}{k}\left[\frac{e^x}{k}\sin kx - \frac{1}{k}\int e^x \sin kx dx\right]$$

$$= -\frac{e^x}{k}\cos kx + \frac{e^x}{k^2}\sin kx - \frac{1}{k^2}\int e^x \sin kx dx$$

so $\quad \left(1 + \frac{1}{k^2}\right)\int e^x \sin kx dx = -\frac{e^x}{k}\cos kx + \frac{e^x}{k^2}\sin kx$

237

$$\frac{k^2+1}{k^2}\int e^x \sin kx\,dx = -\frac{e^x}{k}\cos kx + \frac{e^x}{k^2}\sin kx$$

$$\int e^x \sin kx\,dx = \frac{k^2}{k^2+1}\left(-\frac{e^x}{k}\cos kx + \frac{e^x}{k^2}\sin kx\right)$$

$$= \frac{1}{k^2+1}\left(-ke^x \cos kx + e^x \sin kx\right)$$

so $b_k = \dfrac{1}{\pi}\dfrac{1}{k^2+1}\left[-ke^x \cos kx + e^x \sin kx\right]_0^{2\pi}$

$$= \frac{1}{\pi}\frac{1}{k^2+1}\left[(-ke^{2\pi}+0) - (-k+0)\right] = \frac{-k(e^{2\pi}-1)}{\pi(k^2+1)}$$

Thus, $f(x) = e^x \approx \dfrac{e^{2\pi}-1}{\pi}\left[1 + \dfrac{1}{2}\cos x - \dfrac{1}{2}\sin x + \dfrac{1}{5}\cos 2x - \dfrac{2}{5}\sin 2x\right.$

$$\left. + ... + \frac{1}{n^2+1}\cos nx - \frac{n}{n^2+1}\sin nx\right].$$

20. $g = \text{proj}_{\text{span}\{1, e^x\}} x^2$

$g = \frac{<x^2,1>}{<1,1>}1 + \frac{<x^2,e^x>}{<e^x,e^x>}e^x$

$<x^2, 1> = \displaystyle\int_0^1 x^2 \times 1\,dx = \left[\frac{1}{3}x^3\right]_0^1 = \frac{1}{3} - 0 = \frac{1}{3}$

$<1,1> = \displaystyle\int_0^1 1 \times 1\,dx = [x]_0^1 = 1 - 0 = 1$

$<x^2, e^x> = \displaystyle\int_0^1 x^2 \times e^x\,dx;$ let $u = x^2$, $du = 2x\,dx$, $dv = e^x dx$, $v = e^x$

$$= \left[x^2 e^x - 2\int xe^x dx\right]_0^1;$$ let $u = x$, $du = dx$, $dv = e^x dx$, $v = e^x$

$$= \left[x^2 e^x - 2(xe^x - \int e^x dx)\right]_0^1$$

$$= \left[x^2 e^x - 2xe^x + 2e^x\right]_0^1$$

$$= \left[(e - 2e + 2e) - (0 - 0 + 2)\right] = e - 2$$

$<e^x, e^x> = \displaystyle\int_0^1 e^x \times e^x dx = \int_0^1 e^{2x} dx = \left[\frac{1}{2}e^{2x}\right]_0^1 = \frac{1}{2}(e^2 - 1)$

Thus $g = \frac{1}{1}1 + \frac{e-2}{\frac{1}{2}(e^2-1)}e^x = \frac{1}{3} - 2\frac{e-2}{e^2-1}e^x$

21. $\qquad g = \text{proj}_{\text{span}\{e^x,e^{-x}\}}e^{2x}$

$$g = \frac{<e^{2x},e^x>}{<e^x,e^x>}e^x + \frac{<e^{2x},e^{-x}>}{<e^{-x},e^{-x}>}e^{-x}$$

$$< e^{2x}, e^x > = \int_0^1 e^{2x} \times e^x dx = \int_0^1 e^{3x} dx = \left[\frac{1}{3}e^{3x}\right]_0^1 = \frac{1}{3}(e^3 - 1)$$

$$< e^x, e^x > = \int_0^1 e^x \times e^x dx = \int_0^1 e^{2x} dx = \left[\frac{1}{2}e^{2x}\right]_0^1 = \frac{1}{2}(e^2 - 1)$$

$$< e^{2x}, e^{-x} > = \int_0^1 e^{2x} \times e^{-x} dx = \int_0^1 e^x dx = e - 1$$

$$< e^{-x}, e^{-x} > = \int_0^1 e^{-x} \times e^{-x} dx = \int_0^1 e^{-2x} dx = \left[-\frac{1}{2}e^{-2x}\right]_0^1 = \frac{-1}{2}(e^{-2} - 1)$$

Thus $\quad g = \dfrac{\frac{1}{3}(e^3 - 1)}{\frac{1}{2}(e^2 - 1)}e^x + \dfrac{e - 1}{\frac{-1}{2}(e^{-2} - 1)}e^{-x}$

$$= \dfrac{\frac{1}{3}(e^3 - 1)}{\frac{1}{2}(e^2 - 1)}e^x + \dfrac{e^2(e - 1)}{\frac{1}{2}(e^2 - 1)}e^{-x}$$

$$= \dfrac{e - 1}{\frac{1}{2}(e^2 - 1)}\left[\frac{1}{3}(e^2 + e + 1)e^x + e^2 e^{-x}\right]$$

$$= \dfrac{2}{e + 1}\left[\frac{1}{3}(e^2 + e + 1)e^x + e^2 e^{-x}\right]$$

SECTION 9.5 *QUADRATIC FORMS*

22. (a) $\quad 2x^2 - 4xy + y^2 = \begin{bmatrix} x & y \end{bmatrix}\begin{bmatrix} 2 & -2 \\ -2 & 1 \end{bmatrix}\begin{bmatrix} x \\ y \end{bmatrix}$

(b) Not a quadratic form: not all terms are of degree 2.

(c) $\quad x_1^2 + 5x_1x_2 = \begin{bmatrix} x_1 & x_2 \end{bmatrix}\begin{bmatrix} 1 & 5/2 \\ 5/2 & 0 \end{bmatrix}\begin{bmatrix} x_1 \\ x_2 \end{bmatrix}$

(d) $\quad (2x_1 + \sqrt{2}x_2)^2 = 4x_1^2 + 4\sqrt{2}x_1x_2 + 2x_2^2 = \begin{bmatrix} x_1 & x_2 \end{bmatrix}\begin{bmatrix} 4 & 2\sqrt{2} \\ 2\sqrt{2} & 2 \end{bmatrix}\begin{bmatrix} x_1 \\ x_2 \end{bmatrix}$

(e) $\quad 3x_1^2 + 5x_2^2 - 7x_3^2 - 5x_1x_2 - 6x_2x_3 = \begin{bmatrix} x_1 & x_2 & x_3 \end{bmatrix}\begin{bmatrix} 3 & -5/2 & 0 \\ -5/2 & 5 & -3 \\ 0 & -3 & -7 \end{bmatrix}\begin{bmatrix} x_1 \\ x_2 \\ x_3 \end{bmatrix}$

(f) $\quad 14x_1x_2 - x_3^2 = \begin{bmatrix} x_1 & x_2 & x_3 \end{bmatrix}\begin{bmatrix} 0 & 7 & 0 \\ 7 & 0 & 0 \\ 0 & 0 & -1 \end{bmatrix}\begin{bmatrix} x_1 \\ x_2 \\ x_3 \end{bmatrix}$

23. (a) $2x^2 + 2xy - y^2$

(b) $3xy$

(c) $\pi x_1^2 + 2\pi x_1 x_2 - \pi x_2^2$

(d) $x_1^2 + 4x_2^2 + 7x_3^2 - 6x_1 x_2 - 10x_2 x_3$

(e) $x_1^2 - x_1 x_2 + 2x_1 x_3 + 4x_3^2$

(f) $5x_1^2 + 12x_2^2 - 13x_3^2$

24. (a) $2x_1^2 + 3x_2^2 = [x_1 \quad x_2] \begin{bmatrix} 2 & 0 \\ 0 & 3 \end{bmatrix} \begin{bmatrix} x_1 \\ x_2 \end{bmatrix}$

$\lambda = 2, 3$ since the matrix is diagonal

$\lambda_1 = 3 \longrightarrow \begin{bmatrix} 1 & 0 & 0 \\ 0 & 0 & 0 \end{bmatrix}$ Let $x_1 = 0$ and $x_2 = s$; then $\begin{bmatrix} x_1 \\ x_2 \end{bmatrix} = \begin{bmatrix} 0 \\ s \end{bmatrix} = s \begin{bmatrix} 0 \\ 1 \end{bmatrix}$.

Thus, the maximum is 3 and occurs at $(x_1, x_2) = \pm(0, 1)$.

$\lambda_2 = 2 \longrightarrow \begin{bmatrix} 0 & 0 & 0 \\ 0 & 1 & 0 \end{bmatrix}$ Let $x_1 = t$ and $x_2 = 0$; then $\begin{bmatrix} x_1 \\ x_2 \end{bmatrix} = \begin{bmatrix} t \\ 0 \end{bmatrix} = t \begin{bmatrix} 1 \\ 0 \end{bmatrix}$.

Thus, the minimum is 2 and occurs at $(x_1, x_2) = \pm(1, 0)$.

(b) $2x_1^2 + 3x_1 x_2 + 2x_2^2 = [x_1 \quad x_2] \begin{bmatrix} 2 & 3/2 \\ 3/2 & 2 \end{bmatrix} \begin{bmatrix} x_1 \\ x_2 \end{bmatrix}$

$0 = \begin{vmatrix} \lambda - 2 & -3/2 \\ -3/2 & \lambda - 2 \end{vmatrix} = (\lambda - 2)^2 - (-3/2)^2 = \lambda^2 - 4\lambda + 4 - \dfrac{9}{4}$

$= \lambda^2 - 4\lambda + \dfrac{7}{4} = (\lambda - \dfrac{1}{2})(\lambda - \dfrac{7}{2})$ so $\lambda = \dfrac{1}{2}, \dfrac{7}{2}$

$\lambda_1 = \dfrac{7}{2} \longrightarrow \begin{bmatrix} 3/2 & -3/2 & 0 \\ -3/2 & 3/2 & 0 \end{bmatrix} \longrightarrow \begin{bmatrix} 1 & -1 & 0 \\ 0 & 0 & 0 \end{bmatrix}$

Let $x_2 = s$;

then $x_1 - x_2 = 0$, i.e. $x_1 = x_2 = s$

so $\begin{bmatrix} x_1 \\ x_2 \end{bmatrix} = \begin{bmatrix} s \\ s \end{bmatrix} = s \begin{bmatrix} 1 \\ 1 \end{bmatrix}$

and $(1, 1)/\|(1, 1)\| = (1, 1)/\sqrt{2} = (\frac{1}{\sqrt{2}}, \frac{1}{\sqrt{2}})$.

Thus, the maximum is $\frac{7}{2}$ and occurs at $(x_1, x_2) = \pm(\frac{1}{\sqrt{2}}, \frac{1}{\sqrt{2}})$.

$$\lambda_1 = \tfrac{1}{2} \longrightarrow \begin{bmatrix} -3/2 & -3/2 & 0 \\ -3/2 & -3/2 & 0 \end{bmatrix} \longrightarrow \begin{bmatrix} 1 & 1 & 0 \\ 0 & 0 & 0 \end{bmatrix}$$

Let $x_2 = t$;

then $x_1 + x_2 = 0$, *i.e.* $x_1 = -x_2 = -t$

so $\begin{bmatrix} x_1 \\ x_2 \end{bmatrix} = \begin{bmatrix} -t \\ t \end{bmatrix} = t\begin{bmatrix} -1 \\ 1 \end{bmatrix}$

and $(-1,1)/\|(-1,1)\| = (-1,1)/\sqrt{2} = (-\tfrac{1}{\sqrt{2}}, \tfrac{1}{\sqrt{2}})$.

Thus, the minimum is $\tfrac{1}{2}$ and occurs at $(x_1, x_2) = \pm(-\tfrac{1}{\sqrt{2}}, \tfrac{1}{\sqrt{2}})$.

(c) $x_1^2 + 2x_1 x_2 + x_2^2 = [x_1 \quad x_2]\begin{bmatrix} 1 & 1 \\ 1 & 1 \end{bmatrix}\begin{bmatrix} x_1 \\ x_2 \end{bmatrix}$

$$0 = \begin{vmatrix} \lambda - 1 & -1 \\ -1 & \lambda - 1 \end{vmatrix} = (\lambda - 1)^2 - (-1)^2 = \lambda^2 - 2\lambda + 1 - 1 = \lambda^2 - 2\lambda$$

$$= \lambda(\lambda - 2) \quad \text{so} \quad \lambda = 0, 2$$

$$\lambda_1 = 2 \longrightarrow \begin{bmatrix} 1 & -1 & 0 \\ -1 & 1 & 0 \end{bmatrix} \longrightarrow \begin{bmatrix} 1 & -1 & 0 \\ 0 & 0 & 0 \end{bmatrix}$$

Let $x_2 = s$;

then $x_1 - x_2 = 0$, *i.e.* $x_1 = x_2 = s$

so $\begin{bmatrix} x_1 \\ x_2 \end{bmatrix} = \begin{bmatrix} s \\ s \end{bmatrix} = s\begin{bmatrix} 1 \\ 1 \end{bmatrix}$

and $(1,1)/\|(1,1)\| = (1,1)/\sqrt{2} = (\tfrac{1}{\sqrt{2}}, \tfrac{1}{\sqrt{2}})$.

Thus, the maximum is 2 and occurs at $\pm(\tfrac{1}{\sqrt{2}}, \tfrac{1}{\sqrt{2}})$.

$$\lambda_2 = 0 \longrightarrow \begin{bmatrix} -1 & -1 & 0 \\ -1 & -1 & 0 \end{bmatrix} \longrightarrow \begin{bmatrix} 1 & 1 & 0 \\ 0 & 0 & 0 \end{bmatrix}$$

Let $x_2 = t$;

then $x_1 + x_2 = 0$, *i.e.* $x_1 = -x_2 = -t$

so $\begin{bmatrix} x_1 \\ x_2 \end{bmatrix} = \begin{bmatrix} -t \\ t \end{bmatrix} = t\begin{bmatrix} -1 \\ 1 \end{bmatrix}$

and $(-1,1)/\|(-1,1)\| = (-1,1)/\sqrt{2} = (-\tfrac{1}{\sqrt{2}}, \tfrac{1}{\sqrt{2}})$.

Thus, the minimum is 0 and occurs at $\pm(-\tfrac{1}{\sqrt{2}}, \tfrac{1}{\sqrt{2}})$.

(d) $\quad 2x_1^2 + 3x_1x_2 + x_2^2 = [x_1 \quad x_2]\begin{bmatrix} 2 & 3/2 \\ 3/2 & 1 \end{bmatrix}\begin{bmatrix} x_1 \\ x_2 \end{bmatrix}$

$$0 = \begin{vmatrix} \lambda - 2 & -3/2 \\ -3/2 & \lambda - 1 \end{vmatrix} = (\lambda - 2)(\lambda - 1) - \left(-\frac{3}{2}\right)^2 = \lambda^2 - 3\lambda + 2 - \frac{9}{4} = \lambda^2 - 3\lambda - \frac{1}{4}$$

so $\quad \lambda = \dfrac{3 \pm \sqrt{9+1}}{2} = \dfrac{3 \pm \sqrt{10}}{2}$

$\lambda_1 = \dfrac{3 + \sqrt{10}}{2} \longrightarrow \begin{bmatrix} (-1+\sqrt{10})/2 & -3/2 & 0 \\ -3/2 & (1+\sqrt{10})/2 & 0 \end{bmatrix} \longrightarrow \begin{bmatrix} 1 & 3/(1-\sqrt{10}) & 0 \\ 0 & 0 & 0 \end{bmatrix}$

Let $x_2 = s$;

then $x_1 + \dfrac{3}{1-\sqrt{10}}x_2 = 0$, $\quad i.e. \quad x_1 = \dfrac{-3}{1-\sqrt{10}}x_2 = \dfrac{-3}{1-\sqrt{10}}s$

so $\begin{bmatrix} x_1 \\ x_2 \end{bmatrix} = \begin{bmatrix} -3/(1-\sqrt{10})s \\ s \end{bmatrix} = s\begin{bmatrix} -3/(1-\sqrt{10}) \\ 1 \end{bmatrix} = \dfrac{s}{1-\sqrt{10}}\begin{bmatrix} -3 \\ 1-\sqrt{10} \end{bmatrix}$

and $(-3, 1-\sqrt{10})/\|(-3, 1-\sqrt{10})\| = (-3, 1-\sqrt{10})/\sqrt{20 - 2\sqrt{10}}$

$$= \left(\frac{-3}{\sqrt{20-2\sqrt{10}}}, \frac{1-\sqrt{10}}{\sqrt{20-2\sqrt{10}}}\right).$$

Thus, the maximum is $\frac{3+\sqrt{10}}{2}$ and occurs at $(x_1, x_2) = \pm\left(\frac{-3}{\sqrt{20-2\sqrt{10}}}, \frac{1-\sqrt{10}}{\sqrt{20-2\sqrt{10}}}\right)$.

$\lambda_2 = \frac{3-\sqrt{10}}{2} \longrightarrow \begin{bmatrix} (-1-\sqrt{10})/2 & -3/2 & 0 \\ -3/2 & (1-\sqrt{10})/2 & 0 \end{bmatrix} \longrightarrow \begin{bmatrix} 1 & \frac{3}{1+\sqrt{10}} & 0 \\ 0 & 0 & 0 \end{bmatrix}$

Let $x_2 = t$;

then $x_1 + \dfrac{3}{1+\sqrt{10}}x_2 = 0$, $\quad i.e. \quad x_1 = -\dfrac{3}{1+\sqrt{10}}x_2 = -\dfrac{3}{1+\sqrt{10}}t$

so $\begin{bmatrix} x_1 \\ x_2 \end{bmatrix} = \begin{bmatrix} -3/(1+\sqrt{10})t \\ t \end{bmatrix} = t\begin{bmatrix} \frac{-3}{1+\sqrt{10}} \\ 1 \end{bmatrix} = \dfrac{t}{1+\sqrt{10}}\begin{bmatrix} -3 \\ 1+\sqrt{10} \end{bmatrix}$

and $(-3, 1+\sqrt{10})/\|(-3, 1+\sqrt{10})\| = (-3, 1+\sqrt{10})/\sqrt{20 + 2\sqrt{10}}$

$$= \left(\frac{-3}{\sqrt{20+2\sqrt{10}}}, \frac{1+\sqrt{10}}{\sqrt{20+2\sqrt{10}}}\right)$$

Thus, the minimum is $\frac{3-\sqrt{10}}{2}$ and occurs at $(x_1, x_2) = \pm\left(\frac{-3}{\sqrt{20+2\sqrt{10}}}, \frac{1+\sqrt{10}}{\sqrt{20+2\sqrt{10}}}\right)$..

25. (a) $\quad x_1^2 - 4x_1x_2 - 4x_2x_3 - x_3^2 = [x_1 \quad x_2 \quad x_3]\begin{bmatrix} 1 & -2 & 0 \\ -2 & 0 & -2 \\ 0 & -2 & -1 \end{bmatrix}\begin{bmatrix} x_1 \\ x_2 \\ x_3 \end{bmatrix}$

$$0 = \begin{vmatrix} \lambda - 1 & 2 & 0 \\ 2 & \lambda & 2 \\ 0 & 2 & \lambda + 1 \end{vmatrix} = (\lambda - 1)[\lambda(\lambda + 1) - (2)(2)] - 2[2(\lambda + 1) - (0)(2)]$$

$$= (\lambda - 1)(\lambda^2 + \lambda - 4) - 4(\lambda + 1) = (\lambda^3 - 5\lambda + 4) - 4(\lambda + 1)$$

$$= \lambda^3 - 9\lambda = \lambda(\lambda^2 - 9) = \lambda(\lambda - 3)(\lambda + 3) \quad \text{so} \quad \lambda = 0, 3, -3$$

$$\lambda_1 = 3 \longrightarrow \begin{bmatrix} 2 & 2 & 0 & 0 \\ 2 & 3 & 2 & 0 \\ 0 & 2 & 4 & 0 \end{bmatrix} \longrightarrow \begin{bmatrix} 1 & 1 & 0 & 0 \\ 0 & 1 & 2 & 0 \\ 0 & 2 & 4 & 0 \end{bmatrix} \longrightarrow \begin{bmatrix} 1 & 0 & -2 & 0 \\ 0 & 1 & 2 & 0 \\ 0 & 0 & 0 & 0 \end{bmatrix}$$

Let $x_3 = s$;

then $x_2 + 2x_3 = 0$, $\quad i.e. \quad x_2 = -2x_3 = -2s$

and $x_1 - 2x_3 = 0$, $\quad i.e. \quad x_1 = 2x_3 = 2s$

so $\begin{bmatrix} x_1 \\ x_2 \\ x_3 \end{bmatrix} = \begin{bmatrix} 2s \\ -2s \\ s \end{bmatrix} = s \begin{bmatrix} 2 \\ -2 \\ 1 \end{bmatrix}$

and $(2, -2, 1)/\|(2, -2, 1)\| = (2, -2, 1)/3 = (\frac{2}{3}, -\frac{2}{3}, \frac{1}{3})$.

Thus, the maximum is 3 and occurs at $(x_1, x_2, x_3) = \pm(\frac{2}{3}, -\frac{2}{3}, \frac{1}{3})$.

$$\lambda_3 = -3 \longrightarrow \begin{bmatrix} -4 & 2 & 0 & 0 \\ 2 & -3 & 2 & 0 \\ 0 & 2 & -2 & 0 \end{bmatrix} \longrightarrow \begin{bmatrix} 1 & -1/2 & 0 & 0 \\ 0 & -2 & 2 & 0 \\ 0 & 2 & -2 & 0 \end{bmatrix} \longrightarrow \begin{bmatrix} 1 & 0 & -1/2 & 0 \\ 0 & 1 & -1 & 0 \\ 0 & 0 & 0 & 0 \end{bmatrix}$$

Let $x_3 = t$;

then $x_2 - x_3 = 0$, $\quad i.e. \quad x_2 = x_3 = t$

and $x_1 - \frac{1}{2}x_3 = 0$, $\quad i.e. \quad x_1 = \frac{1}{2}x_3 = \frac{1}{2}t$

so $\begin{bmatrix} x_1 \\ x_2 \\ x_3 \end{bmatrix} = \begin{bmatrix} 1/2t \\ t \\ t \end{bmatrix} = t \begin{bmatrix} 1/2 \\ 1 \\ 1 \end{bmatrix} = \frac{1}{2}t \begin{bmatrix} 1 \\ 2 \\ 2 \end{bmatrix}$

and $(1, 2, 2)/\|(1, 2, 2)\| = (1, 2, 2)/3 = (\frac{1}{3}, \frac{2}{3}, \frac{2}{3})$.

Thus, the minimum is -3 and occurs at $(x_1, x_2, x_3) = \pm(\frac{1}{3}, \frac{2}{3}, \frac{2}{3})$.

25. (b) $\quad 2x_1^2 + 2x_2^2 + 2x_3^2 - 2x_1x_3 = \begin{bmatrix} x_1 & x_2 & x_3 \end{bmatrix} \begin{bmatrix} 2 & 0 & -1 \\ 0 & 2 & 0 \\ -1 & 0 & 2 \end{bmatrix} \begin{bmatrix} x_1 \\ x_2 \\ x_3 \end{bmatrix}$

$$0 = \begin{vmatrix} \lambda - 2 & 0 & 1 \\ 0 & \lambda - 2 & 0 \\ 1 & 0 & \lambda - 2 \end{vmatrix} = (\lambda - 2)[(\lambda - 2)(\lambda - 2) - (0)(0)] + 1[(0)(0) - (1)(\lambda - 2)]$$

$$= (\lambda - 2)^3 + -(\lambda - 2)$$
$$= (\lambda - 2)[(\lambda - 2)^2 - 1]$$

$$= (\lambda - 2)(\lambda^2 - 4\lambda + 3)$$

$$= (\lambda - 2)(\lambda - 3)(\lambda - 1) \quad \text{so} \quad \lambda = 3, 2, 1$$

$$\lambda_1 = 3 \longrightarrow \begin{bmatrix} 1 & 0 & 1 & 0 \\ 0 & 1 & 0 & 0 \\ 1 & 0 & 1 & 0 \end{bmatrix} \longrightarrow \begin{bmatrix} 1 & 0 & 1 & 0 \\ 0 & 1 & 0 & 0 \\ 0 & 0 & 0 & 0 \end{bmatrix}$$

Let $x_3 = s$;

then $x_1 + x_3 = 0$, *i.e.* $x_1 = -x_3 = -s$

and $x_2 = 0$

so $\begin{bmatrix} x_1 \\ x_2 \\ x_3 \end{bmatrix} = \begin{bmatrix} -s \\ 0 \\ s \end{bmatrix} = s \begin{bmatrix} -1 \\ 0 \\ 1 \end{bmatrix}$

and $(-1, 0, 1)/\|(-1, 0, 1)\| = (-1, 0, 1)/\sqrt{2} = (\frac{-1}{\sqrt{2}}, 0, \frac{1}{\sqrt{2}})$.

Thus, the maximum is 3 and occurs at $(x_1, x_2, x_3) = \pm(\frac{-1}{\sqrt{2}}, 0, \frac{1}{\sqrt{2}})$.

$$\lambda_3 = 1 \longrightarrow \begin{bmatrix} -1 & 0 & 1 & 0 \\ 0 & -1 & 0 & 0 \\ 1 & 0 & -1 & 0 \end{bmatrix} \longrightarrow \begin{bmatrix} 1 & 0 & -1 & 0 \\ 0 & 1 & 0 & 0 \\ 0 & 0 & 0 & 0 \end{bmatrix}$$

Let $x_3 = t$;

then $x_1 - x_3 = 0$, *i.e.* $x_1 = x_3 = t$

and $x_2 = 0$

so $\begin{bmatrix} x_1 \\ x_2 \\ x_3 \end{bmatrix} = \begin{bmatrix} t \\ 0 \\ t \end{bmatrix} = t \begin{bmatrix} 1 \\ 0 \\ 1 \end{bmatrix}$

and $(1, 0, 1)/\|(1, 0, 1)\| = (1, 0, 1)/\sqrt{2} = (\frac{1}{\sqrt{2}}, 0, \frac{1}{\sqrt{2}})$.

Thus, the minimum is 1 and occurs at $(x_1, x_2, x_3) = \pm(\frac{1}{\sqrt{2}}, 0, \frac{1}{\sqrt{2}})$.

25. (c) $\quad -2x_1^2 + 5x_2^2 + 7x_3^2 + 12x_1x_3 = \begin{bmatrix} x_1 & x_2 & x_3 \end{bmatrix} \begin{bmatrix} -2 & 0 & 6 \\ 0 & 5 & 0 \\ 6 & 0 & 7 \end{bmatrix} \begin{bmatrix} x_1 \\ x_2 \\ x_3 \end{bmatrix}$

$$0 = \begin{vmatrix} \lambda+2 & 0 & -6 \\ 0 & \lambda-5 & 0 \\ -6 & 0 & \lambda-7 \end{vmatrix} = (\lambda+2)[(\lambda-5)(\lambda-7) - (0)(0)] - 6[(0)(0) - (\lambda-5)(-6)]$$

$$= (\lambda+2)(\lambda-5)(\lambda-7) - 36(\lambda-5)$$

$$= (\lambda-5)[(\lambda+2)(\lambda-7) - 36]$$

$$= (\lambda-5)(\lambda^2 - 5\lambda - 50)$$

$$= (\lambda-5)(\lambda+5)(\lambda-10) \quad \text{so} \quad \lambda = 10, 5, -5$$

$$\lambda_1 = 10 \longrightarrow \begin{bmatrix} 12 & 0 & -6 & 0 \\ 0 & 5 & 0 & 0 \\ -6 & 0 & 3 & 0 \end{bmatrix} \longrightarrow \begin{bmatrix} 1 & 0 & -1/2 & 0 \\ 0 & 1 & 0 & 0 \\ 0 & 0 & 0 & 0 \end{bmatrix}$$

Let $x_3 = s$;

then $x_1 - \frac{1}{2}x_3 = 0, \quad \text{i.e.} \quad x_1 = \frac{1}{2}x_3 = \frac{1}{2}s$

and $x_2 = 0$

so $\begin{bmatrix} x_1 \\ x_2 \\ x_3 \end{bmatrix} = \begin{bmatrix} (1/2)s \\ 0 \\ s \end{bmatrix} = s\begin{bmatrix} 1/2 \\ 0 \\ 1 \end{bmatrix} = \frac{1}{2}s\begin{bmatrix} 1 \\ 0 \\ 2 \end{bmatrix}$

and $(1,0,2)/\|(1,0,2)\| = (1,0,2)/\sqrt{5} = (\frac{1}{\sqrt{5}}, 0, \frac{2}{\sqrt{5}})$.

Thus, the maximum is 10 and occurs at $(x_1, x_2, x_3) = \pm(\frac{1}{\sqrt{5}}, 0, \frac{2}{\sqrt{5}})$.

$$\lambda_3 = -5 \longrightarrow \begin{bmatrix} -3 & 0 & -6 & 0 \\ 0 & -10 & 0 & 0 \\ -6 & 0 & -12 & 0 \end{bmatrix} \longrightarrow \begin{bmatrix} 1 & 0 & 2 & 0 \\ 0 & 1 & 0 & 0 \\ 0 & 0 & 0 & 0 \end{bmatrix}$$

Let $x_3 = t$;

then $x_1 + 2x_3 = 0, \quad \text{i.e.} \quad x_1 = -2x_3 = -2t$

and $x_2 = 0$

so $\begin{bmatrix} x_1 \\ x_2 \\ x_3 \end{bmatrix} = \begin{bmatrix} -2t \\ 0 \\ t \end{bmatrix} = t\begin{bmatrix} -2 \\ 0 \\ 1 \end{bmatrix}$

and $(-2,0,1)/\|(-2,0,1)\| = (-2,0,1)/\sqrt{5} = (\frac{-2}{\sqrt{5}},0,\frac{1}{\sqrt{5}})$.

Thus, the minimum is -5 and occurs at $(x_1,x_2,x_3) = \pm(\frac{-2}{\sqrt{5}},0,\frac{1}{\sqrt{5}})$.

26. (a) $\lambda = 3,\ 0,\ 17$ which are all nonnegative, so A is positive semidefinite.

(b) $\lambda = \pi + 4,\quad \pi - 4,\quad \pi^2 - 16$ which are both positive and negative, so A is indefinite.

(c) $|A_1| = 3 > 0,\quad |A_2| = 9 - 1 = 8 > 0,\quad |A_3| = 4(8) = 32 > 0$, so A is positive definite.

$$\text{Equivalently,}\quad 0 = \begin{vmatrix} \lambda - 3 & 1 & 0 \\ 1 & \lambda - 3 & 0 \\ 0 & 0 & \lambda - 4 \end{vmatrix} = (\lambda - 4)\big[(\lambda - 3)(\lambda - 3) - (1)(1)\big]$$

$$= (\lambda - 4)(\lambda^2 - 6\lambda + 8)$$

$$= (\lambda - 4)(\lambda - 4)(\lambda - 2)$$

so $\lambda = 2, 4, 4$ which are all positive, so A is positive definite.

(d) $0 = \begin{vmatrix} \lambda + 6 & -1 \\ -1 & \lambda + 6 \end{vmatrix} = (\lambda + 6)(\lambda + 6) - (-1)(-1)$

$$= \lambda^2 + 12\lambda + 36 - 1$$

$$= \lambda^2 + 12\lambda + 35$$

$$= (\lambda + 5)(\lambda + 7)$$

so $\lambda = -5, -7$ which are both negative, so A is negative definite.

(e) $0 = \begin{vmatrix} \lambda - 1 & 0 & 2 \\ 0 & \lambda - 1 & -3 \\ 2 & -3 & \lambda \end{vmatrix} = (\lambda - 1)\big[(\lambda - 1)(\lambda) - (-3)(-3)\big] + 2\big[(0)(-3) - (2)(\lambda - 1)\big]$

$$= (\lambda - 1)(\lambda^2 - \lambda - 9) + -4(\lambda - 1)$$

$$= (\lambda - 1)(\lambda^2 - \lambda - 9 - 4)$$

$$= (\lambda - 1)(\lambda^2 - \lambda - 13)$$

so $\lambda = 1$ or $\frac{1 \pm \sqrt{1 - 4(-13)}}{2}$

$= 1$ or $\frac{1 \pm \sqrt{53}}{2}$ which are both positive and negative, so A is indefinite.

(f) $0 = \begin{vmatrix} \lambda+3 & 0 & -1 \\ 0 & \lambda & 0 \\ -1 & 0 & \lambda+1 \end{vmatrix} = (\lambda+3)[(\lambda)(\lambda+1)-(0)(0)] - 1[(0)(0)-(-1)(\lambda)]$

$$= (\lambda+3)(\lambda^2+\lambda) - \lambda$$

$$= \lambda^3 + 4\lambda^2 + 2\lambda$$

$$= \lambda(\lambda^2 + 4\lambda + 2)$$

so $\lambda = 0$ or $\dfrac{-4\pm\sqrt{16-4(2)}}{2}$

$= 0$ or $-2 \pm \sqrt{2}$ which are all nonpositive, so A is negative semidefinite.

SECTION 9.6   *DIAGONALIZING QUADRATIC FORMS; CONIC SECTIONS*

27. (a) $4x_1^2 + 4x_2^2 + 14x_1x_2 = \begin{bmatrix} x_1 & x_2 \end{bmatrix} \begin{bmatrix} 4 & 7 \\ 7 & 4 \end{bmatrix} \begin{bmatrix} x_1 \\ x_2 \end{bmatrix}$

$0 = \begin{vmatrix} \lambda-4 & -7 \\ -7 & \lambda-4 \end{vmatrix} = (\lambda-4)^2 - (-7)^2 = \lambda^2 - 8\lambda + 16 - 49$

$$= \lambda^2 - 8\lambda - 33 = (\lambda-11)(\lambda+3) \quad \text{so} \quad \lambda = 11, -3$$

$\lambda_1 = 11 \longrightarrow \begin{bmatrix} 7 & -7 & 0 \\ -7 & 7 & 0 \end{bmatrix} \longrightarrow \begin{bmatrix} 1 & -1 & 0 \\ 0 & 0 & 0 \end{bmatrix}$

Let $x_2 = s$;

then $x_1 - x_2 = 0$,   *i.e.* $x_1 = x_2 = s$

so $\begin{bmatrix} x_1 \\ x_2 \end{bmatrix} = \begin{bmatrix} s \\ s \end{bmatrix} = s \begin{bmatrix} 1 \\ 1 \end{bmatrix}$

and $(1,1)/\|(1,1)\| = (1,1)/\sqrt{2} = (\frac{1}{\sqrt{2}}, \frac{1}{\sqrt{2}})$

$\lambda_2 = -3 \longrightarrow \begin{bmatrix} -7 & -7 & 0 \\ -7 & -7 & 0 \end{bmatrix} \longrightarrow \begin{bmatrix} 1 & 1 & 0 \\ 0 & 0 & 0 \end{bmatrix}$

Let $x_2 = t$;

then $x_1 + x_2 = 0$,   *i.e.* $x_1 = -x_2 = -t$

so $\begin{bmatrix} x_1 \\ x_2 \end{bmatrix} = \begin{bmatrix} -t \\ t \end{bmatrix} = t \begin{bmatrix} -1 \\ 1 \end{bmatrix}$.

and $(-1,1)/\|(-1,1)\| = (-1,1)/\sqrt{2} = (\frac{-1}{\sqrt{2}}, \frac{1}{\sqrt{2}})$

247

The substitution

$$\begin{bmatrix} x_1 \\ x_2 \end{bmatrix} = \begin{bmatrix} \frac{1}{\sqrt{2}} & -\frac{1}{\sqrt{2}} \\ \frac{1}{\sqrt{2}} & \frac{1}{\sqrt{2}} \end{bmatrix} \begin{bmatrix} y_1 \\ y_2 \end{bmatrix}$$

leads to the quadratic form

$$[y_1 \ \ y_2] \begin{bmatrix} 11 & 0 \\ 0 & -3 \end{bmatrix} \begin{bmatrix} y_1 \\ y_2 \end{bmatrix} = 11y_1^2 - 3y_2^2$$

(b) $\quad 3x_1^2 + 5x_2^2 - 2\sqrt{35}x_1x_2 = [x_1 \ \ x_2] \begin{bmatrix} 3 & -\sqrt{35} \\ -\sqrt{35} & 5 \end{bmatrix} \begin{bmatrix} x_1 \\ x_2 \end{bmatrix}$

$$0 = \begin{vmatrix} \lambda - 3 & \sqrt{35} \\ \sqrt{35} & \lambda - 5 \end{vmatrix} = (\lambda - 3)(\lambda - 5) - (\sqrt{35})(\sqrt{35}) = \lambda^2 - 8\lambda + 15 - 35$$

$$= \lambda^2 - 8\lambda - 20 = (\lambda - 10)(\lambda + 2) \quad \text{so} \quad \lambda = 10, -2$$

$$\lambda_1 = 10 \longrightarrow \begin{bmatrix} 7 & \sqrt{35} & 0 \\ \sqrt{35} & 5 & 0 \end{bmatrix} \longrightarrow \begin{bmatrix} 1 & \sqrt{35}/7 & 0 \\ 0 & 0 & 0 \end{bmatrix}$$

Let $x_2 = s$;

then $x_1 + \frac{1}{7}\sqrt{35}x_2 = 0$, $\quad i.e. \quad x_1 = -\frac{1}{7}\sqrt{35}x_2 = -\frac{1}{7}\sqrt{35}s$

so $\begin{bmatrix} x_1 \\ x_2 \end{bmatrix} = \begin{bmatrix} -(\sqrt{35}/7)s \\ s \end{bmatrix} = s \begin{bmatrix} -(\sqrt{35}/7) \\ 1 \end{bmatrix} = \frac{1}{7}s \begin{bmatrix} -\sqrt{35} \\ 7 \end{bmatrix}$

and $(-\sqrt{35}, 7)/\|(-\sqrt{35}, 7)\| = (-\sqrt{35}, 7)/\sqrt{84} = (\frac{-\sqrt{35}}{\sqrt{84}}, \frac{7}{\sqrt{84}}) = (-\sqrt{\frac{5}{12}}, \sqrt{\frac{7}{12}})$.

$$\lambda_2 = -2 \longrightarrow \begin{bmatrix} -5 & \sqrt{35} & 0 \\ \sqrt{35} & -7 & 0 \end{bmatrix} \longrightarrow \begin{bmatrix} 1 & -\sqrt{35}/5 & 0 \\ 0 & 0 & 0 \end{bmatrix}$$

Let $x_2 = t$;

then $x_1 - \frac{1}{5}\sqrt{35}x_2 = 0$, $\quad i.e. \quad x_1 = \frac{1}{5}\sqrt{35}x_2 = \frac{1}{5}\sqrt{35}t$

so $\begin{bmatrix} x_1 \\ x_2 \end{bmatrix} = \begin{bmatrix} (\sqrt{35}/5)t \\ t \end{bmatrix} = t \begin{bmatrix} \sqrt{35}/5 \\ 1 \end{bmatrix} = \frac{1}{5}t \begin{bmatrix} \sqrt{35} \\ 5 \end{bmatrix}$

and $(\sqrt{35}, 5)/\|(\sqrt{35}, 5)\| = (\sqrt{35}, 5)/\sqrt{60} = (\frac{\sqrt{35}}{\sqrt{60}}, \frac{5}{\sqrt{60}}) = (\sqrt{\frac{7}{12}}, \sqrt{\frac{5}{12}})$.

The substitution

$$\begin{bmatrix} x_1 \\ x_2 \end{bmatrix} = \begin{bmatrix} -\sqrt{\frac{5}{12}} & \sqrt{\frac{7}{12}} \\ \sqrt{\frac{7}{12}} & \sqrt{\frac{5}{12}} \end{bmatrix} \begin{bmatrix} y_1 \\ y_2 \end{bmatrix}$$

leads to the quadratic form

$$[y_1 \ \ y_2] \begin{bmatrix} 10 & 0 \\ 0 & -2 \end{bmatrix} \begin{bmatrix} y_1 \\ y_2 \end{bmatrix} = 10y_1^2 - 2y_2^2$$

27. (c) $-2x_1x_2 - 2x_2x_3 + 2x_1x_3 = [x_1 \quad x_2 \quad x_3] \begin{bmatrix} 0 & -1 & 1 \\ -1 & 0 & -1 \\ 1 & -1 & 0 \end{bmatrix} \begin{bmatrix} x_1 \\ x_2 \\ x_3 \end{bmatrix}$

$$0 = \begin{vmatrix} \lambda & 1 & -1 \\ 1 & \lambda & 1 \\ -1 & 1 & \lambda \end{vmatrix} = \lambda(\lambda^2 - 1) - 1(\lambda + 1) - 1(\lambda + 1)$$

$$= \lambda(\lambda - 1)(\lambda + 1) - 2(\lambda + 1)$$

$$= [\lambda(\lambda - 1) - 2](\lambda + 1)$$

$$= (\lambda^2 - \lambda - 2)(\lambda + 1) = (\lambda - 2)(\lambda + 1)(\lambda + 1) \quad \text{so} \quad \lambda = 2, -1, -1$$

$$\lambda_1 = 2 \longrightarrow \begin{bmatrix} 2 & 1 & -1 & 0 \\ 1 & 2 & 1 & 0 \\ -1 & 1 & 2 & 0 \end{bmatrix} \longrightarrow \begin{bmatrix} 1 & 2 & 1 & 0 \\ 2 & 1 & -1 & 0 \\ -1 & 1 & 2 & 0 \end{bmatrix} \longrightarrow \begin{bmatrix} 1 & 2 & 1 & 0 \\ 0 & -3 & -3 & 0 \\ 0 & 3 & 3 & 0 \end{bmatrix}$$

$$\longrightarrow \begin{bmatrix} 1 & 0 & -1 & 0 \\ 0 & 1 & 1 & 0 \\ 0 & 0 & 0 & 0 \end{bmatrix}$$

Let $x_3 = r$;

then $x_2 + x_3 = 0$, i.e. $x_2 = -x_3 = -r$

and $x_1 - x_3 = 0$, i.e. $x_1 = x_3 = r$

so $\begin{bmatrix} x_1 \\ x_2 \\ x_3 \end{bmatrix} = \begin{bmatrix} r \\ -r \\ r \end{bmatrix} = r \begin{bmatrix} 1 \\ -1 \\ 1 \end{bmatrix}$

and $(1, -1, 1)/\|(1, -1, 1)\| = (1, -1, 1)/\sqrt{3} = \left(\frac{1}{\sqrt{3}}, \frac{-1}{\sqrt{3}}, \frac{1}{\sqrt{3}}\right)$.

$$\lambda_2 = -1 \longrightarrow \begin{bmatrix} -1 & 1 & -1 & 0 \\ 1 & -1 & 1 & 0 \\ -1 & 1 & -1 & 0 \end{bmatrix} \longrightarrow \begin{bmatrix} 1 & -1 & 1 & 0 \\ 0 & 0 & 0 & 0 \\ 0 & 0 & 0 & 0 \end{bmatrix}$$

Let $x_3 = t$ and $x_2 = s$;

then $x_1 - x_2 + x_3 = 0$, i.e. $x_1 = x_2 - x_3 = s - t$

so $\begin{bmatrix} x_1 \\ x_2 \\ x_3 \end{bmatrix} = \begin{bmatrix} s - t \\ s \\ t \end{bmatrix} = \begin{bmatrix} s \\ s \\ 0 \end{bmatrix} + \begin{bmatrix} -t \\ 0 \\ t \end{bmatrix} = s \begin{bmatrix} 1 \\ 1 \\ 0 \end{bmatrix} + t \begin{bmatrix} -1 \\ 0 \\ 1 \end{bmatrix}$.

$(-1, 0, 1) - \frac{(-1,0,1) \cdot (1,1,0)}{(1,1,0) \cdot (1,1,0)}(1, 1, 0) = (-1, 0, 1) - -\frac{1}{2}(1, 1, 0) = (-\frac{1}{2}, \frac{1}{2}, 1) = \frac{1}{2}(-1, 1, 2)$

and $(1, 1, 0)/\|(1, 1, 0)\| = (1, 1, 0)/\sqrt{2} = \left(\frac{1}{\sqrt{2}}, \frac{1}{\sqrt{2}}, 0\right)$

and $(-1,1,2)/\|(-1,1,2)\| = (-1,1,2)/\sqrt{6} = (-\frac{1}{\sqrt{6}}, \frac{1}{\sqrt{6}}, \frac{2}{\sqrt{6}})$

The substitution

$$\begin{bmatrix} x_1 \\ x_2 \\ x_3 \end{bmatrix} = \begin{bmatrix} 1/\sqrt{3} & 1/\sqrt{2} & -1/\sqrt{6} \\ -1/\sqrt{3} & 1/\sqrt{2} & 1/\sqrt{6} \\ 1/\sqrt{3} & 0 & 2/\sqrt{6} \end{bmatrix} \begin{bmatrix} y_1 \\ y_2 \\ y_3 \end{bmatrix}$$

leads to the quadratic form

$$[y_1 \ \ y_2 \ \ y_3] \begin{bmatrix} 2 & 0 & 0 \\ 0 & -1 & 1 \\ 0 & 0 & -1 \end{bmatrix} \begin{bmatrix} y_1 \\ y_2 \\ y_3 \end{bmatrix} = 2y_1^2 - y_2^2 - y_3^2$$

27. (d) $x_1^2 - x_3^2 - 4x_1x_2 - 4x_2x_3 = [x_1 \ \ x_2 \ \ x_3] \begin{bmatrix} 1 & -2 & 0 \\ -2 & 0 & -2 \\ 0 & -2 & -1 \end{bmatrix} \begin{bmatrix} x_1 \\ x_2 \\ x_3 \end{bmatrix}$

$$0 = \begin{vmatrix} \lambda - 1 & 2 & 0 \\ 2 & \lambda & 2 \\ 0 & 2 & \lambda + 1 \end{vmatrix} = (\lambda - 1)[\lambda(\lambda + 1) - 2(2)] - 2[2(\lambda + 1) - 2(0)]$$

$$= (\lambda - 1)(\lambda^2 + \lambda - 4) - 4(\lambda + 1)$$

$$= (\lambda^3 - 5\lambda + 4) - 4(\lambda + 1)$$

$$= \lambda^3 - 9\lambda = \lambda(\lambda^2 - 9) = \lambda(\lambda - 3)(\lambda + 3) \quad \text{so} \quad \lambda = 0, 3, -3$$

$$\lambda_1 = 0 \longrightarrow \begin{bmatrix} -1 & 2 & 0 & 0 \\ 2 & 0 & 2 & 0 \\ 0 & 2 & 1 & 0 \end{bmatrix} \longrightarrow \begin{bmatrix} 1 & -2 & 0 & 0 \\ 0 & 4 & 2 & 0 \\ 0 & 2 & 1 & 0 \end{bmatrix} \longrightarrow \begin{bmatrix} 1 & 0 & 1 & 0 \\ 0 & 1 & 1/2 & 0 \\ 0 & 0 & 0 & 0 \end{bmatrix}$$

Let $x_3 = r$;

then $x_2 + \frac{1}{2}x_3 = 0$, i.e. $x_2 = -\frac{1}{2}x_3 = -\frac{1}{2}r$

and $x_1 + x_3 = 0$, i.e. $x_1 = -x_3 = -r$

so $\begin{bmatrix} x_1 \\ x_2 \\ x_3 \end{bmatrix} = \begin{bmatrix} -r \\ -(1/2)r \\ r \end{bmatrix} = r \begin{bmatrix} -1 \\ -1/2 \\ 1 \end{bmatrix} = \frac{1}{2}r \begin{bmatrix} -2 \\ -1 \\ 2 \end{bmatrix}$

and $(-2, -1, 2)/\|(-2, -1, 2)\| = (-2, -1, 2)/3 = (-\frac{2}{3}, -\frac{1}{3}, \frac{2}{3})$.

$$\lambda_2 = 3 \longrightarrow \begin{bmatrix} 2 & 2 & 0 & 0 \\ 2 & 3 & 2 & 0 \\ 0 & 2 & 4 & 0 \end{bmatrix} \longrightarrow \begin{bmatrix} 1 & 1 & 0 & 0 \\ 0 & 1 & 2 & 0 \\ 0 & 2 & 4 & 0 \end{bmatrix} \longrightarrow \begin{bmatrix} 1 & 0 & -2 & 0 \\ 0 & 1 & 2 & 0 \\ 0 & 0 & 0 & 0 \end{bmatrix}$$

Let $x_3 = s$;

then $x_2 + 2x_3 = 0$,   *i.e.* $x_2 = -2x_3 = -2s$

and $x_1 - 2x_3 = 0$,   *i.e.* $x_1 = 2x_3 = 2s$

so $\begin{bmatrix} x_1 \\ x_2 \\ x_3 \end{bmatrix} = \begin{bmatrix} 2s \\ -2s \\ s \end{bmatrix} = s \begin{bmatrix} 2 \\ -2 \\ 1 \end{bmatrix}$

and $(2, -2, 1)/\|(2, -2, 1)\| = (2, -2, 1)/3 = (\frac{2}{3}, -\frac{2}{3}, \frac{1}{3})$.

$\lambda_3 = -3 \longrightarrow \begin{bmatrix} -4 & 2 & 0 & 0 \\ 2 & -3 & 2 & 0 \\ 0 & 2 & -2 & 0 \end{bmatrix} \longrightarrow \begin{bmatrix} 1 & -1/2 & 0 & 0 \\ 0 & -2 & 2 & 0 \\ 0 & 2 & -2 & 0 \end{bmatrix} \longrightarrow \begin{bmatrix} 1 & 0 & -1/2 & 0 \\ 0 & 1 & -1 & 0 \\ 0 & 0 & 0 & 0 \end{bmatrix}$

Let $x_3 = t$;

then $x_2 - x_3 = 0$,   *i.e.* $x_2 = x_3 = t$

and $x_1 - \frac{1}{2}x_3 = 0$,   *i.e.* $x_1 = \frac{1}{2}x_3 = \frac{1}{2}t$

so $\begin{bmatrix} x_1 \\ x_2 \\ x_3 \end{bmatrix} = \begin{bmatrix} (1/2)t \\ t \\ t \end{bmatrix} = t \begin{bmatrix} 1/2 \\ 1 \\ 1 \end{bmatrix} = \frac{1}{2}t \begin{bmatrix} 1 \\ 2 \\ 2 \end{bmatrix}$

and $(1, 2, 2)/\|(1, 2, 2)\| = (1, 2, 2)/3 = (\frac{1}{3}, \frac{2}{3}, \frac{2}{3})$.

The substitution

$$\begin{bmatrix} x_1 \\ x_2 \\ x_3 \end{bmatrix} = \begin{bmatrix} -2/3 & 2/3 & 1/3 \\ -1/3 & -2/3 & 2/3 \\ 2/3 & 1/3 & 2/3 \end{bmatrix} \begin{bmatrix} y_1 \\ y_2 \\ y_3 \end{bmatrix}$$

leads to the quadratic form

$$\begin{bmatrix} y_1 & y_2 & y_3 \end{bmatrix} \begin{bmatrix} 0 & 0 & 0 \\ 0 & 3 & 0 \\ 0 & 0 & -3 \end{bmatrix} \begin{bmatrix} y_1 \\ y_2 \\ y_3 \end{bmatrix} = 3y_2^2 - 3y_3^2.$$

28. $x^2 - 6xy + y^2 + 8 = 0 = \begin{bmatrix} x & y \end{bmatrix} \begin{bmatrix} 1 & -3 \\ -3 & 1 \end{bmatrix} \begin{bmatrix} x \\ y \end{bmatrix} + 3$

$0 = \begin{vmatrix} \lambda - 1 & 3 \\ 3 & \lambda - 1 \end{vmatrix} = (\lambda - 1)^2 - (3)^2 = \lambda^2 - 2\lambda - 8$

$= (\lambda - 4)(\lambda + 2)$ so $\lambda = 4, -2$ *(hyperbola)*

$\lambda_1 = 4 \longrightarrow \begin{bmatrix} 3 & 3 & 0 \\ 3 & 3 & 0 \end{bmatrix} \longrightarrow \begin{bmatrix} 1 & 1 & 0 \\ 0 & 0 & 0 \end{bmatrix}$

Let $x_2 = s$;

then $x_1 + x_2 = 0$, _i.e._ $x_1 = -x_2 = -s$

so $\begin{bmatrix} x_1 \\ x_2 \end{bmatrix} = \begin{bmatrix} -s \\ s \end{bmatrix} = s \begin{bmatrix} -1 \\ 1 \end{bmatrix}$

and $(-1,1)/\|(-1,1)\| = (-1,1)/\sqrt{2} = (\frac{-1}{\sqrt{2}}, \frac{1}{\sqrt{2}})$.

$\lambda_2 = -2 \longrightarrow \begin{bmatrix} -3 & 3 & 0 \\ 3 & -3 & 0 \end{bmatrix} \longrightarrow \begin{bmatrix} 1 & -1 & 0 \\ 0 & 0 & 0 \end{bmatrix}$

Let $x_2 = t$;

then $x_1 - x_2 = 0$, _i.e._ $x_1 = x_2 = t$

so $\begin{bmatrix} x_1 \\ x_2 \end{bmatrix} = \begin{bmatrix} t \\ t \end{bmatrix} = t \begin{bmatrix} 1 \\ 1 \end{bmatrix}$

and $(1,1)/\|(1,1)\| = (1,1)/\sqrt{2} = (\frac{1}{\sqrt{2}}, \frac{1}{\sqrt{2}})$.

Note that $\det \begin{bmatrix} \frac{1}{\sqrt{2}} & -\frac{1}{\sqrt{2}} \\ \frac{1}{\sqrt{2}} & \frac{1}{\sqrt{2}} \end{bmatrix} = \frac{1}{2} - -\frac{1}{2} = 1$, indicating a rotation.

The substitution

$$\begin{bmatrix} x \\ y \end{bmatrix} = \begin{bmatrix} \frac{1}{\sqrt{2}} & -\frac{1}{\sqrt{2}} \\ \frac{1}{\sqrt{2}} & \frac{1}{\sqrt{2}} \end{bmatrix} \begin{bmatrix} x' \\ y' \end{bmatrix}$$

leads to the conic equation

$$[x' \ y'] \begin{bmatrix} -2 & 0 \\ 0 & 4 \end{bmatrix} \begin{bmatrix} x' \\ y' \end{bmatrix} + 8 = 0$$

$$-2(x')^2 + 4(y')^2 + 8 = 0.$$

$$\frac{(x')^2}{4} - \frac{(y')^2}{2} = 1.$$

29. $x^2 + 4xy + 4y^2 + 4x - 2y + 5 = 0 = [x \ y] \begin{bmatrix} 1 & 2 \\ 2 & 4 \end{bmatrix} \begin{bmatrix} x \\ y \end{bmatrix} + [4 \quad -2] \begin{bmatrix} x \\ y \end{bmatrix} + 5$

$0 = \begin{vmatrix} \lambda - 1 & -2 \\ -2 & \lambda - 4 \end{vmatrix} = (\lambda - 1)(\lambda - 4) - (-2)(-2) = \lambda^2 - 5\lambda + 4 - 4$

$= \lambda^2 - 5\lambda = \lambda(\lambda - 5)$ so $\lambda = 0, 5$ _(parabola)_

$\lambda_1 = 0 \longrightarrow \begin{bmatrix} -1 & -2 & 0 \\ -2 & -4 & 0 \end{bmatrix} \longrightarrow \begin{bmatrix} 1 & 2 & 0 \\ 0 & 0 & 0 \end{bmatrix}$

Let $x_2 = s$;

then $x_1 + 2x_2 = 0$,   i.e. $x_1 = -2x_2 = -2s$

so $\begin{bmatrix} x_1 \\ x_2 \end{bmatrix} = \begin{bmatrix} -2s \\ s \end{bmatrix} = s\begin{bmatrix} -2 \\ 1 \end{bmatrix}$

and $(-2,1)/\|(-2,1)\| = (-2,1)/\sqrt{5} = (\frac{-2}{\sqrt{5}}, \frac{1}{\sqrt{5}})$.

$\lambda_2 = 5 \longrightarrow \begin{bmatrix} 4 & -2 & 0 \\ -2 & 1 & 0 \end{bmatrix} \longrightarrow \begin{bmatrix} 1 & -1/2 & 0 \\ 0 & 0 & 0 \end{bmatrix}$

Let $x_2 = t$;

then $x_1 - \frac{1}{2}x_2 = 0$,   i.e. $x_1 = \frac{1}{2}x_2 = \frac{1}{2}t$

so $\begin{bmatrix} x_1 \\ x_2 \end{bmatrix} = \begin{bmatrix} (1/2)t \\ t \end{bmatrix} = t\begin{bmatrix} 1/2 \\ 1 \end{bmatrix} = \frac{1}{2}t\begin{bmatrix} 1 \\ 2 \end{bmatrix}$

and $(1,2)/\|(1,2)\| = (1,2)/\sqrt{5} = (\frac{1}{\sqrt{5}}, \frac{2}{\sqrt{5}})$.

Note that $\det \begin{bmatrix} \frac{1}{\sqrt{5}} & \frac{-2}{\sqrt{5}} \\ \frac{2}{\sqrt{5}} & \frac{1}{\sqrt{5}} \end{bmatrix} = \frac{1}{5} - -\frac{4}{5} = 1$, indicating a rotation.

The substitution

$$\begin{bmatrix} x \\ y \end{bmatrix} = \begin{bmatrix} \frac{1}{\sqrt{5}} & \frac{-2}{\sqrt{5}} \\ \frac{2}{\sqrt{5}} & \frac{1}{\sqrt{5}} \end{bmatrix} \begin{bmatrix} x' \\ y' \end{bmatrix}$$

leads to the conic equation

$$[x' \;\; y'] \begin{bmatrix} 5 & 0 \\ 0 & 0 \end{bmatrix} \begin{bmatrix} x' \\ y' \end{bmatrix} + [4 \;\; -2] \begin{bmatrix} \frac{1}{\sqrt{5}} & \frac{-2}{\sqrt{5}} \\ \frac{2}{\sqrt{5}} & \frac{1}{\sqrt{5}} \end{bmatrix} \begin{bmatrix} x' \\ y' \end{bmatrix} + 5 = 0$$

$$5(x')^2 + 0(y')^2 + 0x' - \frac{10}{\sqrt{5}}y' + 5 = 0$$

$$-\frac{10}{\sqrt{5}}y' + 5 = -5(x')^2$$

$$y' - \frac{\sqrt{5}}{2} = \frac{\sqrt{5}}{2}(x')^2.$$

30. $6x^2 - 4xy + 3y^2 - 14 = 0 = [x \;\; y]\begin{bmatrix} 6 & -2 \\ -2 & 3 \end{bmatrix}\begin{bmatrix} x \\ y \end{bmatrix} - 14$

$0 = \begin{vmatrix} \lambda - 6 & 2 \\ 2 & \lambda - 3 \end{vmatrix} = (\lambda - 6)(\lambda - 3) - (2)(2) = \lambda^2 - 9\lambda + 18 - 4$

$= \lambda^2 - 9\lambda + 14 = (\lambda - 2)(\lambda - 7)$ so $\lambda = 2, 7$ (*ellipse*)

$$\lambda_1 = 2 \longrightarrow \begin{bmatrix} -4 & 2 & 0 \\ 2 & -1 & 0 \end{bmatrix} \longrightarrow \begin{bmatrix} 1 & -1/2 & 0 \\ 0 & 0 & 0 \end{bmatrix}$$

Let $x_2 = s$;

then $x_1 - \frac{1}{2}x_2 = 0$, i.e. $x_1 = \frac{1}{2}x_2 = \frac{1}{2}s$

so $\begin{bmatrix} x_1 \\ x_2 \end{bmatrix} = \begin{bmatrix} (1/2)s \\ s \end{bmatrix} = s\begin{bmatrix} 1/2 \\ 1 \end{bmatrix} = \frac{1}{2}s\begin{bmatrix} 1 \\ 2 \end{bmatrix}$

and $(1,2)/\|(1,2)\| = (1,2)/\sqrt{5} = (\frac{1}{\sqrt{5}}, \frac{2}{\sqrt{5}})$.

$$\lambda_2 = 7 \longrightarrow \begin{bmatrix} 1 & 2 & 0 \\ 2 & 4 & 0 \end{bmatrix} \longrightarrow \begin{bmatrix} 1 & 2 & 0 \\ 0 & 0 & 0 \end{bmatrix}$$

Let $x_2 = t$;

then $x_1 + 2x_2 = 0$, i.e. $x_1 = -2x_2 = -2t$

so $\begin{bmatrix} x_1 \\ x_2 \end{bmatrix} = \begin{bmatrix} -2t \\ t \end{bmatrix} = t\begin{bmatrix} -2 \\ 1 \end{bmatrix}$

and $(-2,1)/\|(-2,1)\| = (-2,1)/\sqrt{5} = (\frac{-2}{\sqrt{5}}, \frac{1}{\sqrt{5}})$.

Note that $\det \begin{bmatrix} \frac{1}{\sqrt{5}} & \frac{-2}{\sqrt{5}} \\ \frac{2}{\sqrt{5}} & \frac{1}{\sqrt{5}} \end{bmatrix} = \frac{1}{5} - -\frac{4}{5} = 1$, indicating a rotation.

The substitution

$$\begin{bmatrix} x \\ y \end{bmatrix} = \begin{bmatrix} \frac{1}{\sqrt{5}} & \frac{-2}{\sqrt{5}} \\ \frac{2}{\sqrt{5}} & \frac{1}{\sqrt{5}} \end{bmatrix} \begin{bmatrix} x' \\ y' \end{bmatrix}$$

leads to the conic equation

$$[x' \ y'] \begin{bmatrix} 2 & 0 \\ 0 & 7 \end{bmatrix} \begin{bmatrix} x' \\ y' \end{bmatrix} - 14 = 0$$

$$2(x')^2 + 7(y')^2 - 14 = 0$$

$$2(x')^2 + 7(y')^2 = 14$$

$$\frac{(x')^2}{7} + \frac{(y')^2}{2} = 1$$

31. $-3x^2 + 2xy - 3y^2 + 2x + 2y + 7 = 0 = [x \ y] \begin{bmatrix} -3 & 1 \\ 1 & -3 \end{bmatrix} \begin{bmatrix} x \\ y \end{bmatrix} + [2 \ 2] \begin{bmatrix} x \\ y \end{bmatrix} + 7$

$$0 = \begin{vmatrix} \lambda+3 & -1 \\ -1 & \lambda+3 \end{vmatrix} = (\lambda+3)^2 - (-1)^2 = (\lambda^2 + 6\lambda + 9) - 1$$

$$= \lambda^2 + 6\lambda + 8 = (\lambda+2)(\lambda+4) \quad \text{so} \quad \lambda = -2, -4 \quad (\textit{ellipse})$$

$$\lambda_1 = -2 \longrightarrow \begin{bmatrix} 1 & -1 & 0 \\ -1 & 1 & 0 \end{bmatrix} \longrightarrow \begin{bmatrix} 1 & -1 & 0 \\ 0 & 0 & 0 \end{bmatrix}$$

Let $x_2 = s$;

then $x_1 - x_2 = 0$, i.e. $x_1 = x_2 = s$

so $\begin{bmatrix} x_1 \\ x_2 \end{bmatrix} = \begin{bmatrix} s \\ s \end{bmatrix} = s \begin{bmatrix} 1 \\ 1 \end{bmatrix}$

and $(1,1)/\|(1,1)\| = (1,1)/\sqrt{2} = \left(\frac{1}{\sqrt{2}}, \frac{1}{\sqrt{2}}\right)$.

$$\lambda_2 = -4 \longrightarrow \begin{bmatrix} -1 & -1 & 0 \\ -1 & -1 & 0 \end{bmatrix} \longrightarrow \begin{bmatrix} 1 & 1 & 0 \\ 0 & 0 & 0 \end{bmatrix}$$

Let $x_2 = t$;

then $x_1 + x_2 = 0$, i.e. $x_1 = -x_2 = -t$

so $\begin{bmatrix} x_1 \\ x_2 \end{bmatrix} = \begin{bmatrix} -t \\ t \end{bmatrix} = t \begin{bmatrix} -1 \\ 1 \end{bmatrix}$

and $(-1,1)/\|(-1,1)\| = (-1,1)/\sqrt{2} = \left(\frac{-1}{\sqrt{2}}, \frac{1}{\sqrt{2}}\right)$.

Note that det $\begin{bmatrix} \frac{1}{\sqrt{2}} & \frac{-1}{\sqrt{2}} \\ \frac{1}{\sqrt{2}} & \frac{1}{\sqrt{2}} \end{bmatrix} = \frac{1}{2} - -\frac{1}{2} = 1$, indicating a rotation.

The substitution

$$\begin{bmatrix} x \\ y \end{bmatrix} = \begin{bmatrix} \frac{1}{\sqrt{2}} & \frac{-1}{\sqrt{2}} \\ \frac{1}{\sqrt{2}} & \frac{1}{\sqrt{2}} \end{bmatrix} \begin{bmatrix} x' \\ y' \end{bmatrix}$$

leads to the conic equation

$$[x' \quad y'] \begin{bmatrix} -2 & 0 \\ 0 & -4 \end{bmatrix} \begin{bmatrix} x' \\ y' \end{bmatrix} + [2 \quad 2] \begin{bmatrix} \frac{1}{\sqrt{2}} & \frac{-1}{\sqrt{2}} \\ \frac{1}{\sqrt{2}} & \frac{1}{\sqrt{2}} \end{bmatrix} \begin{bmatrix} x' \\ y' \end{bmatrix} + 7 = 0$$

$$-2(x')^2 - 4(y')^2 + \frac{4}{\sqrt{2}}x' + 0y' + 7 = 0$$

$$-2\left[(x')^2 - \frac{2}{\sqrt{2}}x'\right] - 4(y')^2 + 7 = 0$$

$$-2\left[(x')^2 - \frac{2}{\sqrt{2}}x' + \frac{1}{2}\right] - 4(y')^2 + 7 = -1$$

$$-2\left(x' - \frac{1}{\sqrt{2}}\right)^2 - 4(y')^2 + 7 = -1$$

$$-2\left(x' - \frac{1}{\sqrt{2}}\right)^2 - 4(y')^2 = -8$$

$$\frac{(x' - \frac{1}{\sqrt{2}})^2}{4} + \frac{(y')^2}{2} = 1$$

The substitution

$$\begin{bmatrix} x' - \frac{1}{\sqrt{2}} \\ y' \end{bmatrix} = \begin{bmatrix} x'' \\ y'' \end{bmatrix}$$

leads to the conic equation

$$\frac{(x'')^2}{4} + \frac{(y'')^2}{2} = 1.$$

32. $4x^2 - 24xy + 11y^2 + 40x - 70y - 105 = 0 = \begin{bmatrix} x & y \end{bmatrix}\begin{bmatrix} 4 & -12 \\ -12 & 11 \end{bmatrix}\begin{bmatrix} x \\ y \end{bmatrix} + \begin{bmatrix} 40 & -70 \end{bmatrix}\begin{bmatrix} x \\ y \end{bmatrix} - 105$

$$0 = \begin{vmatrix} \lambda - 4 & 12 \\ 12 & \lambda - 11 \end{vmatrix} = (\lambda - 4)(\lambda - 11) - (12)(12) = \lambda^2 - 15\lambda + 44 - 144$$

$$= \lambda^2 - 15\lambda - 100 = (\lambda - 20)(\lambda + 5) \quad \text{so} \quad \lambda = 20, -5 \quad (\textit{hyperbola})$$

$\lambda_1 = 20 \longrightarrow \begin{bmatrix} 16 & 12 & 0 \\ 12 & 9 & 0 \end{bmatrix} \longrightarrow \begin{bmatrix} 1 & 3/4 & 0 \\ 0 & 0 & 0 \end{bmatrix}$

Let $x_2 = s$;

then $x_1 + \frac{3}{4}x_2 = 0$, i.e. $x_1 = \frac{-3}{4}x_2 = \frac{-3}{4}s$

so $\begin{bmatrix} x_1 \\ x_2 \end{bmatrix} = \begin{bmatrix} -(3/4)s \\ s \end{bmatrix} = s\begin{bmatrix} -3/4 \\ 1 \end{bmatrix} = \frac{1}{4}s\begin{bmatrix} -3 \\ 4 \end{bmatrix}$

and $(-3, 4)/\|(-3, 4)\| = (-3, 4)/5 = (\frac{-3}{5}, \frac{4}{5})$.

$\lambda_2 = -5 \longrightarrow \begin{bmatrix} -9 & 12 & 0 \\ 12 & -16 & 0 \end{bmatrix} \longrightarrow \begin{bmatrix} 1 & -4/3 & 0 \\ 0 & 0 & 0 \end{bmatrix}$

Let $x_2 = t$;

then $x_1 - \frac{4}{3}x_2 = 0$, i.e. $x_1 = \frac{4}{3}x_2 = \frac{4}{3}t$

so $\begin{bmatrix} x_1 \\ x_2 \end{bmatrix} = \begin{bmatrix} (4/3)t \\ t \end{bmatrix} = t\begin{bmatrix} 4/3 \\ 1 \end{bmatrix} = \frac{1}{3}t\begin{bmatrix} 4 \\ 3 \end{bmatrix}$

and $(4, 3)/\|(4, 3)\| = (4, 3)/5 = (\frac{4}{5}, \frac{3}{5})$.

Note that $\det \begin{bmatrix} 4/5 & -3/5 \\ 3/5 & 4/5 \end{bmatrix} = \frac{16}{25} - -\frac{9}{25} = 1$, indicating a rotation.

The substitution

$$\begin{bmatrix} x \\ y \end{bmatrix} = \begin{bmatrix} 4/5 & -3/5 \\ 3/5 & 4/5 \end{bmatrix} \begin{bmatrix} x' \\ y' \end{bmatrix}$$

leads to the conic equation

$$[x' \ \ y'] \begin{bmatrix} -5 & 0 \\ 0 & 20 \end{bmatrix} \begin{bmatrix} x' \\ y' \end{bmatrix} + [40 \ \ -70] \begin{bmatrix} 4/5 & -3/5 \\ 3/5 & 4/5 \end{bmatrix} \begin{bmatrix} x' \\ y' \end{bmatrix} - 105 = 0$$

$$-5(x')^2 + 20(y')^2 + -10x' + -80y' - 105 = 0$$

$$-5\left[(x')^2 + 2x'\right] + 20\left[(y')^2 - 4y'\right] - 105 = 0$$

$$-5\left[(x')^2 + 2x' + 1\right] + 20\left[(y')^2 - 4y' + 4\right] - 105 = -5 + 80$$

$$-5(x' + 1)^2 + 20(y' - 2)^2 = 180$$

$$\frac{-(x' + 1)^2}{36} + \frac{(y' - 2)^2}{9} = 1$$

The substitution

$$\begin{bmatrix} x' + 1 \\ y' - 2 \end{bmatrix} = \begin{bmatrix} x'' \\ y'' \end{bmatrix}$$

leads to the conic equation

$$\frac{-(x'')^2}{36} + \frac{(y'')^2}{9} = 1.$$

33. $59x^2 + 24xy + 66y^2 - 170x - 60y - 325 = 0 = [x \ \ y] \begin{bmatrix} 59 & 12 \\ 12 & 66 \end{bmatrix} \begin{bmatrix} x \\ y \end{bmatrix} + [-170 \ \ -60] \begin{bmatrix} x \\ y \end{bmatrix} - 325$

$$0 = \begin{vmatrix} \lambda - 59 & -12 \\ -12 & \lambda - 66 \end{vmatrix} = (\lambda - 59)(\lambda - 66) - (-12)(-12)$$

$$= \lambda^2 - 125\lambda + 3894 - 144$$

$$= \lambda^2 - 125\lambda + 3750 = (\lambda - 50)(\lambda - 75) \quad \text{so} \quad \lambda = 50, 75 \quad (\text{ellipse})$$

$$\lambda_1 = 50 \longrightarrow \begin{bmatrix} -9 & -12 & 0 \\ -12 & -16 & 0 \end{bmatrix} \longrightarrow \begin{bmatrix} 1 & 4/3 & 0 \\ 0 & 0 & 0 \end{bmatrix}$$

Let $x_2 = s$;

then $x_1 + \frac{4}{3}x_2 = 0, \quad i.e. \quad x_1 = -\frac{4}{3}x_2 = -\frac{4}{3}s$

257

so $\begin{bmatrix} x_1 \\ x_2 \end{bmatrix} = \begin{bmatrix} -(4/3)s \\ s \end{bmatrix} = s\begin{bmatrix} -4/3 \\ 1 \end{bmatrix} = \frac{1}{3}s\begin{bmatrix} -4 \\ 3 \end{bmatrix}$

and $(-4,3)/\|(-4,3)\| = (-4,3)/5 = (-\frac{4}{5}, \frac{3}{5})$.

$\lambda_2 = 75 \longrightarrow \begin{bmatrix} 16 & -12 & 0 \\ -12 & 9 & 0 \end{bmatrix} \longrightarrow \begin{bmatrix} 1 & -3/4 & 0 \\ 0 & 0 & 0 \end{bmatrix}$

Let $x_2 = t$;

then $x_1 - \frac{3}{4}x_2 = 0$, i.e. $x_1 = \frac{3}{4}x_2 = \frac{3}{4}t$

so $\begin{bmatrix} x_1 \\ x_2 \end{bmatrix} = \begin{bmatrix} (3/4)t \\ t \end{bmatrix} = t\begin{bmatrix} 3/4 \\ 1 \end{bmatrix} = \frac{1}{4}t\begin{bmatrix} 3 \\ 4 \end{bmatrix}$

and $(3,4)/\|(3,4)\| = (3,4)/5 = (\frac{3}{5}, \frac{4}{5})$.

Note that $\det\begin{bmatrix} 3/5 & -4/5 \\ 4/5 & 3/5 \end{bmatrix} = \frac{9}{25} - -\frac{16}{25} = 1$, indicating a rotation.

The substitution

$$\begin{bmatrix} x \\ y \end{bmatrix} = \begin{bmatrix} 3/5 & -4/5 \\ 4/5 & 3/5 \end{bmatrix}\begin{bmatrix} x' \\ y' \end{bmatrix}$$

leads to the conic equation

$$[x' \quad y']\begin{bmatrix} 75 & 0 \\ 0 & 50 \end{bmatrix}\begin{bmatrix} x' \\ y' \end{bmatrix} + [-170 \quad -60]\begin{bmatrix} 3/5 & -4/5 \\ 4/5 & 3/5 \end{bmatrix}\begin{bmatrix} x' \\ y' \end{bmatrix} - 325 = 0$$

$$75(x')^2 + 50(y')^2 + -150x' + 100y' - 325 = 0$$

$$75[(x')^2 - 2x'] + 50[(y')^2 + 2y'] - 325 = 0$$

$$75[(x')^2 - 2x' + 1] + 50[(y')^2 + 2y' + 1] - 325 = 75 + 50$$

$$75(x' - 1)^2 + 50(y' + 1)^2 - 325 = 125$$

$$75(x' - 1)^2 + 50(y' + 1)^2 = 450$$

$$\frac{(x' - 1)^2}{6} + \frac{(y' + 1)^2}{9} = 1$$

The substitution

$$\begin{bmatrix} x' - 1 \\ y' + 1 \end{bmatrix} = \begin{bmatrix} x'' \\ y'' \end{bmatrix}$$

leads to the conic equation

$$\frac{(x'')^2}{6} + \frac{(y'')^2}{9} = 1.$$

34. (a) $[x \ \ y \ \ z] \begin{bmatrix} 2 & 2 & 0 \\ 2 & -3 & 0 \\ 0 & 0 & 1 \end{bmatrix} \begin{bmatrix} x \\ y \\ z \end{bmatrix} + [0 \ \ -3 \ \ -1] \begin{bmatrix} x \\ y \\ z \end{bmatrix} - 1 = 0$

(b) $[x \ \ y \ \ z] \begin{bmatrix} 12 & -1 & 0 \\ -1 & 1 & -2 \\ 0 & -2 & -1 \end{bmatrix} \begin{bmatrix} x \\ y \\ z \end{bmatrix} + [1 \ \ 1 \ \ 1] \begin{bmatrix} x \\ y \\ z \end{bmatrix} - 6 = 0$

(c) $[x \ \ y \ \ z] \begin{bmatrix} 1 & 0 & 3 \\ 0 & -1 & -1/2 \\ 3 & -1/2 & -1 \end{bmatrix} \begin{bmatrix} x \\ y \\ z \end{bmatrix} + [0 \ \ 16 \ \ -100] \begin{bmatrix} x \\ y \\ z \end{bmatrix} - 8 = 0$

(d) $[x \ \ y \ \ z] \begin{bmatrix} 6 & 3/2 & 2 \\ 3/2 & 0 & 5/2 \\ 2 & 5/2 & 9 \end{bmatrix} \begin{bmatrix} x \\ y \\ z \end{bmatrix} + [-11 \ \ 0 \ \ 17] \begin{bmatrix} x \\ y \\ z \end{bmatrix} = 0$

35. $x^2 - z^2 - 4xy - 4yz - 12x - 3y - 18z + 12 = 0$

$$= [x \ \ y \ \ z] \begin{bmatrix} 1 & -2 & 0 \\ -2 & 0 & -2 \\ 0 & -2 & -1 \end{bmatrix} \begin{bmatrix} x \\ y \\ z \end{bmatrix} + [-12 \ \ -3 \ \ -18] \begin{bmatrix} x \\ y \\ z \end{bmatrix} + 12$$

$$0 = \begin{vmatrix} \lambda - 1 & 2 & 0 \\ 2 & \lambda & 2 \\ 0 & 2 & \lambda + 1 \end{vmatrix} = (\lambda - 1)[\lambda(\lambda + 1) - (2)(2)] - 2[2(\lambda + 1) - (0)(2)]$$

$$= (\lambda - 1)(\lambda^2 + \lambda - 4) - 4(\lambda + 1)$$

$$= (\lambda^3 - 5\lambda + 4) - 4(\lambda + 1)$$

$$= \lambda^3 - 9\lambda = \lambda(\lambda^2 - 9) = \lambda(\lambda - 3)(\lambda + 3) \quad \text{so} \quad \lambda = 0, 3, -3$$

$$\lambda_1 = 0 \longrightarrow \begin{bmatrix} -1 & 2 & 0 & 0 \\ 2 & 0 & 2 & 0 \\ 0 & 2 & 1 & 0 \end{bmatrix} \longrightarrow \begin{bmatrix} 1 & -2 & 0 & 0 \\ 0 & 4 & 2 & 0 \\ 0 & 2 & 1 & 0 \end{bmatrix} \longrightarrow \begin{bmatrix} 1 & 0 & 1 & 0 \\ 0 & 1 & 1/2 & 0 \\ 0 & 0 & 0 & 0 \end{bmatrix}$$

Let $x_3 = r$;

then $x_2 + \frac{1}{2}x_3 = 0$, *i.e.* $x_2 = -\frac{1}{2}x_3 = -\frac{1}{2}r$

and $x_1 + x_3 = 0$, *i.e.* $x_1 = -x_3 = -r$

so $\begin{bmatrix} x_1 \\ x_2 \\ x_3 \end{bmatrix} = \begin{bmatrix} -r \\ -(1/2)r \\ r \end{bmatrix} = r \begin{bmatrix} -1 \\ -1/2 \\ 1 \end{bmatrix} = \frac{1}{2}r \begin{bmatrix} -2 \\ -1 \\ 2 \end{bmatrix}$

and $(-2, -1, 2)/\|(-2, -1, 2)\| = (-2, -1, 2)/3 = (-\frac{2}{3}, -\frac{1}{3}, \frac{2}{3})$.

$$\lambda_2 = 3 \longrightarrow \begin{bmatrix} 2 & 2 & 0 & 0 \\ 2 & 3 & 2 & 0 \\ 0 & 2 & 4 & 0 \end{bmatrix} \longrightarrow \begin{bmatrix} 1 & 1 & 0 & 0 \\ 0 & 1 & 2 & 0 \\ 0 & 2 & 4 & 0 \end{bmatrix} \longrightarrow \begin{bmatrix} 1 & 0 & -2 & 0 \\ 0 & 1 & 2 & 0 \\ 0 & 0 & 0 & 0 \end{bmatrix}$$

Let $x_3 = s$;

then $x_2 + 2x_3 = 0$, i.e. $x_2 = -2x_3 = -2s$

and $x_1 - 2x_3 = 0$, i.e. $x_1 = 2x_3 = 2s$

so $\begin{bmatrix} x_1 \\ x_2 \\ x_3 \end{bmatrix} = \begin{bmatrix} 2s \\ -2s \\ s \end{bmatrix} = s \begin{bmatrix} 2 \\ -2 \\ 1 \end{bmatrix}$

and $(2, -2, 1)/\|(2, -2, 1)\| = (2, -2, 1)/3 = (\frac{2}{3}, -\frac{2}{3}, \frac{1}{3})$.

$$\lambda_3 = -3 \longrightarrow \begin{bmatrix} -4 & 2 & 0 & 0 \\ 2 & -3 & 2 & 0 \\ 0 & 2 & -2 & 0 \end{bmatrix} \longrightarrow \begin{bmatrix} 1 & -1/2 & 0 & 0 \\ 0 & -2 & 2 & 0 \\ 0 & 2 & -2 & 0 \end{bmatrix} \longrightarrow \begin{bmatrix} 1 & 0 & -1/2 & 0 \\ 0 & 1 & -1 & 0 \\ 0 & 0 & 0 & 0 \end{bmatrix}$$

Let $x_3 = t$;

then $x_2 - x_3 = 0$, i.e. $x_2 = x_3 = t$

and $x_1 - \frac{1}{2}x_3 = 0$, i.e. $x_1 = \frac{1}{2}x_3 = \frac{1}{2}t$

so $\begin{bmatrix} x_1 \\ x_2 \\ x_3 \end{bmatrix} = \begin{bmatrix} (1/2)t \\ t \\ t \end{bmatrix} = t \begin{bmatrix} 1/2 \\ 1 \\ 1 \end{bmatrix} = \frac{1}{2}t \begin{bmatrix} 1 \\ 2 \\ 2 \end{bmatrix}$

and $(1, 2, 2)/\|(1, 2, 2)\| = (1, 2, 2)/3 = (\frac{1}{3}, \frac{2}{3}, \frac{2}{3})$.

Note that $\det \begin{bmatrix} -2/3 & 2/3 & 1/3 \\ -1/3 & -2/3 & 2/3 \\ 2/3 & 1/3 & 2/3 \end{bmatrix} = -\frac{2}{3}(-\frac{6}{9}) - \frac{2}{3}(-\frac{6}{9}) + \frac{1}{3}(\frac{3}{9}) = \frac{27}{27} = 1$, indicating a rotation.

The substitution

$$\begin{bmatrix} x \\ y \\ z \end{bmatrix} = \begin{bmatrix} -2/3 & 2/3 & 1/3 \\ -1/3 & -2/3 & 2/3 \\ 2/3 & 1/3 & 2/3 \end{bmatrix} \begin{bmatrix} x' \\ y' \\ z' \end{bmatrix}$$

leads to the quadric equation

$$\begin{bmatrix} x' & y' & z' \end{bmatrix} \begin{bmatrix} 0 & 0 & 0 \\ 0 & 3 & 0 \\ 0 & 0 & -3 \end{bmatrix} \begin{bmatrix} x' \\ y' \\ z' \end{bmatrix} + \begin{bmatrix} -12 & -3 & -18 \end{bmatrix} \begin{bmatrix} -2/3 & 2/3 & 1/3 \\ -1/3 & -2/3 & 2/3 \\ 2/3 & 1/3 & 2/3 \end{bmatrix} \begin{bmatrix} x' \\ y' \\ z' \end{bmatrix} + 12 = 0$$

$$0(x')^2 + 3(y')^2 - 3(z')^2 + -9x' - 12y' - 18z' + 12 = 0$$

$$-9x' + 3[(y')^2 - 4y'] - 3[(z')^2 + 6z'] + 12 = 0$$

$$-9x' + 3[(y')^2 - 4y' + 4] - 3[(z')^2 + 6z' + 9] + 12 = 12 - 27$$

$$-9x' + 3(y' - 2)^2 - 3(z' + 3)^2 = -27$$

$$\frac{x'}{3} - \frac{(y' - 2)^2}{9} + \frac{(z' + 3)^2}{9} = 1$$

(hyperbolic paraboloid)

36. $2xy + 2xz + 2yz + 12x - 14 = 0 = \begin{bmatrix} x & y & z \end{bmatrix} \begin{bmatrix} 0 & 1 & 1 \\ 1 & 0 & 1 \\ 1 & 1 & 0 \end{bmatrix} \begin{bmatrix} x \\ y \\ z \end{bmatrix} + \begin{bmatrix} 12 & 0 & 0 \end{bmatrix} \begin{bmatrix} x \\ y \\ z \end{bmatrix} - 14$

$$0 = \begin{vmatrix} \lambda & -1 & -1 \\ -1 & \lambda & -1 \\ -1 & -1 & \lambda \end{vmatrix} = \lambda(\lambda^2 - 1) + 1(-\lambda - 1) - 1(1 + \lambda)$$

$$= \lambda(\lambda - 1)(\lambda + 1) - 2(\lambda + 1)$$

$$= [\lambda(\lambda - 1) - 2](\lambda + 1)$$

$$= (\lambda^2 - \lambda - 2)(\lambda + 1) = (\lambda - 2)(\lambda + 1)(\lambda + 1) \quad \text{so} \quad \lambda = 2, -1, -1$$

$$\lambda_1 = 2 \longrightarrow \begin{bmatrix} 2 & -1 & -1 & 0 \\ -1 & 2 & -1 & 0 \\ -1 & -1 & 2 & 0 \end{bmatrix} \longrightarrow \begin{bmatrix} 1 & -1/2 & -1/2 & 0 \\ 0 & 3/2 & -3/2 & 0 \\ 0 & -3/2 & 3/2 & 0 \end{bmatrix} \longrightarrow \begin{bmatrix} 1 & 0 & -1 & 0 \\ 0 & 1 & -1 & 0 \\ 0 & 0 & 0 & 0 \end{bmatrix}$$

Let $x_3 = r$;

then $x_2 - x_3 = 0$, i.e. $x_2 = x_3 = r$

and $x_1 - x_3 = 0$, i.e. $x_1 = x_3 = r$

so $\begin{bmatrix} x_1 \\ x_2 \\ x_3 \end{bmatrix} = \begin{bmatrix} r \\ r \\ r \end{bmatrix} = r \begin{bmatrix} 1 \\ 1 \\ 1 \end{bmatrix}$

and $(1,1,1)/\|(1,1,1)\| = (1,1,1)/\sqrt{3} = (\frac{1}{\sqrt{3}} \frac{1}{\sqrt{3}} \frac{1}{\sqrt{3}})$.

$$\lambda_2 = -1 \longrightarrow \begin{bmatrix} -1 & -1 & -1 & 0 \\ -1 & -1 & -1 & 0 \\ -1 & -1 & -1 & 0 \end{bmatrix} \longrightarrow \begin{bmatrix} 1 & 1 & 1 & 0 \\ 0 & 0 & 0 & 0 \\ 0 & 0 & 0 & 0 \end{bmatrix}$$

Let $x_3 = t$ so $x_2 = s$;

then $x_1 + x_2 + x_3 = 0$, i.e. $x_1 = -x_2 - x_3 = -s - t$

so $\begin{bmatrix} x_1 \\ x_2 \\ x_3 \end{bmatrix} = \begin{bmatrix} -s - t \\ s \\ t \end{bmatrix} = \begin{bmatrix} -s \\ s \\ 0 \end{bmatrix} + \begin{bmatrix} -t \\ 0 \\ -t \end{bmatrix} = s \begin{bmatrix} -1 \\ 1 \\ 0 \end{bmatrix} + t \begin{bmatrix} -1 \\ 0 \\ 1 \end{bmatrix}$

$$(-1,0,1) - \frac{(-1,0,1)\cdot(-1,1,0)}{(-1,1,0)\cdot(-1,1,0)}(-1,1,0) = (-1,0,1) - \frac{1}{2}(-1,1,0) = (-\frac{1}{2},-\frac{1}{2},1)$$

$$= -\frac{1}{2}(1,1,-2)$$

and $(-1,1,0)/\|(-1,1,0)\| = (-1,1,0)/\sqrt{2} = (-\frac{1}{\sqrt{2}},\frac{1}{\sqrt{2}},0)$

and $(1,1,-2)/\|(1,1,-2)\| = (1,1,-2)/\sqrt{6} = (\frac{1}{\sqrt{6}},\frac{1}{\sqrt{6}},\frac{-2}{\sqrt{6}})$.

Note that $\det \begin{bmatrix} \frac{1}{\sqrt{3}} & \frac{1}{\sqrt{6}} & -\frac{1}{\sqrt{2}} \\ \frac{1}{\sqrt{3}} & \frac{1}{\sqrt{6}} & \frac{1}{\sqrt{2}} \\ \frac{1}{\sqrt{3}} & -\frac{2}{\sqrt{6}} & 0 \end{bmatrix} = \frac{1}{\sqrt{3}}\left(\frac{2}{\sqrt{12}}\right) - \frac{1}{\sqrt{6}}\left(-\frac{1}{\sqrt{6}}\right) - \frac{1}{\sqrt{2}}\left(\frac{-3}{\sqrt{18}}\right)$

$$= \frac{6}{\sqrt{36}} = 1, \text{indicating a rotation.}$$

The substitution

$$\begin{bmatrix} x \\ y \\ z \end{bmatrix} = \begin{bmatrix} \frac{1}{\sqrt{3}} & \frac{1}{\sqrt{6}} & -\frac{1}{\sqrt{2}} \\ \frac{1}{\sqrt{3}} & \frac{1}{\sqrt{6}} & -\frac{1}{\sqrt{2}} \\ \frac{1}{\sqrt{3}} & -\frac{2}{\sqrt{6}} & 0 \end{bmatrix} \begin{bmatrix} x' \\ y' \\ z' \end{bmatrix}$$

leads to the quadric equation

$$[x'\ y'\ z'] \begin{bmatrix} 2 & 0 & 0 \\ 0 & -1 & 0 \\ 0 & 0 & -1 \end{bmatrix} \begin{bmatrix} x' \\ y' \\ z' \end{bmatrix} + [12\ 0\ 0] \begin{bmatrix} \frac{1}{\sqrt{3}} & \frac{1}{\sqrt{6}} & -\frac{1}{\sqrt{2}} \\ \frac{1}{\sqrt{3}} & \frac{1}{\sqrt{6}} & \frac{1}{\sqrt{2}} \\ \frac{1}{\sqrt{3}} & -\frac{2}{\sqrt{6}} & 0 \end{bmatrix} \begin{bmatrix} x' \\ y' \\ z' \end{bmatrix} - 14 = 0$$

$$2(x')^2 - (y')^2 - (z')^2 + 4\sqrt{3}x' + 2\sqrt{6}y' - 6\sqrt{2}z' - 14 = 0$$

$$2[(x')^2 + 2\sqrt{3}x'] - [(y')^2 - 2\sqrt{6}y'] - [(z')^2 + 6\sqrt{2}z'] - 14 = 0$$

$$2[(x')^2 + 2\sqrt{3}x' + 3] - [(y')^2 - 2\sqrt{6}y' + 6] - [(z')^2 + 6\sqrt{2}z' + 18] - 14 = 6 - 6 - 18$$

$$2(x' + \sqrt{3})^2 - (y' - \sqrt{6})^2 - (z' + 3\sqrt{2})^2 - 14 = 6 - 6 - 18$$

$$2(x' + \sqrt{3})^2 - (y' - \sqrt{6})^2 - (z' + 3\sqrt{2})^2 = -4$$

$$-\frac{(x' + \sqrt{3})^2}{2} + \frac{(y' - \sqrt{6})^2}{4} + \frac{(z' + 3\sqrt{2})^2}{4} = 1$$

(hyperboloid of one sheet)

37. $2x^2 + 2y^2 + 2z^2 - 2xy - 2xz - 2yz + 3x + 3y + 3z = 0 = [x\ \ y\ \ z]\begin{bmatrix} 2 & -1 & -1 \\ -1 & 2 & -1 \\ -1 & -1 & 2 \end{bmatrix}\begin{bmatrix} x \\ y \\ z \end{bmatrix} + [3\ \ 3\ \ 3]\begin{bmatrix} x \\ y \\ z \end{bmatrix}$

$$0 = \begin{vmatrix} \lambda - 2 & 1 & 1 \\ 1 & \lambda - 2 & 1 \\ 1 & 1 & \lambda - 2 \end{vmatrix} = (\lambda - 2)[(\lambda - 2)^2 - 1^2] - 1[(\lambda - 2) - 1] + 1[1 - (\lambda - 2)]$$

$$= (\lambda - 2)(\lambda^2 - 4\lambda + 3) - 2(\lambda - 3)$$

$$= (\lambda - 2)(\lambda - 1)(\lambda - 3) - 2(\lambda - 3)$$

$$= [(\lambda - 2)(\lambda - 1) - 2](\lambda - 3)$$

$$= (\lambda^2 - 3\lambda)(\lambda - 3) = \lambda(\lambda - 3)(\lambda - 3) \quad \text{so} \quad \lambda = 0, 3, 3$$

$$\lambda_1 = 0 \longrightarrow \begin{bmatrix} -2 & 1 & 1 & 0 \\ 1 & -2 & 1 & 0 \\ 1 & 1 & -2 & 0 \end{bmatrix} \longrightarrow \begin{bmatrix} 1 & -1/2 & -1/2 & 0 \\ 0 & -3/2 & 3/2 & 0 \\ 0 & 3/2 & -3/2 & 0 \end{bmatrix} \longrightarrow \begin{bmatrix} 1 & 0 & -1 & 0 \\ 0 & 1 & -1 & 0 \\ 0 & 0 & 0 & 0 \end{bmatrix}$$

Let $x_3 = r$;

then $x_2 - x_3 = 0$, *i.e.* $x_2 = x_3 = r$

and $x_1 - x_3 = 0$, *i.e.* $x_1 = x_3 = r$

so $\begin{bmatrix} x_1 \\ x_2 \\ x_3 \end{bmatrix} = \begin{bmatrix} r \\ r \\ r \end{bmatrix} = r \begin{bmatrix} 1 \\ 1 \\ 1 \end{bmatrix}$

and $(1,1,1)/\|(1,1,1)\| = (1,1,1)/\sqrt{3} = (\frac{1}{\sqrt{3}}, \frac{1}{\sqrt{3}}, \frac{1}{\sqrt{3}})$.

$$\lambda_2 = 3 \longrightarrow \begin{bmatrix} 1 & 1 & 1 & 0 \\ 1 & 1 & 1 & 0 \\ 1 & 1 & 1 & 0 \end{bmatrix} \longrightarrow \begin{bmatrix} 1 & 1 & 1 & 0 \\ 0 & 0 & 0 & 0 \\ 0 & 0 & 0 & 0 \end{bmatrix}$$

Let $x_3 = t$ *and* $x_2 = s$;

then $x_1 + x_2 + x_3 = 0$, *i.e.* $x_1 = -x_2 - x_3 = -s - t$

so $\begin{bmatrix} x_1 \\ x_2 \\ x_3 \end{bmatrix} = \begin{bmatrix} -s - t \\ s \\ t \end{bmatrix} = \begin{bmatrix} -s \\ s \\ 0 \end{bmatrix} + \begin{bmatrix} -t \\ 0 \\ t \end{bmatrix} = s \begin{bmatrix} -1 \\ 1 \\ 0 \end{bmatrix} + t \begin{bmatrix} -1 \\ 0 \\ 1 \end{bmatrix}$

$(-1,0,1) - \frac{(-1,0,1) \cdot (-1,1,0)}{(-1,1,0) \cdot (-1,1,0)}(-1,1,0) = (-1,0,1) - \frac{1}{2}(-1,1,0) = (-\frac{1}{2}, -\frac{1}{2}, 1) = -\frac{1}{2}(1,1,-2)$

and $(-1,1,0)/\|(-1,1,0)\| = (-1,1,0)/\sqrt{2} = (-\frac{1}{\sqrt{2}}, \frac{1}{\sqrt{2}}, 0)$

and $(1,1,-2)/\|(1,1,-2)\| = (1,1,-2)/\sqrt{6} = (\frac{1}{\sqrt{6}}, \frac{1}{\sqrt{6}}, \frac{-2}{\sqrt{6}})$.

Note that $\det \begin{bmatrix} \frac{1}{\sqrt{3}} & \frac{1}{\sqrt{6}} & -\frac{1}{\sqrt{2}} \\ \frac{1}{\sqrt{3}} & \frac{1}{\sqrt{6}} & \frac{1}{\sqrt{2}} \\ \frac{1}{\sqrt{3}} & -\frac{2}{\sqrt{6}} & 0 \end{bmatrix} = \frac{1}{\sqrt{3}}\left(\frac{2}{\sqrt{12}}\right) - \frac{1}{\sqrt{6}}\left(\frac{-1}{\sqrt{6}}\right) - \frac{1}{\sqrt{2}}\left(\frac{-3}{\sqrt{18}}\right)$

$$= \frac{6}{\sqrt{36}} = 1, \quad \text{indicating a rotation.}$$

The substitution

$$\begin{bmatrix} x \\ y \\ z \end{bmatrix} = \begin{bmatrix} \frac{1}{\sqrt{3}} & \frac{1}{\sqrt{6}} & -\frac{1}{\sqrt{2}} \\ \frac{1}{\sqrt{3}} & \frac{1}{\sqrt{6}} & \frac{1}{\sqrt{2}} \\ \frac{1}{\sqrt{3}} & -\frac{2}{\sqrt{6}} & 0 \end{bmatrix} \begin{bmatrix} x' \\ y' \\ z' \end{bmatrix}$$

leads to the quadric equation

$$[x' \ \ y' \ \ z']\begin{bmatrix} 0 & 0 & 0 \\ 0 & 3 & 0 \\ 0 & 0 & 3 \end{bmatrix}\begin{bmatrix} x' \\ y' \\ z' \end{bmatrix} + [3 \ \ 3 \ \ 3]\begin{bmatrix} \frac{1}{\sqrt{3}} & \frac{1}{\sqrt{6}} & -\frac{1}{\sqrt{2}} \\ \frac{1}{\sqrt{3}} & \frac{1}{\sqrt{6}} & \frac{1}{\sqrt{2}} \\ \frac{1}{\sqrt{3}} & -\frac{2}{\sqrt{6}} & 0 \end{bmatrix}\begin{bmatrix} x' \\ y' \\ z' \end{bmatrix} = 0$$

$$0(x')^2 + 3(y')^2 + 3(z')^2 + 3\sqrt{3}x' + 0y' + 0z' = 0$$

$$3\sqrt{3}x' + 3(y')^2 + 3(z')^2 = 0$$

$$x' + \frac{(y')^2}{\sqrt{3}} + \frac{(z')^2}{\sqrt{3}} = 0 \quad \text{(elliptic paraboloid).}$$

38. $-8xy + 6yz + 12x + 20y + 16z = 0 = [x \ \ y \ \ z]\begin{bmatrix} 0 & -4 & 0 \\ -4 & 0 & 3 \\ 0 & 3 & 0 \end{bmatrix}\begin{bmatrix} x \\ y \\ z \end{bmatrix} + [12 \ \ 20 \ \ 16]\begin{bmatrix} x \\ y \\ z \end{bmatrix}$

$$0 = \begin{vmatrix} \lambda & 4 & 0 \\ 4 & \lambda & -3 \\ 0 & -3 & \lambda \end{vmatrix} = \lambda(\lambda^2 - 9) - 4(4\lambda)$$

$$= \lambda(\lambda^2 - 9 - 16) = \lambda(\lambda^2 - 25) = \lambda(\lambda - 5)(\lambda + 5) \quad \text{so} \quad \lambda = 0, 5, -5$$

$$\lambda_1 = 0 \longrightarrow \begin{bmatrix} 0 & 4 & 0 & 0 \\ 4 & 0 & -3 & 0 \\ 0 & -3 & 0 & 0 \end{bmatrix} \longrightarrow \begin{bmatrix} 4 & 0 & -3 & 0 \\ 0 & 4 & 0 & 0 \\ 0 & -3 & 0 & 0 \end{bmatrix} \longrightarrow \begin{bmatrix} 1 & 0 & -3/4 & 0 \\ 0 & 1 & 0 & 0 \\ 0 & 0 & 0 & 0 \end{bmatrix}$$

Let $x_3 = r$;

then $x_1 - \frac{3}{4}x_3 = 0$, *i.e.* $x_1 = \frac{3}{4}x_3 = \frac{3}{4}r$

and $x_2 = 0$

so $\begin{bmatrix} x_1 \\ x_2 \\ x_3 \end{bmatrix} = \begin{bmatrix} (3/4)r \\ 0 \\ r \end{bmatrix} = r\begin{bmatrix} 3/4 \\ 0 \\ 1 \end{bmatrix} = \frac{1}{4}r\begin{bmatrix} 3 \\ 0 \\ 4 \end{bmatrix}$

and $(3,0,4)/\|(3,0,4)\| = (3,0,4)/5 = (\frac{3}{5},0,\frac{4}{5})$.

$$\lambda_2 = 5 \longrightarrow \begin{bmatrix} 5 & 4 & 0 & 0 \\ 4 & 5 & -3 & 0 \\ 0 & -3 & 5 & 0 \end{bmatrix} \longrightarrow \begin{bmatrix} 1 & 4/5 & 0 & 0 \\ 0 & 9/5 & -3 & 0 \\ 0 & -3 & 5 & 0 \end{bmatrix} \longrightarrow \begin{bmatrix} 1 & 0 & 4/3 & 0 \\ 0 & 1 & -5/3 & 0 \\ 0 & 0 & 0 & 0 \end{bmatrix}$$

Let $x_3 = s$;

then $x_2 - \frac{5}{3}x_3 = 0$, i.e. $x_2 = \frac{5}{3}x_3 = \frac{5}{3}s$

and $x_1 + \frac{4}{3}x_3 = 0$, i.e. $x_1 = -\frac{4}{3}x_3 = -\frac{4}{3}s$

so $\begin{bmatrix} x_1 \\ x_2 \\ x_3 \end{bmatrix} = \begin{bmatrix} -(4/3)s \\ (5/3)s \\ s \end{bmatrix} = s \begin{bmatrix} -4/3 \\ 5/3 \\ 1 \end{bmatrix} = \frac{1}{3}s \begin{bmatrix} -4 \\ 5 \\ 3 \end{bmatrix}$

and $(-4,5,3)/\|(-4,5,3)\| = (-4,5,3)/\sqrt{50} = (\frac{-4}{\sqrt{50}}, \frac{5}{\sqrt{50}}, \frac{3}{\sqrt{50}})$.

$$\lambda_3 = -5 \longrightarrow \begin{bmatrix} -5 & 4 & 0 & 0 \\ 4 & -5 & -3 & 0 \\ 0 & -3 & -5 & 0 \end{bmatrix} \longrightarrow \begin{bmatrix} 1 & -4/5 & 0 & 0 \\ 0 & -9/5 & -3 & 0 \\ 0 & -3 & -5 & 0 \end{bmatrix} \longrightarrow \begin{bmatrix} 1 & 0 & 4/3 & 0 \\ 0 & 1 & 5/3 & 0 \\ 0 & 0 & 0 & 0 \end{bmatrix}$$

Let $x_3 = t$;

then $x_2 + \frac{5}{3}x_3 = 0$, i.e. $x_2 = -\frac{5}{3}x_3 = -\frac{5}{3}t$

and $x_1 + \frac{4}{3}x_3 = 0$, i.e. $x_1 = -\frac{4}{3}x_3 = -\frac{4}{3}t$

so $\begin{bmatrix} x_1 \\ x_2 \\ x_3 \end{bmatrix} = \begin{bmatrix} -(4/3)t \\ -(5/3)t \\ t \end{bmatrix} = t \begin{bmatrix} -4/3 \\ -5/3 \\ 1 \end{bmatrix} = \frac{1}{3}t \begin{bmatrix} -4 \\ -5 \\ 3 \end{bmatrix}$

and $(-4,-5,3)/\|(-4,-5,3)\| = (-4,-5,3)/\sqrt{50} = (\frac{-4}{\sqrt{50}}, \frac{-5}{\sqrt{50}}, \frac{3}{\sqrt{50}})$.

Note that $\det \begin{bmatrix} 3/5 & -4/\sqrt{50} & -4/\sqrt{50} \\ 0 & 5/\sqrt{50} & -5/\sqrt{50} \\ 4/5 & 3/\sqrt{50} & 3/\sqrt{50} \end{bmatrix} = \frac{3}{5}(\frac{30}{50}) + \frac{4}{5}(\frac{40}{50}) = \frac{9}{25} + \frac{16}{25} = 1$, indicating a rotation.

The substitution

$$\begin{bmatrix} x \\ y \\ z \end{bmatrix} = \begin{bmatrix} 3/5 & -4/\sqrt{50} & -4/\sqrt{50} \\ 0 & 5/\sqrt{50} & -5/\sqrt{50} \\ 4/5 & 3/\sqrt{50} & 3/\sqrt{50} \end{bmatrix} \begin{bmatrix} x' \\ y' \\ z' \end{bmatrix}$$

leads to the quadric equation

$$[x' \ y' \ z'] \begin{bmatrix} 0 & 0 & 0 \\ 0 & 5 & 0 \\ 0 & 0 & -5 \end{bmatrix} \begin{bmatrix} x' \\ y' \\ z' \end{bmatrix} + [12 \ 20 \ 16] \begin{bmatrix} 3/5 & -4/\sqrt{50} & -4/\sqrt{50} \\ 0 & 5/\sqrt{50} & -5/\sqrt{50} \\ 4/5 & 3/\sqrt{50} & 3/\sqrt{50} \end{bmatrix} \begin{bmatrix} x' \\ y' \\ z' \end{bmatrix} = 0$$

$$0(x')^2 + 5(y')^2 - 5(z')^2 + 20x' + \frac{100}{\sqrt{50}}y' + \frac{-100}{\sqrt{50}}z' = 0$$

$$(y')^2 - (z')^2 + 4x' + \frac{20}{\sqrt{50}}y' - \frac{20}{\sqrt{50}}z' = 0$$

$$(y')^2 - (z')^2 + 4x' + 2\sqrt{2}y' - 2\sqrt{2}z' = 0$$

$$4x' + [(y')^2 + 2\sqrt{2}y'] - [(z')^2 + 2\sqrt{2}z'] = 0$$

$$4x' + [(y')^2 + 2\sqrt{2}y' + 2] - [(z')^2 + 2\sqrt{2}z' + 2] = 0$$

$$4x' + (y' + \sqrt{2})^2 - (z' + \sqrt{2})^2 = 0$$

$$x' + \frac{(y' + \sqrt{2})^2}{4} - \frac{(z' + \sqrt{2})^2}{4} = 0$$

The substitution

$$\begin{bmatrix} x' \\ y' + \sqrt{2} \\ z' + \sqrt{2} \end{bmatrix} = \begin{bmatrix} x'' \\ y'' \\ z'' \end{bmatrix}$$

leads to the quadric equation

$$x'' + \frac{(y'')^2}{4} - \frac{(z'')^2}{4} = 0 \quad (\textit{hyperbolic paraboloid}).$$

39. $3y^2 + 4xz + 4x + 4z + 22 = 0 = \begin{bmatrix} x & y & z \end{bmatrix} \begin{bmatrix} 0 & 0 & 2 \\ 0 & 3 & 0 \\ 2 & 0 & 0 \end{bmatrix} \begin{bmatrix} x \\ y \\ z \end{bmatrix} + \begin{bmatrix} 4 & 0 & 4 \end{bmatrix} \begin{bmatrix} x \\ y \\ z \end{bmatrix} + 22$

$$0 = \begin{vmatrix} \lambda & 0 & -2 \\ 0 & \lambda - 3 & 0 \\ -2 & 0 & \lambda \end{vmatrix} = \lambda(\lambda - 3)(\lambda) - 2(2)(\lambda - 3)$$

$$= (\lambda^2 - 4)(\lambda - 3) = (\lambda + 2)(\lambda - 2)(\lambda - 3) \quad \text{so} \quad \lambda = -2, 2, 3$$

$\lambda_1 = -2 \longrightarrow \begin{bmatrix} -2 & 0 & -2 & 0 \\ 0 & -5 & 0 & 0 \\ -2 & 0 & -2 & 0 \end{bmatrix} \longrightarrow \begin{bmatrix} 1 & 0 & 1 & 0 \\ 0 & -5 & 0 & 0 \\ 0 & 0 & 0 & 0 \end{bmatrix} \longrightarrow \begin{bmatrix} 1 & 0 & 1 & 0 \\ 0 & 1 & 0 & 0 \\ 0 & 0 & 0 & 0 \end{bmatrix}$

Let $x_3 = r$;

then $x_1 + x_3 = 0$, i.e. $x_1 = -x_3 = -r$

and $x_2 = 0$

so $\begin{bmatrix} x_1 \\ x_2 \\ x_3 \end{bmatrix} = \begin{bmatrix} -r \\ 0 \\ r \end{bmatrix} = r \begin{bmatrix} -1 \\ 0 \\ 1 \end{bmatrix}$

and $(-1, 0, 1)/\|(-1, 0, 1)\| = (-1, 0, 1)/\sqrt{2} = (\frac{-1}{\sqrt{2}}, 0, \frac{1}{\sqrt{2}})$.

$$\lambda_2 = 2 \longrightarrow \begin{bmatrix} 2 & 0 & -2 & 0 \\ 0 & -1 & 0 & 0 \\ -2 & 0 & 2 & 0 \end{bmatrix} \longrightarrow \begin{bmatrix} 1 & 0 & -1 & 0 \\ 0 & -1 & 0 & 0 \\ 0 & 0 & 0 & 0 \end{bmatrix} \longrightarrow \begin{bmatrix} 1 & 0 & -1 & 0 \\ 0 & 1 & 0 & 0 \\ 0 & 0 & 0 & 0 \end{bmatrix}$$

Let $x_3 = s$;

then $x_1 - x_3 = 0$, $\quad i.e. \quad x_1 = x_3 = s$

and $x_2 = 0$

$$\text{so} \quad \begin{bmatrix} x_1 \\ x_2 \\ x_3 \end{bmatrix} = \begin{bmatrix} s \\ 0 \\ s \end{bmatrix} = s \begin{bmatrix} 1 \\ 0 \\ 1 \end{bmatrix}$$

and $(1,0,1)/\|(1,0,1)\| = (1,0,1)/\sqrt{2} = (\frac{1}{\sqrt{2}}, 0, \frac{1}{\sqrt{2}})$.

$$\lambda_3 = 3 \longrightarrow \begin{bmatrix} 3 & 0 & -2 & 0 \\ 0 & 0 & 0 & 0 \\ -2 & 0 & 3 & 0 \end{bmatrix} \longrightarrow \begin{bmatrix} 1 & 0 & -2/3 & 0 \\ 0 & 0 & 0 & 0 \\ 0 & 0 & 5/3 & 0 \end{bmatrix} \longrightarrow \begin{bmatrix} 1 & 0 & -2/3 & 0 \\ 0 & 0 & 5/3 & 0 \\ 0 & 0 & 0 & 0 \end{bmatrix} \longrightarrow \begin{bmatrix} 1 & 0 & 0 & 0 \\ 0 & 0 & 1 & 0 \\ 0 & 0 & 0 & 0 \end{bmatrix}$$

Let $x_2 = t$;

then $x_1 = 0$ $\quad$ and $\quad$ $x_3 = 0$

$$\text{so} \quad \begin{bmatrix} x_1 \\ x_2 \\ x_3 \end{bmatrix} = \begin{bmatrix} 0 \\ t \\ 0 \end{bmatrix} = t \begin{bmatrix} 0 \\ 1 \\ 0 \end{bmatrix}.$$

Note that $\det \begin{bmatrix} -1/\sqrt{2} & 1/\sqrt{2} & 0 \\ 0 & 0 & 1 \\ 1/\sqrt{2} & 1/\sqrt{2} & 0 \end{bmatrix} = -1 \left[\left(\frac{-1}{\sqrt{2}} \right) \left(\frac{1}{\sqrt{2}} \right) - \left(\frac{1}{\sqrt{2}} \right) \left(\frac{1}{\sqrt{2}} \right) \right]$

$$= -\left[-\frac{1}{2} - \frac{1}{2} \right] = -(-1) = 1, \quad \text{indicating a rotation.}$$

The substitution

$$\begin{bmatrix} x \\ y \\ z \end{bmatrix} = \begin{bmatrix} -1/\sqrt{2} & 1/\sqrt{2} & 0 \\ 0 & 0 & 1 \\ 1/\sqrt{2} & 1/\sqrt{2} & 0 \end{bmatrix} \begin{bmatrix} x' \\ y' \\ z' \end{bmatrix}$$

leads to the quadric equation

$$\begin{bmatrix} x' & y' & z' \end{bmatrix} \begin{bmatrix} -2 & 0 & 0 \\ 0 & 2 & 0 \\ 0 & 0 & 3 \end{bmatrix} \begin{bmatrix} x' \\ y' \\ z' \end{bmatrix} + \begin{bmatrix} 4 & 0 & 4 \end{bmatrix} \begin{bmatrix} -1/\sqrt{2} & 1/\sqrt{2} & 0 \\ 0 & 0 & 1 \\ 1/\sqrt{2} & 1/\sqrt{2} & 0 \end{bmatrix} + 22 = 0$$

$$-2(x')^2 + 2(y')^2 + 3(z')^2 + 0x' + \frac{8}{\sqrt{2}}y' + 0z' + 22 = 0$$

$$-2(x')^2 + [2(y')^2 + 4\sqrt{2}y'] + 3(z')^2 + 22 = 0$$

267

$$-2(x')^2 + 2\left[(y')^2 + 2\sqrt{2}y'\right] + 3(z')^2 + 22 = 0$$

$$-2(x')^2 + 2\left[(y')^2 + 2\sqrt{2}y' + 2\right] + 3(z')^2 + 22 = 4$$

$$-2(x')^2 + 2(y' + \sqrt{2})^2 + 3(z')^2 = -18$$

$$\frac{(x')^2}{9} - \frac{(y' + \sqrt{2})^2}{9} - \frac{(z')^2}{6} = 1$$

The substitution

$$\begin{bmatrix} x' \\ y' + \sqrt{2} \\ z' \end{bmatrix} = \begin{bmatrix} x'' \\ y'' \\ z'' \end{bmatrix}$$

leads to the quadric equation

$$\frac{(x'')^2}{9} - \frac{(y'')^2}{9} - \frac{(z'')^2}{6} = 1 \quad (\textit{hyperboloid of two sheets}).$$

40. $14x^2 + 14y^2 + 17z^2 - 8xy - 4xz - 4yz + 36x + 36y + 18z + 9 = 0$

$$= \begin{bmatrix} x & y & z \end{bmatrix} \begin{bmatrix} 14 & -4 & -2 \\ -4 & 14 & -2 \\ -2 & -2 & 17 \end{bmatrix} \begin{bmatrix} x \\ y \\ z \end{bmatrix} + \begin{bmatrix} 36 & 36 & 18 \end{bmatrix} \begin{bmatrix} x \\ y \\ z \end{bmatrix} + 9$$

$$0 = \begin{vmatrix} \lambda - 14 & 4 & 2 \\ 4 & \lambda - 14 & 2 \\ 2 & 2 & \lambda - 17 \end{vmatrix} = (\lambda - 14)\left[(\lambda - 14)(\lambda - 17) - (2)(2)\right]$$

$$- 4\left[4(\lambda - 17) - (2)(2)\right] + 2\left[(4)(2) - (2)(\lambda - 14)\right]$$

$$= (\lambda - 14)(\lambda^2 - 31\lambda + 234) - 4(4\lambda - 72) + 2(-2\lambda + 36)$$

$$= (\lambda - 14)(\lambda - 13)(\lambda - 18) - 16(\lambda - 18) + -4(\lambda - 18)$$

$$= \left[(\lambda - 14)(\lambda - 13) - 16 - 4\right](\lambda - 18)$$

$$= (\lambda^2 - 27\lambda + 162)(\lambda - 18)$$

$$= (\lambda - 9)(\lambda - 18)(\lambda - 18) \quad \text{so} \quad \lambda = 9, 18, 18$$

$$\lambda_1 = 9 \longrightarrow \begin{bmatrix} -5 & 4 & 2 & 0 \\ 4 & -5 & 2 & 0 \\ 2 & 2 & -8 & 0 \end{bmatrix} \longrightarrow \begin{bmatrix} 1 & -4/5 & -2/5 & 0 \\ 0 & -9/5 & 18/5 & 0 \\ 0 & 18/5 & -36/5 & 0 \end{bmatrix} \longrightarrow \begin{bmatrix} 1 & 0 & -2 & 0 \\ 0 & 1 & -2 & 0 \\ 0 & 0 & 0 & 0 \end{bmatrix}$$

Let $x_3 = r$;

then $x_2 - 2x_3 = 0$, i.e. $x_2 = 2x_3 = 2r$

and $x_1 - 2x_3 = 0$, i.e. $x_1 = 2x_3 = 2r$

so $\begin{bmatrix} x_1 \\ x_2 \\ x_3 \end{bmatrix} = \begin{bmatrix} 2r \\ 2r \\ r \end{bmatrix} = r \begin{bmatrix} 2 \\ 2 \\ 1 \end{bmatrix}$

and $(2,2,1)/\|(2,2,1)\| = (2,2,1)/3 = \left(\frac{2}{3}, \frac{2}{3}, \frac{1}{3}\right)$

$\lambda_2 = 18 \longrightarrow \begin{bmatrix} 4 & 4 & 2 & 0 \\ 4 & 4 & 2 & 0 \\ 2 & 2 & 1 & 0 \end{bmatrix} \longrightarrow \begin{bmatrix} 1 & 1 & 1/2 & 0 \\ 0 & 0 & 0 & 0 \\ 0 & 0 & 0 & 0 \end{bmatrix}$

Let $x_3 = t$ and $x_2 = s$;

then $x_1 + x_2 + \frac{1}{2}x_3 = 0$, i.e. $x_1 = -x_2 - \frac{1}{2}x_3 = -s - \frac{1}{2}t$

so $\begin{bmatrix} x_1 \\ x_2 \\ x_3 \end{bmatrix} = \begin{bmatrix} -s - (1/2)t \\ s \\ t \end{bmatrix} = \begin{bmatrix} -s \\ s \\ 0 \end{bmatrix} + \begin{bmatrix} -(1/2)t \\ t \\ t \end{bmatrix}$

$= s \begin{bmatrix} -1 \\ 1 \\ 0 \end{bmatrix} + t \begin{bmatrix} -1/2 \\ 0 \\ 1 \end{bmatrix} = s \begin{bmatrix} -1 \\ 1 \\ 0 \end{bmatrix} + \frac{1}{2}t \begin{bmatrix} -1 \\ 0 \\ 2 \end{bmatrix}$

$(-1,0,2) - \dfrac{(-1,0,2) \cdot (-1,1,0)}{(-1,1,0 \cdot (-1,1,0)}(-1,1,0) = (-1,0,2) - \frac{1}{2}(-1,1,0)$

$= \left(-\frac{1}{2}, -\frac{1}{2}, 2\right) = -\frac{1}{2}(1,1,-4)$

and $(-1,1,0)/\|(-1,1,0)\| = (-1,1,0)/\sqrt{2} = \left(\frac{-1}{\sqrt{2}}, \frac{1}{\sqrt{2}}, 0\right)$

and $(1,1,-4)/\|(1,1,-4)\| = (1,1,-4)/\sqrt{18} = \left(\frac{1}{\sqrt{18}}, \frac{1}{\sqrt{18}}, \frac{-4}{\sqrt{18}}\right)$

Note that $\det \begin{bmatrix} 2/3 & 1/\sqrt{18} & -1/\sqrt{2} \\ 2/3 & 1/\sqrt{18} & 1/\sqrt{2} \\ 1/3 & -4/\sqrt{18} & 0 \end{bmatrix} = \left(\frac{2}{3}\right)\left(\frac{4}{\sqrt{36}}\right) - \left(\frac{1}{\sqrt{18}}\right)\left(\frac{-1}{3\sqrt{2}}\right) + \left(\frac{-1}{\sqrt{2}}\right)\left(\frac{-3}{\sqrt{18}}\right)$

$= \frac{8}{3\sqrt{36}} + \frac{1}{3\sqrt{36}} + \frac{3}{\sqrt{36}}$

$= \frac{18}{3\sqrt{36}} = 1$, indicating a rotation.

The substitution

$$\begin{bmatrix} x \\ y \\ z \end{bmatrix} = \begin{bmatrix} 2/3 & 1/\sqrt{18} & -1/\sqrt{2} \\ 2/3 & 1/\sqrt{18} & 1/\sqrt{2} \\ 1/3 & -4/\sqrt{18} & 0 \end{bmatrix} \begin{bmatrix} x' \\ y' \\ z' \end{bmatrix}$$

leads to the quadric equation

$$[x' \quad y' \quad z'] \begin{bmatrix} 9 & 0 & 0 \\ 0 & 18 & 0 \\ 0 & 0 & 18 \end{bmatrix} \begin{bmatrix} x' \\ y' \\ z' \end{bmatrix} + [36 \quad 36 \quad 18] \begin{bmatrix} 2/3 & 1/\sqrt{18} & -1/\sqrt{2} \\ 2/3 & 1/\sqrt{18} & 1/\sqrt{2} \\ 1/3 & -4/\sqrt{18} & 0 \end{bmatrix} \begin{bmatrix} x' \\ y' \\ z' \end{bmatrix} + 9 = 0$$

$$9(x')^2 + 18(y')^2 + 18(z')^2 + 54x' + 0y' + 0z' + 9 = 0$$

$$9\big[(x')^2 + 6x'\big] + 18(y')^2 + 18(z')^2 + 9 = 0$$

$$9\big[(x')^2 + 6x' + 9\big] + 18(y')^2 + 18(z')^2 + 9 = 81$$

$$9(x' + 3)^2 + 18(y')^2 + 18(z')^2 = 72$$

$$\frac{(x'+3)^2}{8} + \frac{(y')^2}{4} + \frac{(z')^2}{4} = 1$$

The substitution

$$\begin{bmatrix} x'+3 \\ y \\ z \end{bmatrix} = \begin{bmatrix} x'' \\ y'' \\ z'' \end{bmatrix}$$

leads to the quadric equation

$$\frac{(x'')^2}{8} + \frac{(y'')^2}{4} + \frac{(z'')^2}{4} = 1 \quad (ellipsoid)$$

SECTION 9.8 *COMPARISON OF PROCEDURES FOR SOLVING LINEAR SYTEMS*

41. (a)   11 additions and   17 multiplications

 (b)   1,225 additions and   1,345 multiplications

 (c)   5,500 additions and   5,825 multiplications

 (d)   9,044,750 additions and   9,089,900 multiplications

42. (a)   12 additions and   27 multiplications

 (b)   2,940 additions and   3,375 multiplications

 (c)   14,400 additions and   15,625 multiplications

 (d)   26,820,300 additions and   27,000,000 multiplications

43. (a)   18 additions and   36 multiplications

   (b)   3,150 additions and   3,600 multiplications

   (c)   15,000 additions and   16,250 multiplications

   (d)   26,910,000 additions and   27,090,000 multiplications

44. (a)   5 additions and   10 multiplications

   (b)   1,015 additions and   1,134 multiplications

   (c)   4,900 additions and   5,224 multiplications

   (d)   8,955,050 additions and   9,000,199 multiplications

45. (a)   20 additions and   43 multiplications

   (b)   16,240 additions and   18,159 multiplications

   (c)   127,400 additions and   135,849 multiplications

   (d)   2,695,470,050 additions and 2,709,060,199 multiplications

SECTION 9.9 LU-DECOMPOSITIONS

46.

$$\begin{bmatrix} 4 & 20 \\ 3 & 2 \end{bmatrix} \longrightarrow \begin{bmatrix} 1 & 5 \\ 3 & 2 \end{bmatrix} \longrightarrow \begin{bmatrix} 1 & 5 \\ 0 & -13 \end{bmatrix} \longrightarrow \begin{bmatrix} 1 & 5 \\ 0 & 1 \end{bmatrix} = U$$

$$\begin{bmatrix} 1 & 0 \\ 0 & 1 \end{bmatrix} \quad \begin{bmatrix} 4 & 0 \\ 0 & 1 \end{bmatrix} \quad \begin{bmatrix} 4 & 0 \\ 3 & 1 \end{bmatrix} \quad \begin{bmatrix} 4 & 0 \\ 3 & -13 \end{bmatrix} = L$$

$$\begin{bmatrix} 4 & 0 & 4 \\ 3 & -13 & -10 \end{bmatrix} \quad \begin{matrix} 4y_1 = 4 \quad so \quad y_1 = 1 \\ 3y_1 - 13y_2 = -10 \quad so \quad 3 - 13y_2 = -10, \ -13y_2 = -13, \ y_2 = 1 \end{matrix}$$

$$\begin{bmatrix} 1 & 5 & 1 \\ 0 & 1 & 1 \end{bmatrix} \quad \begin{matrix} x_1 + 5x_2 = 1 \quad so \quad x_1 + 5 = 1, \ x_1 = -4 \\ x_2 = 1 \end{matrix}$$

47.

$$\begin{bmatrix} -3 & 6 \\ -2 & 1 \end{bmatrix} \longrightarrow \begin{bmatrix} 1 & -2 \\ -2 & 1 \end{bmatrix} \longrightarrow \begin{bmatrix} 1 & -2 \\ 0 & -3 \end{bmatrix} \longrightarrow \begin{bmatrix} 1 & -2 \\ 0 & 1 \end{bmatrix} = U$$

$$\begin{bmatrix} 1 & 0 \\ 0 & 1 \end{bmatrix} \quad \begin{bmatrix} -3 & 0 \\ 0 & 1 \end{bmatrix} \quad \begin{bmatrix} -3 & 0 \\ -2 & 1 \end{bmatrix} \quad \begin{bmatrix} -3 & 0 \\ -2 & -3 \end{bmatrix} = L$$

$$\begin{bmatrix} -3 & 0 & 3 \\ -2 & -3 & -4 \end{bmatrix} \quad \begin{array}{l} -3y_1 = 3 \quad \text{so} \quad y_1 = -1 \\ -2y_1 - 3y_2 = -4 \quad \text{so} \quad 2 - 3y_2 = -4, \ -3y_2 = -6, \ y_2 = 2 \end{array}$$

$$\begin{bmatrix} 1 & -2 & -1 \\ 0 & 1 & 2 \end{bmatrix} \quad \begin{array}{l} x_1 - 2x_2 = -1 \quad \text{so} \quad x_1 - 4 = -1, \ x_1 = 3 \\ x_2 = 2 \end{array}$$

48.

$$\begin{bmatrix} 1 & 2 & -1 \\ 2 & 6 & -6 \\ 3 & 7 & -1 \end{bmatrix} \longrightarrow \begin{bmatrix} 1 & 2 & -1 \\ 0 & 2 & -4 \\ 0 & 1 & 2 \end{bmatrix} \longrightarrow \begin{bmatrix} 1 & 2 & -1 \\ 0 & 1 & -2 \\ 0 & 0 & 4 \end{bmatrix} \longrightarrow \begin{bmatrix} 1 & 2 & -1 \\ 0 & 1 & -2 \\ 0 & 0 & 1 \end{bmatrix} = U$$

$$\begin{bmatrix} 1 & 0 & 0 \\ 0 & 1 & 0 \\ 0 & 0 & 1 \end{bmatrix} \quad \begin{bmatrix} 1 & 0 & 0 \\ 2 & 1 & 0 \\ 3 & 0 & 1 \end{bmatrix} \quad \begin{bmatrix} 1 & 0 & 0 \\ 2 & 2 & 0 \\ 3 & 1 & 1 \end{bmatrix} \quad \begin{bmatrix} 1 & 0 & 0 \\ 2 & 2 & 0 \\ 3 & 1 & 4 \end{bmatrix} = L$$

$$\begin{bmatrix} 1 & 0 & 0 & 2 \\ 2 & 2 & 0 & -4 \\ 3 & 1 & 4 & 14 \end{bmatrix} \quad \begin{array}{l} y_1 = 2 \\ 2y_1 + 2y_2 = -4 \quad \text{so} \quad 4 + 2y_2 = -4, \ 2y_2 = -8, \ y_2 = -4 \\ 3y_1 + y_2 + 4y_3 = 14 \quad \text{so} \quad 6 + -4 + 4y_3 = 14, \ 4y_3 = 12, \ y_3 = 3 \end{array}$$

$$\begin{bmatrix} 1 & 2 & -1 & 2 \\ 0 & 1 & -2 & -4 \\ 0 & 0 & 1 & 3 \end{bmatrix} \quad \begin{array}{l} x_1 + 2x_2 - x_3 = 2 \quad \text{so} \quad x_1 + 4 - 3 = 2, \ x_1 = 1 \\ x_2 - 2x_3 = -4 \quad \text{so} \quad x_2 - 6 = -4, \ x_2 = 2 \\ x_3 = 3 \end{array}$$

49.

$$\begin{bmatrix} 1 & -3 & 2 \\ 2 & 0 & 1 \\ 3 & -7 & 7 \end{bmatrix} \longrightarrow \begin{bmatrix} 1 & -3 & 2 \\ 0 & 6 & -3 \\ 0 & 2 & 1 \end{bmatrix} \longrightarrow \begin{bmatrix} 1 & -3 & 2 \\ 0 & 1 & -1/2 \\ 0 & 0 & 2 \end{bmatrix} \longrightarrow \begin{bmatrix} 1 & -3 & 2 \\ 0 & 1 & -1/2 \\ 0 & 0 & 1 \end{bmatrix} = U$$

$$\begin{bmatrix} 1 & 0 & 0 \\ 0 & 1 & 0 \\ 0 & 0 & 1 \end{bmatrix} \quad \begin{bmatrix} 1 & 0 & 0 \\ 2 & 1 & 0 \\ 3 & 0 & 1 \end{bmatrix} \quad \begin{bmatrix} 1 & 0 & 0 \\ 2 & 6 & 0 \\ 3 & 2 & 1 \end{bmatrix} \quad \begin{bmatrix} 1 & 0 & 0 \\ 2 & 6 & 0 \\ 3 & 2 & 2 \end{bmatrix} = L$$

$$\begin{bmatrix} 1 & 0 & 0 & 8 \\ 2 & 6 & 0 & 1 \\ 3 & 2 & 2 & 25 \end{bmatrix} \quad \begin{array}{l} y_1 = 8 \\ 2y_1 + 6y_2 = 1 \quad \text{so} \quad 16 + 6y_2 = 1, \ 6y_2 = -15, \ y_2 = -\frac{5}{2} \\ 3y_1 + 2y_2 + 2y_3 = 25 \quad \text{so} \quad 24 + -5 + 2y_3 = 25, \ 2y_3 = 6, \ y_3 = 3 \end{array}$$

$$\begin{bmatrix} 1 & -3 & 2 & 8 \\ 0 & 1 & -1/2 & -5/2 \\ 0 & 0 & 1 & 3 \end{bmatrix} \quad \begin{array}{l} x_1 - 3x_2 + 2x_3 = 8 \quad \text{so} \quad x_1 + 3 + 6 = 8, \ x_1 = -1 \\ x_2 - \frac{1}{2}x_3 = -\frac{5}{2} \quad \text{so} \quad x_2 - \frac{3}{2} = -\frac{5}{2}, \ x_2 = -1 \\ x_3 = 3 \end{array}$$

50.

$$\begin{bmatrix} 1 & 1 & 1 & -1 \\ 2 & 5 & 2 & -2 \\ 0 & 1 & 2 & -4 \\ -3 & 1 & 0 & 0 \end{bmatrix} \longrightarrow \begin{bmatrix} 1 & 1 & 1 & -1 \\ 0 & 3 & 0 & 0 \\ 0 & 1 & 2 & -4 \\ 0 & 4 & 3 & -3 \end{bmatrix} \longrightarrow \begin{bmatrix} 1 & 1 & 1 & -1 \\ 0 & 1 & 0 & 0 \\ 0 & 0 & 2 & -4 \\ 0 & 0 & 3 & -3 \end{bmatrix} \longrightarrow$$

$$\begin{bmatrix} 1 & 0 & 0 & 0 \\ 0 & 1 & 0 & 0 \\ 0 & 0 & 1 & 0 \\ 0 & 0 & 0 & 1 \end{bmatrix} \quad \begin{bmatrix} 1 & 0 & 0 & 0 \\ 2 & 1 & 0 & 0 \\ 0 & 0 & 1 & 0 \\ -3 & 0 & 0 & 1 \end{bmatrix} \quad \begin{bmatrix} 1 & 0 & 0 & 0 \\ 2 & 3 & 0 & 0 \\ 0 & 1 & 1 & 0 \\ -3 & 4 & 0 & 1 \end{bmatrix}$$

$$\longrightarrow \begin{bmatrix} 1 & 1 & 1 & -1 \\ 0 & 1 & 0 & 0 \\ 0 & 0 & 1 & -2 \\ 0 & 0 & 0 & 3 \end{bmatrix} \longrightarrow \begin{bmatrix} 1 & 1 & 1 & -1 \\ 0 & 1 & 0 & 0 \\ 0 & 0 & 1 & -2 \\ 0 & 0 & 0 & 1 \end{bmatrix} = U$$

$$\begin{bmatrix} 1 & 0 & 0 & 0 \\ 2 & 3 & 0 & 0 \\ 0 & 1 & 2 & 0 \\ -3 & 4 & 3 & 1 \end{bmatrix} \qquad \begin{bmatrix} 1 & 0 & 0 & 0 \\ 2 & 3 & 0 & 0 \\ 0 & 1 & 2 & 0 \\ -3 & 4 & 3 & 3 \end{bmatrix} = L$$

$$\begin{bmatrix} 1 & 0 & 0 & 0 & 4 \\ 2 & 3 & 0 & 0 & 5 \\ 0 & 1 & 2 & 0 & -3 \\ -3 & 4 & 3 & 3 & -13 \end{bmatrix}$$

$y_1 = 4$

$2y_1 + 3y_2 = 5 \quad$ so $\quad 8 + 3y_2 = 5, \quad 3y_2 = -3, \quad y_2 = -1$

$y_2 + 2y_3 = -3 \quad$ so $-1 + 2y_3 = -3, \quad 2y_3 = -2, \quad y_3 = -1$

$-3y_1 + 4y_2 + 3y_3 + 3y_4 = -13 \quad$ so $\quad -12 + -4 + -3 + 3y_4 = -13, \quad 3y_4 = 6, \quad y_4 = 2$

$$\begin{bmatrix} 1 & 1 & 1 & -1 & 4 \\ 0 & 1 & 0 & 0 & -1 \\ 0 & 0 & 1 & -2 & -1 \\ 0 & 0 & 0 & 1 & 2 \end{bmatrix}$$

$x_1 + x_2 + x_3 - x_4 = 4 \quad$ so $\quad x_1 + -1 + 3 - 2 = 4, \quad x_1 = 4$

$x_2 = -1$

$x_3 - 2x_4 = -1 \quad$ so $\quad x_3 - 4 = -1, \quad x_3 = 3$

$x_4 = 2$

51. Only one row interchange is required and it is performed at the outset:

$$\begin{bmatrix} 0 & 3 & 3 \\ 1 & 0 & -1 \\ -1 & 2 & 0 \end{bmatrix} \longrightarrow \begin{bmatrix} 1 & 0 & -1 \\ 0 & 3 & 3 \\ -1 & 2 & 0 \end{bmatrix} \longrightarrow \begin{bmatrix} 1 & 0 & -1 \\ 0 & 3 & 3 \\ 0 & 2 & -1 \end{bmatrix} \longrightarrow \begin{bmatrix} 1 & 0 & -1 \\ 0 & 1 & 1 \\ 0 & 0 & -3 \end{bmatrix} \longrightarrow \begin{bmatrix} 1 & 0 & -1 \\ 0 & 1 & 1 \\ 0 & 0 & 1 \end{bmatrix} = U$$

$$\begin{bmatrix} 1 & 0 & 0 \\ 0 & 1 & 0 \\ 0 & 0 & 1 \end{bmatrix} \quad \begin{bmatrix} 1 & 0 & 0 \\ 0 & 1 & 0 \\ 0 & 0 & 1 \end{bmatrix} \quad \begin{bmatrix} 1 & 0 & 0 \\ 0 & 1 & 0 \\ -1 & 0 & 1 \end{bmatrix} \quad \begin{bmatrix} 1 & 0 & 0 \\ 0 & 3 & 0 \\ -1 & 2 & 1 \end{bmatrix} \quad \begin{bmatrix} 1 & 0 & 0 \\ 0 & 3 & 0 \\ -1 & 2 & -3 \end{bmatrix} = L$$

Performing the interchange on I gives $\begin{bmatrix} 1 & 0 & 0 \\ 0 & 1 & 0 \\ 0 & 0 & 1 \end{bmatrix} \longrightarrow \begin{bmatrix} 0 & 1 & 0 \\ 1 & 0 & 0 \\ 0 & 0 & 1 \end{bmatrix} = P$

52. Two row interchanges are required:

$$\begin{bmatrix} 0 & 2 & 4 \\ 2 & 4 & 3 \\ 1 & 2 & 3 \end{bmatrix} \longrightarrow \begin{bmatrix} 1 & 2 & 3 \\ 2 & 4 & 3 \\ 0 & 2 & 4 \end{bmatrix} \longrightarrow \begin{bmatrix} 1 & 2 & 3 \\ 0 & 0 & -3 \\ 0 & 2 & 4 \end{bmatrix} \longrightarrow \begin{bmatrix} 1 & 2 & 3 \\ 0 & 2 & 4 \\ 0 & 0 & -3 \end{bmatrix} \longrightarrow \begin{bmatrix} 1 & 2 & 3 \\ 0 & 1 & 2 \\ 0 & 0 & -3 \end{bmatrix} \longrightarrow \begin{bmatrix} 1 & 2 & 3 \\ 0 & 1 & 2 \\ 0 & 0 & 1 \end{bmatrix}$$

Performing the interchanges at the outset:

$$\begin{bmatrix} 0 & 2 & 4 \\ 2 & 4 & 3 \\ 1 & 2 & 3 \end{bmatrix} \longrightarrow \begin{bmatrix} 1 & 2 & 3 \\ 2 & 4 & 3 \\ 0 & 2 & 4 \end{bmatrix} \longrightarrow \begin{bmatrix} 1 & 2 & 3 \\ 0 & 2 & 4 \\ 2 & 4 & 3 \end{bmatrix} \longrightarrow \begin{bmatrix} 1 & 2 & 3 \\ 0 & 2 & 4 \\ 0 & 0 & -3 \end{bmatrix} \longrightarrow \begin{bmatrix} 1 & 2 & 3 \\ 0 & 1 & 2 \\ 0 & 0 & -3 \end{bmatrix} \longrightarrow \begin{bmatrix} 1 & 2 & 3 \\ 0 & 1 & 2 \\ 0 & 0 & 1 \end{bmatrix} = U$$

$$\begin{bmatrix} 1 & 0 & 0 \\ 0 & 1 & 0 \\ 0 & 0 & 1 \end{bmatrix} \quad \begin{bmatrix} 1 & 0 & 0 \\ 0 & 1 & 0 \\ 0 & 0 & 1 \end{bmatrix} \quad \begin{bmatrix} 1 & 0 & 0 \\ 0 & 1 & 0 \\ 0 & 0 & 1 \end{bmatrix} \quad \begin{bmatrix} 1 & 0 & 0 \\ 0 & 1 & 0 \\ 2 & 0 & 1 \end{bmatrix} \quad \begin{bmatrix} 1 & 0 & 0 \\ 0 & 2 & 0 \\ 2 & 0 & 1 \end{bmatrix} \quad \begin{bmatrix} 1 & 0 & 0 \\ 0 & 2 & 0 \\ 2 & 0 & -3 \end{bmatrix} = L$$

Performing the interchanges in reverse order on I gives $\begin{bmatrix} 1 & 0 & 0 \\ 0 & 1 & 0 \\ 0 & 0 & 1 \end{bmatrix} \longrightarrow \begin{bmatrix} 1 & 0 & 0 \\ 0 & 0 & 1 \\ 0 & 1 & 0 \end{bmatrix} \longrightarrow \begin{bmatrix} 0 & 1 & 0 \\ 0 & 0 & 1 \\ 1 & 0 & 0 \end{bmatrix} = P$

CHAPTER 10: COMPLEX VECTOR SPACES

1. Given that $z_1 = 2 + i$ and $z_2 = 3 - 2i$, compute the following.

   (a) $z_1 + z_2$

   (b) $2z_1 - 3z_2$

   (c) $\text{Re}\,(z_1 - iz_2)$

   (d) $z_1 z_2$

   (e) $z_1^2 - z_2$

   (f) $(iz_1 - z_2)(iz_1 + z_2)$

2. Given that $z_1 = 1 - 3i$ and $z_2 = 2 + 4i$, compute the following.

   (a) $z_1 - z_2$

   (b) $3z_1 + \frac{1}{2}z_2$

   (c) $\text{Im}\,(iz_1 + z_2)$

   (d) $iz_1 z_2$

   (e) $2z_1^2 z_2$

   (f) $(z_1 + z_2)^3$

3. Solve for z.

   (a) $(2z + 3) - i = 2 + 5i$

   (b) $(z + 4i) + 2(z - i) = 3 - 2i$

   (c) $z^2 + z + 1 = 0$

4. Solve for z.

   (a) $-3z = (5 - i) - (2 - 10i)$

   (b) $2i - z = 4 + 3i - 2z$

   (c) $2z^2 + 2z + 1 = 0$

5. Given that $A = \begin{bmatrix} 2 & 3 \\ i & -i \end{bmatrix}$ and $\begin{bmatrix} 1 & 1+i & 3 \\ -i & 0 & 2-3i \end{bmatrix}$, compute the following.

   (a) AB

   (b) $AB - iB$

   (c) $B^T A$

   (d) $2A^2$

6. Given that $A = \begin{bmatrix} 2-i & i \\ -i & 2+i \end{bmatrix}$ and $B = \begin{bmatrix} 2 & 4-i \\ 2+i & -3 \\ 0 & i \end{bmatrix}$, compute the following.

   (a) BA

   (b) $iB + 2BA$

   (c) $\det(A)$

   (d) $\frac{1}{2}A^2$

7. Given that $z_1 = 2 - i$ and $z_2 = 3 + 4i$, compute the following.

   (a) $|z_1|$

   (b) $\bar{z}_2$

   (c) $\overline{z_1 - iz_2}$

   (d) $\frac{z_1}{z_2}$

   (e) $|\bar{z}_1 z_2|$

   (f) $\frac{1}{z_1^2} + \frac{1}{z_2}$

8. Given that $z_1 = 1 + i$ and $z_2 = 2 + 3i$, compute the following.

(a) $\overline{z}_1$

(b) $|z_2|$

(c) $\overline{z_1 z_2}$

(d) $\frac{i z_2}{z_1}$

(e) $\frac{z_1 + z_2}{z_1 - z_2}$

(f) $\frac{1}{i z_1} - \frac{i}{z_2}$

9. Solve by Cramer's Rule.

(a) $\begin{aligned} 2x_1 &- ix_2 &= 2 + i \\ x_1 &+ x_2 &= 1 + i \end{aligned}$

(b) $\begin{aligned} x_1 &- x_2 &= 6 + 7i \\ 2x_1 &+ 3x_2 &= 1 - i \end{aligned}$

10. Solve by Cramer's Rule.

(a) $\begin{aligned} x_1 + 2x_2 - x_3 &= 1 - i \\ x_2 + 2x_3 &= 2 \\ x_1 \quad\quad + x_3 &= -4i \end{aligned}$

(b) $\begin{aligned} x_1 - ix_2 \quad\quad &= 1 \\ x_2 - ix_3 &= i \\ -ix_1 \quad\quad + x_3 &= 1 + i \end{aligned}$

11. Solve by Gauss-Jordan elimination.

(a) $\begin{aligned} x_1 + (2 - i)x_2 &= 0 \\ (2 + i)x_1 + 5x_2 &= 0 \end{aligned}$

(b) $\begin{aligned} (1 - i)x_1 + (3 + 4i)x_2 &= 0 \\ (1 - 3i)x_1 + (10 + 5i)x_2 &= 0 \end{aligned}$

12. Solve by Gauss-Jordan elimination.

(a) $\begin{aligned} x_1 - ix_2 \quad\quad &= 0 \\ ix_1 + x_2 \quad\quad &= 0 \\ ix_2 + x_3 &= 0 \end{aligned}$

(b) $\begin{aligned} x_1 + ix_2 + (2 + i)x_3 &= 0 \\ (1 + i)x_1 + (-1 + i)x_2 + (1 + 3i)x_3 &= 0 \\ (1 - i)x_1 + (1 + i)x_2 + (3 - i)x_3 &= 0 \end{aligned}$

13. Solve by using a matrix inverse.

(a) $\begin{aligned} x_1 + (2 + 3i)x_2 &= i \\ x_1 - (1 + i)x_2 &= 2i \end{aligned}$

(b) $\begin{aligned} 2x_1 + ix_2 &= 3 + 3i \\ ix_1 + (1 - i)x_2 &= -1 - i \end{aligned}$

14. Express each complex number in polar form using its principal argument.

(a) 3 (b) $4i$ (c) $-2 + 2i$ (d) $1 + \sqrt{3}i$ (e) $-i$ (f) $-\sqrt{3} - i$

15. Given that $z_1 = 3\left[\cos\left(\frac{\pi}{6}\right) + i\sin\left(\frac{\pi}{6}\right)\right]$ and $z_2 = 4\left[\cos\left(\frac{2\pi}{3}\right) + i\sin\left(\frac{2\pi}{3}\right)\right]$, find the polar form of the following.

(a) $z_1 z_2$

(b) $\frac{z_1}{z_2}$

(c) $\frac{z_2}{z_1}$

(d) $z_1^2 z_2^3$

16. Let $z_1 = 1 + i$, $z_2 = -\sqrt{3} + i$, and $z_3 = -2i$. Use polar form to compute $z_1 z_2 / z_3$.

17. Use polar form to compute the following.

(a) $(1 - i)^6$ (b) $(1 + \sqrt{3}i)^5$ (c) $(\sqrt{3} - i)^7$ (d) $(2 + 2i)^{-3}$

18. Find all square roots of $\sqrt{3} - i$ and express them in polar form.

19. Find all cube roots of i and express them in polar form.

20. Find all fourth roots of $8\sqrt{2} + 8\sqrt{2}i$ and express them in polar form.

21. Find all fifth roots of 1 and express them in polar form.

22. Find all solutions of $z^4 + 16 = 0$, and use your results to factor $z^4 + 16$ into two quadratic factors with real coefficients.

23. Find all solutions of $z^6 + 8 = 0$, and use your results to factor $z^6 + 8$ into three quadratic factors with real coefficients.

24. Let $\mathbf{u} = (2 - i, 3 + 2i)$ and $\mathbf{v} = (i, 4 - i)$. Compute the following.

    (a) $\mathbf{u} + \mathbf{v}$ (b) $2\mathbf{u} - 3i\mathbf{v}$ (c) $\mathbf{u} \cdot \mathbf{v}$

    (d) $\mathbf{u} \cdot \mathbf{v} - \mathbf{v} \cdot \mathbf{u}$ (e) $\|i\mathbf{u} - 2\mathbf{v}\|$ (f) $\|3\mathbf{u} - 2\mathbf{v}\| + \|2\mathbf{u} - 3i\mathbf{v}\|$

25. Let $\mathbf{u} = (1, -i, 1 + 4i)$ and $\mathbf{v} = (i, 3 - i, 2 + i)$. Compute the following.

    (a) $\mathbf{u} - \mathbf{v}$ (b) $2\mathbf{u} + \mathbf{v}$ (c) $\mathbf{u} - 3i\mathbf{v}$

    (d) $\mathbf{v} \cdot \mathbf{u}$ (e) $\|\mathbf{v}\|$ (f) $\|\mathbf{u} + \mathbf{v}\|$

26. Express each of the following, if possible, as a linear combination of $\mathbf{u} = (-i, 3 - 2i, 1 + i)$ and $\mathbf{v} = (2 - i, 4i, i)$.

    (a) $(i, -3 - 5i, 1)$ (b) $(2, 4 - i, 2 + i)$

27. Express each of the following, if possible, as a linear combination of $\mathbf{u} = (i, 2 - i, 1 + i)$, $\mathbf{v} = (3, 3 + i, i)$, and $\mathbf{w} = (-1 + 3i, 5i, -2 + i)$.

    (a) $(5 + 3i, 0, 1 - i)$ (b) $(1 + 2i, -3 - 11i, 6 - 2i)$

28. Express each of the following, if possible, as a linear combination of $\mathbf{u} = (i, 1 + i)$ and $\mathbf{v} = (1 - i, 2 + i)$.

    (a) $(1, -2 + i)$ (b) $(3 - 2i, 0)$

29. Determine whether the set of all pairs of complex numbers (z_1, z_2) is a complex vector space under the operations
$$(z_1, z_2) + (z_1', z_2') = (z_1 + z_1', z_2 + z_2')$$
$$k(z_1, z_2) = (kiz_1, kiz_2).$$

30. Determine whether the set of all pairs of complex numbers (z_1, z_2) is a complex vector space under the operations
$$(z_1, z_2) + (z_1', z_2') = (z_1 + z_1' + i, z_2 + z_2' + i)$$
$$k(z_1, z_2) = (kz_1, kz_2).$$

31. Consider the set of all pairs of complex numbers (z_1, z_2), where $\|(z_1, z_2)\| = 1$. Prove whether the set is a subspace of C^2.

32. Consider the set of all triples of complex numbers (z_1, z_2, z_3), where $z_3 = i(z_1 + z_2)$. Prove whether the set is a subspace of C^3.

33. Consider the set of all 2×2 diagonal matrices of complex numbers. Prove whether the set is a subspace of complex M_{22}.

34. Consider the set of all complex matrices of the form $\begin{bmatrix} z_1 & z_2 \\ z_3 & z_4 \end{bmatrix}$, where $z_1 z_4 - z_2 z_3 = 0$. Prove whether the set is a subspace of complex M_{22}.

35. In each part, determine whether the given vectors span C^3.

(a) $\mathbf{v}_1 = (i, 1, i)$, $\qquad \mathbf{v}_2 = (0, i, 1 - i)$, $\qquad \mathbf{v}_3 = (1 + i, 2i, 0)$

(b) $\mathbf{v}_1 = (i, -2i, 3i)$, $\qquad \mathbf{v}_2 = (1 + 2i, 2 - 3i, 0)$, $\qquad \mathbf{v}_3 = (-1 + 2i, 1, 3 + 3i)$

(c) $\mathbf{v}_1 = (i, 0, 1 + i)$, $\qquad \mathbf{v}_2 = (0, 1, 1 - i)$, $\qquad \mathbf{v}_3 = (1 + 2i, 1, 4)$, $\qquad \mathbf{v}_4 = (-i, i, 0)$

36. In each part, determine whether the given vectors are linearly independent in C^3.

(a) $\mathbf{v}_1 = (1 - i, 2 + i, 3 - 2i)$, $\qquad \mathbf{v}_2 = (2, 1 + 3i, 5 + i)$

(b) $\mathbf{v}_1 = (i, -i, 2)$, $\qquad \mathbf{v}_2 = (3 - i, 0, i)$, $\qquad \mathbf{v}_3 = (4, -1 - i, 2 - i)$

(c) $\mathbf{v}_1 = (1 + i, i, 0)$, $\qquad \mathbf{v}_2 = (2 - i, 0, 1)$, $\qquad \mathbf{v}_3 = (0, 3 + i, -i)$

37. In each part, determine whether the given vectors form a basis for C^3.

(a) $\mathbf{v}_1 = (1, i, -i)$, $\qquad \mathbf{v}_2 = (0, 1 + i, 2i)$, $\qquad \mathbf{v}_3 = (2, 0, 3)$

(b) $\mathbf{v}_1 = (0, 2 - i, i)$, $\qquad \mathbf{v}_2 = (3 + i, i, -1)$, $\qquad \mathbf{v}_3 = (i, 1, 0)$

(c) $\mathbf{v}_1 = (i, 1 + i, -1 + i)$, $\qquad \mathbf{v}_2 = (1, i, -i)$, $\qquad \mathbf{v}_3 = (2 + i, 0, 2)$

In questions 38–39, determine the dimension of and a basis for the solution space of the system.

38.
$$\begin{aligned} x_1 &+ (2 - i)x_2 &= 0 \\ (1 + 2i)x_1 &+ (4 + 3i)x_2 &= 0 \end{aligned}$$

39.
$$\begin{aligned} 5x_1 &+ 5ix_2 &+ (1 + 2i)x_3 &= 0 \\ (2 + i)x_1 &+ (-1 + 2i)x_2 &+ ix_3 &= 0 \\ (3 - i)x_1 &+ (1 + 3i)x_2 &+ (1 + i)x_3 &= 0 \end{aligned}$$

40. Let $\mathbf{u} = (u_1, u_2)$ and $\mathbf{v} = (v_1, v_2)$. Show whether $\langle \mathbf{u}, \mathbf{v} \rangle = 2u_1 \bar{v}_1 + 3iu_2 \bar{v}_2$ defines an inner product on C^2.

41. Let $\mathbf{u} = (u_1, u_2)$ and $\mathbf{v} = (v_1, v_2)$. Show whether $\langle \mathbf{u}, \mathbf{v} \rangle = u_1 \bar{v}_1 + (2 + 3i)u_1 \bar{v}_2 + (2 - 3i)u_2 \bar{v}_1 + 15u_2 \bar{v}_2$ defines an inner product on C^2.

42. Consider the inner product $\langle \mathbf{u}, \mathbf{v} \rangle = u_1 \bar{v}_1 + (1 - i)u_1 \bar{v}_2 + (1 + i)u_2 \bar{v}_1 + 4u_2 \bar{v}_2$ for C^2. Let $\mathbf{u} = (1, i)$ and $\mathbf{v} = (1 - i, 2)$. Compute the following.

(a) $\langle \mathbf{u}, \mathbf{v} \rangle$ $\qquad\qquad$ (b) $\|\mathbf{u}\|$ $\qquad\qquad$ (c) $\|\mathbf{v}\|$ $\qquad\qquad$ (d) $d(\mathbf{u}, \mathbf{v})$

43. Consider the inner product $\langle A, B \rangle = u_1\bar{v}_1 + 2u_2\bar{v}_2 + 2u_3\bar{v}_3 + u_4\bar{v}_4$ for complex M_{22}. Let $A = \begin{bmatrix} 1 & -i \\ i & o \end{bmatrix}$ and $B = \begin{bmatrix} i & 1+i \\ 1-i & 2-3i \end{bmatrix}$. Compute the following.

(a) $\langle A, B \rangle$
(b) $\|A\|$
(c) $\|B\|$
(d) $d(A, B)$

44. Determine whether the following set of vectors is orthonormal under the Euclidean inner product for C^2.

(a) $\mathbf{u} = \left(\frac{1}{\sqrt{2}}, \frac{1}{\sqrt{2}} \right), \mathbf{v} = \left(\frac{i}{\sqrt{2}}, \frac{-i}{\sqrt{2}} \right)$

(b) $\mathbf{u} = \left(\frac{1}{\sqrt{6}} - \frac{2i}{\sqrt{6}}, \frac{i}{\sqrt{6}} \right), \mathbf{v} = \left(\frac{3}{\sqrt{6}} - \frac{i}{\sqrt{6}}, \frac{5}{\sqrt{6}} - \frac{5i}{\sqrt{6}} \right)$

45. Determine whether the following set of vectors is orthonormal under the Euclidean inner product for C^3.

(a) $\mathbf{u} = \left(\frac{1}{\sqrt{2}}, 0, \frac{i}{\sqrt{2}} \right), \quad \mathbf{v} = \left(\frac{i}{\sqrt{2}}, 0, \frac{1}{\sqrt{2}} \right) \quad \mathbf{w} = \left(0, \frac{1}{\sqrt{2}} + \frac{i}{\sqrt{2}}, 0 \right)$

(b) $\mathbf{u} = \left(\frac{1}{\sqrt{6}} + \frac{i}{\sqrt{6}}, \frac{1}{\sqrt{6}} + \frac{i}{\sqrt{6}}, \frac{1}{\sqrt{6}} + \frac{i}{\sqrt{6}} \right), \quad \mathbf{v} = \left(\frac{-2i}{\sqrt{6}}, \frac{i}{\sqrt{6}}, \frac{i}{\sqrt{6}} \right), \quad \mathbf{w} = \left(0, \frac{\sqrt{2}}{\sqrt{6}} - \frac{i}{\sqrt{6}}, \frac{-\sqrt{2}}{\sqrt{6}} + \frac{i}{\sqrt{6}} \right)$

46. Consider C^2 with the Euclidean inner product. Use the Gram–Schmidt process to transform the basis $\{(1, i), (1+i, 0)\}$ into an orthonormal basis.

47. Consider C^3 with the Euclidean inner prduct. Use the Gram–Schmidt process to transform the basis $\{(i, 0, 0), (1, 1, 1), (1+i, i, 0)\}$ into an orthonormal basis.

48. In each part determine A^*, the conjugate transpose of A.

(a) $A = \begin{bmatrix} 1 & 2-i \\ 1+3i & 4i \end{bmatrix}$
(b) $A = [3 \ -4 \ 5]$

(c) $A = \begin{bmatrix} 2-3i & 1 & 0 \\ 0 & 1-2i & 5i \end{bmatrix}$
(d) $A = \begin{bmatrix} 1 & i & i \\ -i & 1+i & i \\ -i & -i & 1-i \end{bmatrix}$

49. In each part determine whether A is Hermitian.

(a) $A = \begin{bmatrix} 3 & 1+i \\ 1-i & 1 \end{bmatrix}$
(b) $A = \begin{bmatrix} i & -i \\ i & i \end{bmatrix}$

(c) $A = \begin{bmatrix} 0 & 3 & 4i \\ -3 & 0 & -5 \\ -4i & 5 & 0 \end{bmatrix}$
(d) $A = \begin{bmatrix} 5 & 2+i & 1-11i \\ 2-i & 12 & 0 \\ 1+11i & 0 & 13 \end{bmatrix}$

50. In each part determine whether A is unitary and, if so, determine its inverse.

(a) $A = \begin{bmatrix} 1/\sqrt{2} & i/\sqrt{2} \\ -1/\sqrt{2} & i/\sqrt{2} \end{bmatrix}$
(b) $A = \begin{bmatrix} i/2 & (\sqrt{3}/2)i \\ \sqrt{3}/2 & -i/2 \end{bmatrix}$

(c) $A = \begin{bmatrix} i/\sqrt{2} & 0 & -i/\sqrt{2} \\ 0 & -1 & 0 \\ -i/\sqrt{2} & 0 & i/\sqrt{2} \end{bmatrix}$
(d) $A = \begin{bmatrix} i/\sqrt{3} & -2i/\sqrt{6} & 0 \\ i/\sqrt{3} & i/\sqrt{6} & -i/\sqrt{2} \\ i/\sqrt{3} & i/\sqrt{6} & i/\sqrt{2} \end{bmatrix}$

In questions 51–54, find a unitary matrix P that diagonalizes A, and determine $P^{-1}AP$.

51. $A = \begin{bmatrix} -3 & 2+2i \\ 2-2i & 4 \end{bmatrix}$

52. $A = \begin{bmatrix} -7i & -24i \\ -24i & 7i \end{bmatrix}$

53. $A = \begin{bmatrix} 1 & i & 0 \\ -i & 0 & i \\ 0 & -i & 1 \end{bmatrix}$

54. $A = \begin{bmatrix} -3 & i & 0 \\ -i & -3 & 0 \\ 0 & 0 & -3 \end{bmatrix}.$

SECTION 10.1   *COMPLEX NUMBERS*

1.   (a) $z_1 + z_2 = (2 + i) + (3 - 2i) = 5 - i$

    (b) $2z_1 - 3z_2 = 2(2 + i) - 3(3 - 2i) = 4 + 2i - 9 + 6i = -5 + 8i$

    (c) $\operatorname{Re}(z_1 - iz_2) = \operatorname{Re}[(2 + i) - i(3 - 2i)] = \operatorname{Re}(2 + i - 3i + 2) = \operatorname{Re}(4 - 2i) = 4$

    (d) $z_1 z_2 = (2 + i)(3 - 2i) = 6 + 3i - 4i + 2 = 8 - i$

    (e) $z_1^2 - z_2 = (2 + i)^2 - (3 - 2i) = (4 + 2i + 2i + -1) - (3 - 2i) = (3 + 4i) - (3 - 2i) = 6i$

    (f) $(iz_1 - z_2)(iz_1 + z_2) = -z_1^2 + iz_1 z_2 - iz_1 z_2 - z_2^2 = -\left(z_1^2 + z_2^2\right)$

$$= -\left[(2 + i)^2 + (3 - 2i)^2\right]$$
$$= -\left[(4 + 2i + 2i + -1) + (9 - 6i - 6i - 4)\right]$$
$$= -[8 - 8i] = -8 + 8i$$

2.   (a) $z_1 - z_2 = (1 - 3i) - (2 + 4i) = -1 - 7i$

    (b) $3z_1 + \frac{1}{2}z_2 = 3(1 - 3i) + \frac{1}{2}(2 + 4i) = (3 - 9i) + (1 + 2i) = 4 - 7i$

    (c) $\operatorname{Im}(iz_1 + z_2) = \operatorname{Im}[i(1 - 3i) + (2 + 4i)] = \operatorname{Im}[(i + 3) + (2 + 4i)]$
$$= \operatorname{Im}(5 + 5i) = 5$$

    (d) $iz_1 z_2 = i(1 - 3i)(2 + 4i) = i(2 + 4i - 6i + 12) = i(14 - 2i) = 2 + 14i$

    (e) $2z_1^2 z_2 = 2(1 - 3i)^2(2 + 4i) = 2(1 - 3i - 3i + -9)(2 + 4i)$
$$= 2(-8 - 6i)(2 + 4i) = -8(4 + 3i)(1 + 2i)$$
$$= -8(4 + 8i + 3i + -6) = -8(-2 + 11i) = 16 - 88i$$

    (f) $(z_1 + z_2)^3 = \left[(1 - 3i) + (2 + 4i)\right]^3 = (3 + i)^3 = (3 + i)(3 + i)^2$
$$= (3 + i)(9 + 3i + 3i + {}^- 1) = (3 + i)(8 + 6i)$$
$$= 24 + 18i + 8i + {}^- 6 = 18 + 26i$$

3.   (a) $(2z + 3) - i = 2 + 5i$

$$2z \qquad\qquad = -1 + 6i$$
$$z = \frac{1}{2}(-1 + 6i) = \frac{-1}{2} + 3i$$

(b) $(z + 4i) + 2(z - i) = 3 - 2i$

$z + 4i + 2z - 2i = 3 - 2i$

$3z + 2i = 3 - 2i$

$3z = 3 - 4i$

$z = \dfrac{1}{3}(3 - 4i) = 1 - \dfrac{4}{3}i$

(c) $z = \dfrac{-1 \pm \sqrt{1 - 4(1)(1)}}{2(1)} = \dfrac{-1 \pm \sqrt{-3}}{2} = \dfrac{-1}{2} \pm \dfrac{\sqrt{3}}{2}i$

4. (a) $-3z = (5 - i) - (2 - 10i)$

$-3z = 3 + 9i$

$z = \dfrac{-1}{3}(3 + 9i) = -1 - 3i$

(b) $2i - z = 4 + 3i - 2z$

$2i + z = 4 + 3i$

$z = 4 + 3i - 2i = 4 + i$

(c) $z = \dfrac{-2 \pm \sqrt{4 - 4(2)(1)}}{2(2)} = \dfrac{-2 \pm \sqrt{-4}}{4} = \dfrac{-2 \pm 2i}{4} = \dfrac{-1}{2} \pm \dfrac{1}{2}i$

5. (a) $AB = \begin{bmatrix} 2 & 3 \\ i & -i \end{bmatrix} \begin{bmatrix} 1 & 1+i & 3 \\ -i & 0 & 2-3i \end{bmatrix} = \begin{bmatrix} 2 +^- 3i & 2 + 2i + 0 & 6 + 6 - 9i \\ i + i^2 & i + i^2 + 0 & 3i - 2i + 3i^2 \end{bmatrix}$

$= \begin{bmatrix} 2 - 3i & 2 + 2i & 12 - 9i \\ -1 + i & -1 + i & -3 + i \end{bmatrix}$

(b) $AB - iB = \begin{bmatrix} 2 - 3i & 2 + 2i & 12 - 9i \\ -1 + i & -1 + i & -3 + i \end{bmatrix} - i \begin{bmatrix} 1 & 1+i & 3 \\ -i & 0 & 2-3i \end{bmatrix}$ from (a)

$= \begin{bmatrix} 2 - 3i & 2 + 2i & 12 - 9i \\ -1 + i & -1 + i & -3 + i \end{bmatrix} + \begin{bmatrix} -i & 1 - i & -3i \\ -1 & 0 & -3 - 2i \end{bmatrix}$

$= \begin{bmatrix} 2 - 4i & 3 + i & 12 - 12i \\ -2 + i & -1 + i & -6 - i \end{bmatrix}$

(c) $B^T A = \begin{bmatrix} 1 & -i \\ 1+i & 0 \\ 3 & 2-3i \end{bmatrix} \begin{bmatrix} 2 & 3 \\ i & -i \end{bmatrix} = \begin{bmatrix} 2 - i^2 & 3 + i^2 \\ 2 + 2i + 0 & 3 + 3i + 0 \\ 6 + 2i - 3i^2 & 9 - 2i + 3i^2 \end{bmatrix}$

$= \begin{bmatrix} 3 & 2 \\ 2 + 2i & 3 + 3i \\ 9 + 2i & 6 - 2i \end{bmatrix}$

(d) $2A^2 = 2\begin{bmatrix} 2 & 3 \\ i & -i \end{bmatrix} \begin{bmatrix} 2 & 3 \\ i & -i \end{bmatrix} = 2\begin{bmatrix} 4 + 3i & 6 - 3i \\ 2i - i^2 & 3i + i^2 \end{bmatrix}$

$= 2\begin{bmatrix} 4 + 3i & 6 - 3i \\ 1 + 2i & -1 + 3i \end{bmatrix} = \begin{bmatrix} 8 + 6i & 12 - 6i \\ 2 + 4i & -2 + 6i \end{bmatrix}$

282

6. (a) $BA = \begin{bmatrix} 2 & 4-i \\ 2+i & -3 \\ 0 & i \end{bmatrix} \begin{bmatrix} 2-i & i \\ -i & 2+i \end{bmatrix} = \begin{bmatrix} (4-2i)+(-4i+i^2) & 2i+(8+4i-2i-i^2) \\ (4-2i+2i-i^2)+3i & (2i+i^2)+(-6-3i) \\ 0+(-i^2) & 0+(2i+i^2) \end{bmatrix}$

$$= \begin{bmatrix} 3-6i & 9+4i \\ 5+3i & -7-i \\ 1 & -1+2i \end{bmatrix}$$

(b) $iB + 2BA = i \begin{bmatrix} 2 & 4-i \\ 2+i & -3 \\ 0 & i \end{bmatrix} + 2 \begin{bmatrix} 3-6i & 9+4i \\ 5+3i & -7-i \\ 1 & -1+2i \end{bmatrix}$ from (a)

$$= \begin{bmatrix} 2i & 1+4i \\ -1+2i & -3i \\ 0 & -1 \end{bmatrix} + \begin{bmatrix} 6-12i & 18+8i \\ 10+6i & -14-2i \\ 2 & -2+4i \end{bmatrix} = \begin{bmatrix} 6-10i & 19+12i \\ 9+8i & -14-5i \\ 2 & -3+4i \end{bmatrix}$$

(c) $\det A = \det \begin{bmatrix} 2-i & i \\ -i & 2+i \end{bmatrix} = (2-i)(2+i) - (-i^2)$

$$= 4 + 2i - 2i - i^2 + i^2 = 4$$

(d) $\frac{1}{2}A^2 = \frac{1}{2} \begin{bmatrix} 2-i & i \\ -i & 2+i \end{bmatrix} \begin{bmatrix} 2-i & i \\ -i & 2+i \end{bmatrix} =$

$$\frac{1}{2} \begin{bmatrix} (4-2i-2i+i^2)-i^2 & (2i-i^2)+(2i+i^2) \\ (-2i+i^2)+(-2i-i^2) & -i^2+(4+2i+2i+i^2) \end{bmatrix}$$

$$= \frac{1}{2} \begin{bmatrix} 4-4i & 4i \\ -4i & 4+4i \end{bmatrix} = \begin{bmatrix} 2-2i & 2i \\ -2i & 2+2i \end{bmatrix}$$

SECTION 10.2 MODULUS; COMPLEX CONJUGATE; DIVISION

7. (a) $|z_1| = |2-i| = \sqrt{4+1} = \sqrt{5}$

(b) $\bar{z}_2 = \overline{3+4i} = 3-4i$

(c) $\overline{z_1 - iz_2} = \overline{(2-i)-i(3+4i)} = \overline{2-i-3i-4i^2} = \overline{6-4i} = 6+4i$

(d) $\dfrac{z_1}{z_2} = \dfrac{2-i}{3+4i} = \dfrac{1}{|3+4i|^2}(2-i)(3-4i) = \dfrac{1}{25}(6-8i-3i+4i^2)$

$$= \frac{1}{25}(2-11i) = \frac{2}{25} + \frac{-11}{25}i$$

(e) $|\bar{z}_1 z_2| = |\overline{(2-i)}(3+4i)| = |(2+i)(3+4i)| = |6+8i+3i+4i^2|$

$$= |2+11i| = \sqrt{4+121} = \sqrt{125} = 5\sqrt{5}$$

283

(f) $\dfrac{1}{z_1^2} + \dfrac{1}{z_2} = \dfrac{1}{(2-i)^2} + \dfrac{1}{3+4i} = \dfrac{1}{4-4i+i^2} + \dfrac{1}{3+4i}$

$$= \dfrac{1}{3-4i} + \dfrac{1}{3+4i} = \dfrac{3+4i}{|3-4i|^2} + \dfrac{3-4i}{|3+4i|^2}$$

$$= \dfrac{3+4i}{25} + \dfrac{3-4i}{25} = \dfrac{6}{25}$$

8. (a) $\overline{z_1} = \overline{1+i} = 1 - i$

(b) $|z_2| = |2+3i| = \sqrt{4+9} = \sqrt{13}$

(c) $\overline{z_1 z_2} = \overline{(1+i)(2+3i)} = \overline{2+3i+2i+3i^2} = \overline{-1+5i} = -1-5i$

(d) $\dfrac{iz_2}{z_1} = \dfrac{i(2+3i)}{1+i} = \dfrac{-3+2i}{1+i} = \dfrac{1}{|1+i|^2}(-3+2i)(1-i)$

$$= \dfrac{-3+3i+2i-2i^2}{2} = \dfrac{-1+5i}{2} = \dfrac{-1}{2} + \dfrac{5}{2}i$$

(e) $\dfrac{z_1+z_2}{z_1-z_2} = \dfrac{(1+i)+(2+3i)}{(1+i)-(2+3i)} = \dfrac{3+4i}{-1-2i} = \dfrac{1}{|-1-2i|^2}(3+4i)(-1+2i)$

$$= \dfrac{-3+6i-4i+8i^2}{5} = \dfrac{-11+2i}{5} = \dfrac{-11}{5} + \dfrac{2}{5}i$$

(f) $\dfrac{1}{iz_1} - \dfrac{i}{z_2} = \dfrac{z_2 - i^2 z_1}{iz_1 z_2} = \dfrac{z_1 + z_2}{iz_1 z_2} = \dfrac{3+4i}{i(-1-5i)}$ from (c), (e).

$$= \dfrac{3+4i}{5-i} = \dfrac{1}{|5-i|^2}(3+4i)(5+i) = \dfrac{15+3i+20i+4i^2}{26} = \dfrac{11+23i}{26} = \dfrac{11}{26} + \dfrac{23}{26}i$$

9. (a) $|A| = \begin{vmatrix} 2 & -i \\ 1 & 1 \end{vmatrix} = 2 + i$

$|A_1| = \begin{vmatrix} 2+i & -i \\ 1+i & 1 \end{vmatrix} = (2+i) + i(1+i) = 2+i+i+i^2 = 1+2i$

$|A_2| = \begin{vmatrix} 2 & 2+i \\ 1 & 1+i \end{vmatrix} = (2+2i) - (2+i) = i$

$x_1 = \dfrac{|A_1|}{|A|} = \dfrac{1+2i}{2+i} = \dfrac{1}{|2+i|^2}(1+2i)(2-i) = \dfrac{2-i+4i-2i^2}{5} = \dfrac{4+3i}{5} = \dfrac{4}{5} + \dfrac{3}{5}i$

$x_2 = \dfrac{|A_2|}{|A|} = \dfrac{i}{2+i} = \dfrac{1}{|2+i|^2}i(2-i) = \dfrac{1}{5}(2i-i^2) = \dfrac{1+2i}{5} = \dfrac{1}{5} + \dfrac{2}{5}i$

(b) $|A| = \begin{vmatrix} 1 & -1 \\ 2 & 3 \end{vmatrix} = 3 + 2 = 5$

$|A_1| = \begin{vmatrix} 6+7i & -1 \\ 1-i & 3 \end{vmatrix} = (18+21i) + (1-i) = 19 + 20i$

$|A_2| = \begin{vmatrix} 1 & 6+7i \\ 2 & 1-i \end{vmatrix} = (1-i) - 2(6+7i) = -11 - 15i$

$x_1 = \dfrac{|A_1|}{|A|} = \dfrac{19+20i}{5} = \dfrac{19}{5} + 4i$

$x_2 = \dfrac{|A_2|}{|A|} = \dfrac{-11-15i}{5} = \dfrac{-11}{5} - 3i$

10. (a) $|A| = \begin{vmatrix} 1 & 2 & -1 \\ 0 & 1 & 2 \\ 1 & 0 & 1 \end{vmatrix} = 1(1) + 0 + 1(5) = 6$

$|A_1| = \begin{vmatrix} 1-i & 2 & -1 \\ 2 & 1 & 2 \\ -4i & 0 & 1 \end{vmatrix} = -4i(5) + 0 + 1(1-i-4) = -3 - 21i$

$|A_2| = \begin{vmatrix} 1 & 1-i & -1 \\ 0 & 2 & 2 \\ 1 & -4i & 1 \end{vmatrix} = 1(2+8i) + 0 + 1(2-2i+2) = 6 + 6i$

$|A_3| = \begin{vmatrix} 1 & 2 & 1-i \\ 0 & 1 & 2 \\ 1 & 0 & -4i \end{vmatrix} = 1(-4i) + 0 + 1(4-1+i) = 3 - 3i$

$x_1 = \dfrac{|A_1|}{|A|} = \dfrac{-3-21i}{6} = \dfrac{1}{2} - \dfrac{7}{2}i$

$x_2 = \dfrac{|A_2|}{|A|} = \dfrac{6+6i}{6} = 1 + i$

$x_3 = \dfrac{|A_3|}{|A|} = \dfrac{3-3i}{6} = \dfrac{1}{2} - \dfrac{1}{2}i$

(b) $|A| = \begin{vmatrix} 1 & -i & 0 \\ 0 & 1 & -i \\ -i & 0 & 1 \end{vmatrix} = 1(1) - i(i^2) = 1 + i$

$|A_1| = \begin{vmatrix} 1 & -i & 0 \\ i & 1 & -i \\ 1+i & 0 & 1 \end{vmatrix} = 1(1) + i(i+i+i^2) + 0 = -1 - i$

$|A_2| = \begin{vmatrix} 1 & 1 & 0 \\ 0 & i & -i \\ -i & 1+i & 1 \end{vmatrix} = 1(i+i+i^2) - 1(-i^2) + 0 = -2 + 2i$

$|A_3| = \begin{vmatrix} 1 & -i & 1 \\ 0 & 1 & i \\ -i & 0 & 1+i \end{vmatrix} = 1(1+i) + 0 + -i(-i^2-1) = 1 + i$

$$x_1 = \frac{|A_1|}{|A|} = \frac{-1-i}{1+i} = \frac{-(1+i)}{1+i} = -1$$

$$x_2 = \frac{|A_2|}{|A|} = \frac{-2+2i}{1+i} = \frac{1}{|1+i|^2}(-2+2i)(1-i) = \frac{-2+2i+2i-2i^2}{2} = \frac{4i}{2} = 2i$$

$$x_3 = \frac{|A_3|}{|A|} = \frac{1+i}{1+i} = 1$$

11. (a) $\begin{bmatrix} 1 & 2-i & 0 \\ 2+i & 5 & 0 \end{bmatrix} \longrightarrow \begin{bmatrix} 1 & 2-i & 0 \\ 0 & 0 & 0 \end{bmatrix}$

Let $x_2 = t$;

then $x_1 + (2-i)x_2 = 0$, i.e., $x_1 = (-2+i)x_2 = (-2+i)t$

so $\begin{bmatrix} x_1 \\ x_2 \end{bmatrix} = \begin{bmatrix} (-2+i)t \\ t \end{bmatrix}$

(b) $\begin{bmatrix} 1-i & 3+4i & 0 \\ 1-3i & 10+5i & 0 \end{bmatrix} \longrightarrow \begin{bmatrix} 1 & -1/2+(7/2)i & 0 \\ 0 & 0 & 0 \end{bmatrix}$

Let $x_2 = t$;

then $x_1 + \left(\frac{-1}{2} + \frac{7}{2}i\right)x_2 = 0$, i.e., $x_1 = \left(\frac{1}{2} - \frac{7}{2}i\right)x_2 = \left(\frac{1}{2} - \frac{7}{2}i\right)t$

so $\begin{bmatrix} x_1 \\ x_2 \end{bmatrix} = \begin{bmatrix} \left(\frac{1}{2} - \frac{7}{2}i\right)t \\ t \end{bmatrix}$

12. (a) $\begin{bmatrix} 1 & -i & 0 & 0 \\ i & 1 & 0 & 0 \\ 0 & i & 1 & 0 \end{bmatrix} \longrightarrow \begin{bmatrix} 1 & -i & 0 & 0 \\ 0 & 0 & 0 & 0 \\ 0 & i & 1 & 0 \end{bmatrix} \longrightarrow \begin{bmatrix} 1 & -i & 0 & 0 \\ 0 & i & 1 & 0 \\ 0 & 0 & 0 & 0 \end{bmatrix} \longrightarrow \begin{bmatrix} 1 & 0 & 1 & 0 \\ 0 & 1 & -i & 0 \\ 0 & 0 & 0 & 0 \end{bmatrix}$

Let $x_3 = t$;

then $x_2 - ix_3 = 0$, i.e., $x_2 = ix_3 = it$

and $x_1 + x_3 = 0$, i.e., $x_1 = -x_3 = -t$

so $\begin{bmatrix} x_1 \\ x_2 \\ x_3 \end{bmatrix} = \begin{bmatrix} -t \\ it \\ t \end{bmatrix}$

(b) $\begin{bmatrix} 1 & i & 2+i & 0 \\ 1+i & -1+i & 1+3i & 0 \\ 1-i & 1+i & 3-i & 0 \end{bmatrix} \longrightarrow \begin{bmatrix} 1 & i & 2+i & 0 \\ 0 & 0 & 0 & 0 \\ 0 & 0 & 0 & 0 \end{bmatrix}$

Let $x_3 = t$ and $x_2 = s$;

then $x_1 + ix_2 + (2+i)x_3 = 0$, i.e., $x_1 = -ix_2 - (2+i)x_3 = -is - (2+i)t$

so $\begin{bmatrix} x_1 \\ x_2 \\ x_3 \end{bmatrix} = \begin{bmatrix} -is - (2+i)t \\ s \\ t \end{bmatrix}$

13. (a) $\begin{bmatrix} x_1 \\ x_2 \end{bmatrix} = \begin{bmatrix} 1 & 2+3i \\ 1 & -1-i \end{bmatrix}^{-1} \begin{bmatrix} i \\ 2i \end{bmatrix} = \dfrac{1}{-3-4i} \begin{bmatrix} -1-i & -2-3i \\ -1 & 1 \end{bmatrix} \begin{bmatrix} i \\ 2i \end{bmatrix}$

$= \dfrac{1}{-3-4i} \begin{bmatrix} 7-5i \\ i \end{bmatrix} = \dfrac{-3+4i}{25} \begin{bmatrix} 7-5i \\ i \end{bmatrix} = \dfrac{1}{25} \begin{bmatrix} -1+43i \\ -4-3i \end{bmatrix} = \begin{bmatrix} -1/25 & + & (43/25)i \\ -4/25 & - & (3/25)i \end{bmatrix}$

(b) $\begin{bmatrix} x_1 \\ x_2 \end{bmatrix} = \begin{bmatrix} 2 & i \\ i & 1-i \end{bmatrix}^{-1} \begin{bmatrix} 3+3i \\ -1-i \end{bmatrix} = \dfrac{1}{3-2i} \begin{bmatrix} 1-i & -i \\ -i & 2 \end{bmatrix} \begin{bmatrix} 3+3i \\ -1-i \end{bmatrix}$

$= \dfrac{1}{3-2i} \begin{bmatrix} 5+i \\ 1-5i \end{bmatrix} = \dfrac{3+2i}{13} \begin{bmatrix} 5+i \\ 1-5i \end{bmatrix} = \dfrac{1}{13} \begin{bmatrix} 13+13i \\ 13-13i \end{bmatrix} = \begin{bmatrix} 1+i \\ 1-i \end{bmatrix}.$

SECTION 10.3 POLAR FORM; DEMOIVRE'S THEOREM

14. (a) $z = 3 = 3 + 0i$

$r = \sqrt{3^2 + 0^2} = \sqrt{9} = 3$

so $3\cos\theta = 3,$ i.e., $\cos\theta = 1$

Thus $\theta = 0$

and $z = 3(\cos 0 + i\sin 0)$

(b) $z = 4i = 0 + 4i;$

$r = \sqrt{0^2 + 4^2} = \sqrt{16} = 4$

so $4\cos\theta = 0,$ i.e., $\cos\theta = 0$

and $4\sin\theta = 4,$ i.e., $\sin\theta = 1$

Thus $\theta = \dfrac{\pi}{2}$

and $z = 4\left(\cos\dfrac{\pi}{2} + i\sin\dfrac{\pi}{2}\right).$

(c) $z = -2 + 2i;$

$r = \sqrt{(-2)^2 + (2)^2} = \sqrt{8} = 2\sqrt{2}$

so $2\sqrt{2}\cos\theta = -2,$ i.e., $\cos\theta = \dfrac{-2}{2\sqrt{2}} = \dfrac{-\sqrt{2}}{2}$

and $2\sqrt{2}\sin\theta = 2,$ i.e., $\sin\theta = \dfrac{2}{2\sqrt{2}} = \dfrac{\sqrt{2}}{2}.$

Thus $\theta = \dfrac{3\pi}{4}$

and $z = 2\sqrt{2}\left(\cos\dfrac{3\pi}{4} + i\sin\dfrac{3\pi}{4}\right).$

(d) $z = 1 + \sqrt{3}i;$

$$r = \sqrt{(1)^2 + (\sqrt{3})^2} = \sqrt{4} = 2$$

so $2\cos\theta = 1,$ i.e., $\cos\theta = \dfrac{1}{2}$

and $2\sin\theta = \sqrt{3},$ i.e., $\sin\theta = \dfrac{\sqrt{3}}{2}.$

Thus $\theta = \dfrac{\pi}{3}$

and $z = 2\left(\cos\dfrac{\pi}{3} + i\sin\dfrac{\pi}{3}\right).$

(e) $z = -i = 0 - 1i$

$$r = \sqrt{(0)^2 + (-1)^2} = \sqrt{1} = 1$$

so $1\cos\theta = 0,$ i.e., $\cos\theta = 0$

and $1\sin\theta = -1,$ i.e., $\sin\theta = -1.$

Thus $\theta = \dfrac{-\pi}{2}$

and $z = \cos\left(\dfrac{-\pi}{2}\right) + i\sin\left(\dfrac{-\pi}{2}\right).$

(f) $z = -\sqrt{3} - 1i;$

$$r = \sqrt{\left(-\sqrt{3}\right)^2 + (-1)^2} = \sqrt{4} = 2$$

so $2\cos\theta = -\sqrt{3},$ i.e., $\cos\theta = \dfrac{-\sqrt{3}}{2}$

and $2\sin\theta = -1,$ i.e., $\sin\theta = \dfrac{-1}{2}.$

Thus $\theta = \dfrac{-5\pi}{6}$

and $z = 2\left[\cos\left(\dfrac{-5\pi}{6}\right) + i\sin\left(\dfrac{-5\pi}{6}\right)\right].$

15. (a) $r = r_1 r_2 = 3 \cdot 4 = 12$

$$\theta = \theta_1 + \theta_2 = \frac{\pi}{6} + \frac{2\pi}{3} = \frac{5\pi}{6}$$

$$z = 12\left[\cos\left(\frac{5\pi}{6}\right) + i\sin\left(\frac{5\pi}{6}\right)\right].$$

(b) $r = \dfrac{r_1}{r_2} = \dfrac{3}{4}$

$$\theta = \theta_1 - \theta_2 = \frac{\pi}{6} - \frac{2\pi}{3} = \frac{-\pi}{2}$$

$$z = \frac{3}{4}\left[\cos\left(\frac{-\pi}{2}\right) + i\sin\left(\frac{-\pi}{2}\right)\right].$$

(c) $r = \dfrac{r_2}{r_1} = \dfrac{4}{3}$

$$\theta = \theta_2 - \theta_1 = \frac{2\pi}{3} - \frac{\pi}{6} = \frac{\pi}{2}$$

$$z = \frac{4}{3}\left(\cos\frac{\pi}{2} + i\sin\frac{\pi}{2}\right).$$

(d) $r = r_1^2 r_2^3 = 3^2 4^3 = 9 \cdot 64 = 576$

$$\theta = 2\theta_1 + 3\theta_2 = 2\left(\frac{\pi}{6}\right) + 3\left(\frac{2\pi}{3}\right) = \frac{\pi}{3} + 2\pi$$

$$z = 576\left(\cos\frac{\pi}{3} + i\sin\frac{\pi}{3}\right).$$

16. (a) $z_1 = 1 + i;$

$$r_1 = \sqrt{1^2 + 1^2} = \sqrt{2}$$

so $\quad \sqrt{2}\cos\theta_1 = 1,$ i.e., $\cos\theta_1 = \dfrac{\sqrt{2}}{2}$

and $\quad \sqrt{2}\sin\theta_1 = 1,$ i.e., $\sin\theta_1 = \dfrac{\sqrt{2}}{2}.$

Thus $\theta_1 = \dfrac{\pi}{4}.$

$z_2 = -\sqrt{3} + i;$

$$r_2 = \sqrt{(-\sqrt{3})^2 + (1)^2} = \sqrt{4} = 2$$

so $\quad 2\cos\theta_2 = -\sqrt{3},$ i.e., $\cos\theta_2 = \dfrac{-\sqrt{3}}{2}$

and $\quad 2\sin\theta_2 = 1,$ i.e., $\sin\theta_2 = \dfrac{1}{2}.$

Thus $\theta_2 = \dfrac{5\pi}{6}.$

$z_3 = 0 - 2i$

$$r_3 = \sqrt{(0)^2 + (-2)^2} = \sqrt{4} = 2$$

so $\quad 2\cos\theta_3 = 0, \quad$ i.e., $\quad \cos\theta_3 = 0$

and $\quad 2\sin\theta_3 = -2 \quad$ i.e., $\quad \sin\theta_3 = -1$.

Thus $\quad \theta_3 = \dfrac{-\pi}{2}$.

Then $z = z_1 z_2 / z_3 = r(\cos\theta + i\sin\theta)$

where $\quad r = r_1 r_2 / r_3 = \sqrt{2}\cdot 2/2 = \sqrt{2}$

and $\quad \theta = \theta_1 + \theta_2 - \theta_3 = \dfrac{\pi}{4} + \dfrac{5\pi}{6} - \left(\dfrac{-\pi}{2}\right) = \dfrac{19}{12}\pi = 2\pi - \dfrac{5\pi}{12}$

so $\quad z = \sqrt{2}\left[\cos\left(\dfrac{-5\pi}{12}\right) + i\sin\left(\dfrac{-5\pi}{12}\right)\right]$.

17. (a) $z_1 = 1 - i$;

$$r = \sqrt{(1)^2 + (-1)^2} = \sqrt{2}$$

so $\quad \sqrt{2}\cos\theta = 1, \quad$ i.e., $\quad \cos\theta = \dfrac{\sqrt{2}}{2}$

and $\quad \sqrt{2}\sin\theta = -1, \quad$ i.e., $\quad \sin\theta = \dfrac{-\sqrt{2}}{2}$.

Thus $\quad \theta = \dfrac{-\pi}{4}, \quad$ so $\quad 6\theta = 6\left(\dfrac{-\pi}{4}\right) = \dfrac{-3\pi}{2} = -2\pi + \dfrac{\pi}{2}$

and $\quad r^6 = (\sqrt{2})^6 = 8$

so $\quad z^6 = 8\left(\cos\dfrac{\pi}{2} + i\sin\dfrac{\pi}{2}\right)$.

b) $z = 1 + \sqrt{3}i$;

$$r = \sqrt{(1)^2 + (\sqrt{3})^2} = \sqrt{4} = 2$$

so $\quad 2\cos\theta = 1, \quad$ i.e., $\quad \cos\theta = \dfrac{1}{2}$

and $\quad 2\sin\theta = \sqrt{3}, \quad$ i.e., $\quad \sin\theta = \dfrac{\sqrt{3}}{2}$.

Thus $\quad \theta = \dfrac{\pi}{3}, \quad$ so $\quad 5\theta = \dfrac{5\pi}{3} = 2\pi - \dfrac{\pi}{3}$

and $\quad r^5 = 2^5 = 32$

so $\quad z^5 = 32\left[\cos\left(\dfrac{-\pi}{3}\right) + i\sin\left(\dfrac{-\pi}{3}\right)\right]$.

(c) $z = \sqrt{3} - i$;

$$r = \sqrt{(\sqrt{3})^2 + (-1)^2} = \sqrt{4} = 2$$

so $2\cos\theta = \sqrt{3}$,   i.e., $\cos\theta = \dfrac{\sqrt{3}}{2}$

and $2\sin\theta = -1$,   i.e., $\sin\theta = \dfrac{-1}{2}$.

Thus $\theta = \dfrac{-\pi}{6}$,   so $7\theta = \dfrac{-7\pi}{6} = -2\pi + \dfrac{5\pi}{6}$

and $r^7 = 2^7 = 128$

so $z^7 = 128\left(\cos\dfrac{5\pi}{6} + i\sin\dfrac{5\pi}{6}\right)$.

(d) $z = 2 + 2i$;

$$r = \sqrt{2^2 + 2^2} = \sqrt{8} = 2\sqrt{2}$$

so $2\sqrt{2}\cos\theta = 2$,   i.e., $\cos\theta = \dfrac{\sqrt{2}}{2}$

and $2\sqrt{2}\sin\theta = 2$,   i.e., $\sin\theta = \dfrac{\sqrt{2}}{2}$.

Thus $\theta = \dfrac{\pi}{4}$,   so $-3\theta = \dfrac{-3\pi}{4}$

and $r^{-3} = \left(2\sqrt{2}\right)^{-3} = \dfrac{\sqrt{2}}{32}$

so $z^{-3} = \dfrac{\sqrt{2}}{32}\left[\cos\left(\dfrac{-3\pi}{4}\right) + i\sin\left(\dfrac{-3\pi}{4}\right)\right]$.

18. $z = \sqrt{3} + -1i$;

$$r = \sqrt{(\sqrt{3})^2 + (-1)^2} = \sqrt{4} = 2$$

so $2\cos\theta = \sqrt{3}$,   i.e., $\cos\theta = \dfrac{\sqrt{3}}{2}$

and $2\sin\theta = -1$,   i.e., $\sin\theta = \dfrac{-1}{2}$.

Thus $\theta = \dfrac{-\pi}{6}$,

and $\dfrac{1}{2}\left(\dfrac{-\pi}{6} + 2k\pi\right) = \dfrac{-\pi}{12}, \dfrac{5\pi}{12}$.

Also $r^{1/2} = 2^{1/2} = \sqrt{2}$,

so $z^{1/2} = \sqrt{2}\left[\cos\left(\dfrac{-\pi}{12}\right) + i\sin\left(\dfrac{-\pi}{12}\right)\right]$ or $\sqrt{2}\left[\cos\left(\dfrac{5\pi}{12}\right) + i\sin\left(\dfrac{5\pi}{12}\right)\right]$.

19. $z = i = 0 + 1i;$

$$r = \sqrt{0^2 + 1^2} = \sqrt{1} = 1$$

so $\quad 1\cos\theta = 0, \quad$ i.e., $\quad \cos\theta = 0$

and $\quad 1\sin\theta = 1, \quad$ i.e., $\quad \sin\theta = 1.$

Thus $\quad \theta = \dfrac{\pi}{2},$

and $\quad \dfrac{1}{3} = (\dfrac{\pi}{2} + 2k\pi) = \dfrac{\pi}{6}, \dfrac{5\pi}{6}, \dfrac{-\pi}{2}.$

Also $\quad r^{1/3} = 1^{1/3} = 1,$

so $\quad z^{1/3} = \cos\dfrac{\pi}{6} + i\sin\dfrac{\pi}{6},$

or $\quad \cos\dfrac{5\pi}{6} + i\sin\dfrac{5\pi}{6},$

or $\quad \cos\left(\dfrac{-\pi}{2}\right) + i\sin\left(\dfrac{-\pi}{2}\right).$

20. $z = 8\sqrt{2} + 8\sqrt{2}i;$

$$r = \sqrt{(8\sqrt{2})^2 + (8\sqrt{2})^2} = \sqrt{128 + 128} = \sqrt{256} = 16$$

so $\quad 16\cos\theta = 8\sqrt{2}, \quad$ i.e., $\quad \cos\theta = \dfrac{\sqrt{2}}{2}$

and $\quad 16\sin\theta = 8\sqrt{2}, \quad$ i.e., $\quad \sin\theta = \dfrac{\sqrt{2}}{2}.$

Thus $\quad \theta = \dfrac{\pi}{4},$

and $\quad \dfrac{1}{4} = (\dfrac{\pi}{4} + 2k\pi) = \dfrac{\pi}{16}, \dfrac{9\pi}{16}, \dfrac{-7\pi}{16}, \dfrac{-15\pi}{16}.$

Also $\quad r^{1/4} = 16^{1/4} = 2,$

so $\quad z^{1/4} = 2\left[\cos\left(\dfrac{\pi}{16}\right) + i\sin\left(\dfrac{\pi}{16}\right)\right] \quad$ or $\quad 2\left[\cos\left(\dfrac{9\pi}{16}\right) + i\sin\left(\dfrac{9\pi}{16}\right)\right]$

or $\quad 2\left[\cos\left(\dfrac{-7\pi}{16}\right) + i\sin\left(\dfrac{-7\pi}{16}\right)\right] \quad$ or $\quad 2\left[\cos\left(\dfrac{-15\pi}{16}\right) + i\sin\left(\dfrac{-15\pi}{16}\right)\right].$

21. $z = 1 = 1 + 0i;$

$$r = \sqrt{1^2 + 0^2} = \sqrt{1} = 1$$

so $\quad 1\cos\theta = 1, \quad$ i.e., $\quad \cos\theta = 1$

Thus $\quad \theta = 0,$

and $\quad \dfrac{1}{5}(0 + 2k\pi) = 0, \dfrac{2\pi}{5}, \dfrac{4\pi}{5}, \dfrac{-2\pi}{5}, \dfrac{-4\pi}{5}.$

Also $\quad r^{1/5} = 1^{1/5} = 1,$

so $\quad z^{1/5} = \cos 0 + i\sin 0 \quad$ or $\quad \cos\left(\dfrac{2\pi}{5}\right) + i\sin\left(\dfrac{2\pi}{5}\right)$

$$\text{or} \quad \cos\left(\frac{4\pi}{5}\right) + i\sin\left(\frac{4\pi}{5}\right) \quad \text{or} \quad \cos\left(\frac{-2\pi}{5}\right) + i\sin\left(\frac{-2\pi}{5}\right)$$

$$\text{or} \quad \cos\left(\frac{-4\pi}{5}\right) + i\sin\left(\frac{-4\pi}{5}\right).$$

22. $z^4 + 16 = 0$ so $z^4 = -16$ and $z = (-16 + 0i)^{1/4}$;

$$r = \sqrt{(-16)^2 + (0)^2} = \sqrt{256} = 16$$

so $\quad 16\cos\theta = -16, \quad$ i.e., $\quad \cos\theta = -1$

Thus $\quad \theta = \pi$,

and $\quad \dfrac{1}{4}(\pi + 2k\pi) = \dfrac{\pi}{4}, \dfrac{3\pi}{4}, \dfrac{-\pi}{4}, \dfrac{-3\pi}{4}$.

Also $\quad r^{1/4} = 16^{1/4} = 2$,

so the roots are $\quad z_1 = 2\left[\cos\left(\dfrac{\pi}{4}\right) + i\sin\left(\dfrac{\pi}{4}\right)\right] = \sqrt{2} + \sqrt{2}i$

$$z_2 = 2\left[\cos\left(\dfrac{3\pi}{4}\right) + i\sin\left(\dfrac{3\pi}{4}\right)\right] = -\sqrt{2} + \sqrt{2}i$$

$$z_3 = 2\left[\cos\left(\dfrac{-\pi}{4}\right) + i\sin\left(\dfrac{-\pi}{4}\right)\right] = \sqrt{2} - \sqrt{2}i = \bar{z}_1$$

$$z_4 = 2\left[\cos\left(\dfrac{-3\pi}{4}\right) + i\sin\left(\dfrac{-3\pi}{4}\right)\right] = -\sqrt{2} - \sqrt{2}i = \bar{z}_2.$$

Note $\quad (z - z_1)(z - z_3) = z^2 - 2\sqrt{2}z + 4$

and $\quad (z - z_2)(z - z_4) = z^2 + 2\sqrt{2}z + 4$

so $\quad z^4 + 16 = (z^2 - 2\sqrt{2}z + 4)(z^2 + 2\sqrt{2}z + 4)$.

23. $z^6 + 8 = 0$ so $z^6 = -8$ and $z = (-8 + 0i)^{1/6}$;

$$r = \sqrt{(-8)^2 + (0)^2} = \sqrt{64} = 8$$

so $\quad 8\cos\theta = -8, \quad$ i.e., $\quad \cos\theta = -1$.

Thus $\quad \theta = \pi$,

and $\quad \dfrac{1}{6}(\pi + 2k\pi) = \dfrac{\pi}{6}, \dfrac{\pi}{2}, \dfrac{5\pi}{6}, \dfrac{-\pi}{6}, \dfrac{-\pi}{2}, \dfrac{-5\pi}{6}$.

Also $\quad r^{1/6} = 8^{1/6} = 2^{3/6} = \sqrt{2}$,

so the roots are $\quad z_1 = \sqrt{2}\left[\cos\left(\dfrac{\pi}{6}\right) + i\sin\left(\dfrac{\pi}{6}\right)\right] = \sqrt{2}\left(\dfrac{\sqrt{3}}{2} + \dfrac{1}{2}i\right)$

$$z_2 = \sqrt{2}\left[\cos\left(\dfrac{\pi}{2}\right) + i\sin\left(\dfrac{\pi}{2}\right)\right] = \sqrt{2}i$$

$$z_3 = \sqrt{2}\left[\cos\left(\dfrac{5\pi}{6}\right) + i\sin\left(\dfrac{5\pi}{6}\right)\right] = \sqrt{2}\left(\dfrac{-\sqrt{3}}{2} + \dfrac{1}{2}i\right)$$

$$z_4 = \sqrt{2}\left[\cos\left(\frac{-\pi}{6}\right) + i\sin\left(\frac{-\pi}{6}\right)\right] = \sqrt{2}\left(\frac{\sqrt{3}}{2} - \frac{1}{2}i\right) = \bar{z}_1$$

$$z_5 = \sqrt{2}\left[\cos\left(\frac{-\pi}{2}\right) + i\sin\left(\frac{-\pi}{2}\right)\right] = \sqrt{2}i = \bar{z}_2$$

$$z_6 = \sqrt{2}\left[\cos\left(\frac{-5\pi}{6}\right) + i\sin\left(\frac{-5\pi}{6}\right)\right] = \sqrt{2}\left(\frac{-\sqrt{3}}{2} - \frac{1}{2}i\right) = \bar{z}_3$$

Note $\quad (z - z_1)(z - z_4) = z^2 - \sqrt{6}z + 2$

and $\quad (z - z_2)(z - z_5) = z^2 + 2$

and $\quad (z - z_3)(z - z_6) = z^2 + \sqrt{6}z + 2$

so $\quad z^6 + 8 = (z^2 - \sqrt{6}z + 2)(z^2 + \sqrt{6}z + 2)(z^2 + 2).$

SECTION 10.4 *COMPLEX VECTOR SPACES*

24.   (a) $\mathbf{u} + \mathbf{v} = (2 - i, 3 + 2i) + (i, 4 - i) = (2, 7 + i)$

    (b) $2\mathbf{u} - 3i\mathbf{v} = (4 - 2i, 6 + 4i) + (3, -3 - 12i) = (7 - 2i, 3 - 8i)$

    (c) $\mathbf{u} \cdot \mathbf{v} = (2 - i, 3 + 2i) \cdot (i, 4 - i) = (2 - i)(-i) + (3 + 2i)(4 + i)$

             $= (-1 - 2i) + (10 + 11i) = 9 + 9i$

    (d) $\mathbf{v} \cdot \mathbf{u} = \overline{\mathbf{u} \cdot \mathbf{v}} = 9 - 9i \quad$ from (c)

       so $\quad \mathbf{u} \cdot \mathbf{v} - \mathbf{v} \cdot \mathbf{u} = (9 + 9i) - (9 - 9i) = 18i$

    (e) $i\mathbf{u} - 2\mathbf{v} = i(2 - i, 3 + 2i) - 2(i, 4 - i) = (1 + 2i, -2 + 3i) + (-2i, -8 + 2i)$

             $= (1, -10 + 5i)$

$$\|i\mathbf{u} - 2\mathbf{v}\| = \|(1, -10 + 5i)\| = \sqrt{(1)(1) + (-10 + 5i)(-10 - 5i)}$$

$$= \sqrt{1 + 100 + 25} = \sqrt{126} = 3\sqrt{14}.$$

    (f) $3\mathbf{u} - 2\mathbf{v} = 3(2 - i, 3 + 2i) - 2(i, 4 - i) = (6 - 3i, 9 + 6i) + (-2i, -8 + 2i)$

             $= (6 - 5i, 1 + 8i)$

$$\|3\mathbf{u} - 2\mathbf{v}\| = \|(6 - 5i, 1 + 8i)\| = \sqrt{(6 - 5i)(6 + 5i) + (1 + 8i)(1 - 8i)}$$

$$= \sqrt{36 + 25 + 1 + 64} = \sqrt{126} = 3\sqrt{14}$$

$$2\mathbf{u} - 3i\mathbf{v} = 2(2 - i, 3 + 2i) - 3i(i, 4 - i) = (4 - 2i, 6 + 4i) + (3, -3 - 12i)$$

$$= (7 - 2i, 3 - 8i)$$

$$\|2\mathbf{u} - 3i\mathbf{v}\| = \|(7 - 2i, 3 - 8i)\| = \sqrt{(7 - 2i)(7 + 2i) + (3 - 8i)(3 + 8i)}$$

$$= \sqrt{49 + 4 + 9 + 64} = \sqrt{126} = 3\sqrt{14}$$

$$\|3\mathbf{u} - 2\mathbf{v}\| + \|2\mathbf{u} - 3i\mathbf{v}\| = 3\sqrt{14} + 3\sqrt{14} = 6\sqrt{14}.$$

25. (a) $\mathbf{u} - \mathbf{v} = (1, -i, 1 + 4i) - (i, 3 - i, 2 + i) = (1 - i, -3, -1 + 3i)$

(b) $2\mathbf{u} + \mathbf{v} = 2(1, -i, 1 + 4i) + (i, 3 - i, 2 + i) = (2 + i, 3 - 3i, 4 + 9i)$

(c) $\mathbf{u} - 3i\mathbf{v} = (1, -i, 1 + 4i) - 3i(i, 3 - i, 2 + i) = (1, -i, 1 + 4i) + (3, -3 - 9i, 3 - 6i)$

$\quad = (4, -3 - 10i, 4 - 2i)$

(d) $\mathbf{v} \cdot \mathbf{u} = (i, 3 - i, 2 + i) \cdot (1, -i, 1 + 4i) = (i)(1) + (3 - i)(i) + (2 + i)(1 - 4i)$

$\quad = i + (1 + 3i) + (6 - 7i) = 7 - 3i$

(e) $\|\mathbf{v}\| = \|(i, 3 - i, 2 + i)\| = \sqrt{(i)(-i) + (3 - i)(3 + i) + (2 + i)(2 - i)}$

$\quad = \sqrt{1 + 9 + 1 + 4 + 1} = \sqrt{16} = 4$

(f) $\mathbf{u} + \mathbf{v} = (1, -i, 1 + 4i) + (i, 3 - i, 2 + i) = (1 + i, 3 - 2i, 3 + 5i)$

$\|\mathbf{u} + \mathbf{v}\| = \|(1 + i, 3 - 2i, 3 + 5i)\| = \sqrt{(1 + i)(1 - i) + (3 - 2i)(3 + 2i) + (3 + 5i)(3 - 5i)}$

$\quad = \sqrt{1 + 1 + 9 + 4 + 9 + 25} = \sqrt{49} = 7.$

26. (a) $\begin{bmatrix} -i & 2 - i & i \\ 3 - 2i & 4i & -3 - 5i \\ 1 + i & i & 1 \end{bmatrix} \longrightarrow \begin{bmatrix} 1 & 1 + 2i & -1 \\ 0 & -7 & -7i \\ 0 & 1 - 2i & 2 + i \end{bmatrix} \longrightarrow \begin{bmatrix} 1 & 1 + 2i & -1 \\ 0 & 1 & i \\ 0 & 0 & 0 \end{bmatrix}$

$\longrightarrow \begin{bmatrix} 1 & 0 & 1 - i \\ 0 & 1 & i \\ 0 & 0 & 0 \end{bmatrix}$

Thus $\quad (-i, 3 - 2i, 1 + i) = (1 - i)\mathbf{u} + i\mathbf{v}.$

(b) $\begin{bmatrix} -i & 2 - i & 2 \\ 3 - 2i & 4i & 4 - i \\ 1 + i & i & 2 + i \end{bmatrix} \longrightarrow \begin{bmatrix} 1 & 1 + 2i & 2i \\ 0 & -7 & -7i \\ 0 & 1 - 2i & 3 + 2i \end{bmatrix} \longrightarrow \begin{bmatrix} 1 & 1 + 2i & 2i \\ 0 & 1 & i \\ 0 & 0 & 1 + i \end{bmatrix}$

Thus, there is no solution.

27. (a) $\begin{bmatrix} i & 3 & -1 + 3i & 5 + 3i \\ 2 - i & 3 + i & 5i & 0 \\ 1 + i & i & -2 + i & 1 - i \end{bmatrix} \longrightarrow \begin{bmatrix} 1 & -3i & 3 + i & 3 - 5i \\ 0 & 6 + 7i & -7 + 6i & -1 + 13i \\ 0 & -3 + 4i & -4 - 3i & -7 + i \end{bmatrix}$

$\longrightarrow \begin{bmatrix} 1 & -3i & 3 + i & 3 - 5i \\ 0 & 1 & i & 1 + i \\ 0 & 0 & 0 & 0 \end{bmatrix} \longrightarrow \begin{bmatrix} 1 & 0 & i & -2i \\ 0 & 1 & i & 1 + i \\ 0 & 0 & 0 & 0 \end{bmatrix}$

Let $\quad c_3 = t;$

then $\quad c_2 + ic_3 = 1 + i,$ i.e., $\quad c_2 = 1 + i - ic_3 = 1 + i - it$

and $c_1 + ic_3 = -2i,$ i.e., $c_1 = -2i - ic_3 = -2i - it$

Thus, there are infinitely many solutions, one of them being (set $t = 0$) :

$$c_3 = 0, \quad c_2 = 1 + i, \quad c_1 = -2i,$$

i.e., $(5 + 3i, 0, 1 - i) = -2i\mathbf{u} + (1 + i)\mathbf{v} + 0\mathbf{w}.$

(b) $\begin{bmatrix} i & 3 & -1+3i & 1+2i \\ 2-i & 3+i & 5i & -3-11i \\ 1+i & i & -2+i & 6-2i \end{bmatrix} \longrightarrow \begin{bmatrix} 1 & -3i & 3+i & 2-i \\ 0 & 6+7i & -7+6i & -6-7i \\ 0 & -3+4i & -4-3i & 3-3i \end{bmatrix}$

$\longrightarrow \begin{bmatrix} 1 & -3i & 3+i & 2-i \\ 0 & 1 & i & -1 \\ 0 & 0 & 0 & i \end{bmatrix}$

Thus, there is no solution.

28. (a) $\begin{bmatrix} i & 1-i & 1 \\ 1+i & 2+i & -2+i \end{bmatrix} \longrightarrow \begin{bmatrix} 1 & -1-i & -i \\ 0 & 2+3i & -3+2i \end{bmatrix} \longrightarrow \begin{bmatrix} 1 & 0 & -1 \\ 0 & 1 & i \end{bmatrix}$

Thus $(1, -2 + i) = -1\mathbf{u} + i\mathbf{v}.$

(b) $\begin{bmatrix} i & 1-i & 3-2i \\ 1+i & 2+i & 0 \end{bmatrix} \longrightarrow \begin{bmatrix} 1 & -1-i & -2-3i \\ 0 & 2+3i & -1+5i \end{bmatrix} \longrightarrow \begin{bmatrix} 1 & 0 & -2-i \\ 0 & 1 & 1+i \end{bmatrix}$

Thus $(3 - 2i, 0) = (-2 - i)\mathbf{u} + (1 + i)\mathbf{v}.$

29. Axiom (1):   If (z_1, z_2) is a pair of complex numbers

and (z_1', z_2') is a pair of complex numbers

then $(z_1 + z_1', z_2 + z_2')$ is a pair of complex numbers.

(2) : $(z_1, z_2) + (z_1', z_2') = (z_1 + z_1', z_2 + z_2')$

$(z_1', z_2') + (z_1, z_2) = (z_1' + z_1, z_2' + z_2) = (z_1 + z_1', z_2 + z_2')$

(3) : $(z_1, z_2) + ((z_1', z_2') + (z_1'', z_2'')) = (z_1, z_2) + (z_1' + z_1'', z_2' + z_2'')$

$= (z_1 + z_1' + z_1'', z_2 + z_2' + z_2'')$

$((z_1, z_2) + (z_1', z_2')) + (z_1'', z_2'') = (z_1 + z_1', z_2 + z_2') + (z_1'', z_2'')$

$= (z_1 + z_1' + z_1'', z_2 + z_2' + z_2'')$

(4) : There is an object $\mathbf{0} = (0, 0)$ which is a pair of complex numbers

and $(z_1, z_2) + \mathbf{0} = (z_1, z_2) + (0, 0)$

$= (z_1 + 0, z_2 + 0)$

$= (z_1, z_2)$

(5) : For each pair of complex numbers $(z_1, z_2),$ there is an

object $(-z_1, -z_2)$ which is a pair of complex numbers and

$(z_1, z_2) + (-z_1, -z_2) = (z_1 + -z_1, z_2 + -z_2)$

$= (0, 0)$

$= \mathbf{0}$

(6) : If (z_1, z_2) is a pair of complex numbers

and k is a complex number

then $k(z_1, z_2) = (kiz_1, kiz_2)$ is a pair of complex numbers.

(7) : $k((z_1, z_2) + (z_1', z_2')) = k(z_1 + z_1', z_2 + z_2')$

$$= (ki(z_1 + z_1'), ki(z_2 + z_2'))$$

$$k(z_1, z_2) + k(z_1', z_2') = (kiz_1, kiz_2) + (kiz_1', kiz_2')$$

$$= (kiz_1 + kiz_1', kiz_2 + kiz_2')$$

$$= (ki(z_1 + z_1'), ki(z_2 + z_2'))$$

(8) : $(k + \ell)(z_1, z_2) = ((k + \ell)iz_1, (k + \ell)iz_2)$

$$k(z_1, z_2) + \ell(z_1, z_2) = (kiz_1, kiz_2) + (\ell iz_1, \ell iz_2)$$

$$= (kiz_1 + \ell iz_1, kiz_2 + \ell iz_2)$$

$$= ((k + \ell)iz_1, (k + \ell)iz_2)$$

(9)   fails: $k(\ell(z_1, z_2)) = k(\ell iz_1, \ell iz_2)$

$$= (ki\ell iz_1, ki\ell iz_2)$$

$$= (-k\ell z_1, -k\ell z_2)$$

$$(k\ell)(z_1, z_2) = (k\ell iz_1, k\ell iz_2)$$

$$= (-k\ell z_1, -k\ell z_2) \quad \text{only if} \quad k = 0 \quad \text{or} \quad \ell = 0$$

$$\text{or} \quad z_1 = z_2 = 0$$

(10)   fails: $1(z_1, z_2) = (1iz_1, 1iz_2)$

$$\neq (z_1, z_2) \quad \text{unless} \quad z_1 = z_2 = 0$$

Since Axioms (9) and (10) fail, this is not a complex vector space.

30. Axiom (1):   If (z_1, z_2) is a pair of complex numbers

and (z_1', z_2') is a pair of complex numbers

then $(z_1 + z_1' + i, z_2 + z_2' + i)$ is a pair of complex numbers.

(2) : $(z_1, z_2) + (z_1', z_2') = (z_1 + z_1' + i, z_2 + z_2' + i)$

$(z_1', z_2') + (z_1, z_2) = (z_1' + z_1 + i, z_2' + z_2 + i)$

$$= (z_1 + z_1' + i, z_2 + z_2' + i)$$

(3) : $(z_1, z_2) + ((z_1', z_2') + (z_1'', z_2''))$

$$= (z_1, z_2) + (z_1' + z_1'' + i, z_2' + z_2'' + i)$$

$$= (z_1 + z_1' + z_1'' + 2i, z_2 + z_2' + z_2'' + 2i)$$

$$((z_1, z_2) + (z_1', z_2')) + (z_1'', z_2'')$$

$$= (z_1 + z_1' + i, z_2 + z_2' + i) + (z_1'', z_2'')$$

$$= (z_1 + z_1' + i + z_1'' + i, z_2 + z_2' + i + z_2'' + i)$$

$$= (z_1 + z_1' + z_1'' + 2i, z_2 + z_2' + z_2'' + 2i)$$

(4) : There is an object $\mathbf{0} = (-i, -i)$ which is a pair of complex numbers

and $(z_1, z_2) + \mathbf{0} = (z_1, z_2) + (-i, -i)$

$$= (z_1 + -i + i, z_2 + -i + i)$$

$$= (z_1, z_2)$$

(5) : For each pair of complex numbers (z_1, z_2), there is an

object $(-z_1 - 2i, -z_2 - 2i)$ which is a pair of complex numbers and

and $(z_1, z_2) + (-z_1 - 2i, -z_2 - 2i)$

$$= (z_1 + -z_1 - 2i + i, z_2 + -z_2 - 2i + i)$$

$$= (-i, -i)$$

$$= \mathbf{0}.$$

(6) : If (z_1, z_2) is a pair of complex numbers

and k is a complex number

then $k(z_1, z_2) = (kz_1, kz_2)$ is a pair of complex numbers.

(7) fails: $k\big((z_1, z_2) + (z_1', z_2')\big) = k(z_1 + z_1' + i, z_2 + z_2' + i)$

$$= (kz_1 + kz_1' + ki, kz_2 + kz_2' + ki)$$

$k(z_1, z_2) + k(z_1', z_2') = (kz_1, kz_2) + (kz_1', kz_2')$

$$= (kz_1 + kz_1' + i, kz_2 + kz_2' + i)$$

$$\neq (kz_1 + kz_1' + ki, kz_2 + kz_2' + ki)) \qquad \text{unless} \quad k = 1$$

(8) fails: $(k + \ell)(z_1, z_2) = \big((k + \ell)z_1, (k + \ell)z_2\big)$

$k(z_1, z_2) + \ell(z_1, z_2) = (kz_1, kz_2) + (\ell z_1, \ell z_2)$

$$= (kz_1 + \ell z_1 + i, kz_2 + \ell z_2 + i)$$

$$= \big((k + \ell)z_1 + i, (k + \ell)z_2 + i\big)$$

$$\neq \big((k + \ell)z_1, (k + \ell)z_2\big)$$

(9) : $k\big(\ell(z_1, z_2)\big) = k(\ell z_1, \ell z_2)$

$$= (k\ell z_1, k\ell z_2)$$

$(k\ell)(z_1, z_2) = (k\ell z_1, k\ell z_2)$

(10) : $1(z_1, z_2) = (1z_1, 1z_2)$

$$= (z_1, z_2)$$

Since Axioms (7) and (8) fail, this is not a complex vector space.

31. Closure under addition:

(z_1, z_2) such that $\|(z_1, z_2)\| = 1$, i.e., $z_1\bar{z}_1 + z_2\bar{z}_2 = 1$

$+ (z_1', z_2')$ such that $\|(z_1', z_2')\| = 1$, i.e., $z_1'\overline{z_1'} + z_2'\overline{z_2'} = 1$

$= (z_1 + z_1', z_2 + z_2')$ such that

$$(z_1 + z_1')\overline{(z_1 + z_1')} + (z_2 + z_2')\overline{(z_2 + z_2')}$$
$$= (z_1 + z_1')(\bar{z}_1 + \overline{z_1'}) + (z_2 + z_2')(\bar{z}_2 + \overline{z_2'})$$
$$= (z_1\bar{z}_1 + z_1\overline{z_1'} + z_1'\bar{z}_1 + z_1'\overline{z_1'}) + (z_2\bar{z}_2 + z_2\overline{z_2'} + z_2'\bar{z}_2 + z_2'\overline{z_2'})$$
$$= (z_1\bar{z}_1 + z_2\bar{z}_2) + (z_1'\overline{z_1'} + z_2'\overline{z_2'}) + (z_1\overline{z_1'} + z_1'\bar{z}_1 + z_2\overline{z_2'} + z_2'\bar{z}_2)$$
$$= 1 + 1 + (z_1\overline{z_1'} + z_1'\bar{z}_1 + z_2\overline{z_2'} + z_2'\bar{z}_2)$$
$$\neq 1 \quad \text{in general}$$

For example, $\quad (1,0) + (0,1) = (1,1)$

but $\quad \|(1,1)\| = \sqrt{1\cdot\bar{1} + 1\cdot\bar{1}} = \sqrt{1\cdot1 + 1\cdot1} = \sqrt{2} \neq 1.$

Since closure under addition fails, the set is not a subspace.

Closure under multiplication:

$k \quad$ such that $\quad k \quad$ is complex

$\cdot (z_1, z_2) \quad$ such that $\quad \|(z_1, z_2)\| = 1, \quad$ i.e., $\quad z_1\bar{z}_1 + z_2\bar{z}_2 = 1$

$= (kz_1, kz_2) \quad$ such that

$$(kz_1)(\overline{kz_1}) + (kz_2)(\overline{kz_2}) = kz_1k\bar{z}_1 + kz_2k\bar{z}_2$$
$$= k^2 z_1\bar{z}_1 + k^2 z_2\bar{z}_2$$
$$= k^2(z_1\bar{z}_1 + z_2\bar{z}_2)$$
$$= k^2(1)$$
$$= k^2$$
$$\neq 1 \quad \text{in general.}$$

For example, $\quad 2(1,0) = (2,0)$

but $\quad \|(2,0)\| = \sqrt{2\cdot\bar{2} + 0\cdot\bar{0}} = \sqrt{2\cdot2 + 0\cdot0} = \sqrt{4} = 2 \neq 1.$

Since closure under multiplication fails, the set is not a subspace.

32. Closure under addition:

$\quad (z_1, z_2, z_3) \quad$ such that $\quad z_3 = i(z_1 + z_2)$

$+ \ (z_1', z_2', z_3') \quad$ such that $z_3' = i(z_1' + z_2')$

$= \ (z_1 + z_1', z_2 + z_2', z_3 + z_3') \quad$ such that

$$z_3 + z_3' = i(z_1 + z_2) + i(z_1' + z_2')$$
$$= iz_1 + iz_2 + iz_1' + iz_2'$$
$$= iz_1 + iz_1' + iz_2 + iz_2'$$
$$= i(z_1 + z_1') + i(z_2 + z_2')$$

Closure under multiplication:

$k \quad$ such that $\quad k \quad$ is complex

$\cdot (z_1, z_2, z_3) \quad$ such that $\quad z_3 = i(z_1 + z_2)$

$= (kz_1, kz_2, kz_3) \quad$ such that

$$kz_3 = ki(z_1 + z_2)$$
$$= i(kz_1 + kz_2)$$

Since both closures hold, the set is a subspace.

33. Closure under addition:

$$\begin{bmatrix} z_1 & 0 \\ 0 & z_2 \end{bmatrix} \quad \text{such that} \quad z_1, z_2 \quad \text{are complex}$$

$$+ \begin{bmatrix} z_1' & 0 \\ 0 & z_2' \end{bmatrix} \quad \text{such that} \quad z_1', z_2' \quad \text{are complex}$$

$$= \begin{bmatrix} z_1 + z_1' & 0 \\ 0 & z_2 + z_2' \end{bmatrix} \quad \text{such that} \quad z_1 + z_1', z_2 + z_2' \quad \text{are complex.}$$

Closure under multiplication:

$$k \quad \text{such that} \quad k \quad \text{is complex}$$

$$\cdot \begin{bmatrix} z_1 & 0 \\ 0 & z_2 \end{bmatrix} \quad \text{such that} \quad z_1, z_2 \quad \text{are complex}$$

$$= \begin{bmatrix} kz_1 & 0 \\ 0 & kz_2 \end{bmatrix} \quad \text{such that} \quad kz_1, kz_2 \quad \text{are complex.}$$

Since both closures hold, the set is a subspace.

34. Closure under addition:

$$\begin{bmatrix} z_1 & z_2 \\ z_3 & z_4 \end{bmatrix} \quad \text{such that} \quad z_1 z_4 - z_2 z_3 = 0$$

$$+ \begin{bmatrix} z_1' & z_2' \\ z_3' & z_4' \end{bmatrix} \quad \text{such that} \quad z_1' z_4' - z_2' z_3' = 0$$

$$= \begin{bmatrix} z_1 + z_1' & z_2 + z_2' \\ z_3 + z_3' & z_4 + z_4' \end{bmatrix} \quad \text{such that}$$

$$(z_1 + z_1')(z_4 + z_4') - (z_2 + z_2')(z_3 + z_3')$$
$$= (z_1 z_4 + z_1 z_4' + z_1' z_4 + z_1' z_4') - (z_2 z_3 + z_2 z_3' + z_2' z_3 + z_2' z_3')$$
$$= (z_1 z_4 - z_2 z_3) + (z_1' z_4' - z_2' z_3') + (z_1 z_4' + z_1' z_4 - z_2 z_3' - z_2' z_3)$$
$$\quad 0 \quad + \quad 0 \quad + (z_1 z_4' + z_1' z_4 - z_2 z_3' - z_2' z_3)$$
$$\neq 0 \quad \text{in general.}$$

For example, $\begin{bmatrix} 1 & 0 \\ 0 & 0 \end{bmatrix} + \begin{bmatrix} 0 & 0 \\ 0 & 1 \end{bmatrix} = \begin{bmatrix} 1 & 0 \\ 0 & 1 \end{bmatrix}$

but $\quad 1 \cdot 1 - 0 \cdot 0 = 1 \neq 0.$

Since closure under addition fails, the set is not a subspace.

Closure under multiplication:

$$k \quad \text{such that} \quad k \quad \text{is complex}$$

$$\cdot \begin{bmatrix} z_1 & z_2 \\ z_3 & z_4 \end{bmatrix} \quad \text{such that} \quad z_1 z_4 - z_2 z_3 = 0$$

$$= \begin{bmatrix} kz_1 & kz_2 \\ kz_3 & kz_4 \end{bmatrix} \quad \text{such that}$$

$$(kz_1)(kz_4) - (kz_2)(kz_3) = k^2 z_1 z_4 - k^2 z_2 z_3$$
$$= k^2(z_1 z_4 - z_2 z_3)$$
$$= k^2(0)$$
$$= 0.$$

35. (a) $\begin{vmatrix} i & 0 & 1+i \\ 1 & i & 2i \\ i & 1-i & 0 \end{vmatrix} = i[0 - 2i(1-i)] + (1+i)[(1-i) - i^2]$

$$= i(-2i - 2) + (1+i)(2 - i)$$
$$= (2 - 2i) + (3 + i)$$
$$= 5 - i \neq 0, \quad \text{so the vectors span } C^3.$$

(b) $\begin{vmatrix} i & 1+2i & -1+2i \\ -2i & 2-3i & 1 \\ 3i & 0 & 3+3i \end{vmatrix} = 3i[(1+2i)(1) - (2-3i)(-1+2i)] +$

$$(3+3i)[i(2-3i) + 2i(1+2i)]$$

$$= 3i[(1+2i) - (4+7i)] + 3(1+i)[(3+2i) + (-4+2i)]$$

$$= 3i(-3 - 5i) + 3(1+i)(-1 + 4i)$$

$$= 3(5 - 3i + -5 + 3i)$$

$$= 3(0) = 0, \quad \text{so the vectors do not span } C^3.$$

(c) $\begin{bmatrix} i & 0 & 1+2i & -i \\ 0 & 1 & 1 & i \\ 1+i & 1-i & 4 & 0 \end{bmatrix} \longrightarrow \begin{bmatrix} 1 & 0 & 2-i & -1 \\ 0 & 1 & 1 & i \\ 0 & 1-i & 1-i & 1+i \end{bmatrix} \longrightarrow \begin{bmatrix} 1 & 0 & 2-i & -1 \\ 0 & 1 & 1 & i \\ 0 & 0 & 0 & 0 \end{bmatrix},$

so the vectors do not span C^3.

36. (a) $\begin{bmatrix} 1-i & 2 \\ 2+i & 1+3i \\ 3-2i & 5+i \end{bmatrix} \longrightarrow \begin{bmatrix} 1 & 1+i \\ 0 & 0 \\ 0 & 0 \end{bmatrix}$, so the vectors are not independent.

(b)
$$\begin{vmatrix} i & 3-i & 4 \\ -i & 0 & -1-i \\ 2 & i & 2-i \end{vmatrix} = -(3-i)[-i(2-i)-2(-1-i)]-i[i(-1-i)+i(4)]$$

$$= -(3-i)(-2i-1+2+2i)-i(-i+1+4i)$$

$$= -(3-i)(1)-i(1+3i)$$

$$= -3+i-i+3 = 0, \quad \text{so the vectors are not independent.}$$

(c)
$$\begin{vmatrix} 1+i & 2-i & 0 \\ i & 0 & 3+i \\ 0 & 1 & -i \end{vmatrix} = (1+i)[0-(3+i)]-(2-i)[-i^2-0]$$

$$= -(1+i)(3+i)-(2-i)(1)$$

$$= -[(2+4i)+(2-i)]$$

$$= -[4+3i] \neq 0, \quad \text{so the vectors are independent.}$$

37. (a)
$$\begin{vmatrix} 1 & 0 & 2 \\ i & 1+i & 0 \\ -i & 2i & 3 \end{vmatrix} = 1[3(1+i)-0]+2[i(2i)+i(1+i)]$$

$$= 3(1+i)+2(-3+i)$$

$$= -3+5i \neq 0, \quad \text{so the vectors form a basis.}$$

(b)
$$\begin{vmatrix} 0 & 3+i & i \\ 2-i & i & 1 \\ i & -1 & 0 \end{vmatrix} = -(3+i)[0-i]+i[-(2-i)-i^2]$$

$$= (3+i)(i)+i(-1+i)$$

$$= -2+2i \neq 0, \quad \text{so the vectors form a basis.}$$

302

(c) $\begin{vmatrix} i & 1 & 2+i \\ 1+i & i & 0 \\ -1+i & -i & 2 \end{vmatrix} = (2+i)[-i(1+i) - i(-1+i)] + 2[i^2 - (1+i)]$

$$= (2+i)[2] + 2[-2-i]$$

$$= 2(0) = 0, \quad \text{so the vectors do not form a basis.}$$

38. $\begin{bmatrix} 1 & 2-i & 0 \\ 1+2i & 4+3i & 0 \end{bmatrix} \longrightarrow \begin{bmatrix} 1 & 2-i & 0 \\ 0 & 0 & 0 \end{bmatrix}$

Let $x_2 = t$;

then $x_1 + (2-i)x_2 = 0$, i.e., $x_1 = -(2-i)x_2 = (-2+i)t$

so $\begin{bmatrix} x_1 \\ x_2 \end{bmatrix} = \begin{bmatrix} (-2+i)t \\ t \end{bmatrix} = t \begin{bmatrix} -2+i \\ 1 \end{bmatrix}$.

Thus, the dimension is 1 and a basis is $\left\{ \begin{bmatrix} -2+i \\ 1 \end{bmatrix} \right\}$.

39. (a) $\begin{bmatrix} 5 & 5i & 1+2i & 0 \\ 2+i & -1+2i & i & 0 \\ 3-i & 1+3i & 1+i & 0 \end{bmatrix} \longrightarrow \begin{bmatrix} 1 & i & 1/5 + (2/5)i & 0 \\ 0 & 0 & 0 & 0 \\ 0 & 0 & 0 & 0 \end{bmatrix}$

Let $x_2 = s$ and $x_3 = t$;

then $x_1 + i(x_2) + \left(\frac{1}{5} + \frac{2}{5}i \right)x_3 = 0$, i.e., $x_1 = -ix_2 - \left(\frac{1}{5} + \frac{2}{5}i \right)x_3$

$$= -is + \left(\frac{-1}{5} - \frac{2}{5}i \right)t$$

so $\begin{bmatrix} x_1 \\ x_2 \\ x_3 \end{bmatrix} = \begin{bmatrix} -is + (-1/5 - (2/5)i)t \\ s \\ t \end{bmatrix} = \begin{bmatrix} -is \\ s \\ 0 \end{bmatrix} + \begin{bmatrix} (-1/5 - (2/5)i)t \\ 0 \\ t \end{bmatrix}$

$$= s \begin{bmatrix} -i \\ 1 \\ 0 \end{bmatrix} + t \begin{bmatrix} -1/5 - (2/5)i \\ 0 \\ 1 \end{bmatrix} = s \begin{bmatrix} -i \\ 1 \\ 0 \end{bmatrix} + \frac{1}{5}t \begin{bmatrix} -1-2i \\ 0 \\ 5 \end{bmatrix}.$$

Thus, the dimension is 2 and a basis is $\left\{ \begin{bmatrix} -i \\ 1 \\ 0 \end{bmatrix}, \begin{bmatrix} -1-2i \\ 0 \\ 5 \end{bmatrix} \right\}$.

40. Axiom (1): $\langle \mathbf{u}, \mathbf{v} \rangle = 2u_1 \overline{v}_1 + 3iu_2 \overline{v}_2$

$\langle \mathbf{v}, \mathbf{u} \rangle = 2v_1 \overline{u}_1 + 3iv_2 \overline{u}_2$

$= \overline{2\overline{v}_1 u_1} + \overline{3(-i)\overline{v}_2 u_2}$

$= \overline{2u_1 \overline{v}_1 - 3iu_2 \overline{v}_2}$

$\neq \overline{2u_1 \overline{v}_1 + 3iu_2 \overline{v}_2} = \overline{\langle \mathbf{u}, \mathbf{v} \rangle}$

(2) : $\langle \mathbf{u} + \mathbf{v}, \mathbf{w} \rangle = \langle (u_1 + v_1, u_2 + v_2), (w_1, w_2) \rangle$

$= 2(u_1 + v_1)\overline{w}_1 + 3i(u_2 + v_2)\overline{w}_2$

$= 2u_1 \overline{w}_1 + 2v_1 \overline{w}_1 + 3iu_2 \overline{w}_2 + 3iv_2 \overline{w}_2$

$\langle \mathbf{u}, \mathbf{w} \rangle + \langle \mathbf{v}, \mathbf{w} \rangle = (2u_1 \overline{w}_1 + 3iu_2 \overline{w}_2) + (2v_1 \overline{w}_1 + 3iv_2 \overline{w}_2)$

$= 2u_1 \overline{w}_1 + 2v_1 \overline{w}_1 + 3iu_2 \overline{w}_2 + 3iv_2 \overline{w}_2$

$= \langle \mathbf{u} + \mathbf{v}, \mathbf{w} \rangle$

(3) : $\langle k\mathbf{u}, \mathbf{v} \rangle = \langle (ku_1, ku_2), (v_1, v_2) \rangle$

$= 2ku_1 \overline{v}_1 + 3iku_2 \overline{v}_2$

$k\langle \mathbf{u}, \mathbf{v} \rangle = k(2u_1 \overline{v}_1 + 3iu_2 \overline{v}_2)$

$= 2ku_1 \overline{v}_1 + 3iku_2 \overline{v}_2$

$= \langle k\mathbf{u}, \mathbf{v} \rangle$

(4) : $\langle \mathbf{v}, \mathbf{v} \rangle = 2v_1 \overline{v}_1 + 3iv_2 \overline{v}_2$ is not real in general;

e.g., $\langle 1, 1 \rangle = 2 + 3i$

Since Axioms (1) and (4) fail, this is not an inner product.

41. Axiom (1): $\langle \mathbf{u}, \mathbf{v} \rangle = u_1 \overline{v}_1 + (2 + 3i)u_1 \overline{v}_2 + (2 - 3i)u_2 \overline{v}_1 + 15u_2 \overline{v}_2$

$\langle \mathbf{v}, \mathbf{u} \rangle = v_1 \overline{u}_1 + (2 + 3i)v_1 \overline{u}_2 + (2 - 3i)v_2 \overline{u}_1 + 15v_2 \overline{u}_2$

$= \overline{\overline{v}_1 u_1} + \overline{(2 - 3i)\overline{v}_1 u_2} + \overline{(2 + 3i)\overline{v}_2 u_1} + \overline{15\overline{v}_2 u_2}$

$= \overline{u_1 \overline{v}_1 + (2 + 3i)u_1 \overline{v}_2 + (2 - 3i)u_2 \overline{v}_1 + 15u_2 \overline{v}_2}$

$= \overline{\langle \mathbf{u}, \mathbf{v} \rangle}$

$(2): \quad \langle \mathbf{u} + \mathbf{v}, \mathbf{w} \rangle = \langle (u_1 + v_1, u_2 + v_2), (w_1, w_2) \rangle$

$$= (u_1 + v_1)\overline{w}_1 + (2 + 3i)(u_1 + v_1)\overline{w}_2 + (2 - 3i)(u_2 + v_2)\overline{w}_1 +$$
$$15(u_2 + v_2)\overline{w}_2$$
$$= u_1\overline{w}_1 + v_1\overline{w}_1 + (2 + 3i)u_1\overline{w}_2 + (2 + 3i)v_1\overline{w}_2 + (2 - 3i)u_2\overline{w}_1 +$$
$$(2 - 3i)v_2\overline{w}_1 + 15u_2\overline{w}_2 + 15v_2\overline{w}_2$$

$\langle \mathbf{u}, \mathbf{w} \rangle + \langle \mathbf{v}, \mathbf{w} \rangle = \left[u_1\overline{w}_1 + (2 + 3i)u_1\overline{w}_2 + (2 - 3i)u_2\overline{w}_1 + 15u_2\overline{w}_2 \right]$
$$+ \left[v_1\overline{w}_1 + (2 + 3i)v_1\overline{w}_2 + (2 - 3i)v_2\overline{w}_1 + 15v_2\overline{w}_2 \right]$$
$$= u_1\overline{w}_1 + v_1\overline{w}_1 + (2 + 3i)u_1\overline{w}_2 + (2 + 3i)v_1\overline{w}_2 +$$
$$(2 - 3i)u_2\overline{w}_1 + (2 - 3i)v_2\overline{w}_1 + 15u_2\overline{w}_2 + 15v_2\overline{w}_2$$
$$= \langle \mathbf{u} + \mathbf{v}, \mathbf{w} \rangle$$

$(3): \quad \langle k\mathbf{u}, \mathbf{v} \rangle = \langle (ku_1, ku_2), (v_1, v_2) \rangle$

$$= ku_1\overline{v}_1 + (2 + 3i)ku_1\overline{v}_2 + (2 - 3i)ku_2\overline{v}_1 + 15ku_2\overline{v}_2$$

$k\langle \mathbf{u}, \mathbf{v} \rangle = k\left[u_1\overline{v}_1 + (2 + 3i)u_1\overline{v}_2 + (2 - 3i)u_2\overline{v}_1 + 15u_2\overline{v}_2 \right]$
$$= ku_1\overline{v}_1 + (2 + 3i)ku_1\overline{v}_2 + (2 - 3i)ku_2\overline{v}_1 + 15ku_2\overline{v}_2$$
$$= \langle k\mathbf{u}, \mathbf{v} \rangle$$

$(4): \quad \langle \mathbf{v}, \mathbf{v} \rangle = v_1\overline{v}_1 + (2 + 3i)v_1\overline{v}_2 + (2 - 3i)v_2\overline{v}_1 + 15v_2\overline{v}_2$

$$= v_1\overline{v}_1 + \left[(2 + 3i)v_1\overline{v}_2 + \overline{(2 + 3i)v_1\overline{v}_2} \right] + 15v_2\overline{v}_2$$
$$= v_1\overline{v}_1 + 2\mathrm{Re}\left[(2 + 3i)v_1\overline{v}_2 \right] + 15v_2\overline{v}_2$$
$$= |v_1|^2 + 2\mathrm{Re}\left[(2 + 3i)v_1\overline{v}_2 \right] + 15|v_2|^2$$
$$\geq |v_1|^2 - 2|(2 + 3i)v_1\overline{v}_2| + 15|v_2|^2$$
$$= |v_1|^2 - 2|2 + 3i||v_1||\overline{v}_2| + 15|v_2|^2$$
$$= |v_1|^2 - 2\sqrt{13}\,|v_1||v_2| + 13\,|v_2|^2 + 2|v_2|^2$$
$$= \left(|v_1| - \sqrt{13}\,|v_2| \right)^2 + 2|v_1|^2 \geq 0$$

Also $\quad \langle \mathbf{v}, \mathbf{v} \rangle = 0 \quad$ implies $\quad \left(|v_1| - \sqrt{13}\,|v_2| \right)^2 = 0 \quad$ and $2|v_2|^2 = 0$

$$|v_1| - \sqrt{13}\,|v_2| = 0 \quad \text{and} \quad |v_2| = 0$$
$$|v_1| = \sqrt{13}\,|v_2| \quad \text{and} \quad v_2 = 0$$
$$v_1 = 0 \quad \text{and} \quad v_2 = 0$$
$$\mathbf{v} = 0$$

and conversely $\quad \langle \mathbf{0}, \mathbf{0} \rangle = 0 \cdot 0 + (2 + 3i)0 \cdot 0 + (2 - 3i)0 \cdot 0 + 15 \cdot 0 \cdot 0$

$$= 0.$$

This is an inner product.

42.   (a) $\langle (1,i),(1-i,2) \rangle = (1)(\overline{1-i}) + (1-i)(1)(\overline{2}) + (1+i)(i)(\overline{1-i}) + 4(i)(\overline{2})$

$$= (1)(1+i) + (1-i)(1)(2) + (1+i)(i)(1+i) + 4(i)(2)$$

$$= (1+i) \quad + \quad (2-2i) \quad + \quad (-2) \quad + \quad 8i$$

$$= 1 + 7i$$

(b) $\|(1,i)\| = [\langle (1,i),(1,i) \rangle]^{1/2}$

$$= [(1)(\overline{1}) + (1-i)(1)(\overline{i}) + (1+i)(i)(\overline{1}) + 4(i)(\overline{i})]^{1/2}$$

$$= [(1)(1) + (1-i)(1)(-i) + (1+i)(i)(1) + 4(i)(-i)]^{1/2}$$

$$= [1 + (-1-i) + (-1+i) + (4)]^{1/2}$$

$$= [3]^{1/2} = \sqrt{3}$$

(c) $\|(1-i,2)\| = [\langle (1-i,2),(1-i,2) \rangle]^{1/2}$

$$= [(1-i)(\overline{1-i}) + (1-i)(1-i)(\overline{2}) + (1+i)(2)(\overline{1-i}) + 4(2)(\overline{2})]^{1/2}$$

$$= [(1-i)(1+i) + (1-i)(1-i)(2) + (1+i)(2)(1+i) + 4(2)(2)]^{1/2}$$

$$= [(2) + (-4i) + (4i) + 16)]^{1/2}$$

$$= [18]^{1/2} = \sqrt{18} = 3\sqrt{2}$$

(d) $d\big((1,i),(1-i,2)\big) = \|(1,i) - (1-i,2)\|$

$$= \|(i,i-2)\|$$

$$= [\langle (i,i-2),(i,i-2) \rangle]^{1/2}$$

$$= [(i)(\overline{i}) + (1-i)(i)(\overline{i-2}) + (1+i)(i-2)(\overline{i}) + 4(i-2)(\overline{i-2})]^{1/2}$$

$$= [(i)(-i) + (1-i)(i)(-2-i) + (1+i)(-2+i)(-i) + $$

$$4(-2+i)(-2-i)]^{1/2}$$

$$= [(1) + (-1-3i) + (-1+3i) + (20)]^{1/2}$$

$$= [19]^{1/2} = \sqrt{19}$$

43. (a) $\left\langle \begin{bmatrix} 1 & -i \\ i & 0 \end{bmatrix}, \begin{bmatrix} i & 1+i \\ 1-i & 2-3i \end{bmatrix} \right\rangle = (1)(\bar{i}) + 2(-i)(\overline{1+i}) + 2(i)(\overline{1-i}) + (0)(\overline{2-3i})$

$$= (1)(-i) + 2(-i)(1-i) + 2(i)(1+i) + 0$$

$$= (-i) + 2(-1-i) + 2(-1+i) + (0)$$

$$= -4 - i$$

(b) $\|A\| = \left[\left\langle \begin{bmatrix} 1 & -i \\ i & 0 \end{bmatrix}, \begin{bmatrix} 1 & -i \\ i & 0 \end{bmatrix} \right\rangle \right]^{1/2}$

$$= \left[(1)(\bar{1}) + 2(-i)(\overline{-i}) + 2(i)(\bar{i}) + (0)(\bar{0}) \right]^{1/2}$$

$$= \left[(1)(1) + 2(-i)(i) + 2(i)(-i) + 0 \right]^{1/2}$$

$$= (1 + 2 + 2 + 0)^{1/2}$$

$$= \sqrt{5}$$

(c) $\|B\| = \left[\left\langle \begin{bmatrix} i & 1+i \\ 1-i & 2-3i \end{bmatrix}, \begin{bmatrix} i & 1+i \\ 1-i & 2-3i \end{bmatrix} \right\rangle \right]^{1/2}$

$$= \left[(i)(\bar{i}) + 2(1+i)(\overline{1+i}) + 2(1-i)(\overline{1-i}) + (2-3i)(\overline{2-3i}) \right]^{1/2}$$

$$= \left[(i)(-i) + 2(1+i)(1-i) + 2(1-i)(1+i) + (2-3i)(2+3i) \right]^{1/2}$$

$$= (1 + 4 + 4 + 13)^{1/2}$$

$$= \sqrt{22}$$

(d) $d(A, B) = \left\| \begin{bmatrix} 1 & -i \\ i & 0 \end{bmatrix} - \begin{bmatrix} i & 1+i \\ 1-i & 2-3i \end{bmatrix} \right\|$

$$= \left\| \begin{bmatrix} 1-i & -1-2i \\ -1+2i & -2+3i \end{bmatrix} \right\|$$

$$= \left[\left\langle \begin{bmatrix} 1-i & -1-2i \\ -1+2i & -2+3i \end{bmatrix}, \begin{bmatrix} 1-i & -1-2i \\ -1+2i & -2+3i \end{bmatrix} \right\rangle \right]^{1/2}$$

$$= \left[(1-i)(\overline{1-i}) + 2(-1-2i)(\overline{-1-2i}) + 2(-1+2i)(\overline{-1+2i}) + (-2+3i)(\overline{-2+3i}) \right]^{1/2}$$

$$= \left[(1-i)(1+i) + 2(-1-2i)(-1+2i) + 2(-1+2i)(-1-2i) + (-2+3i)(-2-3i) \right]^{1/2}$$

$$= (2 + 10 + 10 + 13)^{1/2}$$

$$= \sqrt{35}$$

44. (a) $\langle \mathbf{u}, \mathbf{v} \rangle = \left(\frac{1}{\sqrt{2}}\right)\left(\frac{-i}{\sqrt{2}}\right) + \left(\frac{1}{\sqrt{2}}\right)\left(\frac{i}{\sqrt{2}}\right) = \frac{-i}{2} + \frac{i}{2} = 0$

$\langle \mathbf{u}, \mathbf{u} \rangle = \left(\frac{1}{\sqrt{2}}\right)\left(\frac{1}{\sqrt{2}}\right) + \left(\frac{1}{\sqrt{2}}\right)\left(\frac{1}{\sqrt{2}}\right) = \frac{1}{2} + \frac{1}{2} = 1$

$\langle \mathbf{v}, \mathbf{v} \rangle = \left(\frac{i}{\sqrt{2}}\right)\left(\frac{-i}{\sqrt{2}}\right) + \left(\frac{-i}{\sqrt{2}}\right)\left(\frac{i}{\sqrt{2}}\right) = \frac{1}{2} + \frac{1}{2} = 1$

This set is orthonormal.

(b) $\langle \mathbf{u}, \mathbf{v} \rangle = \left(\frac{1}{\sqrt{6}} - \frac{2i}{\sqrt{6}}\right)\left(\frac{3}{\sqrt{6}} + \frac{i}{\sqrt{6}}\right) + \left(\frac{i}{\sqrt{6}}\right)\left(\frac{5}{\sqrt{6}} + \frac{5i}{\sqrt{3}}\right)$

$= \left(\frac{5}{6} - \frac{5i}{6}\right) + \left(\frac{-5}{6} + \frac{5i}{6}\right) = 0$

$\langle \mathbf{u}, \mathbf{u} \rangle = \left(\frac{1}{\sqrt{6}} - \frac{2i}{\sqrt{6}}\right)\left(\frac{1}{\sqrt{6}} + \frac{2i}{\sqrt{6}}\right) + \left(\frac{i}{\sqrt{6}}\right)\left(\frac{-i}{\sqrt{6}}\right)$

$= \frac{5}{6} + \frac{1}{6} = 1$

$\langle \mathbf{v}, \mathbf{v} \rangle = \left(\frac{3}{\sqrt{6}} - \frac{i}{\sqrt{6}}\right)\left(\frac{3}{\sqrt{6}} + \frac{i}{\sqrt{6}}\right) + \left(\frac{5}{\sqrt{6}} - \frac{5i}{\sqrt{6}}\right)\left(\frac{5}{\sqrt{6}} + \frac{5i}{\sqrt{6}}\right)$

$= \frac{10}{6} + \frac{50}{6} = \frac{60}{6} = 10 \neq 1$

This set is not orthonormal.

45. (a) $\langle \mathbf{u}, \mathbf{v} \rangle = \left(\frac{1}{\sqrt{2}}\right)\left(\frac{-i}{\sqrt{2}}\right) + (0)(0) + \left(\frac{i}{\sqrt{2}}\right)\left(\frac{1}{\sqrt{2}}\right)$

$= \frac{-i}{2} + 0 + \frac{i}{2} = 0$

$\langle \mathbf{u}, \mathbf{w} \rangle = \left(\frac{1}{\sqrt{2}}\right)(0) + (0)\left(\frac{1}{\sqrt{2}} - \frac{i}{\sqrt{2}}\right) + \left(\frac{i}{\sqrt{2}}\right)(0)$

$= 0 + 0 + 0 = 0$

$\langle \mathbf{v}, \mathbf{w} \rangle = \left(\frac{i}{\sqrt{2}}\right)(0) + (0)\left(\frac{1}{\sqrt{2}} - \frac{i}{\sqrt{2}}\right) + \left(\frac{1}{\sqrt{2}}\right)(0)$

$= 0 + 0 + 0 = 0$

$\langle \mathbf{u}, \mathbf{u} \rangle = \left(\frac{1}{\sqrt{2}}\right)\left(\frac{1}{\sqrt{2}}\right) + (0)(0) + \left(\frac{i}{\sqrt{2}}\right)\left(\frac{-i}{\sqrt{2}}\right)$

$= \frac{1}{2} + 0 + \frac{1}{2} = 1$

$\langle \mathbf{v}, \mathbf{v} \rangle = \left(\frac{i}{\sqrt{2}}\right)\left(\frac{-i}{\sqrt{2}}\right) + (0)(0) + \left(\frac{1}{\sqrt{2}}\right)\left(\frac{1}{\sqrt{2}}\right)$

$= \frac{1}{2} + 0 + \frac{1}{2} = 1$

$\langle \mathbf{w}, \mathbf{w} \rangle = (0)(0) + \left(\frac{1}{\sqrt{2}} + \frac{i}{\sqrt{2}}\right)\left(\frac{1}{\sqrt{2}} - \frac{i}{\sqrt{2}}\right) + (0)(0)$

$= 0 + 1 + 0 = 1$

This set is orthonormal.

(b) $\langle \mathbf{u}, \mathbf{v} \rangle = \left(\frac{1}{\sqrt{6}} + \frac{i}{\sqrt{6}} \right) \left(\frac{2i}{\sqrt{6}} \right) + \left(\frac{1}{\sqrt{6}} + \frac{i}{\sqrt{6}} \right) \left(\frac{-i}{\sqrt{6}} \right) + \left(\frac{1}{\sqrt{6}} + \frac{i}{\sqrt{6}} \right) \left(\frac{-i}{\sqrt{6}} \right)$

$\qquad = \left(\frac{-2}{6} + \frac{2i}{6} \right) + \left(\frac{1}{6} + \frac{-i}{6} \right) + \left(\frac{1}{6} + \frac{-i}{6} \right) = 0$

$\langle \mathbf{u}, \mathbf{w} \rangle = \left(\frac{1}{\sqrt{6}} + \frac{i}{\sqrt{6}} \right)(0) + \left(\frac{1}{\sqrt{6}} + \frac{i}{\sqrt{6}} \right) \left(\frac{\sqrt{2}}{\sqrt{6}} + \frac{i}{\sqrt{6}} \right) + \left(\frac{1}{\sqrt{6}} + \frac{i}{\sqrt{6}} \right) \left(\frac{-\sqrt{2}}{\sqrt{6}} - \frac{i}{\sqrt{6}} \right)$

$\qquad = 0 + \left(\frac{\sqrt{2}-1}{6} + \frac{\sqrt{2}+1}{6}i \right) + \left(\frac{1-\sqrt{2}}{6} - \frac{\sqrt{2}+1}{6}i \right) = 0$

$\langle \mathbf{v}, \mathbf{w} \rangle = \left(\frac{-2i}{\sqrt{6}} \right)(0) + \left(\frac{i}{\sqrt{6}} \right) \left(\frac{\sqrt{2}}{\sqrt{6}} + \frac{i}{\sqrt{6}} \right) + \left(\frac{i}{\sqrt{6}} \right) \left(\frac{-\sqrt{2}}{\sqrt{6}} - \frac{i}{\sqrt{6}} \right)$

$\qquad = 0 + \left(\frac{-1}{6} + \frac{\sqrt{2}}{6}i \right) + \left(\frac{1}{6} - \frac{\sqrt{2}}{6}i \right) = 0$

$\langle \mathbf{u}, \mathbf{u} \rangle = \left(\frac{1}{\sqrt{6}} + \frac{i}{\sqrt{6}} \right) \left(\frac{1}{\sqrt{6}} - \frac{i}{\sqrt{6}} \right) + \left(\frac{1}{\sqrt{6}} + \frac{i}{\sqrt{6}} \right) \left(\frac{1}{\sqrt{6}} - \frac{i}{\sqrt{6}} \right) + \left(\frac{1}{\sqrt{6}} + \frac{i}{\sqrt{6}} \right) \left(\frac{1}{\sqrt{6}} - \frac{i}{\sqrt{6}} \right)$

$\qquad = \frac{2}{6} + \frac{2}{6} + \frac{2}{6} = 1$

$\langle \mathbf{v}, \mathbf{v} \rangle = \left(\frac{-2i}{\sqrt{6}} \right) \left(\frac{2i}{\sqrt{6}} \right) + \left(\frac{i}{\sqrt{6}} \right) \left(\frac{-i}{\sqrt{6}} \right) + \left(\frac{i}{\sqrt{6}} \right) \left(\frac{-i}{\sqrt{6}} \right)$

$\qquad = \frac{4}{6} + \frac{1}{6} + \frac{1}{6} = 1$

$\langle \mathbf{w}, \mathbf{w} \rangle = (0)(0) + \left(\frac{\sqrt{2}}{\sqrt{6}} - \frac{i}{\sqrt{6}} \right) \left(\frac{\sqrt{2}}{\sqrt{6}} + \frac{i}{\sqrt{6}} \right) + \left(\frac{-\sqrt{2}}{\sqrt{6}} + \frac{i}{\sqrt{6}} \right) \left(\frac{-\sqrt{2}}{\sqrt{6}} - \frac{i}{\sqrt{6}} \right)$

$\qquad = 0 + \frac{3}{6} + \frac{3}{6} = 1$

This set is orthonormal.

46. $\qquad \mathbf{v}_1 = (1, i)$

$\qquad \mathbf{v}_2 = (1+i, 0) - \frac{\langle (1+i,0), (1,i) \rangle}{\langle (1,i), (1,i) \rangle}(1,i) = (1+i,0) - \frac{1+i}{2}(1,i)$

$\qquad = (1+i,0) - \left(\frac{1+i}{2}, \frac{-1+i}{2} \right) = \left(\frac{1+i}{2}, \frac{1-i}{2} \right) = \frac{1}{2}(1+i, 1-i)$

$\qquad \mathbf{w}_1 = \frac{(1,i)}{\|(1,i)\|} = \frac{(1,i)}{\sqrt{2}} = \left(\frac{1}{\sqrt{2}}, \frac{i}{\sqrt{2}} \right)$

$\qquad \mathbf{w}_2 = \frac{(1+i, 1-i)}{\|(1+i, 1-i)\|} = \frac{(1+i, 1-i)}{2} = \left(\frac{1}{2} + \frac{i}{2}, \frac{1}{2} - \frac{i}{2} \right)$

47. $\qquad \mathbf{v}_1 = (i, 0, 0)$

$\qquad \mathbf{v}_2 = (1,1,1) - \frac{\langle (1,1,1), (i,0,0) \rangle}{\langle (i,0,0), (i,0,0) \rangle}(i,0,0) = (1,1,1) - \frac{-i}{1}(i,0,0)$

$\qquad = (1,1,1) - (1,0,0) = (0,1,1)$

$$\mathbf{v}_3 = (1+i,i,0) - \frac{\langle(1+i,i,0),(i,0,0)\rangle}{\langle(i,0,0),(i,0,0)\rangle}(i,0,0) - \frac{\langle(1+i,i,0),(0,1,1)\rangle}{\langle(0,1,1),(0,1,1)\rangle}(0,1,1)$$

$$= (1+i,i,0) - \frac{1-i}{1}(i,0,0) - \frac{i}{2}(0,1,1)$$

$$= (1+i,i,0) - (1+i,0,0) - \left(0,\frac{i}{2},\frac{i}{2}\right)$$

$$= \left(0,\frac{i}{2},\frac{-i}{2}\right) = \frac{1}{2}(0,i,-i)$$

$$\mathbf{w}_1 = \frac{(i,0,0)}{\|(i,0,0)\|} = \frac{(i,0,0)}{1} = (i,0,0)$$

$$\mathbf{w}_2 = \frac{(0,1,1)}{\|(0,1,1)\|} = \frac{(0,1,1)}{\sqrt{2}} = \left(0,\frac{1}{\sqrt{2}},\frac{1}{\sqrt{2}}\right)$$

$$\mathbf{w}_3 = \frac{(0,i,-i)}{\|(0,i,-i)\|} = \frac{(0,i,-i)}{\sqrt{2}} = \left(0,\frac{i}{\sqrt{2}},\frac{-i}{\sqrt{2}}\right)$$

SECTION 10.6   UNITARY, NORMAL, AND HERMITIAN MATRICES

48. (a) $A^* = \begin{bmatrix} 1 & 1-3i \\ 2+i & -4i \end{bmatrix}$

    (b) $A^* = \begin{bmatrix} 3 \\ -4 \\ 5 \end{bmatrix}$

    (c) $A^* = \begin{bmatrix} 2+3i & 0 \\ 1 & 1+2i \\ 0 & -5i \end{bmatrix}$

    (d) $A^* = \begin{bmatrix} 1 & i & i \\ -i & 1-i & i \\ -i & -i & 1+i \end{bmatrix}$

49. (a) $A^* = \begin{bmatrix} 3 & 1+i \\ 1-i & 1 \end{bmatrix} = A$,   Hermitian

    (b) $A^* = \begin{bmatrix} -i & -i \\ i & -i \end{bmatrix} \neq A$,   not Hermitian

    (c) $A^* = \begin{bmatrix} 0 & -3 & 4i \\ 3 & 0 & 5 \\ -4i & -5 & 0 \end{bmatrix} \neq A$,   not Hermitian

    (d) $A^* = \begin{bmatrix} 5 & 2+i & 1-11i \\ 2-i & 12 & 0 \\ 1+11i & 0 & 13 \end{bmatrix} = A$,   Hermitian

50. (a) $AA^* = \begin{bmatrix} \frac{1}{\sqrt{2}} & \frac{i}{\sqrt{2}} \\ \frac{-1}{\sqrt{2}} & \frac{i}{\sqrt{2}} \end{bmatrix} \begin{bmatrix} \frac{1}{\sqrt{2}} & \frac{-1}{\sqrt{2}} \\ \frac{-i}{\sqrt{2}} & \frac{-i}{\sqrt{2}} \end{bmatrix} = \begin{bmatrix} 1 & 0 \\ 0 & 1 \end{bmatrix} = I$

    so A is unitary and $A^{-1} = A^* = \begin{bmatrix} \frac{1}{\sqrt{2}} & \frac{-1}{\sqrt{2}} \\ \frac{-i}{\sqrt{2}} & \frac{-i}{\sqrt{2}} \end{bmatrix}$.

(b) $\quad AA^* = \begin{bmatrix} \frac{i}{2} & \frac{\sqrt{3}}{2}i \\ \frac{\sqrt{3}}{2} & \frac{-i}{2} \end{bmatrix} \begin{bmatrix} \frac{-i}{2} & \frac{\sqrt{3}}{2} \\ -\frac{\sqrt{3}i}{2} & \frac{i}{2} \end{bmatrix} = \begin{bmatrix} 1 & \frac{-\sqrt{3}}{4} + \frac{\sqrt{3}}{4}i \\ \frac{-\sqrt{3}}{4} - \frac{\sqrt{3}}{4}i & 1 \end{bmatrix} \neq I$

so A is not unitary.

(c) $\quad AA^* = \begin{bmatrix} \frac{i}{\sqrt{2}} & 0 & \frac{-i}{\sqrt{2}} \\ 0 & -1 & 0 \\ \frac{-i}{\sqrt{2}} & 0 & \frac{i}{\sqrt{2}} \end{bmatrix} \begin{bmatrix} \frac{-i}{\sqrt{2}} & 0 & \frac{i}{\sqrt{2}} \\ 0 & -1 & 0 \\ \frac{i}{\sqrt{2}} & 0 & \frac{-i}{\sqrt{2}} \end{bmatrix} = \begin{bmatrix} 1 & 0 & -1 \\ 0 & 1 & 0 \\ -1 & 0 & 1 \end{bmatrix} \neq I$

so A is not unitary.

d) $\quad AA^* = \begin{bmatrix} \frac{i}{\sqrt{3}} & \frac{-2i}{\sqrt{6}} & 0 \\ \frac{i}{\sqrt{3}} & \frac{i}{\sqrt{6}} & \frac{-i}{\sqrt{2}} \\ \frac{i}{\sqrt{3}} & \frac{i}{\sqrt{6}} & \frac{i}{\sqrt{2}} \end{bmatrix} \begin{bmatrix} \frac{-i}{\sqrt{3}} & \frac{-i}{\sqrt{3}} & \frac{-i}{\sqrt{3}} \\ \frac{2i}{\sqrt{6}} & \frac{-i}{\sqrt{6}} & \frac{-i}{\sqrt{6}} \\ 0 & \frac{i}{\sqrt{2}} & \frac{-i}{\sqrt{2}} \end{bmatrix} = \begin{bmatrix} 1 & 0 & 0 \\ 0 & 1 & 0 \\ 0 & 0 & 1 \end{bmatrix} = I$

so A is unitary and $\quad A^{-1} = A^* = \begin{bmatrix} \frac{-i}{\sqrt{3}} & \frac{-i}{\sqrt{3}} & \frac{-i}{\sqrt{3}} \\ \frac{2i}{\sqrt{6}} & \frac{-i}{\sqrt{6}} & \frac{-i}{\sqrt{6}} \\ 0 & \frac{i}{\sqrt{2}} & \frac{-i}{\sqrt{2}} \end{bmatrix}$.

51. $0 = \begin{vmatrix} \lambda+3 & -2-2i \\ -2+2i & \lambda-4 \end{vmatrix} = (\lambda+3)(\lambda-4) - (-2+2i)(-2-2i)$

$$= (\lambda^2 - \lambda - 12) - (4+4)$$

$$= \lambda^2 - \lambda - 20 = (\lambda-5)(\lambda+4) \quad \text{so} \quad \lambda = 5, -4$$

$\lambda = 5 \longrightarrow \begin{bmatrix} 8 & -2-2i & 0 \\ -2+2i & 1 & 0 \end{bmatrix} \longrightarrow \begin{bmatrix} 1 & -1/4 - (1/4)i & 0 \\ 0 & 0 & 0 \end{bmatrix}$

Let $\quad x_2 = s$;

then $\quad x_1 - \left(\frac{1}{4} + \frac{1}{4}i\right)x_2 = 0$, i.e., $\quad x_1 = \left(\frac{1}{4} + \frac{1}{4}i\right)x_2 = \left(\frac{1}{4} + \frac{1}{4}i\right)s$

so $\quad \begin{bmatrix} x_1 \\ x_2 \end{bmatrix} = \begin{bmatrix} (1/4 + (1/4)i)s \\ s \end{bmatrix} = s \begin{bmatrix} 1/4 + (1/4)i \\ 1 \end{bmatrix} = \frac{1}{4}s \begin{bmatrix} 1+i \\ 4 \end{bmatrix}$

$(1+i, 4)/\|(1+i, 4)\| = (1+i, 4)/\sqrt{18} = \left(\frac{1+i}{3\sqrt{2}}, \frac{4}{3\sqrt{2}}\right).$

$\lambda = -4 \longrightarrow \begin{bmatrix} -1 & -2-2i & 0 \\ -2+2i & -8 & 0 \end{bmatrix} \longrightarrow \begin{bmatrix} 1 & 2+2i & 0 \\ 0 & 0 & 0 \end{bmatrix}$

Let $\quad x_2 = t$;

311

then $x_1 + (2 + 2i)x_2 = 0$, i.e., $x_1 = -(2 + 2i)x_2 = -(2 + 2i)t$

so $\begin{bmatrix} x_1 \\ x_2 \end{bmatrix} = \begin{bmatrix} -(2+2i)t \\ t \end{bmatrix} = t\begin{bmatrix} -2 - 2i \\ 1 \end{bmatrix}$

$(-2 - 2i, 1)/\|(-2 - 2i, 1)\| = (-2 - 2i, 1)/3 = \left(\dfrac{-2 - 2i}{3}, \dfrac{1}{3}\right).$

$P = \begin{bmatrix} \frac{1+i}{3\sqrt{2}} & \frac{-2-2i}{3} \\ \frac{4}{3\sqrt{2}} & \frac{1}{3} \end{bmatrix}$, $P^{-1} = P^* = \begin{bmatrix} \frac{1-i}{3\sqrt{2}} & \frac{4}{3\sqrt{2}} \\ \frac{-2+2i}{3} & \frac{1}{3} \end{bmatrix}$

$D = P^{-1}AP = \begin{bmatrix} \frac{1-i}{3\sqrt{2}} & \frac{4}{3\sqrt{2}} \\ \frac{-2+2i}{3} & \frac{1}{3} \end{bmatrix} \begin{bmatrix} -3 & 2+2i \\ 2-2i & 4 \end{bmatrix} \begin{bmatrix} \frac{1+i}{3\sqrt{2}} & \frac{-2-2i}{3} \\ \frac{4}{3\sqrt{2}} & \frac{1}{3} \end{bmatrix}$

$= \begin{bmatrix} \frac{1-i}{3\sqrt{2}} & \frac{4}{3\sqrt{2}} \\ \frac{-2+2i}{3} & \frac{1}{3} \end{bmatrix} \begin{bmatrix} \frac{5+5i}{3\sqrt{2}} & \frac{8+8i}{3} \\ \frac{20}{3\sqrt{2}} & \frac{-4}{3} \end{bmatrix}$

$= \begin{bmatrix} 5 & 0 \\ 0 & -4 \end{bmatrix}.$

52. $0 = \begin{vmatrix} \lambda + 7i & 24i \\ 24i & \lambda - 7i \end{vmatrix} = (\lambda + 7i)(\lambda - 7i) - (24i)(24i)$

$= \lambda^2 + 7^2 + 24^2$

$= \lambda^2 + 25^2 = (\lambda - 25i)(\lambda + 25i)$ so $\lambda = 25i, -25i$

$\lambda = 25i \longrightarrow \begin{bmatrix} 32i & 24i & 0 \\ 24i & 18i & 0 \end{bmatrix} \longrightarrow \begin{bmatrix} 1 & 3/4 & 0 \\ 0 & 0 & 0 \end{bmatrix}$

Let $x_2 = s$;

then $x_1 + \dfrac{3}{4}x_2 = 0$, i.e., $x_1 = \dfrac{-3}{4}x_2 = \dfrac{-3}{4}s$

so $\begin{bmatrix} x_1 \\ x_2 \end{bmatrix} = \begin{bmatrix} (-3/4)s \\ s \end{bmatrix} = s\begin{bmatrix} -3/4 \\ 1 \end{bmatrix} = \dfrac{1}{4}s\begin{bmatrix} -3 \\ 4 \end{bmatrix}$

$(-3, 4)/\|(-3, 4)\| = (-3, 4)/5 = \left(\dfrac{-3}{5}, \dfrac{4}{5}\right).$

$\lambda = -25i \longrightarrow \begin{bmatrix} -18i & 24i & 0 \\ 24i & -32i & 0 \end{bmatrix} \longrightarrow \begin{bmatrix} 1 & -4/3 & 0 \\ 0 & 0 & 0 \end{bmatrix}$

Let $x_2 = t$;

then $x_1 - \frac{4}{3}x_2 = 0$,   i.e., $x_1 = \frac{4}{3}x_2 = \frac{4}{3}t$

so $\begin{bmatrix} x_1 \\ x_2 \end{bmatrix} = \begin{bmatrix} (4/3)t \\ t \end{bmatrix} = t\begin{bmatrix} 4/3 \\ 1 \end{bmatrix} = \frac{1}{3}t\begin{bmatrix} 4 \\ 3 \end{bmatrix}$

$(4,3)/\|(4,3)\| = (4,3)/5 = \left(\frac{4}{5}, \frac{3}{5}\right).$

$P = \begin{bmatrix} -3/5 & 4/5 \\ 4/5 & 3/5 \end{bmatrix}$, $P^{-1} = P^* = \begin{bmatrix} -3/5 & 4/5 \\ 4/5 & 3/5 \end{bmatrix}$

$D = P^{-1}AP = \begin{bmatrix} -3/5 & 4/5 \\ 4/5 & 3/5 \end{bmatrix}\begin{bmatrix} -7i & -24i \\ -24i & 7i \end{bmatrix}\begin{bmatrix} -3/5 & 4/5 \\ 4/5 & 3/5 \end{bmatrix}$

$= \begin{bmatrix} -3/5 & 4/5 \\ 4/5 & 3/5 \end{bmatrix}\begin{bmatrix} -15i & -20i \\ 20i & -15i \end{bmatrix}$

$= \begin{bmatrix} 25i & 0 \\ 0 & -25i \end{bmatrix}.$

53. $0 = \begin{vmatrix} \lambda-1 & -i & 0 \\ i & \lambda & -i \\ 0 & i & \lambda-1 \end{vmatrix} = (\lambda-1)[(\lambda)(\lambda-1) - (i)(-i)] + i[(i)(\lambda-1) - (0)(-i)]$

$= (\lambda-1)(\lambda^2 - \lambda - 1) - (\lambda-1)$

$= (\lambda-1)(\lambda^2 - \lambda - 2) = (\lambda-1)(\lambda-2)(\lambda+1)$ so $\lambda = 1, 2, -1$

$\lambda = 1 \longrightarrow \begin{bmatrix} 0 & -i & 0 & 0 \\ i & 1 & -i & 0 \\ 0 & i & 0 & 0 \end{bmatrix} \longrightarrow \begin{bmatrix} i & 1 & -i & 0 \\ 0 & -i & 0 & 0 \\ 0 & i & 0 & 0 \end{bmatrix} \longrightarrow \begin{bmatrix} 1 & -i & -1 & 0 \\ 0 & 1 & 0 & 0 \\ 0 & 0 & 0 & 0 \end{bmatrix} \longrightarrow$

$\begin{bmatrix} 1 & 0 & -1 & 0 \\ 0 & 1 & 0 & 0 \\ 0 & 0 & 0 & 0 \end{bmatrix}$

Let $x_3 = r$;

then $x_1 - x_3 = 0$,   i.e., $x_1 = x_3 = r$

and $x_2 = 0$

so $\begin{bmatrix} x_1 \\ x_2 \\ x_3 \end{bmatrix} = \begin{bmatrix} r \\ 0 \\ r \end{bmatrix} = r\begin{bmatrix} 1 \\ 0 \\ 1 \end{bmatrix}$

$(1,0,1)/\|(1,0,1)\| = (1,0,1)/\sqrt{2} = \left(\frac{1}{\sqrt{2}}, 0, \frac{1}{\sqrt{2}}\right).$

$$\lambda = 2 \longrightarrow \begin{bmatrix} 1 & -i & 0 & 0 \\ i & 2 & -i & 0 \\ 0 & i & 1 & 0 \end{bmatrix} \longrightarrow \begin{bmatrix} 1 & -i & 0 & 0 \\ 0 & 1 & -i & 0 \\ 0 & i & 1 & 0 \end{bmatrix} \longrightarrow \begin{bmatrix} 1 & 0 & 1 & 0 \\ 0 & 1 & -i & 0 \\ 0 & 0 & 0 & 0 \end{bmatrix}$$

Let $x_3 = s$;

then $x_2 - ix_3 = 0$, i.e., $x_2 = ix_3 = is$

and $x_1 + x_3 = 0$, i.e., $x_1 = -x_3 = -s$

so $\begin{bmatrix} x_1 \\ x_2 \\ x_3 \end{bmatrix} = \begin{bmatrix} -s \\ is \\ s \end{bmatrix} = s \begin{bmatrix} -1 \\ i \\ 1 \end{bmatrix}$

$$(-1, i, 1)/\|(-1, i, 1)\| = (-1, i, 1)/\sqrt{3} = \left(\frac{-1}{\sqrt{3}}, \frac{i}{\sqrt{3}}, \frac{-1}{\sqrt{3}} \right).$$

$$\lambda = -1 \longrightarrow \begin{bmatrix} -2 & -i & 0 & 0 \\ i & -1 & -i & 0 \\ 0 & i & -2 & 0 \end{bmatrix} \longrightarrow \begin{bmatrix} i & -1 & -i & 0 \\ -2 & -i & 0 & 0 \\ 0 & i & -2 & 0 \end{bmatrix} \longrightarrow \begin{bmatrix} 1 & i & -1 & 0 \\ 0 & i & -2 & 0 \\ 0 & i & -2 & 0 \end{bmatrix} \longrightarrow$$

$$\begin{bmatrix} 1 & 0 & 1 & 0 \\ 0 & 1 & 2i & 0 \\ 0 & 0 & 0 & 0 \end{bmatrix}$$

Let $x_3 = t$;

then $x_2 + 2ix_3 = 0$, i.e., $x_2 = -2ix_3 = -2it$

and $x_1 + x_3 = 0$, i.e., $x_1 = -x_3 = -t$

so $\begin{bmatrix} x_1 \\ x_2 \\ x_3 \end{bmatrix} = \begin{bmatrix} -t \\ -2it \\ t \end{bmatrix} = t \begin{bmatrix} -1 \\ -2i \\ 1 \end{bmatrix}$

$$(-1, -2i, 1)/\|(-1, -2i, 1)\| = (-1, -2i, 1)/\sqrt{6} = \left(\frac{-1}{\sqrt{6}}, \frac{-2i}{\sqrt{6}}, \frac{1}{\sqrt{6}} \right).$$

$$P = \begin{bmatrix} \frac{1}{\sqrt{2}} & \frac{-1}{\sqrt{3}} & \frac{-1}{\sqrt{6}} \\ 0 & \frac{i}{\sqrt{3}} & \frac{-2i}{\sqrt{6}} \\ \frac{1}{\sqrt{2}} & \frac{1}{\sqrt{3}} & \frac{1}{\sqrt{6}} \end{bmatrix}, \quad P^{-1} = P^* = \begin{bmatrix} \frac{1}{\sqrt{2}} & 0 & \frac{1}{\sqrt{2}} \\ \frac{-1}{\sqrt{3}} & \frac{-i}{\sqrt{3}} & \frac{1}{\sqrt{3}} \\ \frac{-1}{\sqrt{6}} & \frac{2i}{\sqrt{6}} & \frac{1}{\sqrt{6}} \end{bmatrix}$$

$$D = P^{-1}AP = \begin{bmatrix} \frac{1}{\sqrt{2}} & 0 & \frac{1}{\sqrt{2}} \\ \frac{-1}{\sqrt{3}} & \frac{-i}{\sqrt{3}} & \frac{1}{\sqrt{3}} \\ \frac{-1}{\sqrt{6}} & \frac{2i}{\sqrt{6}} & \frac{1}{\sqrt{6}} \end{bmatrix} \begin{bmatrix} 1 & i & 0 \\ -i & 0 & i \\ 0 & -i & 1 \end{bmatrix} \begin{bmatrix} \frac{1}{\sqrt{2}} & \frac{-1}{\sqrt{3}} & \frac{-1}{\sqrt{6}} \\ 0 & \frac{i}{\sqrt{3}} & \frac{-2i}{\sqrt{6}} \\ \frac{1}{\sqrt{2}} & \frac{1}{\sqrt{3}} & \frac{1}{\sqrt{6}} \end{bmatrix}$$

$$= \begin{bmatrix} \frac{1}{\sqrt{2}} & 0 & \frac{1}{\sqrt{2}} \\ \frac{-1}{\sqrt{3}} & \frac{-i}{\sqrt{3}} & \frac{1}{\sqrt{3}} \\ \frac{-1}{\sqrt{6}} & \frac{2i}{\sqrt{6}} & \frac{1}{\sqrt{6}} \end{bmatrix} \begin{bmatrix} \frac{1}{\sqrt{2}} & \frac{-2}{\sqrt{3}} & \frac{1}{\sqrt{6}} \\ 0 & \frac{2i}{\sqrt{3}} & \frac{2i}{\sqrt{6}} \\ \frac{1}{\sqrt{2}} & \frac{2}{\sqrt{3}} & \frac{-1}{\sqrt{6}} \end{bmatrix}$$

$$= \begin{bmatrix} 1 & 0 & 0 \\ 0 & 2 & 0 \\ 0 & 0 & -1 \end{bmatrix}.$$

54. $0 = \begin{vmatrix} \lambda+3 & -i & 0 \\ i & \lambda+3 & 0 \\ 0 & i & \lambda+3 \end{vmatrix} = (\lambda+3)[(\lambda+3)(\lambda+3) - (i)(-i)]$

$$= (\lambda+3)(\lambda^2 + 6\lambda + 9 - 1)$$

$$= (\lambda+3)(\lambda^2 + 6\lambda + 8) = (\lambda+3)(\lambda+2)(\lambda+4) \quad \text{so} \quad \lambda = -2, -3, -4$$

$\lambda = -2 \longrightarrow \begin{bmatrix} 1 & -i & 0 & 0 \\ i & 1 & 0 & 0 \\ 0 & 0 & 1 & 0 \end{bmatrix} \longrightarrow \begin{bmatrix} 1 & -i & 0 & 0 \\ 0 & 0 & 0 & 0 \\ 0 & 0 & 1 & 0 \end{bmatrix} \longrightarrow \begin{bmatrix} 1 & -i & 0 & 0 \\ 0 & 0 & 1 & 0 \\ 0 & 0 & 0 & 0 \end{bmatrix}$

Let $\quad x_2 = r;$

then $\quad x_1 - ix_2 = 0, \quad$ i.e., $\quad x_1 = ix_2 = ir$

and $\quad x_3 = 0$

so $\quad \begin{bmatrix} x_1 \\ x_2 \\ x_3 \end{bmatrix} = \begin{bmatrix} ir \\ r \\ 0 \end{bmatrix} = r \begin{bmatrix} i \\ 1 \\ 0 \end{bmatrix}$

$(i, 1, 0)/\|(i, 1, 0)\| = (i, 1, 0)/\sqrt{2} = \left(\dfrac{i}{\sqrt{2}}, \dfrac{1}{\sqrt{2}}, 0 \right).$

$\lambda = -3 \longrightarrow \begin{bmatrix} 0 & -i & 0 & 0 \\ i & 0 & 0 & 0 \\ 0 & 0 & 0 & 0 \end{bmatrix} \longrightarrow \begin{bmatrix} i & 0 & 0 & 0 \\ 0 & -i & 0 & 0 \\ 0 & 0 & 0 & 0 \end{bmatrix} \longrightarrow \begin{bmatrix} 1 & 0 & 0 & 0 \\ 0 & 1 & 0 & 0 \\ 0 & 0 & 0 & 0 \end{bmatrix}$

Let $\quad x_3 = s;$

then $\quad x_1 = 0 \quad$ and $\quad x_2 = 0$

so $\quad \begin{bmatrix} x_1 \\ x_2 \\ x_3 \end{bmatrix} = \begin{bmatrix} 0 \\ 0 \\ s \end{bmatrix} = s \begin{bmatrix} 0 \\ 0 \\ 1 \end{bmatrix}$

$(0, 0, 1)/\|(0, 0, 1)\| = (0, 0, 1)/1 = (0, 0, 1).$

$$\lambda = -4 \longrightarrow \begin{bmatrix} -1 & -i & 0 & 0 \\ i & -1 & 0 & 0 \\ 0 & 0 & -1 & 0 \end{bmatrix} \longrightarrow \begin{bmatrix} 1 & i & 0 & 0 \\ 0 & 0 & 0 & 0 \\ 0 & 0 & -1 & 0 \end{bmatrix} \longrightarrow \begin{bmatrix} 1 & i & 0 & 0 \\ 0 & 0 & -1 & 0 \\ 0 & 0 & 0 & 0 \end{bmatrix} \longrightarrow$$

$$\begin{bmatrix} 1 & i & 0 & 0 \\ 0 & 0 & 1 & 0 \\ 0 & 0 & 0 & 0 \end{bmatrix}$$

Let $\quad x_2 = t$;

then $\quad x_1 + i x_2 = 0$, $\quad$ i.e., $\quad x_1 = -i x_2 = -it$

and $\quad x_3 = 0$

so $\quad \begin{bmatrix} x_1 \\ x_2 \\ x_3 \end{bmatrix} = \begin{bmatrix} -it \\ t \\ 0 \end{bmatrix} = t \begin{bmatrix} -i \\ 1 \\ 0 \end{bmatrix}$

$$(-i, 1, 0)/\|(-i, 1, 0)\| = (-i, 1, 0)/\sqrt{2} = \left(\frac{-i}{\sqrt{2}}, \frac{1}{\sqrt{2}}, 0 \right).$$

$$P = \begin{bmatrix} \frac{i}{\sqrt{2}} & \frac{-i}{\sqrt{2}} & 0 \\ \frac{1}{\sqrt{2}} & \frac{1}{\sqrt{2}} & 0 \\ 0 & 0 & 1 \end{bmatrix} \quad , \quad P^{-1} = P^* = \begin{bmatrix} \frac{-i}{\sqrt{2}} & \frac{1}{\sqrt{2}} & 0 \\ \frac{i}{\sqrt{2}} & \frac{1}{\sqrt{2}} & 0 \\ 0 & 0 & 1 \end{bmatrix}$$

$$D = P^{-1} A P = \begin{bmatrix} \frac{-i}{\sqrt{2}} & \frac{1}{\sqrt{2}} & 0 \\ \frac{i}{\sqrt{2}} & \frac{1}{\sqrt{2}} & 0 \\ 0 & 0 & 1 \end{bmatrix} \begin{bmatrix} -3 & i & 0 \\ -i & -3 & 0 \\ 0 & 0 & -3 \end{bmatrix} \begin{bmatrix} \frac{i}{\sqrt{2}} & \frac{-i}{\sqrt{2}} & 0 \\ \frac{1}{\sqrt{2}} & \frac{1}{\sqrt{2}} & 0 \\ 0 & 0 & 1 \end{bmatrix}$$

$$= \begin{bmatrix} \frac{-i}{\sqrt{2}} & \frac{1}{\sqrt{2}} & 0 \\ \frac{i}{\sqrt{2}} & \frac{1}{\sqrt{2}} & 0 \\ 0 & 0 & 1 \end{bmatrix} \begin{bmatrix} \frac{-2i}{\sqrt{2}} & \frac{4i}{\sqrt{2}} & 0 \\ \frac{-2}{\sqrt{2}} & \frac{-4}{\sqrt{2}} & 0 \\ 0 & 0 & -3 \end{bmatrix}$$

$$= \begin{bmatrix} -2 & 0 & 0 \\ 0 & -4 & 0 \\ 0 & 0 & -3 \end{bmatrix}.$$

FINAL EXAM A

1. Consider the vectors $\mathbf{u} = (2, 5, 1)$, $\mathbf{v} = (0, 1, 3)$, $\mathbf{w} = (-1, 0, 2)$. Compute each of the following.

   (a) $2\mathbf{u} - \mathbf{v} + 3\mathbf{w}$
   (b) $\mathbf{u}/\|\mathbf{u}\|$
   (c) $8\mathbf{v} \cdot 2\mathbf{w}$
   (d) $\mathbf{u} \times \mathbf{w}$
   (e) the component of $\mathbf{u}$ orthogonal to $\mathbf{v}$

2. Consider the matrices $\quad A = \begin{bmatrix} 1 & 1 & -1 \\ 1 & 0 & 1 \\ 0 & 3 & -2 \end{bmatrix}$, $\quad B = \begin{bmatrix} 2 & 6 & 6 \\ 2 & 7 & 6 \\ 2 & 7 & 7 \end{bmatrix}$.

   Compute each of the following.

   (a) $3A - 2B$
   (b) AB
   (c) $A^2 + B$
   (d) $A \det A$
   (e) $\det B$
   (f) AB^{-1}

3. Consider the linear system $\quad \begin{cases} 2x + 4y + 6z = 18 \\ 4x + 5y + 6z = 24 \\ 3x + y - 2z = 4. \end{cases}$

   (a) Solve the system using Gauss or Gauss–Jordan elimination.
   (b) Solve the system using Cramer's Rule of Determinants.

4. Consider the plane $6x - y + 2z = 5$.

   (a) Find an equation for the line through $P(1, 2, 3)$ perpendicular to the plane.
   (b) Find an equation for the plane through $P(1, 2, 3)$ parallel to the given plane.

5. Show whether $\{a_0 + a_1 x + a_2 x^2 : a_1^2 - 4a_0 a_2 < 0\}$ is a subspace of P_2.

6. Consider the set $B = \{(1, 1, 0), (0, 1, 1), (1, 0, 1)\}$.

   (a) Show that B is a basis for R^3
   (b) Express $\mathbf{u} = (2, 4, -6)$ as a linear combination of the elements of B.
   (c) Use the Gram–Schmidt process to orthonormalize B.

7. Consider the linear transformation $T : R^3 \rightarrow R^3$ defined by

$$T\left(\begin{bmatrix} x \\ y \\ z \end{bmatrix}\right) = \begin{bmatrix} 3x - 2y \\ -2x + 3y \\ 5z \end{bmatrix}.$$

   (a) Find the standard matrix $[T]$ for the transformation.
   (b) Find a basis for $\ker(T)$.
   (c) Find a basis for $R(T)$.
   (d) If $B = \{(3, 0, 0), (2, 2, 0), (1, 2, -1)\}$, find the matrix $[T]_B$.

317

(e) Find the eigenvalue(s) of the standard matrix $A = [T]$ and, for each eigenvalue, find a basis for the associated eigenspace.

(f) Find a matrix P such that $P^{-1}AP$ is diagonal.

(g) Use your answer to (f) to calculate $T^4 \left(\begin{bmatrix} 2 \\ -2 \\ 4 \end{bmatrix} \right)$.

8. Consider the conic section $2x^2 - 4xy - y^2 - 4x - 8y = -14$. Use orthogonal diagonalization and completing the squares to find the equation of the curve when it is rotated and translated into standard position.

FINAL EXAM A

1. (a) $2\mathbf{u} - \mathbf{v} + 3\mathbf{w} = (4, 10, 2) - (0, 1, 3) + (-3, 0, 6) = (1, 9, 5)$

   (b) $\mathbf{u}/\|\mathbf{u}\| = (2, 5, 1)/\sqrt{4 + 25 + 1} = \frac{1}{\sqrt{30}}(2, 5, 1)$

   (c) $8\mathbf{v}\cdot 2\mathbf{w} = 16\mathbf{v}\cdot\mathbf{w} = 16(0, 1, 3)\cdot(-1, 0, 2) = 16(6) = 96$

   (d) $\mathbf{u} \times \mathbf{w} = \begin{vmatrix} \mathbf{i} & \mathbf{j} & \mathbf{k} \\ 2 & 5 & 1 \\ -1 & 0 & 2 \end{vmatrix} = \mathbf{i}(10) - \mathbf{j}(5) + \mathbf{k}(5) = (10, -5, 5)$

   (e) $\mathbf{u} - \dfrac{\mathbf{u}\cdot\mathbf{v}}{\mathbf{v}\cdot\mathbf{v}}\mathbf{v} = (2, 5, 1) - \dfrac{(2, 5, 1)\cdot(0, 1, 3)}{(0, 1, 3)\cdot(0, 1, 3)}(0, 1, 3)$

   $= (2, 5, 1) - \dfrac{8}{10}(0, 1, 3)$

   $= \left(2, \dfrac{21}{5}, \dfrac{-7}{5}\right)$

2. (a) $3A - 2B = \begin{bmatrix} 3 & 3 & -3 \\ 3 & 0 & 3 \\ 0 & 9 & -6 \end{bmatrix} - \begin{bmatrix} 4 & 12 & 12 \\ 4 & 14 & 12 \\ 4 & 14 & 14 \end{bmatrix} = \begin{bmatrix} -1 & -9 & -15 \\ -1 & -14 & -9 \\ -4 & -5 & -20 \end{bmatrix}$

   (b) $AB = \begin{bmatrix} 1 & 1 & -1 \\ 1 & 0 & 1 \\ 0 & 3 & -2 \end{bmatrix}\begin{bmatrix} 2 & 6 & 6 \\ 2 & 7 & 6 \\ 2 & 7 & 7 \end{bmatrix} = \begin{bmatrix} 2 & 6 & 5 \\ 4 & 13 & 13 \\ 2 & 7 & 4 \end{bmatrix}$

   (c) $A^2 + B = \begin{bmatrix} 1 & 1 & -1 \\ 1 & 0 & 1 \\ 0 & 3 & -2 \end{bmatrix}\begin{bmatrix} 1 & 1 & -1 \\ 1 & 0 & 1 \\ 0 & 3 & -2 \end{bmatrix} + \begin{bmatrix} 2 & 6 & 6 \\ 2 & 7 & 6 \\ 2 & 7 & 7 \end{bmatrix}$

   $= \begin{bmatrix} 2 & -2 & 2 \\ 1 & 4 & -3 \\ 3 & -6 & 7 \end{bmatrix} + \begin{bmatrix} 2 & 6 & 6 \\ 2 & 7 & 6 \\ 2 & 7 & 7 \end{bmatrix} = \begin{bmatrix} 4 & 4 & 8 \\ 3 & 11 & 3 \\ 5 & 1 & 14 \end{bmatrix}$

   (d) $A \det A = A[1(-3) - 1(1)] = A(-4) = \begin{bmatrix} -4 & -4 & 4 \\ -4 & 0 & -4 \\ 0 & -12 & 8 \end{bmatrix}$

   (e) $\det B = 2(7) - 2(0) + 2(-6) = 2$

   (f) $B^{-1} = \dfrac{\text{adj } B}{\det B} = \dfrac{1}{2}\begin{bmatrix} 7 & -2 & 0 \\ 0 & 2 & -2 \\ -6 & 0 & 2 \end{bmatrix}^T = \dfrac{1}{2}\begin{bmatrix} 7 & 0 & -6 \\ -2 & 2 & 0 \\ 0 & -2 & 2 \end{bmatrix}$

   $AB^{-1} = \dfrac{1}{2}\begin{bmatrix} 1 & 1 & -1 \\ 1 & 0 & 1 \\ 0 & 3 & -2 \end{bmatrix}\begin{bmatrix} 7 & 0 & -6 \\ -2 & 2 & 0 \\ 0 & -2 & 2 \end{bmatrix} = \dfrac{1}{2}\begin{bmatrix} 5 & 4 & -8 \\ 7 & -2 & -4 \\ -6 & 10 & -4 \end{bmatrix}$

3. (a) $\begin{bmatrix} 2 & 4 & 6 & 18 \\ 4 & 5 & 6 & 24 \\ 3 & 1 & -2 & 4 \end{bmatrix} \longrightarrow \begin{bmatrix} 1 & 2 & 3 & 9 \\ 0 & -3 & -6 & -12 \\ 0 & -5 & -11 & -23 \end{bmatrix} \longrightarrow \begin{bmatrix} 1 & 2 & 3 & 9 \\ 0 & 1 & 2 & 4 \\ 0 & 0 & -1 & -3 \end{bmatrix} \longrightarrow \begin{bmatrix} 1 & 2 & 3 & 9 \\ 0 & 1 & 2 & 4 \\ 0 & 0 & 1 & 3 \end{bmatrix}$

To finish by Gaussian,

$$z = 3$$

$$y + 2z = 4 \quad \text{so} \quad y + 6 = 4 \quad , \quad y = -2$$

$$x + 2y + 3z = 9 \quad \text{so} \quad x + -4 + 9 = 9 \quad , \quad x = 4$$

To finish by Gauss-Jordan,

$$\begin{bmatrix} 1 & 2 & 3 & 9 \\ 0 & 1 & 2 & 4 \\ 0 & 0 & 1 & 3 \end{bmatrix} \longrightarrow \begin{bmatrix} 1 & 0 & -1 & 1 \\ 0 & 1 & 2 & 4 \\ 0 & 0 & 1 & 3 \end{bmatrix} \longrightarrow \begin{bmatrix} 1 & 0 & 0 & 4 \\ 0 & 1 & 0 & -2 \\ 0 & 0 & 1 & 3 \end{bmatrix} \begin{matrix} x = 4 \\ y = -2 \\ z = 3 \end{matrix}$$

(b) $|A| = \begin{vmatrix} 2 & 4 & 6 \\ 4 & 5 & 6 \\ 3 & 1 & -2 \end{vmatrix} = 2(-16) - 4(-26) + 6(-11) = 6$

$|A_1| = \begin{vmatrix} 18 & 4 & 6 \\ 24 & 5 & 6 \\ 4 & 1 & -2 \end{vmatrix} = 18(-16) - 4(-72) + 6(4) = 24 \quad , \quad \text{so} \quad x = \dfrac{24}{6} = 4$

$|A_2| = \begin{vmatrix} 2 & 18 & 6 \\ 4 & 24 & 6 \\ 3 & 4 & -2 \end{vmatrix} = 2(-72) - 18(-26) + 6(-56) = -12 \quad , \quad \text{so} \quad y = \dfrac{-12}{6} = -2$

$|A_3| = \begin{vmatrix} 2 & 4 & 18 \\ 4 & 5 & 24 \\ 3 & 1 & 4 \end{vmatrix} = 2(-4) - 4(-56) + 18(-11) = 18 \quad , \quad \text{so} \quad z = \dfrac{18}{6} = 3$

4. Note $\mathbf{n} = (6, -1, 2)$.

(a) $x = 1 + 6t$

$y = 2 + -1t$

$z = 3 + 2t$

(b) $6(x - 1) + -1(y - 2) + 2(z - 3) = 0$

$6x + -y + 2z = 10$

5. Let $U = \{a_0 + a_1 x + a_2 x^2 : a_1^2 - 4a_0 a_2 < 0\}$.

Consider $a_0 + a_1 x + a_2 x^2$ and $b_0 + b_1 x + b_2 x^2$ in U,

that is $a_1^2 - 4a_0 a_2 < 0$ and $b_1^2 - 4b_0 b_2 < 0$.

Is $(a_0 + a_1 x + a_2 x^2) + (b_0 + b_1 x + b_2 x^2)$ in U?

$= (a_0 + b_0) + (a_1 + b_1)x + (a_2 + b_2)x^2$

That is, is it true that $(a_1 + b_1)^2 - 4(a_0 + b_0)(a_2 + b_2) < 0$?

i.e., $a_1^2 + 2a_1 b_1 + b_1^2 - 4a_0 a_2 - 4a_0 b_2 - 4b_0 a_2 - 4b_0 b_2 < 0$?

i.e., $(a_1^2 - 4a_0 a_2) + (b_1^2 - 4b_0 b_2) + (2a_1 b_1 - 4a_0 b_2 - 4b_0 a_2) < 0$?

The first two parenthesized terms are negative,

but there is no guarantee that the third term is negative.

For example, $x^2 + 1$ and $-x^2 - 1$ are in U,

but $(x^2 + 1) + (-x^2 - 1) = 0$ is not in U.

Since U is not closed under addition, it is not a subspace of P_2.

6. (a) $\begin{vmatrix} 1 & 0 & 1 \\ 1 & 1 & 0 \\ 0 & 1 & 1 \end{vmatrix} = 1(1) - 1(-1) = 2 \neq 0$

(b) $\begin{bmatrix} 1 & 0 & 1 & 2 \\ 1 & 1 & 0 & 4 \\ 0 & 1 & 1 & -6 \end{bmatrix} \longrightarrow \begin{bmatrix} 1 & 0 & 1 & 2 \\ 0 & 1 & -1 & 2 \\ 0 & 1 & 1 & -6 \end{bmatrix} \longrightarrow \begin{bmatrix} 1 & 0 & 1 & 2 \\ 0 & 1 & -1 & 2 \\ 0 & 0 & 2 & -8 \end{bmatrix} \longrightarrow \begin{bmatrix} 1 & 0 & 0 & 6 \\ 0 & 1 & 0 & -2 \\ 0 & 0 & 1 & -4 \end{bmatrix}$

Thus, $\mathbf{u} = 6(1,1,0) + -2(0,1,1) + -4(1,0,1)$.

(c) $\mathbf{v}_1 = \mathbf{u}_1 = (1,1,0)$

$\mathbf{v}_2 = \mathbf{u}_2 - \dfrac{\mathbf{u}_2 \cdot \mathbf{v}_1}{\mathbf{v}_1 \cdot \mathbf{v}_1} \mathbf{v}_1 = (0,1,1) - \dfrac{(0,1,1,) \cdot (1,1,0)}{(1,1,0) \cdot (1,1,0)}(1,1,0)$

$\qquad = (0,1,1) - \dfrac{1}{2}(1,1,0) = \left(\dfrac{-1}{2}, \dfrac{1}{2}, 1\right) = \dfrac{1}{2}(-1,1,2)$

$\mathbf{v}_3 = \mathbf{u}_3 - \dfrac{\mathbf{u}_3 \cdot \mathbf{v}_1}{\mathbf{v}_1 \cdot \mathbf{v}_1} \mathbf{v}_1 - \dfrac{\mathbf{u}_3 \cdot \mathbf{v}_2}{\mathbf{v}_2 \cdot \mathbf{v}_2} \mathbf{v}_2$

$\qquad = (1,0,1) - \dfrac{(1,0,1) \cdot (1,1,0)}{(1,1,0) \cdot (1,1,0)}(1,1,0) - \dfrac{(1,0,1) \cdot \left(\frac{-1}{2}, \frac{1}{2}, 1\right)}{\left(\frac{-1}{2}, \frac{1}{2}, 1\right) \cdot \left(\frac{-1}{2}, \frac{1}{2}, 1\right)}\left(\dfrac{-1}{2}, \dfrac{1}{2}, 1\right)$

$\qquad = (1,0,1) - \dfrac{1}{2}(1,1,0) - \dfrac{\frac{1}{2}}{\frac{3}{2}}\left(\dfrac{-1}{2}, \dfrac{1}{2}, 1\right) = \left(\dfrac{2}{3}, \dfrac{-2}{3}, \dfrac{2}{3}\right) = \dfrac{2}{3}(1,-1,1)$

$\mathbf{w}_1 = (1,1,0)/\|(1,1,0)\| = (1,1,0)/\sqrt{2}$

$\mathbf{w}_2 = (-1,1,2)/\|(-1,1,2)\| = (-1,1,2)/\sqrt{6}$

$\mathbf{w}_3 = (1,-1,1)/\|(1,-1,1)\| = (1,-1,1)/\sqrt{3}$

7. (a) $[T] = [T(\mathbf{e}_1) \vdots T(\mathbf{e}_2) \vdots T(\mathbf{e}_3)] = \begin{bmatrix} 3 & -2 & 0 \\ -2 & 3 & 0 \\ 0 & 0 & 5 \end{bmatrix}$

(b) $\begin{bmatrix} 3 & -2 & 0 & 0 \\ -2 & 3 & 0 & 0 \\ 0 & 0 & 5 & 0 \end{bmatrix} \longrightarrow \begin{bmatrix} 1 & -2/3 & 0 & 0 \\ 0 & 5/3 & 0 & 0 \\ 0 & 0 & 5 & 0 \end{bmatrix} \longrightarrow \begin{bmatrix} 1 & 0 & 0 & 0 \\ 0 & 1 & 0 & 0 \\ 0 & 0 & 1 & 0 \end{bmatrix}$

Thus, $x = y = z = 0$; $\ker T = \{(0,0,0)\}$ and has no basis.

(c) Noting the leading ones in part (b), a basis for $R(T)$ is $\left\{ \begin{bmatrix} 3 \\ -2 \\ 0 \end{bmatrix}, \begin{bmatrix} -2 \\ 3 \\ 0 \end{bmatrix}, \begin{bmatrix} 0 \\ 0 \\ 5 \end{bmatrix} \right\}$.

Since $R(T)$ is 3–dimensional, another good basis would be $\left\{ \begin{bmatrix} 1 \\ 0 \\ 0 \end{bmatrix}, \begin{bmatrix} 0 \\ 1 \\ 0 \end{bmatrix}, \begin{bmatrix} 0 \\ 0 \\ 1 \end{bmatrix} \right\}$.

(d) $[T]_B = \left[[T(\mathbf{u}_1)]_B \vdots [T(\mathbf{u}_2)]_B \vdots [T(\mathbf{u}_3)]_B \right]$

$\qquad = \left[\begin{bmatrix} 9 \\ -6 \\ 0 \end{bmatrix}_B \vdots \begin{bmatrix} 2 \\ 2 \\ 0 \end{bmatrix}_B \vdots \begin{bmatrix} -1 \\ 4 \\ -5 \end{bmatrix}_B \right]$

$\qquad = \begin{bmatrix} 3 & 2 & 1 \\ 0 & 2 & 2 \\ 0 & 0 & -1 \end{bmatrix}^{-1} \begin{bmatrix} 9 & 2 & -1 \\ -6 & 2 & 4 \\ 0 & 0 & -5 \end{bmatrix}$

$$= \frac{1}{-6} \begin{bmatrix} -2 & 0 & 0 \\ 2 & -3 & 0 \\ 2 & -6 & 6 \end{bmatrix}^T \begin{bmatrix} 9 & 2 & -1 \\ -6 & 2 & 4 \\ 0 & 0 & -5 \end{bmatrix}$$

$$= \frac{1}{6} \begin{bmatrix} 2 & -2 & -2 \\ 0 & 3 & 6 \\ 0 & 0 & -6 \end{bmatrix} \begin{bmatrix} 9 & 2 & -1 \\ -6 & 2 & 4 \\ 0 & 0 & -5 \end{bmatrix}$$

$$= \frac{1}{6} \begin{bmatrix} 30 & 0 & 0 \\ -18 & 6 & -18 \\ 0 & 0 & 30 \end{bmatrix} = \begin{bmatrix} 5 & 0 & 0 \\ -3 & 1 & -3 \\ 0 & 0 & 5 \end{bmatrix}.$$

(e)
$$0 = \begin{vmatrix} \lambda - 3 & 2 & 0 \\ 2 & \lambda - 3 & 0 \\ 0 & 0 & \lambda - 5 \end{vmatrix} = (\lambda - 5)[(\lambda - 3)(\lambda - 3) - (2)(2)]$$

$$= (\lambda - 5)[(\lambda^2 - 6\lambda + 9) - 4]$$

$$= (\lambda - 5)(\lambda^2 - 6\lambda + 5)$$

$$= (\lambda - 5)(\lambda - 5)(\lambda - 1) \quad , \quad \text{so} \quad \lambda = 1, 5, 5$$

$$\lambda_1 = 1 \longrightarrow \begin{bmatrix} -2 & 2 & 0 & 0 \\ 2 & -2 & 0 & 0 \\ 0 & 0 & -4 & 0 \end{bmatrix} \longrightarrow \begin{bmatrix} 1 & -1 & 0 & 0 \\ 0 & 0 & 0 & 0 \\ 0 & 0 & 1 & 0 \end{bmatrix} \longrightarrow \begin{bmatrix} 1 & -1 & 0 & 0 \\ 0 & 0 & 1 & 0 \\ 0 & 0 & 0 & 0 \end{bmatrix}$$

Let $x_2 = r$;

then $x_1 - x_2 = 0$, i.e., $x_1 = x_2 = r$

and $x_3 = 0$

so $\begin{bmatrix} x_1 \\ x_2 \\ x_3 \end{bmatrix} = \begin{bmatrix} r \\ r \\ 0 \end{bmatrix} = r \begin{bmatrix} 1 \\ 1 \\ 0 \end{bmatrix}$; $B = \left\{ \begin{bmatrix} 1 \\ 1 \\ 0 \end{bmatrix} \right\}$.

$$\lambda_2 = 5 \longrightarrow \begin{bmatrix} 2 & 2 & 0 & 0 \\ 2 & 2 & 0 & 0 \\ 0 & 0 & 0 & 0 \end{bmatrix} \longrightarrow \begin{bmatrix} 1 & 1 & 0 & 0 \\ 0 & 0 & 0 & 0 \\ 0 & 0 & 0 & 0 \end{bmatrix}$$

Let $x_2 = s$ and $x_3 = t$;

then $x_1 + x_2 = 0$, i.e., $x_1 = -x_2 = -s$

so $\begin{bmatrix} x_1 \\ x_2 \\ x_3 \end{bmatrix} = \begin{bmatrix} -s \\ s \\ t \end{bmatrix} = \begin{bmatrix} -s \\ s \\ 0 \end{bmatrix} + \begin{bmatrix} 0 \\ 0 \\ t \end{bmatrix} = s \begin{bmatrix} -1 \\ 1 \\ 0 \end{bmatrix} + t \begin{bmatrix} 0 \\ 0 \\ 1 \end{bmatrix}$;

$$B = \left\{ \begin{bmatrix} -1 \\ 1 \\ 0 \end{bmatrix}, \begin{bmatrix} 0 \\ 0 \\ 1 \end{bmatrix} \right\}.$$

(f) $P = \begin{bmatrix} 1 & -1 & 0 \\ 1 & 1 & 0 \\ 0 & 0 & 1 \end{bmatrix}$

$$P^{-1} = \frac{1}{2} \begin{bmatrix} 1 & -1 & 0 \\ 1 & 1 & 0 \\ 0 & 0 & 2 \end{bmatrix}^T = \frac{1}{2} \begin{bmatrix} 1 & 1 & 0 \\ -1 & 1 & 0 \\ 0 & 0 & 2 \end{bmatrix} \quad ; \quad D = P^{-1}AP = \begin{bmatrix} 1 & 0 & 0 \\ 0 & 5 & 0 \\ 0 & 0 & 5 \end{bmatrix}.$$

(g) $\quad T^4\left(\begin{bmatrix} 2 \\ -2 \\ 4 \end{bmatrix}\right) = A^4 \begin{bmatrix} 2 \\ -2 \\ 4 \end{bmatrix} = PD^4P^{-1} \begin{bmatrix} 2 \\ -2 \\ 4 \end{bmatrix}$

$$= \begin{bmatrix} 1 & -1 & 0 \\ 1 & 1 & 0 \\ 0 & 0 & 1 \end{bmatrix} \begin{bmatrix} 1 & 0 & 0 \\ 0 & 625 & 0 \\ 0 & 0 & 625 \end{bmatrix} \frac{1}{2} \begin{bmatrix} 1 & 1 & 0 \\ -1 & 1 & 0 \\ 0 & 0 & 2 \end{bmatrix} \begin{bmatrix} 2 \\ -2 \\ 4 \end{bmatrix}$$

$$= \begin{bmatrix} 1 & -625 & 0 \\ 1 & 625 & 0 \\ 0 & 0 & 625 \end{bmatrix} \begin{bmatrix} 1 & 1 & 0 \\ -1 & 1 & 0 \\ 0 & 0 & 2 \end{bmatrix} \begin{bmatrix} 1 \\ -1 \\ 2 \end{bmatrix}$$

$$= \begin{bmatrix} 1 & -625 & 0 \\ 1 & 625 & 0 \\ 0 & 0 & 625 \end{bmatrix} \begin{bmatrix} 0 \\ -2 \\ 4 \end{bmatrix} = \begin{bmatrix} 1250 \\ -1250 \\ 2500 \end{bmatrix}$$

8. $\quad 2x^2 - 4xy - y^2 - 4x - 8y = -14$

$$[x\ y] \begin{bmatrix} 2 & -2 \\ -2 & -1 \end{bmatrix} \begin{bmatrix} x \\ y \end{bmatrix} + [-4\ -8] \begin{bmatrix} x \\ y \end{bmatrix} = -14$$

$$0 = \begin{vmatrix} \lambda - 2 & 2 \\ 2 & \lambda + 1 \end{vmatrix} = (\lambda^2 - \lambda - 2) - 4 = \lambda^2 - \lambda - 6 = (\lambda - 3)(\lambda + 2), \quad \text{so } \lambda = 3, -2 \text{ (hyperbola)}$$

$$\lambda_1 = 3 \longrightarrow \begin{bmatrix} 1 & 2 & 0 \\ 2 & 4 & 0 \end{bmatrix} \longrightarrow \begin{bmatrix} 1 & 2 & 0 \\ 0 & 0 & 0 \end{bmatrix}$$

Let $\quad x_2 = s$;

then $\quad x_1 + 2x_2 = 0$, i.e., $\quad x_1 = -2x_2 = -2s$

so $\quad \begin{bmatrix} x_1 \\ x_2 \end{bmatrix} = \begin{bmatrix} -2s \\ s \end{bmatrix} = s \begin{bmatrix} -2 \\ 1 \end{bmatrix}$

and $\quad (-2, 1)/\|(-2, 1)\| = (-2, 1)/\sqrt{5} = (-2/\sqrt{5}, 1/\sqrt{5})$

$$\lambda_2 = -2 \longrightarrow \begin{bmatrix} -4 & 2 & 0 \\ 2 & -1 & 0 \end{bmatrix} \longrightarrow \begin{bmatrix} 1 & -1/2 & 0 \\ 0 & 0 & 0 \end{bmatrix}$$

Let $\quad x_2 = t$;

then $\quad x_1 - \dfrac{1}{2}x_2 = 0$, i.e., $\quad x_1 = \dfrac{1}{2}x_2 = \dfrac{1}{2}t$

so $\quad \begin{bmatrix} x_1 \\ x_2 \end{bmatrix} = \begin{bmatrix} (1/2)t \\ t \end{bmatrix} = t \begin{bmatrix} 1/2 \\ 1 \end{bmatrix} = \dfrac{1}{2}t \begin{bmatrix} 1 \\ 2 \end{bmatrix}$

and $\quad (1, 2)/\|(1, 2)\| = (1, 2)/\sqrt{5} = (1/\sqrt{5}, 2/\sqrt{5})$.

Note that $\quad \det \begin{bmatrix} 1/\sqrt{5} & -2/\sqrt{5} \\ 2/\sqrt{5} & 1/\sqrt{5} \end{bmatrix} = \dfrac{1}{5} - \dfrac{-4}{5} = 1$, indicating a rotation.

$$[x'\ y'] \begin{bmatrix} -2 & 0 \\ 0 & 3 \end{bmatrix} \begin{bmatrix} x' \\ y' \end{bmatrix} + [-4\ -8] \begin{bmatrix} 1/\sqrt{5} & -2/\sqrt{5} \\ 2/\sqrt{5} & 1/\sqrt{5} \end{bmatrix} \begin{bmatrix} x' \\ y' \end{bmatrix} = -14$$

$$-2(x')^2 + 3(y')^2 + \dfrac{-20}{\sqrt{5}}x' + 0y' = -14$$

$$-2(x')^2 + 3(y')^2 - 4\sqrt{5}x' = -14$$

$$-2\left[(x')^2 + 2\sqrt{5}x'\right] + 3(y')^2 = -14$$

$$-2\left[(x')^2 + 2\sqrt{5}x' + 5\right] + 3(y')^2 = -14 - 10$$
$$-2\left(x' + \sqrt{5}\right)^2 + 3(y')^2 = -24$$
$$2\left(x' + \sqrt{5}\right)^2 - 3(y')^2 = 24$$

Substituting the translation $\left(x' + \sqrt{5}, y'\right) = (x'', y'')$ gives

$$2(x'')^2 - 3(y'')^2 = 24 \quad \text{or} \quad \frac{(x'')^2}{12} - \frac{(y'')^2}{8} = 1.$$

FINAL EXAM B

1. Consider the vectors $\mathbf{u} = (0, 1, 0)$, $\mathbf{v} = (1, 2, 3)$, $\mathbf{w} = (-1, 1, 1)$. Compute each of the following.
   - (a) $3\mathbf{u} + 2\mathbf{v} - \mathbf{w}$
   - (b) $\mathbf{u} \cdot \mathbf{w}$
   - (c) $\mathbf{v}/\|\mathbf{v}\|$
   - (d) $\mathbf{u} \cdot \mathbf{v} \times \mathbf{w}$
   - (e) $\mathbf{w} \times 13\mathbf{v}$

2. Consider the matrices $A = \begin{bmatrix} 0 & 1 & 5 \\ 3 & -6 & 9 \\ 2 & 6 & 1 \end{bmatrix}$, $B = \begin{bmatrix} 1 & 0 & 0 \\ 1 & 2 & 3 \\ 0 & 1 & 1 \end{bmatrix}$.

   Compute each of the following.
   - (a) $B - 2A$
   - (b) $A^T + B^2$
   - (c) AB
   - (d) BA
   - (e) $\det B$
   - (f) A^{-1}

3. Consider the linear system $\begin{cases} x + y + 2z = 9 \\ 2x + 4y - 3z = 1 \\ 3x + 6y - 5z = 0 \end{cases}$.
   - (a) Solve the system using Gauss or Gauss–Jordan elimination.
   - (b) Solve the system using Cramer's Rule of Determinants.

4. Consider the planes $3x + 2y - 4z = 6$ and $x - 3y - 2z = 4$.
   - (a) Find an equation for the line of intersection.
   - (b) Find an equation for the plane through $P(2, 3, -1)$ perpendicular to the line of intersection.
   - (c) Find an equation for the plane through $P(2, 3, -1)$ containing the line of intersection.

5. Show whether $\{(a, b, a - b) : a, b \text{ are real}\}$ is a subspace of R^3.

6. Consider the set $B = \{(1, 1, 1), (-1, 1, 0), (1, 2, 1)\}$.
   - (a) Show that B is a basis for R^3.
   - (b) Express $\mathbf{u} = (1, 0, 0)$ as a linear combination of the elements of B.
   - (c) Use the Gram–Schmidt process to orthonormalize B.

7. Consider the function $T : R^2 \rightarrow R^2$ defined by

$$T\left(\begin{bmatrix} x \\ y \end{bmatrix}\right) = \begin{bmatrix} 2x - y \\ -8x + 4y \end{bmatrix}.$$

   - (a) Show that T is a linear transformation.
   - (b) Find the matrix $[T]$ that represents T in the standard basis.
   - (c) Find $\ker(T)$ and state its dimension.
   - (d) Find $R(T)$ and state its dimension.
   - (e) Find the matrix $[T]_B$ that represents T relative to the basis $B = \{(1, 2), (3, -1)\}$.

8. Consider the linear operator $T : R^3 \rightarrow R^3$ defined by

$$T(\mathbf{x}) = A\mathbf{x} \quad \text{where} \quad A = \begin{bmatrix} 2 & 0 & -2 \\ 0 & 3 & 0 \\ 0 & 0 & 3 \end{bmatrix}$$

(a) Find the eigenvalue(s) of A.

(b) Find square matrices P, D such that $D = P^{-1}AP$ is diagonal.

(c) Use your answer to part (b) to compute $T^5 \left(\begin{bmatrix} 1 \\ 2 \\ 3 \end{bmatrix} \right)$.

9. Find the standard matrix representing the planar operator that first reflects across the line $y = x$, then shears horizontally by a factor 2.

FINAL EXAM B

1. (a) $3\mathbf{u} + 2\mathbf{v} - \mathbf{w} = (0,3,0) + (2,4,6) - (-1,1,1) = (3,6,5)$

   (b) $\mathbf{u}\cdot\mathbf{w} = (0,1,0)\cdot(-1,1,1) = (0)(-1) + (1)(1) + (0)(1) = 1$

   (c) $\mathbf{v}/\|\mathbf{v}\| = (1,2,3)/\sqrt{1^2 + 2^2 + 3^2} = \frac{1}{\sqrt{14}}(1,2,3)$

   (d) $\mathbf{u}\cdot\mathbf{v} \times \mathbf{w} = (0,1,0)\cdot(1,2,3) \times (-1,1,1) = \begin{vmatrix} 0 & 1 & 0 \\ 1 & 2 & 3 \\ -1 & 1 & 1 \end{vmatrix}$

   $$= -1(1 - -3) = -4$$

   (e) $\mathbf{w} \times 13\mathbf{v} = (-1,1,1) \times 13(1,2,3) = 13(-1,1,1) \times (1,2,3)$

   $$= 13\begin{vmatrix} \mathbf{i} & \mathbf{j} & \mathbf{k} \\ -1 & 1 & 1 \\ 1 & 2 & 3 \end{vmatrix} = 13[\mathbf{i}(1) - \mathbf{j}(-4) + \mathbf{k}(-3)] = 13(1,4,-3)$$

2. (a) $B - 2A = \begin{bmatrix} 1 & 0 & 0 \\ 1 & 2 & 3 \\ 0 & 1 & 1 \end{bmatrix} - \begin{bmatrix} 0 & 2 & 10 \\ 6 & -12 & 18 \\ 4 & 12 & 2 \end{bmatrix} = \begin{bmatrix} 1 & -2 & -10 \\ -5 & 14 & -15 \\ -4 & -11 & -1 \end{bmatrix}$

   (b) $A^T + B^2 = \begin{bmatrix} 0 & 3 & 2 \\ 1 & -6 & 6 \\ 5 & 9 & 1 \end{bmatrix} + \begin{bmatrix} 1 & 0 & 0 \\ 1 & 2 & 3 \\ 0 & 1 & 1 \end{bmatrix}\begin{bmatrix} 1 & 0 & 0 \\ 1 & 2 & 3 \\ 0 & 1 & 1 \end{bmatrix}$

   $$= \begin{bmatrix} 0 & 3 & 2 \\ 1 & -6 & 6 \\ 5 & 9 & 1 \end{bmatrix} + \begin{bmatrix} 1 & 0 & 0 \\ 3 & 7 & 9 \\ 1 & 3 & 4 \end{bmatrix} = \begin{bmatrix} 1 & 3 & 2 \\ 4 & 1 & 15 \\ 6 & 12 & 5 \end{bmatrix}$$

   (c) $AB = \begin{bmatrix} 0 & 1 & 5 \\ 3 & -6 & 9 \\ 2 & 6 & 1 \end{bmatrix}\begin{bmatrix} 1 & 0 & 0 \\ 1 & 2 & 3 \\ 0 & 1 & 1 \end{bmatrix} = \begin{bmatrix} 1 & 7 & 8 \\ -3 & -3 & -9 \\ 8 & 13 & 19 \end{bmatrix}$

   (d) $BA = \begin{bmatrix} 1 & 0 & 0 \\ 1 & 2 & 3 \\ 0 & 1 & 1 \end{bmatrix}\begin{bmatrix} 0 & 1 & 5 \\ 3 & -6 & 9 \\ 2 & 6 & 1 \end{bmatrix} = \begin{bmatrix} 0 & 1 & 5 \\ 12 & 7 & 26 \\ 5 & 0 & 10 \end{bmatrix}$

   (e) $\det B = \begin{vmatrix} 1 & 0 & 0 \\ 1 & 2 & 3 \\ 0 & 1 & 1 \end{vmatrix} = 1(2 - 3) = -1$

   (f) $A^{-1} = \begin{bmatrix} 0 & 1 & 5 \\ 3 & -6 & 9 \\ 2 & 6 & 1 \end{bmatrix}^{-1} = \dfrac{\text{adj } A}{\det A} = \dfrac{1}{(0)(-60) + (1)(15) + (5)(30)}\begin{bmatrix} -60 & 15 & 30 \\ 29 & -10 & 2 \\ 39 & 15 & -3 \end{bmatrix}^T$

   $$= \frac{1}{165}\begin{bmatrix} -60 & 29 & 39 \\ 15 & -10 & 15 \\ 30 & 2 & -3 \end{bmatrix}$$

3. (a)
$$\begin{bmatrix} 1 & 1 & 2 & 9 \\ 2 & 4 & -3 & 1 \\ 3 & 6 & -5 & 0 \end{bmatrix} \longrightarrow \begin{bmatrix} 1 & 1 & 2 & 9 \\ 0 & 2 & -7 & -17 \\ 0 & 3 & -11 & -27 \end{bmatrix} \longrightarrow \begin{bmatrix} 1 & 1 & 2 & 9 \\ 0 & 1 & -7/2 & -17/2 \\ 0 & 0 & -1/2 & -3/2 \end{bmatrix}$$

$$\longrightarrow \begin{bmatrix} 1 & 1 & 2 & 9 \\ 0 & 1 & -7/2 & -17/2 \\ 0 & 0 & 1 & 3 \end{bmatrix}$$

To finish by Gaussian,

$$z = 3$$

$$y - \frac{7}{2}z = \frac{-17}{2} \quad \text{so} \quad y - \frac{21}{2} = \frac{-17}{2} \ , \quad y = \frac{4}{2} = 2$$

$$x + y + 2z = 9 \quad \text{so} \quad x + 2 + 6 = 9 \ , \quad x = 1$$

To finish by Gauss–Jordan,

$$\begin{bmatrix} 1 & 1 & 2 & 9 \\ 0 & 1 & -7/2 & -17/2 \\ 0 & 0 & 1 & 3 \end{bmatrix} \longrightarrow \begin{bmatrix} 1 & 0 & 11/2 & 35/2 \\ 0 & 1 & -7/2 & -17/2 \\ 0 & 0 & 1 & 3 \end{bmatrix}$$

$$\longrightarrow \begin{bmatrix} 1 & 0 & 0 & 1 \\ 0 & 1 & 0 & 2 \\ 0 & 0 & 1 & 3 \end{bmatrix} \begin{matrix} x = 1 \\ y = 2 \\ z = 3 \end{matrix}$$

(b) $\quad |A| = \begin{vmatrix} 1 & 1 & 2 \\ 2 & 4 & -3 \\ 3 & 6 & -5 \end{vmatrix} = 1(-2) - 1(-1) + 2(0) = -1$

$$|A_1| = \begin{vmatrix} 9 & 1 & 2 \\ 1 & 4 & -3 \\ 0 & 6 & -5 \end{vmatrix} = 9(-2) - 1(-17) + 0 = -1 \ , \quad \text{so} \quad x = \frac{-1}{-1} = 1$$

$$|A_2| = \begin{vmatrix} 1 & 9 & 2 \\ 2 & 1 & -3 \\ 3 & 0 & -5 \end{vmatrix} = -9(-1) + 1(-11) + 0 = -2 \ , \quad \text{so} \quad y = \frac{-2}{-1} = 2$$

$$|A_3| = \begin{vmatrix} 1 & 1 & 9 \\ 2 & 4 & 1 \\ 3 & 6 & 0 \end{vmatrix} = 9(0) - 1(3) + 0 = -3 \ , \quad \text{so} \quad z = \frac{-3}{-1} = 3$$

4. (a) $\quad \mathbf{n}_1 = (3, 2, -4); \mathbf{n}_2 = (1, -3, -2)$

$\mathbf{u} = \mathbf{n}_1 \times \mathbf{n}_2 = (3, 2, -4) \times (1, -3, -2)) = (-16, 2, -11)$

$$y = 0 \longrightarrow \begin{matrix} 3x - 4z = 6 \\ x - 2z = 4 \end{matrix} \longrightarrow \begin{bmatrix} 3 & -4 & 6 \\ 1 & -2 & 4 \end{bmatrix} \longrightarrow \begin{bmatrix} 1 & -2 & 4 \\ 3 & -4 & 6 \end{bmatrix} \longrightarrow \begin{bmatrix} 1 & -2 & 4 \\ 0 & 2 & -6 \end{bmatrix}$$

$$\longrightarrow \begin{bmatrix} 1 & 0 & -2 \\ 0 & 1 & -3 \end{bmatrix}$$

Thus, a point on the line is $Q(-2, 0, -3)$.

$$\begin{aligned} x &= -2 + -16t = -2 - 16t \\ y &= 0 + 2t = 2t \\ z &= -3 + -11t = -3 - 11t \end{aligned}$$

(b) $\mathbf{n} = \mathbf{n}_1 \times \mathbf{n}_2 = (-16, 2, -11)$; $P(2, 3, -1)$

$\quad - 16(x - 2) + 2(y - 3) + -11(z - -1) = 0$

$\quad - 16x + 2y - 11z = -15$

$\quad 16x - 2y + 11z = 15$

(c) $\vec{QP} = (4, 3, 2)$

$\quad \mathbf{n} = (4, 3, 2) \times (-16, 2, -11) = (-37, 12, 56)$; $P(2, 3, -1)$

$\quad - 37(x - 2) + 12(y - 3) + 56(z - -1) = 0$

$\quad - 37x + 12y + 56z = -94$

5. Let $U = \{(a, b, a - b) : a, b \text{ are real}\}$

$\quad$ Consider $\mathbf{u} = (a, b, a - b)$ $\quad$ and $\quad$ $\mathbf{v} = (c, d, c - d)$ $\quad$ in $\quad$ U; $\quad$ that is, $\quad$ a, b, c, d $\quad$ are real.

$\quad$ Is $\quad$ $\mathbf{u} + \mathbf{v} = (a, b, a - b) + (c, d, c - d)$ $\quad$ in $\quad$ U?

$\qquad = (a + c, b + d, a - b + c - d)$

$\qquad = (a + c, b + d, (a + c) - (b + d))$ $\quad$ and $\quad$ $a + c$, $b + d$ $\quad$ are real.

$\qquad$ Yes, $\quad$ $\mathbf{u} + \mathbf{v}$ $\quad$ is in $\quad$ $U,$ $\quad$ so $\quad$ U $\quad$ is closed under addition.

$\quad$ Is $\quad$ $k\mathbf{u} = k(a, b, a - b)$ $\quad$ in $\quad$ U $\quad$ for all real $\quad$ k?

$\qquad = (ka, kb, k(a - b))$

$\qquad = (ka, kb, ka - kb)$ $\quad$ and $\quad$ ka , kb $\quad$ are real.

$\qquad$ Yes, $\quad$ $k\mathbf{u}$ $\quad$ is in $\quad$ $U,$ $\quad$ so $\quad$ U $\quad$ is closed under scalar multiplication.

$\quad$ Thus, $\quad$ U $\quad$ is a subspace of $\quad$ R^3.

6. (a) $\begin{vmatrix} 1 & -1 & 1 \\ 1 & 1 & 2 \\ 1 & 0 & 1 \end{vmatrix} = 1(-3) + 0 + 1(2) = -1 \ne 0$

(b) $\begin{bmatrix} 1 & -1 & 1 & 1 \\ 1 & 1 & 2 & 0 \\ 1 & 0 & 1 & 0 \end{bmatrix} \longrightarrow \begin{bmatrix} 1 & -1 & 1 & 1 \\ 0 & 2 & 1 & -1 \\ 0 & 1 & 0 & -1 \end{bmatrix} \longrightarrow \begin{bmatrix} 1 & -1 & 1 & 1 \\ 0 & 1 & 0 & -1 \\ 0 & 2 & 1 & -1 \end{bmatrix} \longrightarrow \begin{bmatrix} 1 & -1 & 1 & 1 \\ 0 & 1 & 0 & -1 \\ 0 & 0 & 1 & 1 \end{bmatrix}$

$\qquad \longrightarrow \begin{bmatrix} 1 & 0 & 1 & 0 \\ 0 & 1 & 0 & -1 \\ 0 & 0 & 1 & 1 \end{bmatrix} \longrightarrow \begin{bmatrix} 1 & 0 & 0 & -1 \\ 0 & 1 & 0 & -1 \\ 0 & 0 & 1 & 1 \end{bmatrix}$

$\qquad$ Thus, $\quad$ $(1, 0, 0) = -1(1, 1, 1) + -1(-1, 1, 0) + 1(1, 2, 1)$.

(c) $\mathbf{v}_1 = \mathbf{u}_1 = (1, 1, 1)$

$\quad \mathbf{v}_2 = \mathbf{u}_2 - \dfrac{\mathbf{u}_2 \cdot \mathbf{v}_1}{\mathbf{v}_1 \cdot \mathbf{v}_1} = (-1, 1, 0) - \dfrac{(-1, 1, 0) \cdot (1, 1, 1)}{(1, 1, 1) \cdot (1, 1, 1)} (1, 1, 1)$

$\qquad = (-1, 1, 0) - 0(1, 1, 1) = (-1, 1, 0)$

$\quad \mathbf{v}_3 = \mathbf{u}_3 - \dfrac{\mathbf{u}_3 \cdot \mathbf{v}_1}{\mathbf{v}_1 \cdot \mathbf{v}_1} \mathbf{v}_1 - \dfrac{\mathbf{u}_3 \cdot \mathbf{v}_2}{\mathbf{v}_2 \cdot \mathbf{v}_2} \mathbf{v}_2$

$\qquad = (1, 2, 1) - \dfrac{(1, 2, 1) \cdot (1, 1, 1)}{(1, 1, 1) \cdot (1, 1, 1)} (1, 1, 1) - \dfrac{(1, 2, 1) \cdot (-1, 1, 0)}{(-1, 1, 0) \cdot (-1, 1, 0)} (-1, 1, 0)$

$\qquad = (1, 2, 1) - \dfrac{4}{3}(1, 1, 1) - \dfrac{1}{2}(-1, 1, 0) = \left(\dfrac{1}{6}, \dfrac{1}{6}, \dfrac{-2}{6} \right) = \dfrac{1}{6}(1, 1, -2)$

$$\mathbf{w}_1 = (1,1,1)/\|(1,1,1)\| = (1,1,1)/\sqrt{3}$$
$$\mathbf{w}_2 = (-1,1,0)/\|(-1,1,0)\| = (-1,1,0)/\sqrt{2}$$
$$\mathbf{w}_3 = (1,1,-2)/\|(1,1,-2)\| = (1,1,-2)/\sqrt{6}$$

7. (a)
$$T(\mathbf{u} + \mathbf{v}) = T\left(\begin{bmatrix} x_1 \\ y_1 \end{bmatrix} + \begin{bmatrix} x_2 \\ y_2 \end{bmatrix}\right)$$

$$= T\left(\begin{bmatrix} x_1 + x_2 \\ y_1 + y_2 \end{bmatrix}\right)$$

$$= \begin{bmatrix} 2(x_1 + x_2) - (y_1 + y_2) \\ -8(x_1 + x_2) + 4(y_1 + y_2) \end{bmatrix}$$

$$= \begin{bmatrix} 2x_1 + 2x_2 - y_1 - y_2 \\ -8x_1 - 8x_2 + 4y_1 + 4y_2 \end{bmatrix}$$

$$T(\mathbf{u}) + T(\mathbf{v}) = T\left(\begin{bmatrix} x_1 \\ y_1 \end{bmatrix}\right) + T\left(\begin{bmatrix} x_2 \\ y_2 \end{bmatrix}\right)$$

$$= \begin{bmatrix} 2x_1 - y_1 \\ -8x_1 + 4y_1 \end{bmatrix} + \begin{bmatrix} 2x_2 - y_2 \\ -8x_2 + 4y_2 \end{bmatrix}$$

$$= \begin{bmatrix} 2x_1 - y_1 + 2x_2 - y_2 \\ -8x_1 + 4y_1 - 8x_2 + 4y_2 \end{bmatrix}$$

$$= \begin{bmatrix} 2x_1 + 2x_2 - y_1 - y_2 \\ -8x_1 - 8x_2 + 4y_1 + 4y_2 \end{bmatrix} = T(\mathbf{u} + \mathbf{v})$$

$$T(k\mathbf{u}) = T\left(k\begin{bmatrix} x \\ y \end{bmatrix}\right)$$

$$= T\left(\begin{bmatrix} kx \\ ky \end{bmatrix}\right)$$

$$= \begin{bmatrix} 2kx - ky \\ -8kx + 4ky \end{bmatrix}$$

$$kT(\mathbf{u}) = kT\left(\begin{bmatrix} x \\ y \end{bmatrix}\right)$$

$$= k\begin{bmatrix} 2x - y \\ -8x + 4y \end{bmatrix}$$

$$= \begin{bmatrix} k(2x - y) \\ k(-8x + 4y) \end{bmatrix}$$

$$= \begin{bmatrix} 2kx - ky \\ -8kx + 4ky \end{bmatrix} = T(k\mathbf{u})$$

(b) $[T] = \begin{bmatrix} T(\mathbf{e}_1) \vdots T(\mathbf{e}_2) \end{bmatrix} = \begin{bmatrix} 2 & -1 \\ -8 & 4 \end{bmatrix}$

(c) $\begin{bmatrix} 2 & -1 & 0 \\ -8 & 4 & 0 \end{bmatrix} \longrightarrow \begin{bmatrix} 1 & -1/2 & 0 \\ 0 & 0 & 0 \end{bmatrix}$

Let $y = t$;

then $x - \dfrac{1}{2}y = 0$, i.e., $x = \dfrac{1}{2}y = \dfrac{1}{2}t$

so $\begin{bmatrix} x \\ y \end{bmatrix} = \begin{bmatrix} (1/2)t \\ t \end{bmatrix} = t\begin{bmatrix} 1/2 \\ 1 \end{bmatrix} = \dfrac{1}{2}t\begin{bmatrix} 1 \\ 2 \end{bmatrix}$

A basis for $\ker(T)$ is $\left\{\begin{bmatrix} 1 \\ 2 \end{bmatrix}\right\}$, and $\ker(T)$ is 1–dimensional.

(d) Noting the leading ones in part (c), a basis for $R(T)$ is $\left\{\begin{bmatrix} 2 \\ -8 \end{bmatrix}\right\}$,

and $R(T)$ is 1–dimensional.

(e) $[T]_B = \left[[T(\mathbf{u}_1)]_B \vdots [T(\mathbf{u}_2)]_B\right]$

$= \left[\left[T\left(\begin{bmatrix} 1 \\ 2 \end{bmatrix}\right)\right]_B \vdots \left[T\left(\begin{bmatrix} 3 \\ -1 \end{bmatrix}\right)\right]_B\right]$

$= \left[\begin{bmatrix} 0 \\ 0 \end{bmatrix}_B \vdots \begin{bmatrix} 7 \\ -28 \end{bmatrix}_B\right]$

$= \begin{bmatrix} 1 & 3 \\ 2 & -1 \end{bmatrix}^{-1} \begin{bmatrix} 0 & 7 \\ 0 & -28 \end{bmatrix}$

$= \dfrac{1}{-7}\begin{bmatrix} -1 & -3 \\ -2 & 1 \end{bmatrix}\begin{bmatrix} 0 & 7 \\ 0 & -28 \end{bmatrix}$

$= \begin{bmatrix} -1 & -3 \\ -2 & 1 \end{bmatrix}\begin{bmatrix} 0 & -1 \\ 0 & 4 \end{bmatrix} = \begin{bmatrix} 0 & -11 \\ 0 & 6 \end{bmatrix}$.

8. (a) $0 = \begin{vmatrix} \lambda-2 & 0 & 2 \\ 0 & \lambda-3 & 0 \\ 0 & 0 & \lambda-3 \end{vmatrix} = (\lambda-2)(\lambda-3)^2$ so $\lambda = 2, 3, 3$

(b) $\lambda_1 = 2 \longrightarrow \begin{bmatrix} 0 & 0 & 2 & 0 \\ 0 & -1 & 0 & 0 \\ 0 & 0 & -1 & 0 \end{bmatrix} \longrightarrow \begin{bmatrix} 0 & 0 & 1 & 0 \\ 0 & 1 & 0 & 0 \\ 0 & 0 & -1 & 0 \end{bmatrix} \longrightarrow \begin{bmatrix} 0 & 1 & 0 & 0 \\ 0 & 0 & 1 & 0 \\ 0 & 0 & 0 & 0 \end{bmatrix}$

Let $x = r$;
$y = z = 0$

so $\begin{bmatrix} x \\ y \\ z \end{bmatrix} = \begin{bmatrix} r \\ 0 \\ 0 \end{bmatrix} = r\begin{bmatrix} 1 \\ 0 \\ 0 \end{bmatrix}$

$\lambda_2 = 3 \longrightarrow \begin{bmatrix} 1 & 0 & 2 & 0 \\ 0 & 0 & 0 & 0 \\ 0 & 0 & 0 & 0 \end{bmatrix}$

Let $y = s$ and $z = t$;
$x + 2z = 0$,   i.e., $x = -2z = -2t$

so $\begin{bmatrix} x \\ y \\ z \end{bmatrix} = \begin{bmatrix} -2t \\ s \\ t \end{bmatrix} = \begin{bmatrix} -2t \\ 0 \\ t \end{bmatrix} + \begin{bmatrix} 0 \\ s \\ 0 \end{bmatrix} = t\begin{bmatrix} -2 \\ 0 \\ 1 \end{bmatrix} + s\begin{bmatrix} 0 \\ 1 \\ 0 \end{bmatrix}$

$P = \begin{bmatrix} 1 & 0 & -2 \\ 0 & 1 & 0 \\ 0 & 0 & 1 \end{bmatrix}$

$P^{-1} = \dfrac{1}{1}\begin{bmatrix} 1 & 0 & 0 \\ 0 & 1 & 0 \\ 2 & 0 & 1 \end{bmatrix}^T = \begin{bmatrix} 1 & 0 & 2 \\ 0 & 1 & 0 \\ 0 & 0 & 1 \end{bmatrix}$; $D = P^{-1}AP = \begin{bmatrix} 2 & 0 & 0 \\ 0 & 3 & 0 \\ 0 & 0 & 3 \end{bmatrix}$.

331

(c) $T^5 \left(\begin{bmatrix} 1 \\ 2 \\ 3 \end{bmatrix} \right) = A^5 \begin{bmatrix} 1 \\ 2 \\ 3 \end{bmatrix} = PD^5P^{-1} \begin{bmatrix} 1 \\ 2 \\ 3 \end{bmatrix}$

$$= \begin{bmatrix} 1 & 0 & -2 \\ 0 & 1 & 0 \\ 0 & 0 & 1 \end{bmatrix} \begin{bmatrix} 32 & 0 & 0 \\ 0 & 243 & 0 \\ 0 & 0 & 243 \end{bmatrix} \begin{bmatrix} 1 & 0 & 2 \\ 0 & 1 & 0 \\ 0 & 0 & 1 \end{bmatrix} \begin{bmatrix} 1 \\ 2 \\ 3 \end{bmatrix}$$

$$= \begin{bmatrix} 32 & 0 & -486 \\ 0 & 243 & 0 \\ 0 & 0 & 243 \end{bmatrix} \begin{bmatrix} 1 & 0 & 2 \\ 0 & 1 & 0 \\ 0 & 0 & 1 \end{bmatrix} \begin{bmatrix} 1 \\ 2 \\ 3 \end{bmatrix}$$

$$= \begin{bmatrix} 32 & 0 & -422 \\ 0 & 243 & 0 \\ 0 & 0 & 243 \end{bmatrix} \begin{bmatrix} 1 \\ 2 \\ 3 \end{bmatrix} = \begin{bmatrix} -1234 \\ 486 \\ 729 \end{bmatrix}$$

9. Let $T_1 =$ reflection across line $y = x$

$$[T_1] = [T(e_1) \vdots T(e_2)] = \left[T\left(\begin{bmatrix} 1 \\ 0 \end{bmatrix} \right) \vdots T\left(\begin{bmatrix} 0 \\ 1 \end{bmatrix} \right) \right] = \begin{bmatrix} 0 & 1 \\ 1 & 0 \end{bmatrix}$$

Let $T_2 =$ horizontal shear by 2

$$[T_2] = [T(e_1) \vdots T(e_2)] = \left[T\left(\begin{bmatrix} 1 \\ 0 \end{bmatrix} \right) \vdots T\left(\begin{bmatrix} 0 \\ 1 \end{bmatrix} \right) \right] = \begin{bmatrix} 1 & 2 \\ 0 & 1 \end{bmatrix}$$

$[T_2 \circ T_1] = [T_2][T_1]$

$$= \begin{bmatrix} 1 & 2 \\ 0 & 1 \end{bmatrix} \begin{bmatrix} 0 & 1 \\ 1 & 0 \end{bmatrix}$$

$$= \begin{bmatrix} 2 & 1 \\ 1 & 0 \end{bmatrix}$$

1. Consider the vectors $\mathbf{u} = (3, 1, 2)$, $\mathbf{v} = (2, 0, -7)$, $\mathbf{w} = (-4, 6, 5)$. Compute each of the following.

   (a) $5\mathbf{u} - \mathbf{v} + 2\mathbf{w}$
   (b) $(\mathbf{u} \cdot 3\mathbf{v})\mathbf{w}$
   (c) $\mathbf{u} \cdot \mathbf{w} \times \mathbf{v}$
   (d) $(\mathbf{v} - \mathbf{w})/\|\mathbf{v} - \mathbf{w}\|$
   (e) $\text{proj}_{\mathbf{u}} \mathbf{v}$ (the component of $\mathbf{v}$ parallel to $\mathbf{u}$).

2. Consider the matrices $A = \begin{bmatrix} 3 & 1 & -1 \\ 2 & 0 & 1 \\ 0 & 3 & -5 \end{bmatrix}$, $B = \begin{bmatrix} 3 & 2 & -1 \\ 1 & 6 & 3 \\ 2 & -4 & 0 \end{bmatrix}$.

   Compute each of the following.

   (a) $2A + 3B$
   (b) BA
   (c) $B^2 - 4AB^T$
   (d) $A^{-1} \det A$
   (e) $\left(AB^{-1}\right)^{-1}$

3. Consider the linear system $\begin{cases} x + y + 2z = 8 \\ -x - 2y + 3z = 1 \\ 3x - 7y + 4z = 10 \,. \end{cases}$

   (a) Solve the system using Gauss or Gauss–Jordan elimination.
   (b) Solve the system by inverting the coefficient matrix and multiplying by the right–hand side.

4. Consider $B = \left\{ 2x + 3, 3x^2 + 1, -5x^2 + x - 1 \right\}$.

   (a) Prove that B is a basis for P_2.
   (b) Express $-x^2 - 2$ as a linear combination of the elements of B.
   (c) If $T : P_2 \to P_2$ is a linear transformation, and $T(2x + 3) = x^2 - 1$, $T(3x^2 + 1) = x^2 - 2x$, $T(-5x^2 + x - 1) = -x^2 + 3x$, compute $T(-x^2 - 2)$.

5. Consider the bases $B = \{(-3, 0, -3), (-3, 2, -1), (1, 6, -1)\}$
   and $B' = \{(-6, -6, 0), (-2, -6, 4), (-2, -3, 7)\}$.
   (a) Compute the transition matrix from B to B'.
   (b) Compute the coordinates $[(-5, 8, -5)]_B$.
   (c) Use your answers to parts (a) and (b) to compute $[(-5, 8, -5)]_{B'}$.

6. Consider the transformation $T : R^5 \to R^4$ given by $T(\mathbf{x}) = A\mathbf{x}$, where

$$A = \begin{bmatrix} 1 & 4 & 5 & 0 & 9 \\ 3 & -2 & 1 & 0 & -1 \\ -1 & 0 & -1 & 0 & -1 \\ 2 & 3 & 5 & 1 & 8 \end{bmatrix}.$$

   (a) Find a basis for the range, $R(T)$.
   (b) Find a basis for the kernel, $\ker(T)$.

333

7. Consider the transormation $T : R^3 \rightarrow R^3$ given by $T(x, y, z) = (x + 2y - z, -y, x + 7z)$.
   Consider the bases $B = \{(1, 0, 0), (0, 1, 0), (0, 0, 1)\}$ and $B' = \{(1, 0, 0), (1, 1, 0), (1, 1, 1)\}$.

   (a) Compute the matrix of T with respect to B.
   (b) Compute the matrix of T with respect to B'.

8. Consider the matrix $A = \begin{bmatrix} -1 & 4 & -2 \\ -3 & 4 & 0 \\ -3 & 1 & 3 \end{bmatrix}$.

   (a) Find a matrix P that diagonalizes A, and find $P^{-1}AP$.
   (b) Use your answer to part (a) to compute A^4.

FINAL EXAM C

1. (a) $5\mathbf{u} - \mathbf{v} + 2\mathbf{w} = (15, 5, 10) - (2, 0, -7) + (-8, 12, 10) = (5, 17, 27)$

(b) $(\mathbf{u}\cdot 3\mathbf{v})\mathbf{w} = 3(\mathbf{u}\cdot\mathbf{v})\mathbf{w} = 3[(3)(2) + (1)(0) + (2)(-7)](-4, 6, 5) = -24(-4, 6, 5) = (96, -144, -120)$

(c) $\mathbf{u}\cdot\mathbf{w} \times \mathbf{v} = (3, 1, 2)\cdot(-4, 6, 5) \times (2, 0, -7)$

$$= \begin{vmatrix} 3 & 1 & 2 \\ -4 & 6 & 5 \\ 2 & 0 & -7 \end{vmatrix} = 3(-42) + -1(18) + 2(-12) = -168$$

(d) $(\mathbf{v} - \mathbf{w})/\|\mathbf{v} - \mathbf{w}\| = (6, -6, -12)/\|6, -6, -12\|$

$$= 6(1, -1, -2)/\|6(1, -1, -2)\| = (1, -1, -2)/\|(1, -1, -2)\| = (1, -1, -2)/\sqrt{6}$$

(e) $\mathrm{proj}_{\mathbf{u}}\mathbf{v} = \dfrac{\mathbf{v}\cdot\mathbf{u}}{\mathbf{u}\cdot\mathbf{u}}\mathbf{u} = \dfrac{(2, 0, -7)\cdot(3, 1, 2)}{(3, 1, 2)\cdot(3, 1, 2)}(3, 1, 2) = \dfrac{-8}{14}(3, 1, 2) = \dfrac{-4}{7}(3, 1, 2)$

2. (a) $2A + 3B = \begin{bmatrix} 6 & 2 & -2 \\ 4 & 0 & 2 \\ 0 & 6 & -10 \end{bmatrix} + \begin{bmatrix} 9 & 6 & -3 \\ 3 & 18 & 9 \\ 6 & -12 & 0 \end{bmatrix} = \begin{bmatrix} 15 & 8 & -5 \\ 7 & 18 & 11 \\ 6 & -6 & -10 \end{bmatrix}$

(b) $BA = \begin{bmatrix} 3 & 2 & -1 \\ 1 & 6 & 3 \\ 2 & -4 & 0 \end{bmatrix}\begin{bmatrix} 3 & 1 & -1 \\ 2 & 0 & 1 \\ 0 & 3 & -5 \end{bmatrix} = \begin{bmatrix} 13 & 0 & 4 \\ 15 & 10 & -10 \\ -2 & 2 & -6 \end{bmatrix}$

(c) $B^2 - 4AB^T = \begin{bmatrix} 3 & 2 & -1 \\ 1 & 6 & 3 \\ 2 & -4 & 0 \end{bmatrix}\begin{bmatrix} 3 & 2 & -1 \\ 1 & 6 & 3 \\ 2 & -4 & 0 \end{bmatrix} - 4\begin{bmatrix} 3 & 1 & -1 \\ 2 & 0 & 1 \\ 0 & 3 & -5 \end{bmatrix}\begin{bmatrix} 3 & 1 & 2 \\ 2 & 6 & -4 \\ -1 & 3 & 0 \end{bmatrix}$

$$= \begin{bmatrix} 9 & 22 & 3 \\ 15 & 26 & 17 \\ 2 & -20 & -14 \end{bmatrix} - 4\begin{bmatrix} 12 & 6 & 2 \\ 5 & 5 & 4 \\ 11 & 3 & -12 \end{bmatrix}$$

$$= \begin{bmatrix} 9 & 22 & 3 \\ 15 & 26 & 17 \\ 2 & -20 & -14 \end{bmatrix} - \begin{bmatrix} 48 & 24 & 8 \\ 20 & 20 & 16 \\ 44 & 12 & -48 \end{bmatrix} = \begin{bmatrix} -39 & -2 & -5 \\ -5 & 6 & 1 \\ -42 & -32 & 34 \end{bmatrix}$$

(d) $A^{-1}\det A = \mathrm{adj}\,A = \begin{bmatrix} -3 & 10 & 6 \\ 2 & -15 & -9 \\ 1 & -5 & -2 \end{bmatrix}^{\mathrm{T}} = \begin{bmatrix} -3 & 2 & 1 \\ 10 & -15 & -5 \\ 6 & -9 & -2 \end{bmatrix}$

(e) $\left(AB^{-1}\right)^{-1} = \left(B^{-1}\right)^{-1}A^{-1} = BA^{-1}$

$$= \begin{bmatrix} 3 & 2 & -1 \\ 1 & 6 & 3 \\ 2 & -4 & 0 \end{bmatrix}\frac{1}{3(-3) + 2(2) + 0(1)}\begin{bmatrix} -3 & 2 & 1 \\ 10 & -15 & -5 \\ 6 & -9 & -2 \end{bmatrix} \quad \text{from part (d)}$$

$$= \frac{1}{-5}\begin{bmatrix} 3 & 2 & -1 \\ 1 & 6 & 3 \\ 2 & -4 & 0 \end{bmatrix}\begin{bmatrix} -3 & 2 & 1 \\ 10 & -15 & -5 \\ 6 & -9 & -2 \end{bmatrix} = \frac{-1}{5}\begin{bmatrix} 5 & -15 & -5 \\ 75 & -115 & -35 \\ -46 & 64 & 22 \end{bmatrix}.$$

3. (a) $\begin{bmatrix} 1 & 1 & 2 & 8 \\ -1 & -2 & 3 & 1 \\ 3 & -7 & 4 & 10 \end{bmatrix} \longrightarrow \begin{bmatrix} 1 & 1 & 2 & 8 \\ 0 & -1 & 5 & 9 \\ 0 & -10 & -2 & -14 \end{bmatrix} \longrightarrow \begin{bmatrix} 1 & 1 & 2 & 8 \\ 0 & 1 & -5 & -9 \\ 0 & 0 & -52 & -104 \end{bmatrix}$

$\longrightarrow \begin{bmatrix} 1 & 1 & 2 & 8 \\ 0 & 1 & -5 & -9 \\ 0 & 0 & 1 & 2 \end{bmatrix}$

To finish by Gaussian,

$$z = 2$$

$$y - 5z = -9 \quad \text{so} \quad y - 10 = -9 \; , \quad y = 1$$

$$x + y + 2z = 8 \quad \text{so} \quad x + 1 + 4 = 8 \; , \quad x = 3$$

To finish by Gauss–Jordan,

$\begin{bmatrix} 1 & 1 & 2 & 8 \\ 0 & 1 & -5 & -9 \\ 0 & 0 & 1 & 2 \end{bmatrix} \longrightarrow \begin{bmatrix} 1 & 0 & 7 & 17 \\ 0 & 1 & -5 & -9 \\ 0 & 0 & 1 & 2 \end{bmatrix} \longrightarrow \begin{bmatrix} 1 & 0 & 0 & 3 \\ 0 & 1 & 0 & 1 \\ 0 & 0 & 1 & 2 \end{bmatrix} \begin{matrix} x = 3 \\ y = 1 \\ z = 2 \end{matrix}$

(b) $\begin{bmatrix} x \\ y \\ z \end{bmatrix} = \begin{bmatrix} 1 & 1 & 2 \\ -1 & -2 & 3 \\ 3 & -7 & 4 \end{bmatrix}^{-1} \begin{bmatrix} 8 \\ 1 \\ 10 \end{bmatrix} = \frac{1}{52} \begin{bmatrix} 13 & 13 & 13 \\ -18 & -2 & 10 \\ 7 & -5 & -1 \end{bmatrix}^{T} \begin{bmatrix} 8 \\ 1 \\ 10 \end{bmatrix}$

$= \frac{1}{52} \begin{bmatrix} 13 & -18 & 7 \\ 13 & -2 & -5 \\ 13 & 10 & -1 \end{bmatrix} \begin{bmatrix} 8 \\ 1 \\ 10 \end{bmatrix} = \frac{1}{52} \begin{bmatrix} 156 \\ 52 \\ 104 \end{bmatrix} = \begin{bmatrix} 3 \\ 1 \\ 2 \end{bmatrix}$

4. (a) $\begin{vmatrix} 3 & 1 & -1 \\ 2 & 0 & 1 \\ 0 & 3 & -5 \end{vmatrix} = 3(-3) - 2(-2) + 0 = -5 \neq 0$

(b) $\begin{bmatrix} 3 & 1 & -1 & -2 \\ 2 & 0 & 1 & 0 \\ 0 & 3 & -5 & -1 \end{bmatrix} \longrightarrow \begin{bmatrix} 1 & 1/3 & -1/3 & -2/3 \\ 0 & -2/3 & 5/3 & 4/3 \\ 0 & 3 & -5 & -1 \end{bmatrix} \longrightarrow \begin{bmatrix} 1 & 1/3 & -1/3 & -2/3 \\ 0 & 1 & -5/2 & -2 \\ 0 & 0 & 5/2 & 5 \end{bmatrix}$

$\longrightarrow \begin{bmatrix} 1 & 1/3 & -1/3 & -2/3 \\ 0 & 1 & -5/2 & -2 \\ 0 & 0 & 1 & 2 \end{bmatrix} \longrightarrow \begin{bmatrix} 1 & 0 & 1/2 & 0 \\ 0 & 1 & -5/2 & -2 \\ 0 & 0 & 1 & 2 \end{bmatrix} \longrightarrow \begin{bmatrix} 1 & 0 & 0 & -1 \\ 0 & 1 & 0 & 3 \\ 0 & 0 & 1 & 2 \end{bmatrix}$

Thus, $\quad -x^2 - 2 = -1(2x + 3) + 3(3x^2 + 1) + 2(-5x^2 + x - 1)$.

(c) $T(-x^2 - 2) = T[-1(2x + 3) + 3(3x^2 + 1) + 2(-5x^2 + x - 1)]$

$= -1T(2x + 3) + 3T(3x^2 + 1) + 2T(-5x^2 + x - 1)$

$= -1(x^2 - 1) + 3(x^2 - 2x) + 2(-x^2 + 3x)$

$= 1$

5. (a) $P_{B',B} = \left[\left[\begin{pmatrix} -3 \\ 0 \\ -3 \end{pmatrix} \right]_{B'} \; : \; \left[\begin{pmatrix} -3 \\ 2 \\ -1 \end{pmatrix} \right]_{B'} \; : \; \left[\begin{pmatrix} 1 \\ 6 \\ -1 \end{pmatrix} \right]_{B'} \right]$

$$= \begin{bmatrix} -6 & -2 & -2 \\ -6 & -6 & -3 \\ 0 & 4 & 7 \end{bmatrix}^{-1} \begin{bmatrix} -3 & -3 & 1 \\ 0 & 2 & 6 \\ -3 & -1 & -1 \end{bmatrix} = \frac{1}{144} \begin{bmatrix} -30 & 42 & -24 \\ 6 & -42 & 24 \\ -6 & -6 & 24 \end{bmatrix}^T \begin{bmatrix} -3 & -3 & 1 \\ 0 & 2 & 6 \\ -3 & -1 & -1 \end{bmatrix}$$

$$= \frac{1}{24} \begin{bmatrix} -5 & 7 & -4 \\ 1 & -7 & 4 \\ -1 & -1 & 4 \end{bmatrix}^T \begin{bmatrix} -3 & -3 & 1 \\ 0 & 2 & 6 \\ -3 & -1 & -1 \end{bmatrix}$$

$$= \frac{1}{24} \begin{bmatrix} -5 & 1 & -1 \\ 7 & -7 & -1 \\ -4 & 4 & 4 \end{bmatrix} \begin{bmatrix} -3 & -3 & 1 \\ 0 & 2 & 6 \\ -3 & -1 & -1 \end{bmatrix} = \frac{1}{24} \begin{bmatrix} 18 & 18 & 2 \\ -18 & -34 & -34 \\ 0 & 16 & 16 \end{bmatrix}$$

(b) $$\left[\begin{pmatrix} -5 \\ 8 \\ -5 \end{pmatrix} \right]_B = \begin{bmatrix} -3 & -3 & 1 \\ 0 & 2 & 6 \\ -3 & -1 & -1 \end{bmatrix}^{-1} \begin{bmatrix} -5 \\ 8 \\ -5 \end{bmatrix} = \frac{1}{48} \begin{bmatrix} 4 & -18 & 6 \\ -4 & 6 & 6 \\ -20 & 18 & -6 \end{bmatrix}^T \begin{bmatrix} -5 \\ 8 \\ -5 \end{bmatrix}$$

$$= \frac{1}{24} \begin{bmatrix} 2 & -9 & 3 \\ -2 & 3 & 3 \\ -10 & 9 & -3 \end{bmatrix}^T \begin{bmatrix} -5 \\ 8 \\ -5 \end{bmatrix}$$

$$= \frac{1}{24} \begin{bmatrix} 2 & -2 & -10 \\ -9 & 3 & 9 \\ 3 & 3 & -3 \end{bmatrix} \begin{bmatrix} -5 \\ 8 \\ -5 \end{bmatrix} = \frac{1}{24} \begin{bmatrix} 24 \\ 24 \\ 24 \end{bmatrix} = \begin{bmatrix} 1 \\ 1 \\ 1 \end{bmatrix}$$

(c) $$\left[\begin{pmatrix} -5 \\ 8 \\ -5 \end{pmatrix} \right]_{B'} = P_{B',B} \left[\begin{pmatrix} -5 \\ 8 \\ -5 \end{pmatrix} \right]_B$$

$$= \frac{1}{24} \begin{bmatrix} 18 & 18 & 2 \\ -18 & -34 & -34 \\ 0 & 16 & 16 \end{bmatrix} \begin{bmatrix} 1 \\ 1 \\ 1 \end{bmatrix} = \frac{1}{24} \begin{bmatrix} 38 \\ -86 \\ 32 \end{bmatrix} = \frac{1}{12} \begin{bmatrix} 19 \\ -43 \\ 16 \end{bmatrix}$$

6. (a) $$\begin{bmatrix} 1 & 4 & 5 & 0 & 9 \\ 3 & -2 & 1 & 0 & -1 \\ -1 & 0 & -1 & 0 & -1 \\ 2 & 3 & 5 & 1 & 8 \end{bmatrix} \longrightarrow \begin{bmatrix} 1 & 4 & 5 & 0 & 9 \\ 0 & -14 & -14 & 0 & -28 \\ 0 & 4 & 4 & 0 & 8 \\ 0 & -5 & -5 & 1 & -10 \end{bmatrix} \longrightarrow \begin{bmatrix} 1 & 0 & 1 & 0 & 1 \\ 0 & 1 & 1 & 0 & 2 \\ 0 & 0 & 0 & 0 & 0 \\ 0 & 0 & 0 & 1 & 0 \end{bmatrix}$$

$$\longrightarrow \begin{bmatrix} 1 & 0 & 1 & 0 & 1 \\ 0 & 1 & 1 & 0 & 2 \\ 0 & 0 & 0 & 1 & 0 \\ 0 & 0 & 0 & 0 & 0 \end{bmatrix}$$

Noting the leading ones, a basis for $R(T)$ is $\left\{ \begin{bmatrix} 1 \\ 3 \\ -1 \\ 2 \end{bmatrix}, \begin{bmatrix} 4 \\ -2 \\ 0 \\ 3 \end{bmatrix}, \begin{bmatrix} 0 \\ 0 \\ 0 \\ 1 \end{bmatrix} \right\}$.

(b) From part (a), the homogeneous system has solutions as follows:

$$\text{Let} \quad x_3 = s \quad \text{and} \quad x_5 = t;$$

$$\text{then} \quad x_4 = 0$$

$$\text{and} \quad x_2 + x_3 + 2x_5 = 0 \quad , \quad \text{i.e.,} \quad x_2 = -x_3 - 2x_5 = -s - 2t$$

$$\text{and} \quad x_1 + x_3 + x_5 = 0 \quad , \quad \text{i.e.,} \quad x_1 = -x_3 - x_5 = -s - t$$

$$\text{so} \quad \begin{bmatrix} x_1 \\ x_2 \\ x_3 \\ x_4 \\ x_5 \end{bmatrix} = \begin{bmatrix} -s-t \\ -s-2t \\ s \\ 0 \\ t \end{bmatrix} = \begin{bmatrix} -s \\ -s \\ s \\ 0 \\ 0 \end{bmatrix} + \begin{bmatrix} -t \\ -2t \\ 0 \\ 0 \\ t \end{bmatrix} = s\begin{bmatrix} -1 \\ -1 \\ 1 \\ 0 \\ 0 \end{bmatrix} + t\begin{bmatrix} -1 \\ -2 \\ 0 \\ 0 \\ 1 \end{bmatrix}$$

A basis for $\ker(T)$ is $\left\{ \begin{bmatrix} -1 \\ -1 \\ 1 \\ 0 \\ 0 \end{bmatrix}, \begin{bmatrix} -1 \\ -2 \\ 0 \\ 0 \\ 1 \end{bmatrix} \right\}.$

7. (a) $[T]_B = [T] = [T(e_1) \vdots T(e_2) \vdots T(e_3)]$

$$= \begin{bmatrix} 1 & 2 & -1 \\ 0 & -1 & 0 \\ 1 & 0 & 7 \end{bmatrix}$$

(b) $[T]_{B'} = \left[[T(1,0,0)]_{B'} \vdots [T(1,1,0)]_{B'} \vdots [T(1,1,1)]_{B'} \right]$

$$= \left[[(1,0,1)]_{B'} \vdots [(3,-1,1)]_{B'} \vdots [(2,-1,8)]_{B'} \right]$$

$$= \begin{bmatrix} 1 & 1 & 1 \\ 0 & 1 & 1 \\ 0 & 0 & 1 \end{bmatrix}^{-1} \begin{bmatrix} 1 & 3 & 2 \\ 0 & -1 & -1 \\ 1 & 1 & 8 \end{bmatrix}$$

$$= \frac{1}{1} \begin{bmatrix} 1 & 0 & 0 \\ -1 & 1 & 0 \\ 0 & -1 & 1 \end{bmatrix}^T \begin{bmatrix} 1 & 3 & 2 \\ 0 & -1 & -1 \\ 1 & 1 & 8 \end{bmatrix}$$

$$= \begin{bmatrix} 1 & -1 & 0 \\ 0 & 1 & -1 \\ 0 & 0 & 1 \end{bmatrix} \begin{bmatrix} 1 & 3 & 2 \\ 0 & -1 & -1 \\ 1 & 1 & 8 \end{bmatrix} = \begin{bmatrix} 1 & 4 & 3 \\ -1 & -2 & -9 \\ 1 & 1 & 8 \end{bmatrix}$$

8. (a) $0 = \begin{vmatrix} \lambda+1 & -4 & 2 \\ 3 & \lambda-4 & 0 \\ 3 & -1 & \lambda-3 \end{vmatrix} = 2[-3 - 3(\lambda-4)] + 0 + (\lambda-3)[(\lambda+1)(\lambda-4) - 3(-4)]$

$$= 2[-3\lambda + 9] + (\lambda-3)[\lambda^2 - 3\lambda + 8]$$

$$= -6(\lambda-3) + (\lambda-3)(\lambda^2 - 3\lambda + 8)$$

$$= (\lambda - 3)(-6 + \lambda^2 - 3\lambda + 8)$$

$$= (\lambda - 3)(\lambda^2 - 3\lambda + 2)$$

$$= (\lambda - 3)(\lambda - 2)(\lambda - 1) \quad \text{so} \quad \lambda = 1, 2, 3$$

$$\lambda_1 = 1 \longrightarrow \begin{bmatrix} 2 & -4 & 2 & 0 \\ 3 & -3 & 0 & 0 \\ 3 & -1 & -2 & 0 \end{bmatrix} \longrightarrow \begin{bmatrix} 1 & -2 & 1 & 0 \\ 0 & 3 & -3 & 0 \\ 0 & 5 & -5 & 0 \end{bmatrix} \longrightarrow \begin{bmatrix} 1 & 0 & -1 & 0 \\ 0 & 1 & -1 & 0 \\ 0 & 0 & 0 & 0 \end{bmatrix}$$

Let $x_3 = r$;

then $x_2 - x_3 = 0$, i.e., $x_2 = x_3 = r$

and $x_1 - x_3 = 0$, i.e., $x_1 = x_3 = r$

so $\begin{bmatrix} x_1 \\ x_2 \\ x_3 \end{bmatrix} = \begin{bmatrix} r \\ r \\ r \end{bmatrix} = r \begin{bmatrix} 1 \\ 1 \\ 1 \end{bmatrix}$

$$\lambda_2 = 2 \longrightarrow \begin{bmatrix} 3 & -4 & 2 & 0 \\ 3 & -2 & 0 & 0 \\ 3 & -1 & -1 & 0 \end{bmatrix} \longrightarrow \begin{bmatrix} 1 & -4/3 & 2/3 & 0 \\ 0 & 2 & -2 & 0 \\ 0 & 3 & -3 & 0 \end{bmatrix} \longrightarrow \begin{bmatrix} 1 & 0 & -2/3 & 0 \\ 0 & 1 & -1 & 0 \\ 0 & 0 & 0 & 0 \end{bmatrix}$$

Let $x_3 = s$;

then $x_2 - x_3 = 0$, i.e., $x_2 = x_3 = s$

and $x_1 - \dfrac{2}{3}x_3 = 0$, i.e., $x_1 = \dfrac{2}{3}x_3 = \dfrac{2}{3}s$

so $\begin{bmatrix} x_1 \\ x_2 \\ x_3 \end{bmatrix} = \begin{bmatrix} (2/3)s \\ s \\ s \end{bmatrix} = s \begin{bmatrix} 2/3 \\ 1 \\ 1 \end{bmatrix} = \dfrac{1}{3}s \begin{bmatrix} 2 \\ 3 \\ 3 \end{bmatrix}$

$$\lambda_3 = 3 \longrightarrow \begin{bmatrix} 4 & -4 & 2 & 0 \\ 3 & -1 & 0 & 0 \\ 3 & -1 & 0 & 0 \end{bmatrix} \longrightarrow \begin{bmatrix} 1 & -1 & 1/2 & 0 \\ 0 & 2 & -3/2 & 0 \\ 0 & 2 & -3/2 & 0 \end{bmatrix} \longrightarrow \begin{bmatrix} 1 & 0 & -1/4 & 0 \\ 0 & 1 & -3/4 & 0 \\ 0 & 0 & 0 & 0 \end{bmatrix}$$

Let $x_3 = t$;

then $x_2 - \dfrac{3}{4}x_3 = 0$, i.e., $x_2 = \dfrac{3}{4}x_3 = \dfrac{3}{4}t$

and $x_1 - \dfrac{1}{4}x_3 = 0$, i.e., $x_1 = \dfrac{1}{4}x_3 = \dfrac{1}{4}t$

so $\begin{bmatrix} x_1 \\ x_2 \\ x_3 \end{bmatrix} = \begin{bmatrix} (1/4)t \\ (3/4)t \\ t \end{bmatrix} = t \begin{bmatrix} 1/4 \\ 3/4 \\ 1 \end{bmatrix} = \dfrac{1}{4}t \begin{bmatrix} 1 \\ 3 \\ 4 \end{bmatrix}$

$$P = \begin{bmatrix} 1 & 2 & 1 \\ 1 & 3 & 3 \\ 1 & 3 & 4 \end{bmatrix} \quad ; \quad P^{-1} = \frac{1}{1}\begin{bmatrix} 3 & -1 & 0 \\ -5 & 3 & -1 \\ 3 & -2 & 1 \end{bmatrix}^{T} = \begin{bmatrix} 3 & -5 & 3 \\ -1 & 3 & -2 \\ 0 & -1 & 1 \end{bmatrix}$$

$$D = P^{-1}AP = \begin{bmatrix} 1 & 0 & 0 \\ 0 & 2 & 0 \\ 0 & 0 & 3 \end{bmatrix}.$$

(b) $\quad A^4 = PD^4P^{-1} = \begin{bmatrix} 1 & 2 & 1 \\ 1 & 3 & 3 \\ 1 & 3 & 4 \end{bmatrix}\begin{bmatrix} 1 & 0 & 0 \\ 0 & 16 & 0 \\ 0 & 0 & 81 \end{bmatrix}\begin{bmatrix} 3 & -5 & 3 \\ -1 & 3 & -2 \\ 0 & -1 & 1 \end{bmatrix}$

$$= \begin{bmatrix} 1 & 2 & 1 \\ 1 & 3 & 3 \\ 1 & 3 & 4 \end{bmatrix}\begin{bmatrix} 3 & -5 & 3 \\ -16 & 48 & -32 \\ 0 & -81 & 81 \end{bmatrix}$$

$$= \begin{bmatrix} -29 & 10 & 20 \\ -45 & -104 & 150 \\ -45 & -185 & 231 \end{bmatrix}$$

1. Consider the vectors $\mathbf{u} = (2, -1, 3)$, $\mathbf{v} = (1, 1, 4)$, $\mathbf{w} = (0, 2, 0)$. Compute each of the following.

   (a) $3\mathbf{u} + \mathbf{v} - 2\mathbf{w}$
   (b) $2\mathbf{v}\cdot(\mathbf{w} + \mathbf{u})$
   (c) $\|\mathbf{u}\|\mathbf{v} - \|\mathbf{v}\|\mathbf{u}$
   (d) $\mathbf{u} \times (\mathbf{v} \times \mathbf{w})$

2. Consider the matrices

$$A = \begin{bmatrix} 1 & -2 & 3 \\ 0 & 5 & 0 \\ 2 & 1 & 0 \end{bmatrix} \quad , \quad B = \begin{bmatrix} 1 & 0 & 1 \\ 2 & 0 & 0 \\ 0 & -1 & 1 \end{bmatrix} \quad , \quad C = \begin{bmatrix} 1 & 3 & 0 \\ 0 & 0 & 2 \\ 1 & 0 & 1 \end{bmatrix}$$

   Compute each of the following.

   (a) $A - B$
   (b) $3B - 4C$
   (c) $AB - BC$
   (d) $A^2(B^2 + C^2)$

3. Consider the following system.
$$\begin{cases} x - y - z = 0 \\ 2x - y - z = 3 \\ 3x - 4z = 1 \end{cases}$$

   (a) Solve by Gauss or Gauss–Jordan elimination.
   (b) Solve by finding the inverse of the coefficient matrix and multiplying by the right–hand–side.

4. Consider the set $S = \{(1, 2, 7), (6, 2, 2), (1, 0, -1), (5, 2, 3)\}$.

   (a) Show whether the span of S is R^3.
   (b) Find a subset of S which is a basis for the span of S.

5. Consider the bases $B = \{(1, 0), (0, 1)\}$ and $B' = \{(4, 5), (2, 3)\}$ for R^2.

   (a) Find the transition matrix from B to B'.
   (b) Find $[(11, 14)]_{B'}$.

6. Prove whether the function $F : M_{22} \to R^1$ defined by $F(A) = \det A$ is a linear transformation.

7. Let T by multiplication by the matrix

$$A = \begin{bmatrix} 1 & 2 & 2 & -1 & 1 \\ 0 & 2 & 2 & -2 & -1 \\ 2 & 6 & 2 & -4 & 1 \\ 1 & 4 & 0 & -3 & 0 \end{bmatrix}.$$

   (a) Find a basis for $R(T)$.
   (b) Find a basis for $\ker(T)$.

8. Consider $T : R^3 \rightarrow R^3$ defined by $T(x, y, z) = (y + z, z - x, x + y + 3z)$.

   Consider the bases $B = \{(1, 0, 0), (1, 2, 0), (1, 2, 3)\}$ and $B' = \{(1, 1, 1), (1, 1, 0), (1, 0, 0)\}$.

   (a) Compute $[T]_{B',B}$ (the matrix for T with respect to the basis B for the domain and B' for the range).

   (b) Use your answer to part (a) to compute $T(1, -1, 2)$.

9. Let $A = \begin{pmatrix} 3 & -2 & 0 \\ -2 & 3 & 0 \\ 0 & 0 & 5 \end{pmatrix}$.

   (a) Find a matrix P that diagonalizes A (i.e., $P^{-1}AP$ is diagonal).

   (b) Find $P^{-1}AP$.

   (c) Use your answers to parts (a) and (b) to compute A^4.

FINAL EXAM D

1. (a) $3\mathbf{u} + \mathbf{v} - 2\mathbf{w} = (6, -3, 9) + (1, 1, 4) - (0, 4, 0) = (7, -6, 13)$

   (b) $2\mathbf{v} \cdot (\mathbf{w} + \mathbf{u}) = 2(1, 1, 4) \cdot (2, 1, 3) = 2(2 + 1 + 12) = 30$

   (c) $\|\mathbf{u}\|\mathbf{v} - \|\mathbf{v}\|\mathbf{u} = \|(2, -1, 3)\|(1, 1, 4) - \|(1, 1, 4)\|(2, -1, 3)$

$$= \sqrt{14}(1, 1, 4) - \sqrt{18}(2, -1, 3)$$
$$= \left(\sqrt{14} - 2\sqrt{18}, \sqrt{14} + \sqrt{18}, 4\sqrt{14} - 3\sqrt{18}\right)$$
$$= \left(\sqrt{14} - 6\sqrt{2}, \sqrt{14} + 3\sqrt{2}, 4\sqrt{14} - 9\sqrt{2}\right)$$

   (d) $\mathbf{u} \times (\mathbf{v} \times \mathbf{w}) = (2, -1, 3) \times [(1, 1, 4) \times (0, 2, 0)]$

$$= (2, -1, 3) \times \begin{vmatrix} \mathbf{i} & \mathbf{j} & \mathbf{k} \\ 1 & 1 & 4 \\ 0 & 2 & 0 \end{vmatrix}$$

$$= (2, -1, 3) \times [\mathbf{i}(-8) + \mathbf{j}(0) + \mathbf{k}(2)] = (2, -1, 3) \times (-8, 0, 2)$$

$$= \begin{vmatrix} \mathbf{i} & \mathbf{j} & \mathbf{k} \\ 2 & -1 & 3 \\ -8 & 0 & 2 \end{vmatrix}$$

$$= i(-2) + j(-28) + k(-8) = (-2, -28, -8)$$

2. (a) $A - B = \begin{bmatrix} 1 & -2 & 3 \\ 0 & 5 & 0 \\ 2 & 1 & 0 \end{bmatrix} - \begin{bmatrix} 1 & 0 & 1 \\ 2 & 0 & 0 \\ 0 & -1 & 1 \end{bmatrix} = \begin{bmatrix} 0 & -2 & 2 \\ -2 & 5 & 0 \\ 2 & 2 & -1 \end{bmatrix}$

   (b) $3B - 4C = \begin{bmatrix} 3 & 0 & 3 \\ 6 & 0 & 0 \\ 0 & -3 & 3 \end{bmatrix} - \begin{bmatrix} 4 & 12 & 0 \\ 0 & 0 & 8 \\ 4 & 0 & 4 \end{bmatrix} = \begin{bmatrix} -1 & -12 & 3 \\ 6 & 0 & -8 \\ -4 & -3 & -1 \end{bmatrix}$

   (c) $AB - BC = \begin{bmatrix} 1 & -2 & 3 \\ 0 & 5 & 0 \\ 2 & 1 & 0 \end{bmatrix}\begin{bmatrix} 1 & 0 & 1 \\ 2 & 0 & 0 \\ 0 & -1 & 1 \end{bmatrix} - \begin{bmatrix} 1 & 0 & 1 \\ 2 & 0 & 0 \\ 0 & -1 & 1 \end{bmatrix}\begin{bmatrix} 1 & 3 & 0 \\ 0 & 0 & 2 \\ 1 & 0 & 1 \end{bmatrix}$

$$= \begin{bmatrix} -3 & -3 & 4 \\ 10 & 0 & 0 \\ 4 & 0 & 2 \end{bmatrix} - \begin{bmatrix} 2 & 3 & 1 \\ 2 & 6 & 0 \\ 1 & 0 & -1 \end{bmatrix} = \begin{bmatrix} -5 & -6 & 3 \\ 8 & -6 & 0 \\ 3 & 0 & 3 \end{bmatrix}$$

   (d) $A^2(B^2 + C^2) = \begin{bmatrix} 1 & -2 & 3 \\ 0 & 5 & 0 \\ 2 & 1 & 0 \end{bmatrix}\begin{bmatrix} 1 & -2 & 3 \\ 0 & 5 & 0 \\ 2 & 1 & 0 \end{bmatrix} \times$

$$\left(\begin{bmatrix} 1 & 0 & 1 \\ 2 & 0 & 0 \\ 0 & -1 & 1 \end{bmatrix}\begin{bmatrix} 1 & 0 & 1 \\ 2 & 0 & 0 \\ 0 & -1 & 1 \end{bmatrix} + \begin{bmatrix} 1 & 3 & 0 \\ 0 & 0 & 2 \\ 1 & 0 & 1 \end{bmatrix}\begin{bmatrix} 1 & 3 & 0 \\ 0 & 0 & 2 \\ 1 & 0 & 1 \end{bmatrix} \right)$$

$$= \begin{bmatrix} 7 & -9 & 3 \\ 0 & 25 & 0 \\ 2 & 1 & 6 \end{bmatrix}\left(\begin{bmatrix} 1 & -1 & 2 \\ 2 & 0 & 2 \\ -2 & -1 & 1 \end{bmatrix} + \begin{bmatrix} 1 & 3 & 6 \\ 2 & 0 & 2 \\ 2 & 3 & 1 \end{bmatrix} \right)$$

$$= \begin{bmatrix} 7 & -9 & 3 \\ 0 & 25 & 0 \\ 2 & 1 & 6 \end{bmatrix} \begin{bmatrix} 2 & 2 & 8 \\ 4 & 0 & 4 \\ 0 & 2 & 2 \end{bmatrix} = \begin{bmatrix} -22 & 20 & 26 \\ 100 & 0 & 100 \\ 8 & 16 & 32 \end{bmatrix}$$

3. (a) $\begin{bmatrix} 1 & -1 & -1 & 0 \\ 2 & -1 & -1 & 3 \\ 3 & 0 & -4 & 1 \end{bmatrix} \longrightarrow \begin{bmatrix} 1 & -1 & -1 & 0 \\ 0 & 1 & 1 & 3 \\ 0 & 3 & -1 & 1 \end{bmatrix} \longrightarrow \begin{bmatrix} 1 & -1 & -1 & 0 \\ 0 & 1 & 1 & 3 \\ 0 & 0 & -4 & -8 \end{bmatrix} \longrightarrow \begin{bmatrix} 1 & -1 & -1 & 0 \\ 0 & 1 & 1 & 3 \\ 0 & 0 & 1 & 2 \end{bmatrix}$

To finish by Gaussian,

$z = 2$

$y + z = 3$ so $y + 2 = 3$, $y = 1$

$x - y - z = 0$ so $x - 1 - 2 = 0$, $x = 3$

To finish by Gauss–Jordan,

$$\begin{bmatrix} 1 & -1 & -1 & 0 \\ 0 & 1 & 1 & 3 \\ 0 & 0 & 1 & 2 \end{bmatrix} \longrightarrow \begin{bmatrix} 1 & 0 & 0 & 3 \\ 0 & 1 & 1 & 3 \\ 0 & 0 & 1 & 2 \end{bmatrix} \longrightarrow \begin{bmatrix} 1 & 0 & 0 & 3 \\ 0 & 1 & 0 & 1 \\ 0 & 0 & 1 & 2 \end{bmatrix} \begin{matrix} x = 3 \\ y = 1 \\ z = 2 \end{matrix}$$

(b) $\begin{bmatrix} x \\ y \\ z \end{bmatrix} = \begin{bmatrix} 1 & -1 & -1 \\ 2 & -1 & -1 \\ 3 & 0 & -4 \end{bmatrix}^{-1} \begin{bmatrix} 0 \\ 3 \\ 1 \end{bmatrix} = \dfrac{1}{-4} \begin{bmatrix} 4 & 5 & 3 \\ -4 & -1 & -3 \\ 0 & -1 & 1 \end{bmatrix}^{T} \begin{bmatrix} 0 \\ 3 \\ 1 \end{bmatrix}$

$$= \dfrac{1}{4} \begin{bmatrix} -4 & 4 & 0 \\ -5 & 1 & 1 \\ -3 & 3 & -1 \end{bmatrix} \begin{bmatrix} 0 \\ 3 \\ 1 \end{bmatrix} = \dfrac{1}{4} \begin{bmatrix} 12 \\ 4 \\ 8 \end{bmatrix} = \begin{bmatrix} 3 \\ 1 \\ 2 \end{bmatrix}$$

4. (a) $\begin{bmatrix} 1 & 6 & 1 & 5 & b_1 \\ 2 & 2 & 0 & 2 & b_2 \\ 7 & 2 & -1 & 3 & b_3 \end{bmatrix} \longrightarrow \begin{bmatrix} 1 & 6 & 1 & 5 & b_1 \\ 0 & -10 & -2 & -8 & b_2 - 2b_1 \\ 0 & -40 & -8 & -32 & b_3 - 7b_1 \end{bmatrix}$

$$\longrightarrow \begin{bmatrix} 1 & 6 & 1 & 5 & b_1 \\ 0 & 1 & 1/5 & 4/5 & (2b_1 - b_2)/10 \\ 0 & 0 & 0 & 0 & b_1 - 4b_2 + b_3 \end{bmatrix}$$

Since the system is only consistent if $b_1 - 4b_2 + b_3 = 0$,

span (S) is the plane $x - 4y + z = 0$,   not R^3.

(b) Noting the columns with leading ones in part (a),

a basis for   span (S) is $\{(1, 2, 7), (6, 2, 2)\}$.

(Any other pair of vectors in S also constitutes a basis for   span (S)).

5. (a) $P_{B',B} = \left[[(1,0)]_{B'} \vdots [(0,1)]_{B'} \right]$

$$= \begin{bmatrix} 4 & 2 \\ 5 & 3 \end{bmatrix}^{-1} \begin{bmatrix} 1 & 0 \\ 0 & 1 \end{bmatrix}$$

$$= \frac{1}{2} \begin{bmatrix} 3 & -2 \\ -5 & 4 \end{bmatrix} \begin{bmatrix} 1 & 0 \\ 0 & 1 \end{bmatrix} = \frac{1}{2} \begin{bmatrix} 3 & -2 \\ -5 & 4 \end{bmatrix}$$

(b) $[(11,14)]_{B'} = P_{B',B}[(11,14)]_B$

$$= \frac{1}{2} \begin{bmatrix} 3 & -2 \\ -5 & 4 \end{bmatrix} \begin{bmatrix} 11 \\ 14 \end{bmatrix} = \frac{1}{2} \begin{bmatrix} 5 \\ 1 \end{bmatrix}$$

6. $\quad F(\mathbf{u}+\mathbf{v}) = F(A+B)$

$\qquad\qquad = \det(A+B)$

$\quad F(\mathbf{u})+F(\mathbf{v}) = F(A)+F(B)$

$\qquad\qquad = \det A + \det B$

$\qquad\qquad \neq F(\mathbf{u}+\mathbf{v}) \quad$ in general.

$\qquad\qquad$ For example, $\quad \begin{vmatrix} 1 & 0 \\ 0 & 1 \end{vmatrix} \neq \begin{vmatrix} 1 & 0 \\ 0 & 0 \end{vmatrix} + \begin{vmatrix} 0 & 0 \\ 0 & 1 \end{vmatrix}$

$\quad F(k\mathbf{u}) = F(kA)$

$\qquad\qquad = \det(kA)$

$\qquad\qquad = k^2 \det(a) \quad$ since $\quad A \quad$ is a $\quad 2 \times 2$ matrix

$\quad kF(\mathbf{u}) = kF(A)$

$\qquad\qquad = k \det(A)$

$\qquad\qquad \neq F(k\mathbf{u}) \quad$ unless $\quad k = 0$ or 1

$\qquad\qquad$ For example, $\quad \begin{vmatrix} 2 & 0 \\ 0 & 2 \end{vmatrix} \neq 2 \begin{vmatrix} 1 & 0 \\ 0 & 1 \end{vmatrix}$

On both counts, F is not a linear transformation.

7. (a)
$$\begin{bmatrix} 1 & 2 & 2 & -1 & 1 \\ 0 & 2 & 2 & -2 & -1 \\ 2 & 6 & 2 & -4 & 1 \\ 1 & 4 & 0 & -3 & 0 \end{bmatrix} \longrightarrow \begin{bmatrix} 1 & 2 & 2 & -1 & 1 \\ 0 & 2 & 2 & -2 & -1 \\ 0 & 2 & -2 & -2 & -1 \\ 0 & 2 & -2 & -2 & -1 \end{bmatrix} \longrightarrow \begin{bmatrix} 1 & 2 & 2 & -1 & 1 \\ 0 & 1 & 1 & -1 & -1/2 \\ 0 & 0 & -4 & 0 & 0 \\ 0 & 0 & -4 & 0 & 0 \end{bmatrix}$$

$$\longrightarrow \begin{bmatrix} 1 & 2 & 2 & -1 & 1 \\ 0 & 1 & 1 & -1 & -1/2 \\ 0 & 0 & 1 & 0 & 0 \\ 0 & 0 & 0 & 0 & 0 \end{bmatrix} \longrightarrow \begin{bmatrix} 1 & 0 & 0 & 1 & 2 \\ 0 & 1 & 1 & -1 & -1/2 \\ 0 & 0 & 1 & 0 & 0 \\ 0 & 0 & 0 & 0 & 0 \end{bmatrix} \longrightarrow \begin{bmatrix} 1 & 0 & 0 & 1 & 2 \\ 0 & 1 & 0 & -1 & -1/2 \\ 0 & 0 & 1 & 0 & 0 \\ 0 & 0 & 0 & 0 & 0 \end{bmatrix}$$

Noting the columns with leading ones,
a basis for $\quad R(T) \quad$ is $\quad \{(1,0,2,1),(2,2,6,4),(2,2,2,0)\}$.

(b) From part (a), the homogeneous system has solutions as follows:

$\qquad$ Let $\quad x_4 = s \quad$ and $\quad x_5 = t$;

$\qquad$ then $\quad x_3 = 0$

345

and $x_2 - x_4 - \frac{1}{2}x_5 = 0$, i.e., $x_2 = x_4 + \frac{1}{2}x_5 = s + \frac{1}{2}t$

and $x_1 + x_4 + 2x_5 = 0$, i.e., $x_1 = -x_4 - 2x_5 = -s - 2t$

so
$$
\begin{bmatrix} x_1 \\ x_2 \\ x_3 \\ x_4 \\ x_5 \end{bmatrix} = \begin{bmatrix} -s - 2t \\ s + (1/2)t \\ 0 \\ s \\ t \end{bmatrix} = \begin{bmatrix} -s \\ s \\ 0 \\ s \\ 0 \end{bmatrix} + \begin{bmatrix} -2t \\ (1/2)t \\ 0 \\ 0 \\ t \end{bmatrix}
$$

$$
= s \begin{bmatrix} -1 \\ 1 \\ 0 \\ 1 \\ 0 \end{bmatrix} + t \begin{bmatrix} -2 \\ 1/2 \\ 0 \\ 0 \\ 0 \end{bmatrix} = s \begin{bmatrix} -1 \\ 1 \\ 0 \\ 1 \\ 0 \end{bmatrix} + \frac{1}{2}t \begin{bmatrix} -4 \\ 1 \\ 0 \\ 0 \\ 2 \end{bmatrix}
$$

so a basis for $\ker(T)$ is
$$
\left\{ \begin{bmatrix} -1 \\ 1 \\ 0 \\ 1 \\ 0 \end{bmatrix}, \begin{bmatrix} -4 \\ 1 \\ 0 \\ 0 \\ 2 \end{bmatrix} \right\}.
$$

8. (a) $[T]_{B',B} = \left[[T(1,0,0)]_{B'} \vdots [T(1,2,0)]_{B'} \vdots [T(1,2,3)]_{B'} \right]$

$= \left[[(0,-1,1)]_{B'} \vdots [(2,-1,3)]_{B'} \vdots [(5,2,12)]_{B'} \right]$

$= \begin{bmatrix} 1 & 1 & 1 \\ 1 & 1 & 0 \\ 1 & 0 & 0 \end{bmatrix}^{-1} \begin{bmatrix} 0 & 2 & 5 \\ -1 & -1 & 2 \\ 1 & 3 & 12 \end{bmatrix}$

$= \dfrac{1}{-1} \begin{bmatrix} 0 & 0 & -1 \\ 0 & -1 & 1 \\ -1 & 1 & 0 \end{bmatrix}^{T} \begin{bmatrix} 0 & 2 & 5 \\ -1 & -1 & 2 \\ 1 & 3 & 12 \end{bmatrix}$

$= \begin{bmatrix} 0 & 0 & 1 \\ 0 & 1 & -1 \\ 1 & -1 & 0 \end{bmatrix} \begin{bmatrix} 0 & 2 & 5 \\ -1 & -1 & 2 \\ 1 & 3 & 12 \end{bmatrix} = \begin{bmatrix} 1 & 3 & 12 \\ -2 & -4 & -10 \\ 1 & 3 & 3 \end{bmatrix}$

(b) $[T(1,-1,2)]_{B'} = [T]_{B',B}[(1,-1,2)]_B$

$= \begin{bmatrix} 1 & 3 & 12 \\ -2 & -4 & -10 \\ 1 & 3 & 3 \end{bmatrix} \begin{bmatrix} 1 & 1 & 1 \\ 0 & 2 & 2 \\ 0 & 0 & 3 \end{bmatrix}^{-1} \begin{bmatrix} 1 \\ -1 \\ 2 \end{bmatrix}$

$= \begin{bmatrix} 1 & 3 & 12 \\ -2 & -4 & -10 \\ 1 & 3 & 3 \end{bmatrix} \dfrac{1}{6} \begin{bmatrix} 6 & 0 & 0 \\ -3 & 3 & 0 \\ 0 & -2 & 2 \end{bmatrix}^{T} \begin{bmatrix} 1 \\ -1 \\ 2 \end{bmatrix}$

$$= \frac{1}{6} \begin{bmatrix} 1 & 3 & 12 \\ -2 & -4 & -10 \\ 1 & 3 & 3 \end{bmatrix} \begin{bmatrix} 6 & -3 & 0 \\ 0 & 3 & -2 \\ 0 & 0 & 2 \end{bmatrix} \begin{bmatrix} 1 \\ -1 \\ 2 \end{bmatrix}$$

$$= \frac{1}{6} \begin{bmatrix} 1 & 3 & 12 \\ -2 & -4 & -10 \\ 1 & 3 & 3 \end{bmatrix} \begin{bmatrix} 9 \\ -7 \\ 4 \end{bmatrix}$$

$$= \frac{1}{6} \begin{bmatrix} 36 \\ -30 \\ 0 \end{bmatrix} = \begin{bmatrix} 6 \\ -5 \\ 0 \end{bmatrix}$$

so $T(1,-1,2) = 6(1,1,1) + -5(1,1,0) + 0(1,0,0) = (1,1,6)$.

9. (a) $\quad 0 = \begin{vmatrix} \lambda - 3 & 2 & 0 \\ 2 & \lambda - 3 & 0 \\ 0 & 0 & \lambda - 5 \end{vmatrix} = (\lambda - 5)[(\lambda - 3)(\lambda - 3) - 2(2)]$

$$= (\lambda - 5)(\lambda^2 - 6\lambda + 5)$$

$$= (\lambda - 5)(\lambda - 5)(\lambda - 1) \quad \text{so} \quad \lambda = 1, 5, 5$$

$$\lambda_1 = \begin{bmatrix} -2 & 2 & 0 & 0 \\ 2 & -2 & 0 & 0 \\ 0 & 0 & -4 & 0 \end{bmatrix} \longrightarrow \begin{bmatrix} 1 & -1 & 0 & 0 \\ 0 & 0 & 0 & 0 \\ 0 & 0 & -4 & 0 \end{bmatrix} \longrightarrow \begin{bmatrix} 1 & -1 & 0 & 0 \\ 0 & 0 & 1 & 0 \\ 0 & 0 & 0 & 0 \end{bmatrix}$$

Let $\quad x_2 = r$;

then $\quad x_1 - x_2 = 0$, i.e., $\quad x_1 = x_2 = r$

and $\quad x_3 = 0$

so $\quad \begin{bmatrix} x_1 \\ x_2 \\ x_3 \end{bmatrix} = \begin{bmatrix} r \\ r \\ 0 \end{bmatrix} = r \begin{bmatrix} 1 \\ 1 \\ 0 \end{bmatrix}$

$$\lambda_2 = 5 \longrightarrow \begin{bmatrix} 2 & 2 & 0 & 0 \\ 2 & 2 & 0 & 0 \\ 0 & 0 & 0 & 0 \end{bmatrix} \longrightarrow \begin{bmatrix} 1 & 1 & 0 & 0 \\ 0 & 0 & 0 & 0 \\ 0 & 0 & 0 & 0 \end{bmatrix}$$

Let $\quad x_2 = s$ and $\quad x_3 = t$;

then $\quad x_1 + x_2 = 0$, i.e., $\quad x_1 = -x_2 = -s$

so $\quad \begin{bmatrix} x_1 \\ x_2 \\ x_3 \end{bmatrix} = \begin{bmatrix} -s \\ s \\ t \end{bmatrix} = \begin{bmatrix} -s \\ s \\ 0 \end{bmatrix} + \begin{bmatrix} 0 \\ 0 \\ t \end{bmatrix} = s \begin{bmatrix} -1 \\ 1 \\ 0 \end{bmatrix} + t \begin{bmatrix} 0 \\ 0 \\ 1 \end{bmatrix}$

$$P = \begin{bmatrix} 1 & -1 & 0 \\ 1 & 1 & 0 \\ 0 & 0 & 1 \end{bmatrix}$$

(b) $\quad P^{-1} = \dfrac{1}{2}\begin{bmatrix} 1 & -1 & 0 \\ 1 & 1 & 0 \\ 0 & 0 & 2 \end{bmatrix}^{T} = \dfrac{1}{2}\begin{bmatrix} 1 & 1 & 0 \\ -1 & 1 & 0 \\ 0 & 0 & 2 \end{bmatrix}$

$$P^{-1}AP = \dfrac{1}{2}\begin{bmatrix} 1 & 1 & 0 \\ -1 & 1 & 0 \\ 0 & 0 & 2 \end{bmatrix}\begin{bmatrix} 3 & -2 & 0 \\ -2 & 3 & 0 \\ 0 & 0 & 5 \end{bmatrix}\begin{bmatrix} 1 & -1 & 0 \\ 1 & 1 & 0 \\ 0 & 0 & 1 \end{bmatrix}$$

$$= \dfrac{1}{2}\begin{bmatrix} 1 & 1 & 0 \\ -1 & 1 & 0 \\ 0 & 0 & 2 \end{bmatrix}\begin{bmatrix} 1 & -5 & 0 \\ 1 & 5 & 0 \\ 0 & 0 & 5 \end{bmatrix}$$

$$= \dfrac{1}{2}\begin{bmatrix} 2 & 0 & 0 \\ 0 & 10 & 0 \\ 0 & 0 & 10 \end{bmatrix} = \begin{bmatrix} 1 & 0 & 0 \\ 0 & 5 & 0 \\ 0 & 0 & 5 \end{bmatrix}$$

(c) $\quad A^4 = PD^4P^{-1}$

$$= \begin{bmatrix} 1 & -1 & 0 \\ 1 & 1 & 0 \\ 0 & 0 & 1 \end{bmatrix}\begin{bmatrix} 1 & 0 & 0 \\ 0 & 625 & 0 \\ 0 & 0 & 625 \end{bmatrix}\dfrac{1}{2}\begin{bmatrix} 1 & 1 & 0 \\ -1 & 1 & 0 \\ 0 & 0 & 2 \end{bmatrix}$$

$$= \dfrac{1}{2}\begin{bmatrix} 1 & -1 & 0 \\ 1 & 1 & 0 \\ 0 & 0 & 1 \end{bmatrix}\begin{bmatrix} 1 & 1 & 0 \\ -625 & 625 & 0 \\ 0 & 0 & 1250 \end{bmatrix}$$

$$= \dfrac{1}{2}\begin{bmatrix} 626 & -624 & 0 \\ -624 & 626 & 0 \\ 0 & 0 & 1250 \end{bmatrix} = \begin{bmatrix} 313 & -312 & 0 \\ -312 & 313 & 0 \\ 0 & 0 & 625 \end{bmatrix}$$